AF342522

LIQUID CRYSTALS WITH NANO AND MICROPARTICLES

Volume I

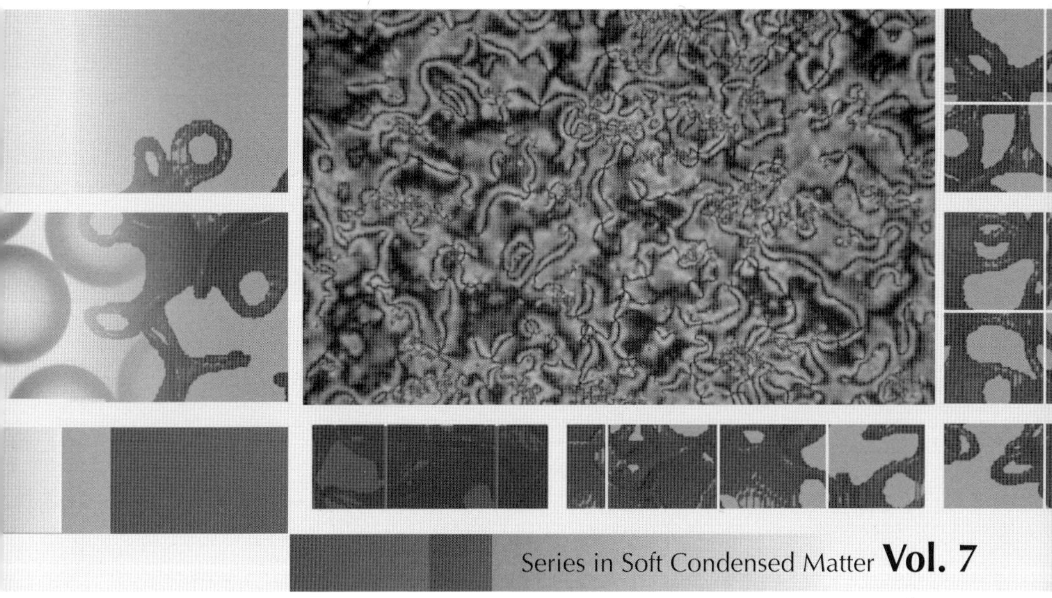

Series in Soft Condensed Matter **Vol. 7**

LIQUID CRYSTALS WITH NANO AND MICROPARTICLES

Volume I

Editors

Jan P F Lagerwall • Giusy Scalia

Seoul National University, South Korea

World Scientific

NEW JERSEY · LONDON · SINGAPORE · BEIJING · SHANGHAI · HONG KONG · TAIPEI · CHENNAI · TOKYO

Published by

World Scientific Publishing Co. Pte. Ltd.
5 Toh Tuck Link, Singapore 596224
USA office: 27 Warren Street, Suite 401-402, Hackensack, NJ 07601
UK office: 57 Shelton Street, Covent Garden, London WC2H 9HE

Library of Congress Cataloging-in-Publication Data
Liquid crystals with nano and microparticles / [edited by] Jan P.F.
   Lagerwall (Seoul National University, South Korea), Giusy Scalia
(Seoul National University, South Korea).
      pages cm. -- (Series in soft condensed matter ; vol. 7)
   Includes bibliographical references and index.
   ISBN 978-981-4619-25-7 (hardcover-set : alk. paper) -- ISBN 978-981-3203-67-9
   (hardcover-Vol. I : alk. paper) -- ISBN 978-981-3203-68-6 (hardcover-Vol. II : alk. paper)
   1. Liquid crystals. 2. Colloidal crystals. 3. Nanoparticles. I. Lagerwall, Jan P. F.
II. Scalia, Giusy.
   TA418.9.L54L58 2015
   530.4'29--dc23
                                                      2014020840

British Library Cataloguing-in-Publication Data
A catalogue record for this book is available from the British Library.

Desk Editor: Christopher Teo

Printed in Singapore

Preface

Liquid crystals and colloids are traditional soft condensed matter research fields with well-known applications ranging from displays of all kinds to cosmetic and food products that are with us in the everyday life. In the last century the coupling of the two research fields was sporadic, while the last 10 years brought a change: the interest in the merged field, a segment of anisotropic soft matter covering liquid crystal colloids and colloidal liquid crystals, became a hot topic.

The maturity of traditional fields with many skilled researchers, new experimental techniques, new materials, more efficient application of mathematical tools, and better computing facilities fostered a fast growth of this new field. It is important to list some new or upgraded experimental approaches that have been crucial for these developments: multiphoton confocal polarization microscopy, use of markers such as fluorescent dyes and quantum dots, atomic force microscopy, particle and defect manipulation with laser tweezers based on complex light beams, microfluidic techniques, high resolution lithographic techniques, 3D printing of submicrometer objects, emerging new materials like graphene etc. On the modelling and theoretical side, one can identify more proficient use of mathematical tools originating from topology and geometry. This together with efficient numerical computation schemes supported by multicore and graphic processors enable to numerically solve equations of complex physical models and visualize predicted structures. The synergy of experimental and modelling approaches allows to understand observed complex superstructures in liquid crystal colloids and design new ones for particular applications.

The liquid crystal colloids can be roughly divided in two classes depending on the size of the inclusions: mesoscale ranging from supra- to sub-micron, and nanoscale ranging from supra-nanometer to nanometer inclusion sizes. In case of mesoscale objects, the particles are surrounded by an area where nematic order is substantially perturbed and possibly accompanied by topological defects. This provides strong effective interactions among inclusions that allows the formation of colloidal particle assemblies. The effect that depends on surface anchoring properties and shape asymmetry, in general decreases upon approaching nanoscale. The sharing of liquid crystal deformations accompanying mezo-size inclusions leads to fascinating colloidal structures that include singular and nonsingular defects, which comply with topological properties of the orientational ordering field. In the nematic liquid crystals effective interactions based on localised or entangling disclination line defects provide the stability of colloidal structures with 1D, 2D, and 3D particle arrangements that can partially self-assemble or can be assembled by the assistance of laser tweezers. In nematic colloids the disclination networks may include also knots and links or can be accompanied by solitons. The resulting robust arrays of inclusions in liquid crystals lead to tuneable colloidal crystals that, when adding also the functionality of particles, may further lead to interesting photonic or metamaterial applications.

For the nanoscale inclusions there are at least three different situations that need to be recognised. The first situation is covering homogeneous dispersions with low concentrations of nanoparticles of different shapes and functionalities in the thermotropic liquid crystal solvents. In the second situation a high concentration of cylinder or disc-like nano-particles in an isotropic solvent directly leads to a lyotropic kind of a liquid crystal phase. In both cases physical properties of the resulting homogenous liquid crystal phases can be designed by selecting properties of nano-colloidal particles and their concentrations. The third situation covers the cases where constrained thermotropic liquid crystals have inhomogeneous orientational order that provides general spatially depended force fields that affect nano inclusions. This is reflected in the tendency of nanoparticles to concentrate in areas of depressed liquid crystalline order. Particularly singular point and line defects attract the particles and provide a means to self-assemble complex spatial distributions of nano-colloidal inclusions which again may find a way to photonic applications.

The editors have done an excellent and timely job in collecting 27 chapters written by the experts working on the front of the new field. In the 900 pages practically all relevant aspects of this fast developing anisotropic soft matter research field are addressed. The book starts with fundamentals of liquid crystals and colloidal dispersions and then continues with characterisation methods including advanced polarization microscopies, atomic force microscopy, spectroscopic & scattering techniques. It concludes with optical tweezers as a micron scale manipulation tool. The rest of the collection is devoted to different colloidal systems. The first segment covers structures based on micron scale particles dispersed in nematic and smectic solvents where topological properties of the media play crucial roles and includes examples of electrically driven dynamics of such colloidal systems. In the next segment numerous liquid crystal nanocolloids from inorganic to organic particles dispersed in calamitic, discotic, lyotropic, polymeric, elastomeric and polymer stabilised liquid crystals are described. The last segment is devoted to the colloidal liquid crystals constituted by tiny anisotropic objects ranging from carbon nanotubes to cellulose nanocrystals, dispersed in isotropic solvents.

This impressive book, devoted to the fast developing field of anisotropic soft matter, is covering the whole span from basic science to applications of liquid crystalline colloids and thus provides a much needed overview. It addresses a broad audience from physicists, chemists, material scientists, to engineers, and will be welcome by the readers ranging from experienced researchers to beginners in the field and students.

Ljuldjana, June 2016

Slobodan Žumer
University of Ljuldjana
and
Jozef Stefan Institute

Contents

Chapter 1

Introduction

Giusy Scalia[*] and Jan P. F. Lagerwall[†]

*University of Luxembourg, Physics & Materials Science Research Unit,
162a, avenue de la faiencerie, 1511 Luxembourg, Luxembourg*
[*]giusy.scalia@solcanta.com, [†]jan.lagerwall@lcsoftmatter.com

Liquid crystals are amazing materials. They are amazing because they combine, in a single phase, the fluidity of ordinary liquids with the long-range order that we otherwise find only in crystalline solids. This unique combination reflects the ability of the constituents to self-organize into ordered structures while maintaining a degree of translational freedom that is absent in the solid state. In fact, as counterintuitive as it may seem to the novice, the drive for liquid crystalline ordering is typically dominated by entropic effects, i.e. the ordered structures appear because these states minimize the constraints on the entities building up the phase.

The combination of order and mobility also gives rise to a responsiveness that is truly extraordinary. This responsiveness is put to very good use in the Liquid Crystal Displays (LCDs) that now totally dominate the market for information displays, from small-scale watch and phone displays to high-definition television sets. These devices constitute an astounding demonstration of the possibilities of applying liquid crystals, yet they have a relatively limited focus. Fundamentally, the technology is built on the reaction of a nematic liquid crystal, confined between aligning layers that provide a well-defined ground state, to an externally applied electric field, and the modulation in the optical properties that this response gives rise to. This effect was first studied by Vsevolod Frederiks in the 1920s but it took until the late 1960s until its usefulness for display devices was realized,[1] and then another 30-40 years to develop the supporting technology to the extent that today's impressive displays could be realized.

While displays may be the only example of liquid crystals that most people today are aware of, these materials can in fact be so much more

"

than nematics modulating the brightness of the pixels in a TV. Academic liquid crystal research has during the last two decades been moving away from display-related activities and started to explore the vast untapped potential of liquid crystals.[2,3] Their response to entirely different stimuli than electric fields, like light, chemical environment and mechanical stresses, is increasingly coming into the spotlight, and very different types of liquid crystal are being studied in diverse contexts, often transcending boundaries to fields that previously had little contact with liquid crystal research.

A strong trend in this new development, with many exciting secondary branches growing out during recent years, has been the study of nano- and microparticles in liquid crystals. This is the topic of the present book. It has been known since Bernal's seminal experimental work on suspensions of Tobacco Mosaic Virus (TMV)[4] and Onsager's theoretical explanation of the observations,[5] that suspensions of anisometric nanoparticles form liquid crystal phases already at quite low concentration. With the explosion of novel nanoparticle types during the last decades, totally synthetic or derived from natural precursors, the playground of nanoparticle-based liquid crystals has dramatically expanded and we now know that suspensions of, for instance, carbon nanotubes, graphene flakes, mineral nanorods or -platelets, viruses and cellulose rods, can all form liquid crystal phases, often with surprising as well as useful consequences.

Nanoparticles are sometimes defined from a functional point of view, with the requirement that novel chemical, physical or biological properties arise that are present neither on the atomic nor on the bulk scale of the same material. Examples are the ballistic electrical conductivity of carbon nanotubes and the antibacterial action of silver nanoparticles, neither property of which is present in a macroscopic bulk material of carbon and silver, respectively. Another definition is geometrical, the requirement being that the particle is in the nanoscopic range (1 nm to a few hundreds of nanometers) at least in one dimension. The simplest cases are more or less spherical nanoparticles, like C_{60} fullerenes or the smallest gold nanoparticles, but there are also more complex particles like carbon nanotubes (CNTs) or graphene flakes, frequently with size far beyond the nanoscopic range in one (CNTs) or two (graphene flakes) dimensions. The same holds for some rod-like viruses which can reach the micron scale in length.

Also regular molecular liquid crystals, whether the thermotropic class found in displays or the lyotropic phases formed by amphiphiles in water, have been studied in connection to nanoparticles, in particular in the context of using the liquid crystalline long-range order for aligning or positioning nanoparticles that are introduced as guests. Since nanoparticles are generally processed in a liquid host to keep them separated (dispersed), it would seem a natural extension to use a liquid that can also provide a controlled organization of the particles at the same time as it provides the dispersion, i.e. to use a liquid crystalline host.

Many new intriguing phenomena arise in such systems, often related to the subtle balance between long-term stable dispersion *versus* aggregation of the nanoparticles. The interaction between the orientational field (the director field) of the liquid crystal and the particle guests is of great fundamental interest, but also key to the possibilities of using nanoparticle-liquid crystal dispersions in any applied context. The research in this field has indeed often been motivated by the application prospects but there is also a considerable drive from a curiosity-centered point of view. The interplay between a long-range ordered liquid and guest particles that are frequently on the same scale as the building blocks of the host phase in two dimensions, but orders of magnitude larger in the third, is far from trivial. We are right at the borderline where a continuum approximation of the physics breaks down, but not necessarily in all dimensions!

Perhaps even more impressive results have been achieved with the slightly simpler situation of microparticles in liquid crystals. This case is simpler because the scale makes experimental observation easier and less ambiguous and because the chemistry for stabilization at this scale is better developed, but the physics is no less intriguing. Here the guest particles are so large that they act as defects in the liquid crystal and they induce a well-defined deformation of the director field in their vicinity. This gives rise to a fascinating new set of elasticity-driven interaction schemes, where the particles can self-organize into chains or 2D crystals of various symmetry and geometry. This is a field that certainly started out from a curiosity-driven point of view, but lately new horizons for applications based on microparticles organized by liquid crystals are becoming apparent, in particular in the area of photonics.

When dealing with particles in liquid crystals, whether as guests or as the actual constituents that build up the phase, you enter the realm of colloids. In its most general definition, a colloid is a dispersion of inclusions (solid particles, liquid droplets or gaseous bubbles) in a medium of molecules that are much smaller than the inclusions. The dispersion should be reasonably stable (but not necessarily thermodynamically stable; most colloids are in fact kinetically stabilized) in order to make an analysis from a colloid point of view meaningful. For such systems a range of fascinating phenomena arise, due to the colloidal, and thus heterogeneous, nature of the system. Examples are strongly non-Newtonian flow behavior or peculiar light scattering effects. But the heterogeneity also complicates the systems, both in terms of their theoretical analysis and their experimental preparation. Liquid crystals with dispersed nano- or microparticles are no exception and their study thus requires a researcher to address them from a colloid science perspective.

The book you are holding in your hands has been put together as an attempt to summarize the present knowledge of liquid crystalline colloids or, in a fully non-exclusive terminology, of systems with nano- and microinclusions in liquid crystals, but also to introduce the fundamental concepts of the field to the beginner. It has been our privilege as editors to work with outstanding researchers as chapter authors, each contributing with a vital aspect of this strongly interdisciplinary research field. The authors are internationally recognized as leaders in the field they write about, giving an up-to-date as well as explanatory introduction to this new and exciting development of liquid crystal research. The result is a text book that we believe can be of great benefit to readers ranging from the young graduate student looking for a helpful introduction, to the experienced senior researcher who needs a reference source or is seeking to broaden her or his expertise. Because the field is so broad, no single researcher can capture it in full, making the individual contribution of each expert author so much more valuable.

The book is conceptually divided into five parts. First the fundamental concepts of liquid crystal and colloid science are introduced in three chapters, in a language that should be understandable for advanced graduate students in e.g. physics, chemistry or materials science, who are basically beginners in this particular field of research. Because these chapters need to introduce concepts and phenomena that span the full range of diverse liquid crystalline and colloidal systems that are discussed in the following more applied chapters, they are a bit longer. The purpose here is not to introduce the most recent research results or review the field, but rather to give clear yet concise explanations of concepts and phenomena that play key roles in the following chapters. One of us first gives a phenomenological overview of colloids and liquid crystals—thermotropic as well as lyotropic—and then Paul van der Schoot gives a 'pedestrian' introduction to the theory of colloids, focusing on the concepts that are most important for the topic of this book, such as dispersion stability of spheres, rods and discs and the parameters that influence the stability. Mikhail Osipov ends the introductory section with an equally compact introduction to the theoretical description of liquid crystals with inclusions. Due to the complexity of the topic, this chapter is on a slightly more advanced level than the preceding ones.

In Part 2 the most central methods for studying inclusions in liquid crystals are introduced in five chapters. Taewoo Lee and Ivan Smalyukh give a concise overview of optical microscopy, conventional as well as novel variations, in Chap. 5. This is followed by two chapters on scattering/spectroscopy techniques that are very useful for studying liquid crystals with inclusions. Goran Ungar and co-authors give an introduction to X-ray scattering, and Helen Gleeson on Raman spectroscopy. In Chap. 8 Miha Skarabot introduces us to the art of manipulating inclusions in liquid crystals using optical tweezers, and in the closing chapter of this part, written by Christian Bahr and Benjamin Schulz, we learn how we can address the surface topography of liquid crystals, with nanoscale resolution, using atomic force microscopy (AFM).

The rest of the book deals with specific examples of liquid crystal particle suspensions, first in Part 3 with three chapters on micron scale inclusions. Igor Mušević gives a brief overview of the study of solid microparticles in bulk liquid crystals in Chap. 10, followed by Ralf Stannarius' and Kirsten Harth's overview of inclusions in freely suspended smectic films in Chap. 11. Oleg Lavrentovich then wraps up this part with a focus on motion of particles in liquid crystals, enabled by electrophoresis or electroosmosis.

Part 4 is devoted to nanoscale guests in liquid crystalline hosts, starting with a chapter on nanoparticles in discotic liquid crystals by Sandeep Kumar. This chapter also introduces some of the synthesis schemes for metallic and semiconducting nanoparticles, which thus sets the stage for the following chapter by Torsten Hegmann and co-authors. In their chapter they discuss how metallic and semiconducting nanoparticles can be coated with different types of ligands to allow dispersion in thermotropic calamitic nematics, as well as how the electrooptic behavior of the nematic liquid crystal is affected by the presence of the particles. In Chap. 15 Irena Drevenšek-Olenik covers inorganic nanorods of other types dispersed in thermotropic nematics, with an emphasis on the alignment of the rods by the liquid crystal host as well as the effects on electrooptic behavior.

Gold nanoparticles can even be a component of the mesogens themselves, providing a very interesting way of introducing the nanoparticle 'guests', that gives rise to liquid crystal phases with unusual properties, as Wiktor Lewandowski and Ewa Gorecka teach us in Chap. 16. Together with Schymura, Park and Dierking one of us then introduces carbon nanotubes in non-polymeric calamitic liquid crystals, followed by Yang Yang's and Yan Ji's overview of carbon nanotube-doped liquid crystal elastomers in Chap. 18. Very interesting phenomena can arise when the nanoparticles are magnetic or ferroelectric, and this is what Yuriy Reznikov and co-authors describe in Chap. 19. The next chapter, written by us with co-workers, is devoted to the use of lyotropic liquid crystals as host for nanoparticle dispersion and organization.

Then Emmanuelle Lacaze and Delphine Coursault describe how controlled sets of defects in smectic and cholesteric liquid crystals can be used to organize nanoparticles over large scales, with fascinating consequences for the optical properties of the composite material. In Chap. 22, Shin-Woong Kang and Sudarshan Kundu close this part with a very new development that is in a sense complementary to the previous chapters, namely how we can *create* organic polymer nanoparticles and networks by polymerizing a liquid crystal under carefully controlled conditions.

The final five chapters of the book give examples of nanoparticles that form liquid crystal phases if they are brought into suspension at sufficient concentration. Cecile Zakri and Philippe Poulin discuss the development of nematic phases in carbon nanotube suspensions, followed by N. Fresneau's and Stéphane Campidelli's introduction to the corresponding case for graphene oxide flakes, and then Jangkun Song describes how electrooptic switching with relevance for displays can be achieved in such graphene oxide liquid crystals. While water is often used for carbon nanotube and graphene oxide suspensions, the organic pigments described by Susanne Klein and co-authors in Chap. 26 form (highly colorful) nematic liquid crystals in nonpolar solvents, which simplifies the task of addressing them with electric fields. This provides the second example of particle-based liquid crystals that can be considered for use in display applications. Also chiral nematics, or cholesterics, can arise in nanoparticle suspensions, as one of us describes with the example of cellulose nanocrystals, in collaboration with local co-authors as well as Christina Schütz and Lennart Bergström, in the book's final chapter.

The research on particles in liquid crystals is young and still highly explorative in character, with many different directions being pursued in parallel and stimulating challenges being encountered on different levels and of varying character. It is impossible to know today where these thrusts will lead, but one thing is certain, and that is that this is a flowering research field with potential for exciting studies, fundamental and applied, for many years to come. We will see the unique self-organizing processes of liquid crystals, and the related exceptional responsiveness, taking exciting new forms when applied to nano- and microparticles, forming or being embedded in a liquid crystal phase. It is our belief and hope that this book can serve as a source of inspiration as well as guidance in the process.

Acknowledgments

We are grateful to a number of people, in addition to the chapter authors, who have helped in the realization of this book by providing very valuable feedback (in alphabetical order): Nicholas Abbott (University of Wisconsin Madison), Eric Anglaret (University of Montpellier), Ute Baumeister (Martin Luther University Halle-Wittenberg), Dirk Broer (Eindhoven University of Technology), Alexey Eremin (University of Magdeburg), Venkata Subba Rao Jampani (University of Luxembourg), Nadia Kapernaum (University of Stuttgart), Daniel Krüerke (Klinik Arlesheim), Sven Lagerwall (Chalmers University of Technology), Sabine Laschat (University of Stuttgart), Joseph Maclennan (University of Colorado), Alenka Mertelj (University of Ljubljana), Piero Morales (ENEA), Anupam Sengupta (Massachusetts Institute of Technology), Yoichi Takanishi (Kyoto University), Eugene Terentjev (Cambridge University), Carsten Tschierske (Martin Luther University Halle-Wittenberg), Epifanio Virga (University of Pavia), Dong Ki Yoon (KAIST), Hiroyuki Yoshida (Osaka University).

References

1. T. J. Sluckin, D. A. Dunmur, and H. Stegemeyer, *Crystals that flow: Classic papers from the history of liquid crystals.* Taylor and Francis, London (2004).
2. Q. Li (Ed.), *Liquid Crystals Beyond Displays: Chemistry, Physics, and Applications.* Wiley (2012).
3. J. P. F. Lagerwall and G. Scalia, A new era for liquid crystal research: Applications of liquid crystals in soft matter nano-, bio- and microtechnology, *Curr. Appl. Phys.* **12**(6), 1387–1412 (2012).
4. F. C. Bawden, N. W. Pirie, J. D. Bernal, and I. Fankuchen, Liquid crystalline substances from virus-infected plants, *Nature.* **138**(3503), 1051–1052 (1936).
5. L. Onsager, The effects of shape on the interaction of colloidal particles, *Ann. N. Y. Acad. Sci.* **51**(4), 627–659 (1949).

Part 1

Fundamentals

Chapter 2

A phenomenological introduction to liquid crystals and colloids

Jan P. F. Lagerwall

*University of Luxembourg, Physics & Materials Science Research Unit,
162a, avenue de la faiencerie, 1511 Luxembourg, Luxembourg*
jan.lagerwall@lcsoftmatter.com

This chapter aims to give the reader an overview of the full scope of the liquid crystalline state of matter and a first contact with colloids. The ambition is to introduce and explain all key phenomena and concepts that will be needed in the following chapters in a concise yet understandable way. We begin by introducing the nematic phase and defining the director concept. We then introduce the two classes of liquid crystals, thermotropics and lyotropics, discussing similarities and differences and defining necessary help concepts such as mesogenicity, amphiphilicity and micelle formation. In the context of lyotropic liquid crystals we also introduce some key concepts of colloids, which form a minimum base that the following more detailed chapter on colloids by Paul van der Schoot takes as a starting point. Thermotropic smectic and lyotropic lamellar phases are then discussed together, emphasizing shared aspects as well as their respective unique features. This is followed by columnar phases of disc-shaped thermotropic molecules and in lyotropic suspensions of nanorods, and then we introduce the modifications of the phase structures that chirality typically induces.

In the second section we quantify nematic ordering by introducing the orientational order parameter in three and two dimensions. Section three is devoted to the anisotropic optical and viscous properties of liquid crystals, followed by an introduction to liquid crystal elasticity in Sec. 4, where we introduce the three basic deformations splay, twist and bend. This prepares us for an introduction to topological defects in Sec. 5. Section 6 is a more practical intermission, dealing with the experimental study of liquid crystals, covering typical sample cells for thermotropic as well as lyotropic liquid crystals, means of aligning samples, applying external fields etc. We are then ready to go through the liquid crystal response to applied electric or magnetic fields, key to the application of liquid crystals in displays, in Sec. 7.

In Sec. 8 we revisit the effects of chirality, now going into the special physical properties like selective reflection, optical activity and spontaneous polarization that may appear in chiral liquid crystal phases. In Sec. 9 we give a very brief overview of typical chemical structural features of the molecules that build thermotropic and lyotropic liquid crystals, respectively, and to some extent how variations of these features influence the properties of the macroscopic liquid crystal phase. Finally, we end the chapter by giving a minimum explanation to why nematic liquid crystal phases form in section 10, summarizing the fundamental ideas and outcomes of the Maier-Saupe and Onsager theories for thermotropics and lyotropics, respectively, both of which will be important in later chapters of the book.

Contents

1. Liquid crystal classes and phases

What makes liquid crystals unique is that they combine fluidity with (quasi) long-range order. This means that they can flow and adapt their shape to the volume of their container, as in regular liquids, but, in contrast to such liquids, the orientation or position—or both—of a certain building block has a specific relation to those of building blocks a long distance away. This is a situation we normally find only in a crystal and, as in a crystal, this long-range correlation gives rise to anisotropic macroscopic physical properties. Liquid crystals are therefore sometimes referred to as anisotropic liquids.

We speak of building blocks rather than molecules because liquid crystals are truly diverse, with many phases formed by molecule aggregates or particles rather than by individual molecules. The latter category is referred to as **thermotropic** liquid crystals while the former comprises the class of **lyotropics**.[a] Being intermediate between the anisotropic crystalline solid state and the ordinary isotropic liquid, liquid crystals are said to be **mesomorphic** and molecules capable of forming liquid crystal phases are called **mesogenic** molecules or **mesogens** (*meso* = in between).

1.1. *The nematic phase and the director concept*

In the simplest and best studied liquid crystal phase, the **nematic** (abbreviated N), the positions of building blocks is as dynamic and disordered as in ordinary isotropic liquids and the long-range order is of purely orientational type. Its description takes place via the introduction of the **director**, abbreviated **n**. This is a sign-invariant (**n** = -**n**) unit vector that indicates the principal symmetry axis of the phase, cf. Fig. 1. Here two cartoons of a nematic phase are drawn, one with disc-shaped and one with rod-shaped building blocks. Although far from perfectly oriented, these discs or rods tend to align with their individual principal symmetry axes along **n**. Reflecting the continuity of the fluid phase, **n** varies smoothly without discrete changes (except in defects), hence one often speaks of the **director field** **n(r)**, where **r** is the space coordinate.

For a nematic phase to form, the building blocks must be anisometric (anisotropic in shape). Indeed, liquid crystal phases are most often built up by units that are effectively either rod- or disc-shaped, (although more complex anisometric molecules have become quite important in recent years,

---

[a]We use the most inclusive definition of the term lyotropic, following the convention of Sluckin, Dunmur and Stegemeyer,[1] while others prefer a more restrictive interpretation.

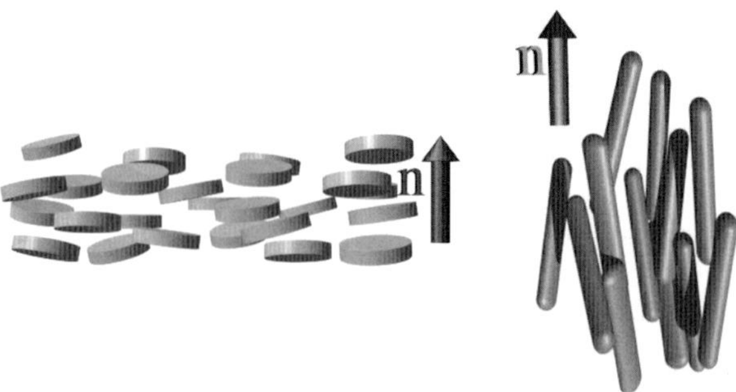

Fig. 1.   Two cartoons of a nematic phase, built from disc- and rod-shaped building blocks, respectively, drawn with a vertical director **n**. From Ref. 32.

see Sec. 9). When one wants to emphasize the shape of the building blocks one often speaks of **calamitic** and **discotic** liquid crystals for these two cases, respectively.

The achiral nematic phase is generally uniaxial, i.e. it has full cylindrical rotational symmetry around **n** (point group $D_{\infty h}$ in Schönfließ notation). Biaxial nematics were found among lyotropic liquid crystals in 1980,[2,3] whereas the possible existence of thermotropic biaxial nematics is a hot issue of current debate. The symmetry of any *chiral* liquid crystal phase is reduced by the absence of mirror planes (the index h in $D_{\infty h}$ signifies a horizontal mirror plane). This reduction has several important consequences for the physical properties of the phase, as will be discussed in Sec. 8. Until then, all symmetry notations will refer to the *achiral* version of the phase considered.

1.2. *Thermotropic liquid crystals*

The name thermotropic reflects the fact that temperature is the fundamental thermodynamic control parameter determining the phase. Two temperatures are particularly important, namely those defining the beginning and end of the liquid crystalline regime, cf. Fig. 2. The **melting point** is, as for other materials, the temperature where the solid crystal melts, only for liquid crystals it is not into an isotropic liquid but into a liquid crystalline state. Unique to liquid crystals is the **clearing point**, at which the highest-temperature liquid crystal phase turns into an isotropic liquid. It owes its name to the fact that a bulk liquid crystal scatters light whereas the isotropic liquid state of the same material is clear.

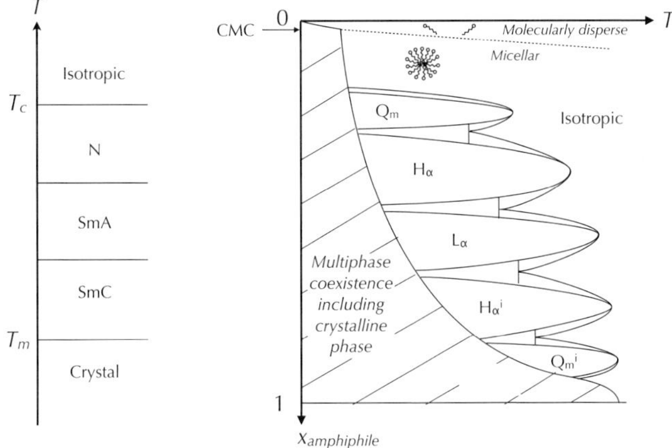

Fig. 2. A comparison between a generic phase sequence of thermotropic calamitic liquid crystals (left) and a generic phase diagram of a lyotropic liquid crystal formed by surfactant in water (right), both highly simplified. The vertical axis of each diagram corresponds to the main thermodynamic control parameter, *temperature T* for thermotropics and *amphiphile concentration x* for the lyotropic. In the former case the liquid crystalline regime is bounded by the melting point T_m and the clearing point T_c, in the latter it is located between the concentration x_{high} of the most concentrated liquid crystal phase and the high-concentration end of the isotropic micellar liquid regime, at $x_{low} > CMC$. For surfactant-based lyotropics the temperature (horizontal axis) acts as a secondary control parameter. For particle-based liquid crystals its influence is generally fully negligible and the system is then said to be 'athermal'. From Ref. 32.

1.3. *Lyotropic liquid crystals and colloids*

Lyotropic liquid crystals form only upon addition of a solvent. The building block is frequently not one but many molecules (typically on the order of 100), organized into an aggregate called a **micelle**. Such lyotropic liquid crystals thus belong to the category of associated **colloids**, a term we will say more about in a moment. The micelle formation is a result of the **amphiphilic** character of the constituent molecules, i.e. they have one end that is liked by the solvent and one that the solvent avoids. Most often the solvent is water and the typical amphiphile is the **surfactant**[b] found in commercial soaps and detergents. Surfactants have a polar and thus **hydrophilic** (liked by water) head group and a nonpolar **hydrophobic** (avoided by water), alternatively referred to as **lipophilic** (liked by fat), tail.

---

[b]Surfactant is short for *surf*ace-*acti*ve ag*ent,* the name reflecting the fact that they reduce the surface tension of water considerably.

When a surfactant is placed in an aqueous environment the head group is easily accommodated but the inability of the nonpolar end chain to form hydrogen bonds leads to an increase in free energy for the water molecules in contact with the chain.[4] It is this **hydrophobic effect** acting on only a part of the surfactant molecule that drives the micelle formation: beyond a limiting amphiphile concentration, the free energy of the whole system is reduced by ordering the amphiphiles into aggregates in which the nonpolar tails are directed inwards, protected from contact with the water by the polar head groups which together form a 'shell' around the hydrophobic 'core', cf. Fig. 3 (note that these cartoons for simplicity have been drawn with a highly unrealistic degree of chain order). If the aggregates are finite we call them micelles and the concentration where association begins is called the **Critical Micelle Concentration**, abbreviated **CMC**. Typical CMC values lie in the 1-10 mM range (about 0.01-0.1 wt.-%). Note that the CMC does not constitute the onset of liquid crystalline order. This typ-

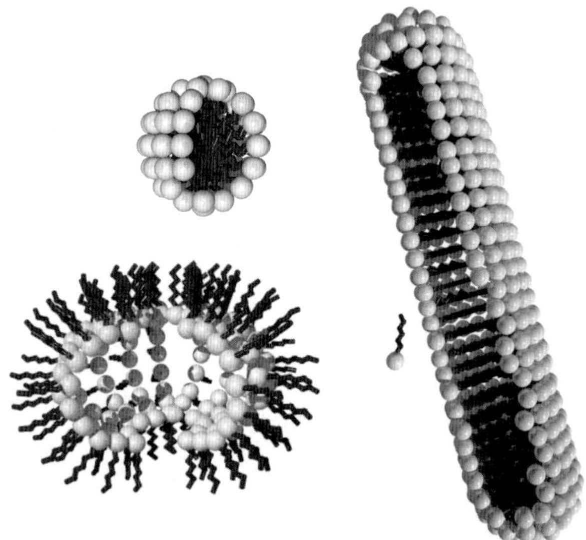

Fig. 3. Highly simplified cartoons of a spherical and a rod-shaped micelle of normal type (top left and right), as well as of an inverse micelle (bottom left). In order to reveal the micelle interior a sector of amphiphiles has been left out in each case. In reality the polar head groups (depicted as white balls) constitute an essentially complete shell around (normal) or within (inverse) the non-polar chains (black zigzags). Note that the order is grossly exaggerated in all three drawings, in particular for the non-polar tail (drawn black), which in reality is highly flexible. From Ref. 32.

ically happens around 25-40% surfactant, while the micellar phase at lower concentrations is isotropic in all properties. This phase can be compared to the isotropic phase of a thermotropic material heated above its clearing point; the building blocks are there but they are not long-range ordered. We see here that the main thermodynamic control parameter for lyotropics is not the temperature but the solute concentration. Low concentrations correspond to high temperatures of thermotropics, as illustrated in Fig. 2.

If, rather than water, oil is added as a solvent (generally, both solvents are required but with oil in large excess) then the reverse micelle structure is favorable. Indeed, under such circumstances one may observe inverted lyotropic phases (indicated with a superscript i), where the micelles have a polar interior and non-polar exterior. Often the micelles are spherical and thus rather unsuitable for building liquid crystal phases (they may build up cubic phases), but with the right concentration of the right amphiphile, sometimes with the aid of an appropriate co-surfactant, the micelles may take a rod- or disc-like shape. Such micelles are appropriate building blocks for developing a lyotropic nematic phase. The full details regulating the micelle shape are outside the scope of this book but, in brief, it is the relationship between the effective sizes of the hydrophilic and hydrophobic molecule parts, respectively, that dictates the final shape of the micellar aggregate. An in-depth treatment of these issues can be found e.g. in Ref. 5.

Although actually a very dynamic and fairly flexible construct, the micelle in surfactant-based lyotropic liquid crystals plays the part of the rigid core in thermotropics, whilst the isotropic solvent takes the role of the thermotropic mesogen's flexible end chains, ensuring the fluidity of the phase. The isotropic solvent is often referred to as the ***continuous phase*** while the micelles, being individually dispersed in the host, together constitute the ***disperse phase***. The fact that one phase is dispersed in another, in units that are larger than the solvent molecules, means that lyotropic liquid crystals belong to the materials class of colloids. In its most general definition, a colloid is a dispersion of particles, droplets or bubbles that are substantially larger than the molecules of the surrounding medium. This means that the disperse phase units have a size in the range of approximately 1 nm - 1μm, and sometimes this size range is used to define the term colloid.

Colloids can be solutions as well as non-equilibrium suspensions of lyophobic particles, where the difference refers to the thermodynamic state: a solution forms spontaneously and is thus thermodynamically stable, representing a minimum in free energy, but a suspension is a *kinetically* stabilized state corresponding to a local, but not global, minimum in free energy. The term *lyophobic* indicates that the disperse phase units are not soluble in the continuous phase but would in fact prefer to aggregate and phase separate from the host liquid on a macroscopic scale, e.g. oil floating on top of water or sand grains sedimenting to the bottom of a container with water in which the sand was dispersed. The kinetic stabilization means that an energy barrier that is considerably larger than the thermal energy separates the stabilized local minimum from the global minimum. In the case of colloids this amounts to the disperse phase units experiencing a repulsive force that prevents them from aggregating.

Micelles form spontaneously and the surfactant-based lyotropic phases are thus colloidal solutions, in thermodynamic equilibrium. In contrast, the other groups of lyotropic liquid crystals, where nanoparticles like inorganic nanorods (Chapters 23 and 26) or -platelets (Chapters 24 and 25), viruses or cellulose nanorods (Chap. 27) are the building blocks, generally need kinetic stabilization to appear. We often use the more specific term colloidal **suspension**, which by definition is thermodynamically unstable. Some refer to these liquid crystals simply as colloidal liquid crystals. This subclass of lyotropic liquid crystals attracts greatly increasing interest today.[6–13] Also in this case surfactants are used, but not for generating micelles that build the phase. They rather play the role of stabilizer, coating the nanoparticles to make them more compatible with the continuous phase and prevent aggregation. In Chap. 3 Paul van der Schoot will go into the different colloidal stabilization mechanisms—as well as possible mechanisms of aggregation—in detail.

As we will see in Sec. 10, building block anisometry is one requirement for lyotropic liquid crystal formation, the other that there is a sufficient volume fraction of blocks present. In an amphiphile solution, the concentration must generally be some 100 - 500 times the CMC before an anisotropic phase arises. When this happens, it may be because anisometric micelles become long-range ordered in their orientation without losing their liquid-like short-range positional correlation. Such a lyotropic nematic phase is however quite rare among surfactant-based lyotropics, where the columnar and lamellar phases, exhibiting positional as well as orientational order, strongly dominate.[14] The reverse situation prevails in many particle-based lyotropics, where nematic phases are the norm and columnar and lamellar phases are uncommon. This can be understood as a result of the large spread in length of many nanoparticles (they are polydisperse[c]), which means that no distinct lamellar thickness can be defined, and due to other disruptive phenomena—aggregation or gelation—occurring at concentrations that are lower than the threshold concentration for the more ordered phases. These issues will play a role in the final part of the book, Chapters 23–27.

Before ending this section, we should add that polymer solutions may form unassociated yet thermodynamically stable lyotropic liquid crystals, if the polymer chain is stiff enough. The most famous example is perhaps that of polyaramide chains processed in organic solvents via a liquid crystalline state into Kevlar® or Twaron® fibers, while a less well known but very important example is that of solutions of double-stranded DNA.[15,16] A somewhat intermediate position is taken by the chromonic class of lyotropic liquid crystals,[17] where the constituent molecules do not aggregate into micelles but instead stack up into columns of varying lengths. The molecules forming chromonic liquid crystals, which are generally dyes (hence the name), are amphiphilic but of somewhat different type than the classic examples: the main surface of a chromonic molecule is hydrophobic (thus forming the interior of the stack) whereas its border is water soluble. In the remaining part of this chapter we will mainly deal with amphiphile-based lyotropics, largely due to their benefits as illustrative teaching example.

1.4. *The smectic and lamellar phases*

The nematic phase is the only liquid crystal phase that exhibits no long-range positional order and thus the only anisotropic 3D liquid. All other liquid crystal phases exhibit quasi-long-range positional order in one, two or three dimensions. We will now discuss the most important positionally ordered liquid crystal phases briefly, starting with the family of phases with one-dimensional (1D) positional order: the **smectic** (in thermotropics and particle-based lyotropics) and **lamellar** (in amphiphile-based lyotropics) phases.

Common to smectic and lamellar phases is a layered structure. In the lamellar case, for which the basic shorthand notation L is used, we have a periodic stack of parallel molecular bilayers separated by water, cf. Fig. 4 a-b. Within each bilayer the hydrophobic chains can be in a liquid-like state

---

[c]The IUPAC recommendation is actually to use *disperse* and *non-disperse* rather than *polydisperse* and *monodisperse*, since the former term is a tautology and the latter a contradiction. We will, however, use the two latter terms in this book for the simple reason that essentially everyone uses them, whereas the IUPAC-promoted terms often cause confusion despite their linguistic superiority.

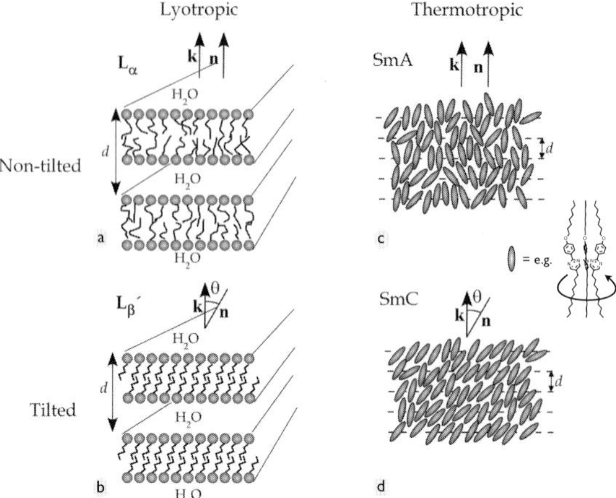

Fig. 4. Schematic drawings of the most important amphiphile-based lamellar and thermotropic smectic phases, the amphiphiles of the former drawn with a ball for the polar head group. The mesogens in the thermotropic smectics are drawn as ellipsoids reflecting their fast rotation around the main axis of inertia, effectively averaging out the details of the molecular structure in many respects. The distance d along the layer normal **k** is the repeat distance in each phase. From Ref. 32.

(a) or they can be 'frozen' in an extended all-*trans* conformation with a common well-defined orientation throughout the bilayer (b). This difference is the distinguishing factor between the two most important categories of amphiphile-based lamellar lyotropic polymorphism. In the modern notation the status of the chains is represented by a Greek letter appended as an index to the basic L shorthand: α indicates liquid-like disordered chains and β is used when the chains are in a stiff ordered state.

The fluctuations of the disordered chains in the L$_\alpha$ phase are unbiased in the lamellar plane, hence their average direction is along the bilayer normal **k**. Such a phase thus has the same uniaxial (cylindrical) $D_{\infty h}$ rotational symmetry as the nematic phase, with the director **n** parallel to **k**. The L$_\alpha$ phase is of great biological importance, because it occurs in our cell membranes, the main component of which is phospholipids. The L$_\beta$ and L$_{\beta'}$ phases are often referred to as *gel phases*, reflecting their low degree of fluidity. Most common synthetic surfactants do not develop L$_\beta$/L$_{\beta'}$ phases, their sole lamellar phase being L$_\alpha$. Phospholipids, in contrast, generally form L_α as well as $L_\beta/L_{\beta'}$ phases. The transition between them (the 'main transition') is largely thermally controlled.

The prime in $L_{\beta'}$ indicates that the chains, and thus **n**, tilt away from **k** whereas in L_β we have $\mathbf{n}\|\mathbf{k}$. The tilt is a result of an enhanced molecular packing of tilted compared to orthogonally organized lipids, which largely can be traced back to a mismatch between the cross section areas of the head group (larger cross section) and the chains (smaller cross section). This is the most common case, hence the majority of lipids form $L_{\beta'}$ rather than L_β on cooling from L_α.

In thermotropics the analog to L_α is the smectic-A phase, abbreviated SmA. It (generally) has the same uniaxial cylindrical $D_{\infty h}$ rotational symmetry with $\mathbf{n}\|\mathbf{k}$ but the molecules are organized in monolayers as they are not amphiphilic and there is no solvent. Furthermore, the layers are normally not as well-defined as in the lyotropic lamellar case (where the solvent 'seals off' adjacent bilayers from each other), cf. Fig. 4c. The mesogens can diffuse considerably along **k** and they may 'stick out' (interdigitate) outside their current 'home' layer. Smectic phases are generally formed by rod-like molecules, but there are a few examples of smectic phases from discotics, then requiring a strongly asymmetric folding of the terminal chains.[18]

While the SmA phase is almost always uniaxial a few examples of biaxial SmA phases appear to have been identified.[19,20] Much more important as biaxial smectic is however the family of smectic-C-type phases, characterized by a tilted director and in this respect thus a thermotropic relative of the lyotropic $L_{\beta'}$ phase. Note, however, that smectics are viscous fluid, not gel-like, phases. The SmC tilt angle, generally given the symbol θ, is usually temperature dependent, often approaching zero on heating towards the SmA phase, while it at lower temperatures often saturates in the range 20 - 30°.[d]

There are several versions of the basic smectic-C-type structure, distinguished by different interlayer tilting direction correlation schemes (see e.g. Ref. 21 for a review of smectic liquid crystals). In the fundamental SmC phase the tilt in adjacent layers is in the same direction, giving the phase C_{2h} rotational symmetry. For the purpose of this book, it suffices to consider only SmC (in its achiral and chiral versions) as tilted smectic, as it is essentially the only one so far where experiments with inclusions have been reported (discussed by Stannarius and Harth in Chap. 11). One often defines the **SmC tilt plane** as the plane spanned by the director **n** and the layer normal **k**, cf. Fig. 5. In addition, when considering the physics

---

[d]If the smectic-C phase follows on cooling directly from a nematic phase or from the isotropic liquid state, θ is often large (around 45°) and close to temperature-independent. The same holds in case of a transition from a SmA phase with strong first-order character.

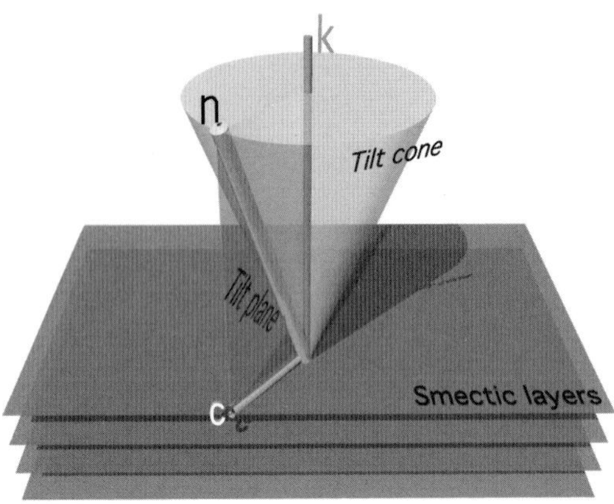

Fig. 5. The geometry of the SmC phase calls for the definition of many new help concepts, such as the tilt plane, the tilt cone and the C-director **c**. From Ref. 32.

of the SmC phase, it is convenient to define an additional vector field,[22] closely related to the director. Reflecting the phase in which it finds use, it is called the **C-director**, abbreviated **c**, and it is defined as the projection of the actual director **n** onto the smectic layer plane, cf. Fig. 5.

If we want to define a SmC state completely, it is not sufficient to give the value of θ, we must also tell in which direction **n** tilts. This is generally done by defining some (arbitrary) reference axis in the smectic layer plane and then stating the angle φ between this reference axis and the tilting direction, cf. Fig. 5. However, while the *magnitude* of tilt θ critically influences the free energy of a SmC phase (θ is the primary order parameter of the SmA-SmC transition), φ has no impact on the energy. As a result any value of φ is equally good, yielding a range of degenerate SmC states that define a cone (the *SmC tilt cone*), with opening angle 2θ and symmetry axis along **k**, cf. Fig. 5.

Basically, the smectic layer thickness is the projection of the average mesogen length on **k** (taking conformational disorder into account),[21] whereas the thickness of the lamellar bilayer is twice the projection of the average amphiphile length. We should stress, however, that the bilayer thickness is not the periodicity of the lamellar phase: its period is the sum of the bilayer thickness and the thickness of the water layer separating two adjacent bilayers. This means that the translational periodicity in lyotropic lamellar phases is a function of water content. There are several other types of lamellar and smectic phases, but they are outside the scope of this book.

1.5. *The columnar phases*

The next step in long-range positional order in liquid crystal phases is encountered among the columnar phases. Now the building blocks are positioned on a 2D lattice, but in the third direction there is no long-range positional correlation, cf. Fig. 6. In the thermotropic case the columnar order is typically formed by discotic mesogens, the aromatic cores stacking up as in piles of coins, each pile being located on a point of a lattice that is hexagonal (Fig. 6a) or close to hexagonal (Fig. 6b). Within a pile the molecule positions are often not long-range correlated (the stack is internally disordered), hence the structures can be regarded as 1D liquids. Moreover, the peripheral chains of each mesogen are in a disordered fluctuating state, giving the interstitial volume 'between the columns' very low degree of order. This aspect has been ignored in the cartoons in Fig. 6.

The average orientation of the disc can be flat, i.e. **n** is along the column axis, giving the phase D_{6h} symmetry with a C_6 rotation axis along the columns and six C_2 axes perpendicular to them. The positional lattice is truly hexagonal. The discs may however also be more or less uniformly tilted within the columns. If there is correlation in the tilting direction between adjacent columns the phase loses its D_{6h} symmetry, the hexagonal lattice shrinking along the tilting direction into a rectangular one, as in

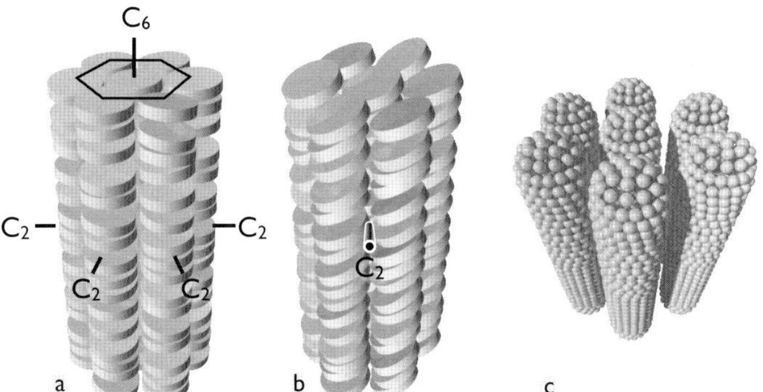

Fig. 6. Cartoons of three different columnar phases. Parts a) and b) both depict thermotropic phases, the columns being formed by disc-shaped mesogens stacking with their cores on top of each other. If the cores are non-tilted or randomly tilted the phase has hexagonal point group symmetry D_{6h} (a) but if they are tilted in a well-defined common direction the symmetry gets reduced to rectangular (b). The lyotropic hexagonal columnar phase (c) is formed by uniformly aligned rod micelles positionally organized on a hexagonal lattice in the plane perpendicular to the micelle long axis (defining **n**). From Ref. 32.

Fig. 6b. Note that the remaining C_2 rotation axis is perpendicular to the columns: there is no longer any rotational symmetry axis along the columns. Reflecting their respective symmetries these two cases of columnar mesomorphology are denoted Col_h and Col_r, respectively.[e] See e.g. the review of Laschat *et al.*[18] for more details.

In the lyotropic columnar phases we have either rod-shaped nanoparticles or 'infinitely' long rod-shaped micelles[14] positionally correlated on a 2D lattice in a plane perpendicular to the rods, i.e. perpendicular to **n**, cf. Fig. 6c. The disorder of the system is mainly found in the water (or other solvent) found between the columns, just like the disordered peripheral chains of discotic mesogens in thermotropic columnar phases. Most often the packing of rod micelles in the plane perpendicular to **n** is hexagonal and the normal columnar phase is then labelled H_α. We can also have a hexagonal columnar phase of inverted micelles (water inside, oil between the micelles) which then gets the label H_α^i. For the normal as well as the inverted columnar phases the packing is not restricted to being hexagonal, but rectangular as well as square lyotropic columnar phases also occur, denoted R and C, respectively.[24]

Lyotropic nomenclature is unfortunately not fully consistent. For hexagonal columnar phases a relatively commonly occurring alternative to the notation used in this book is H_1 and H_2 for the normal and inverted structures, respectively. Some researchers still use an older terminology for lyotropics, in which lamellar phases are referred to as *neat* and columnar as *middle* phases.

1.6. *Chiral liquid crystal phases*

With the introduction of chirality into liquid crystals, another fascinating as well as useful aspect of this class of ordered soft matter arises. In most cases, chiral liquid crystals are a result of chiral molecules being present, either as chiral dopants in an achiral host phase or by the use of mesogens or nanoparticles that are chiral in themselves. In both cases the presence of stereoisomerically enriched[f] chiral species, leading to a sample that is

---

[e]Sometimes an additional index *o* (ordered) or *d* (disordered) is added, referring to the presence or absence of a medium-range positional correlation along the column axis. The IUPAC recommendation is *not* to use these indices,[23] as in both cases the positional order along the column is liquid-like, only with different correlation lengths.

[f]Racemates, where all stereoisomers of a chiral species are present at equal amounts, are effectively non-chiral in their physical properties. The star is thus used only when one stereoisomer dominates over the other(s).

chiral on the macroscopic scale, is often indicated by adding a star to the shorthand of the fundamental corresponding achiral phase, e.g. N* for a chiral nematic phase. In terms of symmetry, the definition of chirality tells that no mirror planes are present, hence the index h in all symmetries mentioned so far must be removed for the chiral version of a phase.

The chiral nematic phase (often referred to with the historically motivated[1] term **cholesteric** phase) is the best studied chiral liquid crystal, a result of its simplicity, ubiquity, beauty as well as applicability. The molecular chirality is here amplified by the phase to the macroscopic scale as a helical director modulation along an axis that is perpendicular to **n**, cf. Fig. 7. This gives rise to spectacular physical properties which will be discussed in Sec. 8.

Fig. 7.   Cartoons of the helical director modulation in the chiral nematic (or cholesteric) phase for the case of rod- and disc-shaped building blocks, respectively. Each rod or disc represents either a mesogen (thermotropics) or micelle or nanoparticle (lyotropics) with the corresponding shape. Note that, for clarity, the pitch has been drawn orders of magnitude smaller than in reality and the local degree of order is much too high. From Ref. 32.

In smectic phases, a helical director modulation perpendicular to **n** would break the layers and is thus not admitted.[g] The SmA* phase therefore has the same structure as an achiral SmA phase. Nevertheless, its physical properties are quite different from its achiral analog. The phase is still chiral, despite the absence of a helix. In contrast to SmA*, the chiral SmC* phase does allow a helical superstructure, but it applies to the C-director **c** rather than the normal director **n**. In other words, the tilting *direction* precesses helically along the smectic layer normal, as illustrated in Fig. 8.

The **pitch** p (periodicity of the helix) can be anywhere from some hundred nanometers to infinity, for cholesterics as well as SmC*-type phases. It depends on the one hand on the so-called 'helical twisting power' (HTP) of the chiral molecule (i.e. it is structure-specific), on the other on its enantiomeric enrichment ('enantiomeric excess', *ee*), third on the temperature.

---

[g]A special case where chirality in fact does break up layers is the class of Twist Grain Boundary (TGB*) phases.

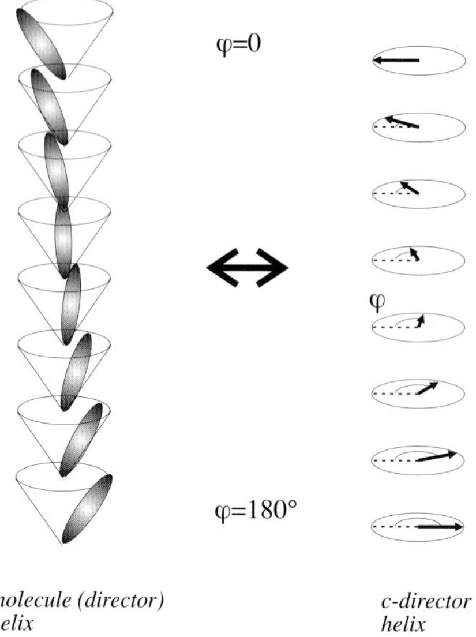

Fig. 8. The helical modulation of the chiral smectic-C (SmC*) phase applies to the director tilting direction φ or, equivalently, to the C-director **c**. To the left a cartoon of the molecular order is shown, each layer being represented by a tilt cone on which the actual director is indicated with an ellipse. The right drawing shows the corresponding modulation in **c** (represented by the black arrow) and φ. Half a period of the helical structure is drawn, the twist greatly exaggerated for reasons of clarity. A real short-pitch SmC* phase has a helical pitch on the order of 100 smectic layers. From Ref. 32.

The typically rather strong temperature dependence of the pitch (at least for thermotropics), which can give rise to a color that changes on heating or cooling (see Section 8), is the basis for the common use of N* liquid crystals in temperature sensors. The handedness of the helix depends on which stereoisomer builds up the phase or is added to the achiral host phase. Quantitatively, the *inverse* pitch depends linearly on *ee*, going from 0 (infinite pitch) at the racemate to p_0^{-1} at 100% *ee*, where p_0 is the minimum pitch that can be obtained with this particular system.

1.7. *Enantiotropic versus monotropic phases*

One final pair of fundamental terms should be defined in this discussion of liquid crystal phases. Some thermotropic substances show a larger number of liquid crystalline phases on cooling than on heating, the reason being that some of them may occur only as metastable supercooled phases, when cooling the substance past its melting point. If crystallization then does not set in immediately (generally because of kinetic hinderance of some kind), a phase transition into a new liquid crystalline state may instead take place, the new phase being referred to as a **monotropic** phase. Sooner or later the supercooled phase will however be replaced by the crystalline state corresponding to the global energy minimum (except if a glass transition takes place, which can occur for some substances).

When heating the substance the monotropic liquid crystal phase will not reform, but the substance will stay in the crystalline state until it melts directly into the first **enantiotropic** phase of the compound, i.e. the first thermodynamically stable liquid crystal or isotropic liquid phase, forming on heating as well as on cooling. The term 'enantiotropic' applies to any thermodynamically stable phase, regardless of whether the compound exhibits monotropic phases or not, but the distinction is generally called upon only when discussing substances exhibiting metastable phases on cooling.

When stating the phase sequence of a substance with monotropic phases these are enclosed in parentheses, together with the transition temperatures into each phase (which must refer to a cooling run). A compound with a monotropic SmA phase underneath an enantiotropic nematic phase could thus have the phase sequence:

Cr. 30 (SmA 27) N 42 Iso. $/^{\circ}$C

Note that the melting point (30°C) is higher than the N-SmA transition (27°C)! Furthermore, all enantiotropic transition temperatures are generally given on heating, since transition temperatures can be determined with greater accuracy in this direction.

2. Nematic order and how to quantify it: The orientational order parameter

The definition of the director provides a first qualitative description of the long-range orientational order of a nematic phase and enters as the natural variable in what is referred to as the *elastic continuum description* of the free energy of a nematic.[22] But apart from the *direction* of the anisotropy axis, one often desires also a quantitative measure of the anisotropy, or degree of orientational order. The parameter filling our needs is nowadays often called 'the nematic order parameter' S, even when applied to non-liquid crystalline systems such as dried films of nanorods.

For three-dimensional systems this parameter, introduced in 1939 by P.H. Hermanns and P. Platzek[25] and adopted for liquid crystals in 1942 by Viktor Tsvetkov,[26] has the form:

$$S = \frac{1}{2}\langle 3\cos^2\beta - 1\rangle \tag{1}$$

Here we have introduced the angle β, describing the deviation in orientation away from **n** of a particular building block at a particular moment in time, cf. Fig. 9. The deviation is averaged over the ensemble of building blocks constituting the phase considered, as indicated by the pointed brackets. In the figure we again use the angle φ to define the tilting direction, this time of the building block with respect to **n**.

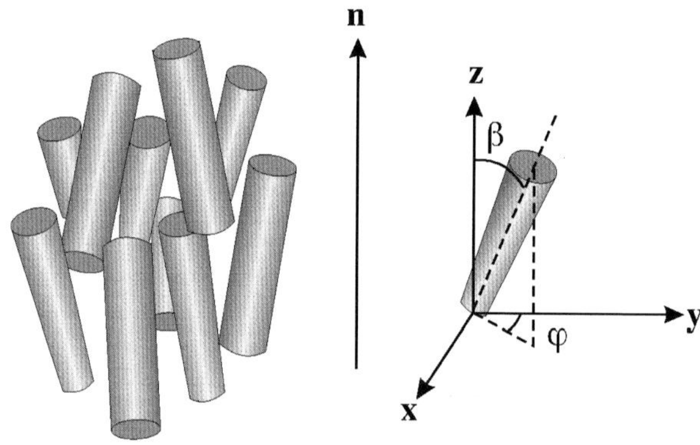

Fig. 9.   Graphical depiction of the concepts required for defining the orientational order parameter. The building blocks of the liquid crystal phase are depicted as rods, on the average oriented along **n** but each deviating by some angle β in a direction φ. From Ref. 32.

The order parameter Eq. (1) has the desirable property of being zero for total disorder, since in three dimensions $\langle\cos^2\beta\rangle = 1/3$ for a random orientational distribution, and 1 for perfect order (in which case $\langle\cos^2\beta\rangle = 1$). You may recognize the expression as the second Legendre polynomial, and the order parameter is often referred to as $\langle P_2\rangle$ to emphasize this equivalence,[h] but we will use the simpler shorthand S. In fact, the full scalar orientational order parameter[i] is an expansion in Legendre polynomials, the

---

[h]Actually, the IUPAC recommendation is to use $\langle P_2\rangle$ as shorthand for the scalar orientational order parameter[23] but S is still very commonly employed.
[i]A complete description of the orientationally ordered state requires a tensorial order parameter which includes both **n** and S.[22]

first term of which is $S = \langle P_2 \rangle$, but for many considerations it suffices to use this first term.

It has been empirically as well as theoretically established[1,22] that the isotropic-nematic transition in a system of building blocks of constant size and shape is first-order, i.e. the order parameter jumps discretely at the phase transition from zero to a non-zero value, for thermotropics typically around $S = 0.4$. On cooling a thermotropic nematic, S increases, initially fast but rapidly approaching saturation around $S = 0.6 - 0.7$, cf. Fig. 10. If smectic phases develop on further cooling the orientational order may increase discretely by a small amount at that phase transition as well, but inter-smectic transitions like SmA-SmC generally do not affect S markedly. In thermotropic liquid crystals, the orientational order rarely increases beyond $S \sim 0.8$, columnar phases being an exception.

In lyotropic liquid crystals one can basically distinguish two subclasses as far as the orientational order is concerned. Among surfactant-based lyotropics, the hexagonal phases have very high order parameters in the range of $S \approx 0.9$.[27] The same holds for nematic phases formed not by surfactant micelles but by colloidal suspensions of anisometric nanoparticles (viruses, carbon nanotubes, bentonite platelets, ...). In both cases the order parameter is largely insensitive to temperature. Micellar nematic phases, on the other hand can have a considerable temperature dependence of the order parameter, reflecting the temperature dependence of the length and stiffness (represented by the persistence length) of the micelles.[14] As a result their order parameter versus temperature curve may look qualitatively similar to Fig. 10. Moreover, the value S_{NI} at the transition point (which is here defined by a temperature and a concentration) can here be very low, sometimes substantially lower than S_{NI} of thermotropics. It is

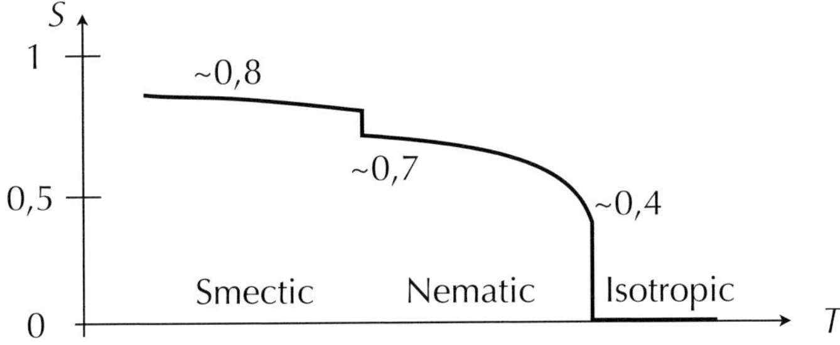

Fig. 10. Typical temperature dependence of the orientational order parameter in a thermotropic material exhibiting a nematic-smectic phase sequence. From Ref. 32.

typically $S_{NI} \approx 0.3$[28–31] but some experimental works report values as low as $S_{NI} \approx 0.1$.[29,30] The difference is most likely a result of the fact that the building blocks themselves change with temperature and concentration, varying in length, polydispersity as well as stiffness.

For a two-dimensional ensemble, e.g. rods restricted to a single plane like a substrate or thin flat film, the average $\langle \cos^2 \beta \rangle = 1/2$ for a random distribution, hence the corresponding expression for S in 2D is:

$$S_{2D} = \langle 2\cos^2 \beta - 1 \rangle \tag{2}$$

Since we know of no 2D liquid crystal phases with in-plane director[j] this order parameter should not be needed for describing the liquid crystal itself. However, if one wishes to describe the orientational distribution of nanorods such as carbon nanotubes or cellulose nanocrystals, which can easily reach several microns in length, dispersed within a liquid crystal phase that is filled into a standard sample cell (typically on the order of a few microns in thickness, thus thin enough to restrict the orientational fluctuations of the long nanorods to the cell plane), then S_{2D} is often the proper order parameter to use. The same holds for a dry film of nanorods produced by evaporating the solvent from an originally liquid crystalline suspensions of rods.

3. The anisotropic optical and viscous properties of liquid crystals

The macroscopic anisotropy of liquid crystals, a property shared with no other fluid, is the basis for their successful commercial exploitation. The anisotropy takes on several faces. We wait with the discussion of the response to electric and magnetic fields until Sec. 7 and we first restrict ourselves to achiral phases, the special properties arising as a result of chirality being the topic of Sec. 8.

3.1. *Optical anisotropy*

The anisometry of the building blocks and the long-range orientational order together generally render liquid crystals optically anisotropic, i.e. their refractive index $n_{\parallel}$ parallel to **n** is different from that perpendicular to the director, $n_{\perp}$. For a uniaxial material, these two indices are the

---

[j]Free-standing films of smectics, discussed in Chap. 11, can be considered 2D liquid crystals, but **n** is never in the film plane, since this is also the smectic layer plane.

extreme refractive index values and the director defines the optic axis. The magnitude of optical anisotropy, the **birefringence**, is defined as $\Delta n = n_{\parallel} - n_{\perp}$. Consequently, if $n_{\parallel}$ is the maximum refractive index, $\Delta n > 0$ and we call the liquid crystal positive uniaxial (this is the general case for rod-shaped mesogens), whereas if $\Delta n < 0$ the phase is negative uniaxial (this is the standard case for discotics).

A birefringent material can affect the polarization of light, changing its ellipticity, the main oscillation direction as well as handedness continuously. This is the basis for the use of liquid crystals in most electrooptic devices like displays, where the substance is placed between crossed polarizers. In the bright state the director/optic axis is oriented such that the light leaving the liquid crystal is linearly polarized with the electric field oscillations in the direction transmitted by the exit polarizer (the analyzer). Light thus passes through. In the dark state the director is reoriented such that no birefringence effect takes place. The polarization of the light then remains unchanged linear, with the oscillation direction perpendicular to the transmission direction of the analyzer, which thus absorbs the light. The function of liquid crystal displays is well described in numerous books and we thus refer the reader to other sources for a more complete explanation of their operation.

The dark state just described may be achieved by establishing a so-called **homeotropic** director geometry (Fig. 11, left), a term used when $\mathbf{n}$ and consequently the optic axis are perpendicular to the sample interface plane. Light passing through the sample at normal incidence (the light ray is perpendicular to the sample interface plane) thus propagates exactly along the optic axis, rendering the apparent birefringence zero.[k] In contrast, the maximum effective birefringence is experienced when the propagation direction is perpendicular to the optic axis. Again considering the case of normal incidence, this corresponds to $\mathbf{n}$ being in the sample interface plane. In liquid crystal science this geometry is referred to as **planar** alignment.[l]

In Fig. 11 the two principal alignment types are illustrated for the case of flat samples of smectic-A phase. Hometropic alignment corresponds to

---

[k]While the exact origin of the term *homeotropic* is obscure, it may be understood as a condensed form of *homeoisotropic* meaning *like isotropic*, referring to the fact that the birefringence effectively vanishes for light propagating along the optic axis.

[l]An older term sometimes encountered is *homogeneous alignment*. There are many reasons to avoid this term, the most important of which is its misleading character: *homeotropic* alignment is *homogeneous* in the proper sense of the word and a *planar* sample without a well-defined direction of $\mathbf{n}$ in the sample plane is an example of a highly *inhomogeneous* director field.

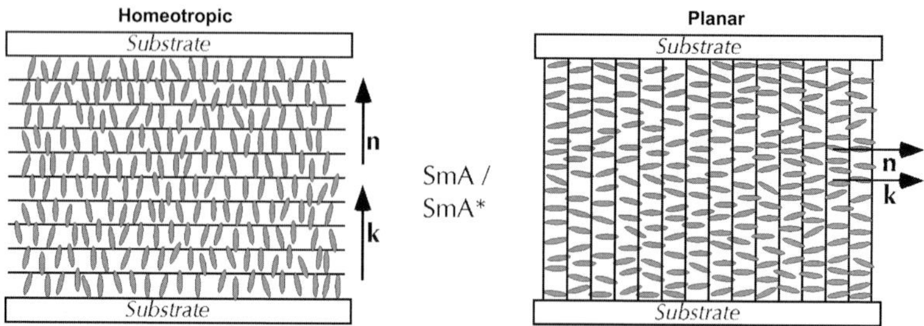

Fig. 11.   Schematic drawing of homeotropic and planar alignment, respectively, here illustrated for the case of a SmA phase. Normal light incidence means the light beam is propagating vertically in the picture. Note that the drawing is not to scale: a smectic layer is three orders of magnitude thinner than the typical distance between the sample substrates. From Ref. 32.

smectic layers in the sample plane whereas the planar alignment is equivalent to a geometry where the layers are standing up. The nematic cases are identical apart from the absence of layers, but the SmC case is somewhat different. Here one usually maintains the *layer* geometries in Fig. 11 in the definition of the concepts homeotropic and planar, although the director is then not along the viewing direction in the former case (it is therefore sometimes referred to as *quasi-homeotropic*) and not necessarily in the sample interface plane in the latter.

A planar nematic sample where **n** has no restriction to any particular direction in the sample plane is referred to as **degenerate planar**. The director and thus the optic axis change direction randomly (but continuously, except at defects) in the plane throughout the sample area. When observing a sample that is cooled from the isotropic phase into a nematic with degenerate planar alignment between crossed polarizers, many softly curving black 'brushes' appear, as seen in Fig. 12, often emanating from crosses or cusps that are defects in the director field. Along a black brush, **n** is parallel to one of the polarizers and the random turns of these lines reflect the absence of an influence that tells along *which* in-plane direction the director should align. Moreover, one often also sees a number of randomly curving 'threads' or 'streaks' that are bright rather than dark. A few of them are present in Fig. 12. These are defect lines, separating areas between which the director is rotated by half a turn (π radians, $\mathbf{n} \to -\mathbf{n}$). Most of these defects, called **schlieren** after the German word for streak, *Schliere*, quickly diminish in length and gradually disappear as the director field 'heals out', becoming more uniform in order to minimize energy.

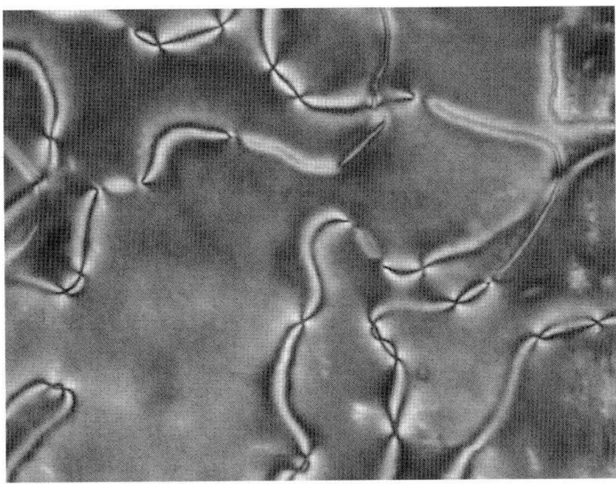

Fig. 12. An example of the characteristic schlieren texture exhibited by nematic liquid crystals in degenerate planar alignment.

These defects give the name to the feature-rich degenerate planar texture shown in Fig. 12, very characteristic of the nematic phase, referred to as a *schlieren texture*.

The magnitude of the birefringence depends on the degree of orientational order S and the polarizability anisotropy $\Delta\alpha$ of the building blocks of the phase, according to:

$$\Delta n \propto S\Delta\alpha \tag{3}$$

i.e. it is a linear function of the nematic order parameter and the difference in polarizability along and perpendicular to the principal symmetry axis of the building block. While $\Delta\alpha$ is largely temperature independent the order parameter generally changes strongly at temperatures close to the transition to the isotropic phase, as discussed above, hence Δn decreases rapidly as a thermotropic liquid crystal is heated towards its clearing point, cf. Fig. 13. Any other influence on the degree of order, e.g. the addition of particles that disturb the nematic organization, will have the same type of very visible influence on Δn.

The linear aromatic core commonly found in calamitic thermotropic mesogens (see Sec. 9) results in a high value of $\Delta\alpha$, hence thermotropic calamitics belong to some of the strongest birefringent materials known. Most lyotropic liquid crystals, in contrast, are formed by molecules or particles without aromatic moieties (carbon nanotubes are a striking exception, being *entirely* aromatic), making $\Delta\alpha$ rather small. Consequently, a lyotropic nematic typically has orders of magnitude smaller birefringence

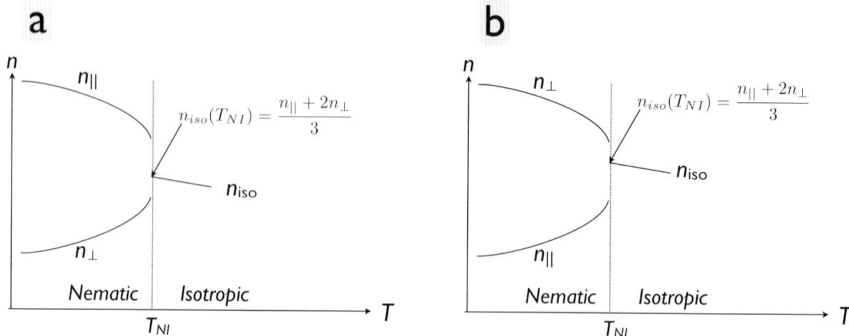

Fig. 13. Typical temperature dependencies of the refractive indices of a positive (a) and negative (b) uniaxial thermotropic nematic, below and above the clearing point. From Ref. 32.

than its thermotropic counterpart, although $S(T)$ may be greater for the lyotropic.

If we cool a nematic-forming thermotropic down from its isotropic into its nematic phase, the isotropic refractive index will split up in $n_\parallel$ and $n_\perp$ at the phase transition, cf. Fig. 13. Within the isotropic-nematic phase coexistence range (for a pure compound only a single temperature, as follows from Gibbs' phase rule), these three refractive indices are related as:

$$n_{iso}(T_{NI}) = \frac{n_\parallel(T_{NI}) + 2n_\perp(T_{NI})}{3} \tag{4}$$

a result of the geometrical averaging taking place in the isotropic phase. This holds regardless of whether the material has positive (Fig. 13a) or negative (b) optical anisotropy. As a result, the isotropic refractive index at the phase transition is closer to the greater nematic refractive index for a negative uniaxial material, whereas it is closer to the smaller one for a positive material. The decrease in n_{iso} upon heating through the isotropic phase is a result of the dependence of the refractive index on the density of the phase, which decreases on further heating.

The visible effect of birefringence is generally not simply one of bright or dark, but one of color. This is because the exact change in polarization that light undergoes on passage through the liquid crystal depends on its wavelength, or color. Therefore, a liquid crystal between crossed polarizers illuminated by white light will often appear strongly colored. The color depends on the magnitude of Δn and the thickness of the sample, as is graphically summarized in a **Michel-Lévy** chart, cf. Fig. 14. This chart is an invaluable aid to the polarizing microscopist and thus has a very good

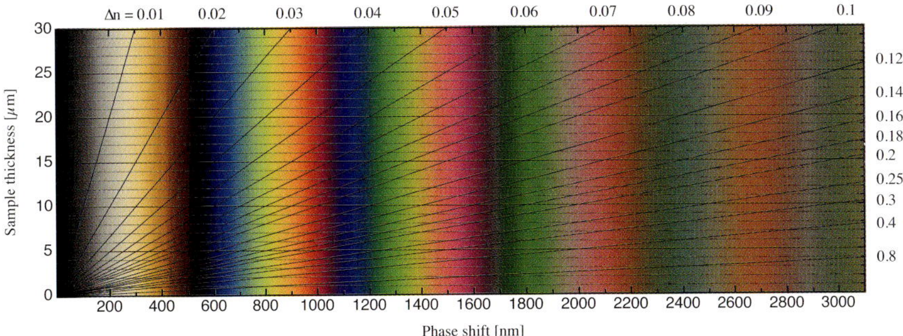

Fig. 14. Calculated Michel-Lévy diagram optimized for typical values of birefringence of thermotropic liquid crystals. The colors are only approximately correct (in particular, the true color at about 530 nm phase shift is in fact a deep violet). From Ref. 32.

place on the wall in any lab where liquid crystals are studied.

The horizontal axis of the diagram corresponds to the phase shift between ordinary and extraordinary light components introduced by the birefringent sample and the vertical axis corresponds to the sample thickness. The color between crossed polarizers of a sample with a particular value of birefringence can thus be determined, as a function of sample thickness, by drawing a straight line from the origin. Several such lines are drawn in the diagram for different Δn values, allowing one to quickly locate the line roughly corresponding to the sample presently under study. The Michel-Lévy chart shown in Fig. 14 is actually rather unique because it has been drawn on a scale optimized for thermotropic liquid crystals.[m] Most Michel-Lévy diagrams are drawn with inorganic crystals in mind, typically having about an order of magnitude lower birefringence than thermotropic liquid crystals. They may, however, work quite well for lyotropics.

For typical thermotropic birefringence values of $\Delta n \approx 0.1$ one finds that a regime of strong colors (varying quasi-periodically over two - three orders) for sample thicknesses in the range $d \approx 3\mu$m to $d \approx 20\mu$m, is surrounded by a grey-white regime for very thin cells ($d \approx 1 - 2\mu$m) and a regime with a slow periodic variation between pallid and rather uninformative green and pink tones for very thick cells. The latter is one of the reasons why thermotropic liquid crystal cells are rarely much thicker than some tens of microns (cf. Sec. 6). Conversely, if we know the sample thickness, we can use the chart to estimate Δn or at least track changes in birefringence.

---

[m]The colors of a standard Michel-Lévy diagram may however be more accurate, because the colors in Fig. 14 are only approximate, cf. Ref. 32.

This very brief discussion of the optical anisotropy of liquid crystals has been done using the simplest case of uniaxial birefringence. The optical situation gets more complicated in case of a biaxial phase, which has two optic axes and three extreme values of refractive index n_1, n_2 and n_3. When working with liquid crystals we often deal with uniaxial phases (N, SmA, L$_\alpha$, ...), and even the biaxial phases (SmC, ...) are often very weakly so, such that we in a first approximation can neglect the biaxiality.

3.2. *The viscous properties of liquid crystals*

Figure 15a shows a classic set-up for defining shear viscosity: a fluid is encapsulated between a stationary bottom plate and a top plate that moves with velocity v, as indicated by the long thick arrow. Since the fluid at each plate is at rest with respect to that plate (assuming no-slip boundary conditions), the fluid velocity as measured in the external reference frame increases continuously from zero at the bottom plate to v at the top plate, as illustrated by the arrows increasing in length from bottom to top. The resulting shear flow is counteracted by dissipative forces described by the shear viscosity of the fluid. As we are here considering a liquid crystal, these forces are strongly influenced by the orientational order. It makes a great difference if the flow is along or perpendicular to **n**, and for the latter case it also makes a difference if the flow velocity gradient is along or perpendicular to the director. In the 1930's these three situations, depicted by three orthogonal director orientations in Fig. 15a, were for the first time successfully realized for measuring the three corresponding viscosities, η_1,

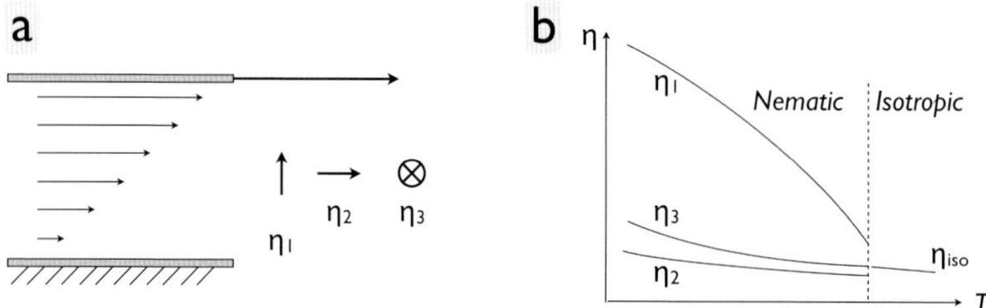

Fig. 15. a) The three Mięsowicz viscosities are defined by considering a classic shear flow experiment, except that **n** is blocked by an external magnetic field, giving three different orthogonal director orientations (indicated to the right of the shear flow schematic by arrows above η_1, η_2 and η_3) with respect to the flow direction. b) The isotropic viscosity splits into the three Mięsowicz viscosities below the transition to the nematic phase, η_3 often essentially following the isotropic viscosity value, whereas η_1 is higher and η_2 lower than the viscosity in the isotropic phase. From Ref. 32.

η_2 and η_3, by the Polish physicist Marian Miȩsowicz.[33] These three special viscosity values of a nematic are nowadays consequently referred to as the **Miȩsowicz viscosities**.

It is probably intuitively clear that the lowest of the three shear viscosities is η_2, corresponding to flow along the director. The largest viscous resistance is obtained when the director is perpendicular to the flow but parallel to the velocity gradient, i.e. η_1 is the largest Miȩsowicz viscosity. The η_3 value, finally, is of intermediate magnitude, generally considerably closer to η_2 than η_1. A typical temperature dependence is sketched in Fig. 15b. In a very approximate way the Miȩsowicz viscosities are sufficient for understanding the basic viscous behavior of liquid crystals. For instance, if we make no particular effort to control the director orientation during flow, the flow will align the director for minimum dissipation, i.e. **n** will be more or less along the flow.[n] This also means that if one attempts to measure the viscosity of a nematic with a standard viscometer, one will generally measure a viscosity not far from η_2, obtaining a value on the order of a Poise for thermotropics. Flow alignment can be very useful, sometimes even essential, for achieving uniformly aligned samples of liquid crystals that are difficult to align by means of field application or surface action (see Section 6), e.g. when dealing with lyotropic liquid crystals. However, for liquid crystals with positional order the minimum dissipation is along the layers or columns, i.e. not necessarily along **n**.

While η_1, η_2 and η_3 bear a close resemblance to the scalar viscosity η in an isotropic liquid there are in a nematic also new types of viscosity that have no correspondence in an isotropic liquid. Consider a nematic with positive dielectric anisotropy, $\Delta\epsilon > 0$, that is initially aligned uniformly with the director $\mathbf{n}_0$ along a particular direction in the xy plane. This is the minimum energy situation and there is no flow. If we now apply an electric field along the $\hat{z}$ direction the field will, as explained in Sec. 7, tend to rotate the director far from surfaces by an angle ϕ around an axis in the xy plane, cf. Fig. 16a, experiencing a counteracting viscous torque given by:

$$\Gamma = -\gamma_1 \cdot \frac{d\phi}{dt} \tag{5}$$

The change in direction is counteracted by a viscosity γ_1. This viscosity is called the **rotational viscosity**. The coefficient γ_1 also determines the

---

[n]In reality the situation is more complicated. The director **n** and the flow velocity v are strongly interacting. If **n** is perpendicular to the flow lines, it suffers a large torque. But even if **n** is along the flow lines it suffers a (smaller) torque and will tend to form an angle with v.[22]

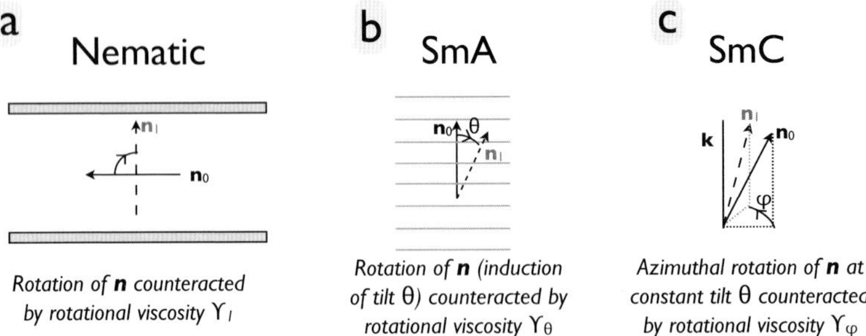

Fig. 16. Three main rotational viscosities are considered in the study of liquid crystals, not related to bulk material flow but to reorientation of the director. In the nematic phase the rotational viscosity γ_1 (a) relates to director reorientation in the liquid crystal at rest. In SmA and SmC a related viscosity is denoted γ_θ, corresponding to an induction (SmA) or variation (SmC) of a director tilt θ (b). Finally, because the steady-state tilt in SmC is non-zero, there is a rotational viscosity γ_φ describing the weak resistance against azimuthal rotations at constant tilt angle (c). From Ref. 32.

speed of back relaxation of the director when we take the field away (assuming that the surfaces promote the original planar alignment $\mathbf{n}_0$). It is a technically very important characteristic as it influences the maximum frequency at which a nematic device can be driven. The complete hydrodynamics of nematics requires five independent viscosities for its general description[22] as worked out by Ericksen and Leslie, but this theory is beyond the scope of this chapter.

In smectics the viscosities are essentially different in character. In SmC we have two characteristic rotational viscosities, different from γ_1. Because the director is tilted with respect to the layer normal we have the possibility of reorientation of the tilting direction φ around the tilt cone, cf. Fig. 16c. The corresponding viscosity is denoted γ_φ, and it is very low, as the free energy is degenerate in φ. In contrast, a rotation of $\mathbf{n}$ that changes the SmC tilt angle θ affects the free energy. Such a motion is thus very limited, described by the viscosity γ_θ, cf. Fig. 16b.

4. Liquid crystal elasticity

An ordinary liquid shows no shape elasticity, can sustain no dilatation (stretching) and can only be compressed with difficulty. A liquid crystal is not an ordinary liquid. In addition to the fundamental behavior of ordinary liquids it exhibits a unique type of elastic response. While it is probably no surprise that liquid crystal phases with long-range positional order can exhibit solid-like elasticity as a response to mechanically induced changes in a lamellar, smectic or columnar structure, it may to the newcomer be more mysterious at first that elastic deformation and restoration exists also in nematics. This is not the standard solid-like elasticity related to shape change, but an orientational elasticity connected to deformations in the director field. We will in this introductory chapter discuss only this type of elasticity, which is quite unique to liquid crystals. It is the only type of elasticity existing in nematics, but it is just as important in smectics and lamellar phases. In columnar phases the 2D lattice makes director field distortions more complicated, but also there they play a role.

4.1. *Deformations in the director field*

The non-deformed elastic ground state of an achiral nematic is one where (ignoring thermally activated fluctuations) the director field is totally uniform, i.e. $\mathbf{n}$ points in the same direction everywhere throughout the sample. An elastic deformation in the case of a nematic results from a *local* reorientation $\delta\mathbf{n}$ of the director, leading to a director field distortion transmitted over a larger scale. Since distortions in the director field cost energy, the nematic tries to reestablish the uniform director field, not by a force as in solid elasticity but by an elastic *torque*. The strength of the torque can be calculated by differentiating the elastic free energy. The starting point for analyzing elastic deformations and their consequences in a nematic is thus to establish the simplest possible mathematical expression for the elastic contributions to the free energy. This was first done successfully by Oseen in 1928 and in 1958 Frank introduced the notation and terminology that is still used today.[1] Consequently, the result is nowadays often referred to as the **Oseen–Frank theory.**

We cannot go into the details of the work of Oseen and Frank here but simply state the results and discuss the meaning. The main conclusion was that, neglecting surface effects, *any* generic deformation of the nematic director field can be described as a linear combination of three elementary elastic deformations: **splay**, **twist** and **bend**. These three fundamental distortions, defined graphically in Fig. 17, are independent of one another, i.e. a twist can only be compensated by a twist of opposite handedness, not by any combination of splay and bend, and analogously for the other deformations. As a result the elastic free energy density of a bulk nematic

Splay   **Twist**   **Bend**

$K_1 \left(\nabla \cdot \mathbf{n} \right)^2 \neq 0$ $K_2 \left(\mathbf{n} \cdot \left(\nabla \times \mathbf{n} \right) \right)^2 \neq 0$ $K_3 \left(\mathbf{n} \times \left(\nabla \times \mathbf{n} \right) \right)^2 \neq 0$

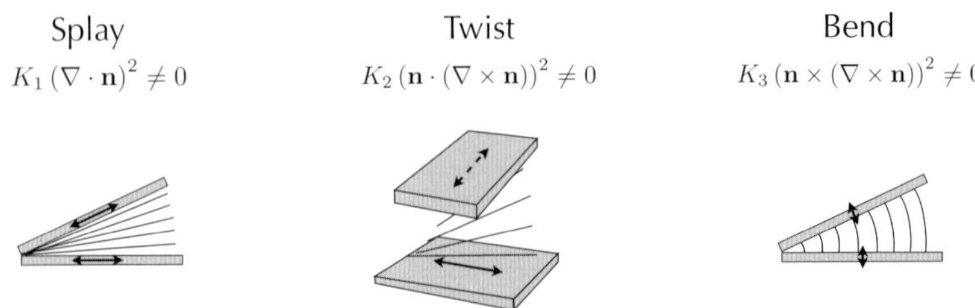

Fig. 17.   Graphical definitions of the three elementary director field deformations splay, twist and bend, together with their corresponding terms in the elastic free energy density and their respective elastic constants K_1, K_2 and K_3. The drawings illustrate how each deformation can be produced in practice by encapsulating a nematic between flat substrates, the insides of which are prepared such as to ensure uniform planar or homeotropic director orientation at the substrate (the preferred director is indicated with a thick double-headed arrow). Redrawn after de Gennes and Prost.[22]

can be written as a sum of three terms,[o] each giving the total contribution due to splay, twist and bend deformations in the sample, respectively:

$$g_{deform.} = \frac{1}{2} K_1 \left(\nabla \cdot \mathbf{n} \right)^2 + \frac{1}{2} K_2 \left(\mathbf{n} \cdot \left(\nabla \times \mathbf{n} \right) \right)^2 + \frac{1}{2} K_3 \left(\mathbf{n} \times \left(\nabla \times \mathbf{n} \right) \right)^2 \quad (6)$$

Each deformation is described by the appropriate combination of the vector operators divergence ($\nabla \cdot \mathbf{n}$) and curl ($\nabla \times \mathbf{n}$) squared (the handedness or direction of a deformation cannot play a role in an achiral system, hence linear terms are ruled out) and the energy cost for a certain deformation is proportional to the respective elastic constant, K_1 for splay, K_2 for twist and K_3 for bend. These constants are very important material parameters, critically dictating the behavior of a nematic, e.g. in a display device or as a host for creating regular patterns of colloidal inclusions (see Chapters 10 and 11). Since they represent a 1D energy density (the multiplication of each elastic constant by a squared derivative turns the complete term into a 3D energy density) they have the dimension J/m=N, i.e. a force, with a magnitude typically in the pN range. They must be positive to ensure stability. For thermotropics, K_1 and K_2 often have about the same value whereas K_3 is about twice that value. It can be convenient to approximate them all equal to a single value K, an approximation referred to as the 'one-constant approximation'. For lyotropics the differences in the three

---

[o]A fourth term, described by the saddle-splay constant K_{24}, must sometimes be included, but it is often ignored in the simplest elasticity description. Many cases can be adequately described without taking it into account and we thus omit it in this short introduction to liquid crystal elasticity.

elastic constants can be much stronger, in particular for particle-based lyotropics, for which $K_1 \approx 3K_2 \ll K_3$. When particles are long and stiff it is not uncommon that K_3 is an order of magnitude larger than the other constants.

Some aspects of the meaning of Eq. (6) can be made clearer by making some simplifications. First, since divergence and curl essentially are two types of spatial derivatives of a vector field, we may see each term in Eq. (6) as proportional to $\delta\mathbf{n}^2$, exposing an analogy with Hooke's law for solid elasticity: for solid and nematic elasticity alike the energy is proportional to the square of the deformation magnitude. Second, since a spatial derivative yields an inverse length, each term in Eq. (6) is proportional to $1/R^2$, where R is the characteristic length of each particular deformation. This means that the energy of the deformation gets negligible if it is not strongly localized. The characteristic length is the pitch in case of a twist deformation, the radius of curvature of a bend deformation, and the distance to the 'source' of a splay deformation. Note that the former is independent of location for a twist of constant magnitude, i.e. the energy cost of a uniform twist deformation depends on how tightly twisted $\mathbf{n}(\mathbf{r})$ is but not on which point in the sample we consider. In contrast, the characteristic length of bend and splay is only defined once we have chosen a position, and it is not uniform. This means that the energy cost of a bend or splay deformation varies throughout the sample (which is natural, since a bend or splay locally gets less and less apparent the further away from the center of curvature or 'source' that we are).

The $1/R^2$ dependence and the small magnitude of the elastic constants means that elastic deformations cost very little energy if their characteristic length is not very small, so little in fact that large-scale deformations are all the time thermally generated in a nematic liquid crystal. It is these constantly generated random large-scale deformations that yield the non-uniformity in $\mathbf{n}(\mathbf{r})$ of a bulk nematic, thereby giving rise to its characteristic turbidity: since $\mathbf{n}(\mathbf{r})$ changes randomly over distances that are large (but not too large) on an optical scale, so does the effective refractive index for a light beam going through the sample, and strong scattering results.

The expression of the elastic free energy density Eq. (6) is an important result and it is also very useful in practice. Probably the most common use is to find the equilibrium state under a certain set of boundary conditions by minimizing the free energy, which must contain any other relevant terms, e.g. electric field terms. It is also the foundation for our ability to control the director orientation throughout the sample in a simple manner, an absolute prerequisite for using nematics in devices such as displays. By using substrates prepared for inducing planar or homeotropic anchoring (see Sec. 6 for a description of how this is achieved in practice), in the former case with one direction in the substrate plane being the preferred direction of **n**, we can rely on minimization of liquid crystal elastic energy to transmit this alignment also into the bulk. In case of antagonistic boundary conditions, the liquid crystal will develop the least deformed state accommodating the boundary conditions. Also particles can be prepared such that they induce specific **n(r)** around the particle, with a consequent elastic response by the liquid crystal. This is the foundation for one of the most active fields of research on particles in liquid crystals, introduced by Igor Musevic in Chap. 10.

We end this brief introduction to liquid crystal elasticity by pointing out that this is a *continuum* theory: it relies fundamentally on the assumption that the liquid crystal's true discrete molecular nature can be neglected, the fluid being treated as a continuum instead. This assumption is perfectly valid as long as the objects and phenomena under discussion have sizes that are very large on a molecular scale. Since this is indeed the case in most practical uses of liquid crystals, the elasticity theory is valid and extremely useful in the vast majority of situations. In this book we will however among many other things also discuss very small particles in liquid crystals. In case of micron size particles elasticity theory is still applicable but when going down to nanoparticles one must be careful. The particles are now of the same scale as molecules and the continuum elasticity approximation may break down. In case of greatly anisometric nanoparticles, such as carbon nanotubes, an intermediate situation prevails making the treatment of the system anything but straight-forward.

5. Defects in the director field

So far we have discussed deformations in general, without considering the special case of singularities in **n(r)**. The director fields shown in Fig. 17 are smooth and locally defect-free despite their deformed state. In a nematic that has not been deliberately aligned in a particular way we will frequently have defects, points or lines along which **n(r)** is not defined. A defect line in a liquid crystal is called a ***disclination***. Some examples of director fields with disclinations are shown in Fig. 18 together with exemplifying polarizing micrographs showing the basic textural characteristics. The drawings are two-dimensional as is the plane of observation in the microscope. The

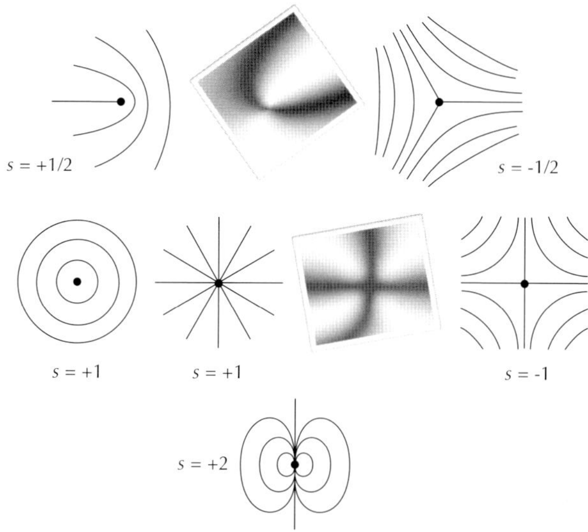

Fig. 18.   Examples of disclinations of magnitude $\frac{1}{2}$, 1 and 2, of positive and negative sign, in a planar-aligned nematic. For the $s = \pm\frac{1}{2}$ and $s = \pm1$ cases, polarizing micrographs are provided as illustrations how these disclinations can be recognized from the sample texture. Further tricks are needed to also determine the sign of the disclination.

lines in the drawings illustrate $\mathbf{n}(\mathbf{r})$ and the black dots indicate the defect locations. In a real 3D sample these disclinations could appear by preparing a nematic sample with substrates ensuring a degenerate planar anchoring (the micrographs were taken on such a sample). The dots in the pictures would then be either head-on views of defect lines, running between the bottom and top substrates, or the defect line may have 'escaped' (see below) into a point defect stuck to the surface.

You will notice in the figure that each disclination has been given a magnitude (or strength, sometimes called winding number) and a sign. In fact, when two or more disclinations are present in a sample, these parameters are of fundamental importance for determining the behavior of the sample as a whole. A simple way to determine the strength, here denoted by s, is illustrated in Fig. 19. Take some kind of linear object with a distinct head-tail asymmetry (we use a match) and place it along the director at an arbitrary starting point (**1** in the figure) near the disclination. Also the initial direction of the head of the object is arbitrary, but remember which direction you chose. Now move the object one full turn around the

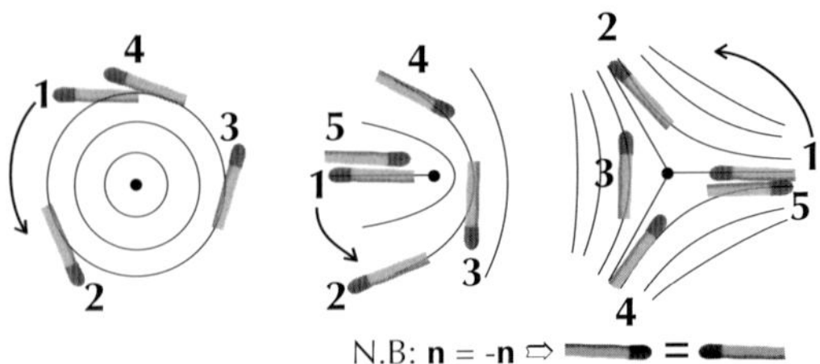

Fig. 19.   Determination of magnitude and sign of disclinations (see text for explanation).

disclination (you can go clockwise or anticlockwise), always making sure that the *object orientation follows the variations of the director field*, until the object is back at point **1**. In the left example in Fig. 19 the match was moved one turn anti-clockwise around the disclination and as a result the match itself also rotated one full turn anti-clockwise. The director thus rotates in the *same sense* (we attribute a positive sign to this) and by the *same number of turns* (the disclination magnitude is the ratio of the number of turns) as we go around the disclination. We characterize this disclination by $s = +1$. Note that $\mathbf{n(r)}$ is continuous, the lines only being representative examples. You are thus free to do parallel displacements of your object from one line to another. In fact, for most disclinations you *must* do such a displacement to complete the loop.

When doing the same thing around the second disclination we see that the director again rotates anti-clockwise when we follow $\mathbf{n(r)}$ in an anti-clockwise loop around the disclination, hence its sign must be positive. But the match has not come to its original orientation: it has only rotated half a turn. While a half-turn rotation is no symmetry operation for our match, it is for the director ($\mathbf{n} = -\mathbf{n}$), hence this disclination is perfectly allowed. Its magnitude is $1/2$, since the director rotated only half a turn as a result of the full circumvention of the disclination. When following the procedure for the third defect in Fig. 19, finally, we again end up with a director that has been rotated only half a turn, but in addition it has been rotated in the *opposite* sense: while we went around the disclination anti-clockwise, the match rotated clockwise. Hence, this defect is an $s = -\frac{1}{2}$ disclination.

It turns out that line defects of integer strength are thermodynamically unstable, because the liquid crystal can decrease its free energy by smoothly inclining the director around the defect line towards one of the bounding surfaces, thereby removing the line discontinuity and transferring it to a point defect at the surface. Thus, spontaneously formed integer disclinations are in essence always point defects stuck at one of the bounding substrates of our sample. This way of smoothing out a line defect (called *escape in the third dimension*) is not available for half-integer defects, hence these are always line discontinuities. For a richer discussion of these issues, see e.g. the text book by de Gennes and Prost.[22]

What happens if two $s = +1$ disclinations form close to each other? In Fig. 20a we have sketched this situation. The director field gets strongly distorted between the disclinations, the more the closer the singularities. If we were to push them closer to each other the effect on the director field would be like tightening a spring. We would have to do work on the system to achieve this, whereas, on the other hand, the energy stored in the strongly distorted director field would allow the system to push the defects away from each other if nothing keeps them in place, i.e. *two disclinations of the same sign repel each other.* If we nevertheless were to push the defects closer and closer until the point that they overlap we would get an $s = +2$ pattern. Thus *merging two disclinations* simply creates a new disclination with sign and strength given by the *sum of the original disclinations.*

If we apply this new result to two disclinations of the same strength but opposite sign, as in Fig. 20b, we notice that the net result should be no disclination at all. Indeed, we see in the figure that the director field is uniformly vertical already quite close to the two disclinations, which in a configuration like this, close to each other but not merged, constitute an *elastic dipole.* As the distortion of the director field gets smaller the closer the disclinations, they are effectively attracted and it is not too difficult to realize that if they eventually are allowed to merge they will annihilate each other, leaving behind a deformation-free director field. This phenomenon is often seen after cooling a nematic from the isotropic phase in the pres-

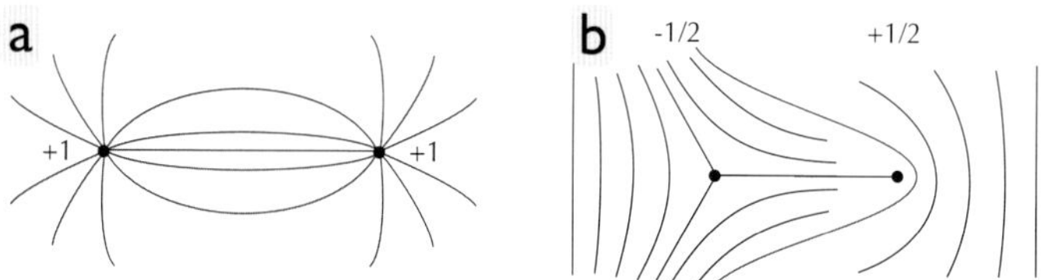

Fig. 20.   Two like-signed disclinations repel each other (a), effectively creating distortions to the director field corresponding to their sum. If the disclinations have opposite signs (b) they tend to compensate each other, reducing the total director field distortion and thus effectively being attracted by each other. If they are kept from merging and thus annihilating, they constitute an elastic dipole.

ence of boundaries that induce degenerate planar alignment. Because of the tendency of opposite sign defects to annihilate, stable elastic dipoles are difficult to realize in a pure nematic, but they can be prepared relatively easily by adding particles, drops or bubbles, each inclusion creating a bulk point defect in the director field. This process and its interesting consequences are discussed in detail in Chap. 10. Disclinations with $|s| > 1$ are rarely observed since the elastic energy density of the deformed director field that surrounds a singularity increases as s^2. The energy density is thus reduced by splitting an $|s| = 2$ disclination into two $|s| = 1$, or one $|s| = 1$ into two $|s| = \frac{1}{2}$. In real samples one must however consider the full energy, i.e. the energy density must be integrated over the volume surrounding the defect, and this can lead to defect configurations that are unexpected by considerations of 2D director field distortions. An example where such phenomena are observed is that of liquid crystal shells.[34]

The elasticity theory described above was developed for nematics but it can be extended and modified to phases with partial positional order. For each particular phase one must however take into account the special restrictions imposed by its symmetry, an issue we will now demonstrate using the examples of SmA and SmC phases. It is rather easy to realize that two out of the three elementary deformations are actually not allowed by the SmA structure, as illustrated in Fig. 21. Considering first twist (left-hand drawing) we see that, since the director also defines the layers through its double role as layer normal, a twist in the director field also entails a twist in the layer structure. This would require breaking up the layers, which is incompatible with an ordinary SmA phase. As for director bend, the middle drawing illustrates that this also gives problems with the layer structure. Since a bend in $\mathbf{n}(\mathbf{r})$ corresponds to a splay in the layers, the

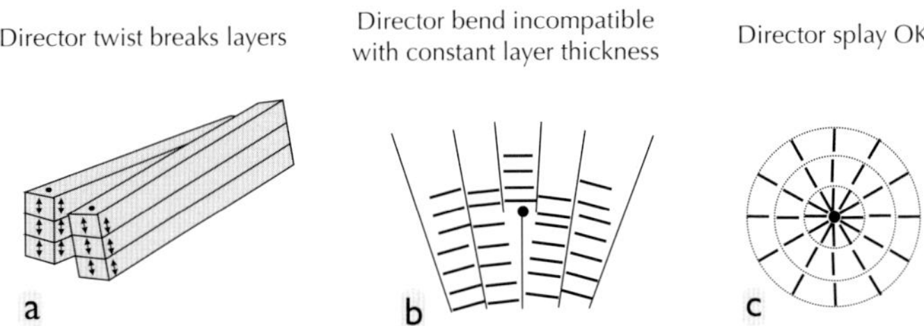

Fig. 21. The geometry of SmA does not allow twist (a) and bend (b) in $\mathbf{n}(\mathbf{r})$ but splay (c) occurs. The director is to the left illustrated with double-headed arrows, in the middle and to the right with lines thicker than the lines indicating smectic layer boundaries .

layer thickness would have to change constantly, a situation that does not occur in reality since the layer thickness is defined by the effective length and inclination of the molecules. If a director bend were to appear in SmA it would induce a network of dislocations in the layered structure.

While director twist and bend are not allowed the *layers* are allowed to bend, for instance into a cylindrical roll (Fig. 21c). They can also easily undulate with a layer thickness essentially constant. This corresponds to mainly splay in the director field and the deformation energy density can be written:

$$g^{SmA} = \frac{1}{2}K_1(\nabla \cdot \mathbf{n})^2 + \frac{1}{2}B(\delta d)^2 \tag{7}$$

where the second term represents the ordinary (solid-like) elasticity due to slight changes in layer thickness d. In the case of a perfectly circular cylindrical (or spherical) shape, $\delta d = 0$ and only the splay term prevails.

Although SmC is less symmetric and thus in some sense more ordered than SmA (SmC occurs at lower temperatures) it actually allows more fluctuations in the director field than SmA. This is because the addition of a tilting direction gives a new freedom for deformations which do not interfere with the layered structure. In fact, the projection of $\mathbf{n}$ onto the layer plane, the C-director $\mathbf{c}$, behaves in many respects similar to the normal director in the nematic. The best illustration is perhaps the helical structure of a chiral SmC* phase, where $\mathbf{c}$ perfectly mimics the twisted structure that $\mathbf{n}$ shows in a chiral nematic phase, cf. Fig. 8. But also $\mathbf{n}$ itself has gained new degrees of freedom. By making a drawing of the helical SmC* structure, as in Fig. 8 (a 3D model is even better), it is not difficult to realize that $\mathbf{n}$ undergoes a combination of bend and twist deformation in the helix. If we instead have an achiral SmC phase such deformations can be induced thermally as temporary fluctuations if their characteristic length is large.

The characteristic texture of a quasi-homeotropic SmC sample very much reminds of the schlieren texture of a planar-aligned nematic (the changing curvature of the schlieren reflecting variations in $\mathbf{c}$), but there is one important difference: there are only integer disclinations in the SmC texture. Because the sign invariance of the director, $\mathbf{n} = -\mathbf{n}$, does not apply to the C-director ($\mathbf{c} \neq -\mathbf{c}$ because $\mathbf{c}$ and $-\mathbf{c}$ correspond to opposite director tilting directions, hence physically different states) half-integer disclinations as in the top row of Fig. 18 are not possible in a SmC phase.

Very interesting things happen when we allow also curved surfaces in 3D, e.g. a drop or a shell or a liquid crystal surrounding an inclusion with a curved boundary. You can easily see by looking at the meridians drawn on a globe of the Earth that the topology of a sphere requires a total defect sum of $s = +2$. The south and north pole each constitute an $s = +1$ defect in the meridians, but the rest of the earth's surface is free of defects in this 'director field'. There are many other ways that one could draw a continuous director field on the globe but regardless of choice, a summation of all defects on the surface will always end with a total of $s = +2$. The same holds if we make an ellipsoid or a tube with end caps out of the sphere by pulling at it. As long as there are no holes in the surface, the disclination sum is $+2$.

6. How liquid crystals are studied: Containment, alignment control, field application and some other practical issues

The fluidity of liquid crystals generally requires the encapsulation of a sample for experimental studies, e.g. in a polarizing microscope. For thermotropics, the standard container is referred to as a 'cell' and it consists of two planar glass substrates assembled in parallel with a well-defined distance, often laterally somewhat displaced to one another in one direction (to allow for electrical connections), cf. the left drawing in Fig. 22. The substrate distance (the 'cell gap') is typically in the range $1 - 100 \mu m$. Thinner cells are difficult to realize with accuracy, thicker may not be very useful as thermally induced fluctuations render thick samples scattering. Furthermore, the director tends to become non-uniform in thick samples and the high birefringence of thermotropics means that optimal optical performance is obtained for cells with thickness in the range 2-10 μm.

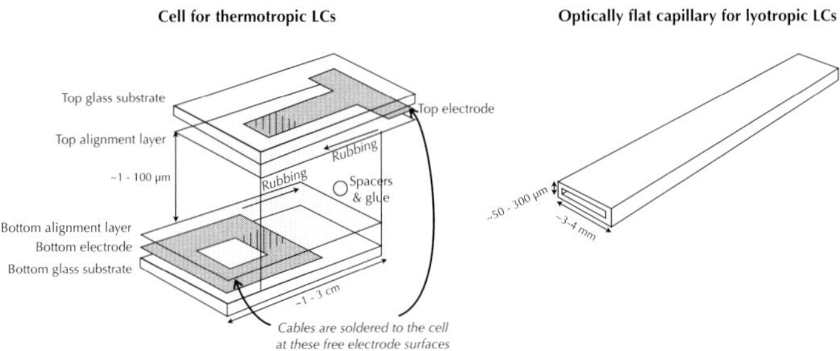

Fig. 22. Drawings of a cell typically used for studying thermotropic liquid crystals (left) and a flat capillary used for studying lyotropic samples (right). The active area in the cell is the hatched area, defined by the overlap of the top and bottom electrodes. From Ref. 32.

A uniform director field, preferably with a selectable direction of **n**, is of great importance to the study of liquid crystals, since the physical properties of liquid crystals to such a great extent are linked to the director. In a standard cell filled with a calamitic thermotropic this is achieved by coating the inner substrate surfaces with an appropriate alignment agent, typically polymers like polyimide (PI), nylon (PA, from the proper chemical name of this class of polymers: polyamide) or polyvinyl alcohol (PVA) or a surfactant.[p] The latter induces hometropic alignment since the polar head groups adsorb on the glass, leaving the alkyl chains pointing more or less normal to the surface (see Sec. 9.3 for an introduction to typical surfactant design), seeding the homeotropic liquid crystal ordering. The polymers generally induce planar alignment because the aromatic cores of mesogens like to be in close contact with them. Normally one also requires a selected direction in the plane for **n** and this can be achieved by mechanically rubbing the coated substrates, giving the alignment layer a uniformly grooved structure. When the cell is filled with the liquid crystal, the mesogens tend to align along the grooves, giving the uniform director orientation. More advanced patterning of **n**(**r**) along the surface is possible via the so-called photoalignment technique, where the substrates are coated with a photo-sensitive polymer and the alignment direction is set by illuminating with polarized UV light.

The above mentioned alignment layers work well for most calamitic thermotropics (although there are several exceptions). For discotic materials alignment is a much trickier issue. A clean surface may induce homeotropic alignment in some substances, but others will exhibit a random alignment. The development of a reliable and convenient method for controlling alignment of discotics is an active research area.[35–38]

For lyotropic liquid crystals the standard container is a capillary with rectangular cross section, cf. the right drawing in Fig. 22. It is typically substantially thicker than the cells used for thermotropics (reflecting the much lower birefringence of lyotropics), often in the range 50 - 300 μm. Alignment layers for control of the director in lyotropics unfortunately do not exist, a lack that makes many investigations of lyotropic samples difficult. Often the polar glass substrates induce a steady-state alignment of amphiphile-based lyotropics that is homeotropic but this may vary from phase to phase

---

[p]A word of warning may be appropriate here. Commercially available cells made for homeotropic alignment sometimes have ionic surfactants as the alignment layer. While they work very well for ensuring the alignment, they will also have consequences for the ionic content of the sample, influencing investigations in electric fields.

     J. P. F. Lagerwall

and from amphiphile to amphiphile. While some lyotropic phases prefer to align planarly (e.g. chiral nematics from cellulose nanocrystal suspensions), we know of no surface that ensures a stable *uniform* planar director orientation. When this is needed in a lyotropic sample, it can sometimes be achieved by application of a strong magnetic field or by shear flow. The easiest way to shear-align a lyotropic phase in the capillary is to suck the liquid crystal into the capillary with relatively high speed, e.g. by attaching the capillary to a syringe via rubber tubing and sucking vacuum with the syringe until the capillary is filled. Unfortunately a field- or shear-induced alignment is not necessarily an equilibrium condition, in particular if the surface promotes homeotropic alignment. In the worst case it persists only while the field/shear flow is applied, and even when no immediate relaxation is seen, the induced alignment may be replaced by a homeotropic or inhomogeneous state after a day or two. Alignment control of lyotropics is a field where our current standing is insufficient and where new research is called for.

The study of liquid crystals is not always done in cells or capillaries or in any other confining container. One can rather easily draw free-standing films[39] of smectic or lamellar phases (the latter however requires humidity control since otherwise the water in the lamellar film will quickly evaporate[40]) which offer some quite unique possibilities to study liquid crystals. Typically, one places a drop of the substance on a substrate next to a small hole that has been drilled through it, and then pulls it over the hole for instance with an inclined cover slip. Kirsten Harth and Ralf Stannarius describe the interesting physics of the free-standing smectic films that can be made in this way, with particular focus on inclusions, in Chap. 11. Another very interesting container-free geometry that has been applied to study smectics, pioneered by Stannarius, is one of bubbles. This is achieved by blowing gas into a smectic sample until a bubble forms.[41,42] A variation that in principle can be applied to any liquid crystal phase is shells that are suspended in a fluid that is immiscible with the liquid crystal—e.g. water—with the same or a different fluid inside the shell. The inner and outer interfaces are stabilized by polymers or surfactants, at the same time controlling the alignment. Such shells are best prepared using a microfluidic set-up that was originally developed in the lab of David Weitz.[34] Nematic, smectic as well as cholesteric phases, and even liquid crystal elastomers, have been studied in this way.[43–48] All these alternatives to cells or capillaries must however be regarded as non-standard techniques. They are typically more challenging in terms of preparing the samples with control of thickness and alignment and keeping them intact over longer periods of time.

It is often important to be able to apply an electric or magnetic field over the sample, in experiments as well as in applications. While magnetic field application is done simply by placing the sample in the field of an external magnet, electric field application is generally achieved by equipping the cells with transparent electrodes, which are then connected to an external voltage source. The standard electrode material is indium tin oxide (ITO), the best compromise known until today in terms of transparency and electrical conductivity. For quantitative measurements it may be important to know the exact effective electrode area (the 'active area') and the ITO layer is therefore usually patterned on the top and bottom substrates such that a well-defined area of overlap results, typically about 20 mm^2 in size, cf. Fig. 22.

6.1. *Director anchoring at boundaries*

In many cases it is important to quantify how strong effect a surface has on the orientation of **n** in its vicinity, i.e. what is the **anchoring strength** of the surface on the director. If we want to be able to dynamically modulate the orientation of **n**, e.g. by an electric field in a display, we need to consider the counteracting/restoring forces, which are mediated by the elasticicity of the liquid crystal but ultimately governed by the anchoring strength: if there is no steady-state anchoring of **n** there will be no back relaxation when the field is removed, as no well defined ground state to relax back to is defined. We thus want strong enough anchoring to define the ground state unambiguously and to drive rapid back relaxation (for this we also want high elastic constant and low rotational viscosities) but the anchoring (and the liquid crystal elasticicity) should not be so strong that we need excessive electric fields to switch the director.

Anchoring can be considered from a thermodynamic as well as from a kinetic perspective, both aspects potentially important for real situations. In terms of thermodynamics, we consider the interfacial tension (the interfacial energy per unit area) of the liquid crystal with the bounding material, e.g. a polymer- or surfactant-coated glass substrate in case of a standard cell for thermotropics, or air in case of a smectic free-standing film or bubble. An ordinary isotropic liquid has only one value of the interfacial tension once the phase on the other side of the interface has been chosen, but in a liquid crystal also the interfacial tension becomes anisotropic. For instance, the ability of aromatic rings to participate, albeit weakly, in hydrogen bonding renders the interfacial tension of most thermotropic liquid crystals in contact with water lower for a planar-aligned interface than for one that is homeotropic-aligned. The aliphatic end chains cannot participate in hydrogen bonding, hence an interface where the water molecules encounter only end chains will yield greater surface energy than one where the aromatic cores are, at least partially, in contact with the water molecules. This explains why thermotropic liquid crystals align planarly at an interface to pure water:[49] the surface free energy is minimum for this alignment. The kinetic aspect refers to any barrier that must be passed in order to switch from one alignment to another. This becomes important if bistable devices are targeted, since they by definition need to have *two* different types of anchoring that both represent minima in free energy, at similar values. The strength of anchoring of the director into one of these states is then determined by the barrier that opposes a director reorientation to the other stable state, i.e. the state is kinetically stabilized.

Since monostability is the situation of most applications of liquid crystals (and much easier to achieve) it often suffices to consider the thermodynamic aspect, i.e. the anisotropy in interfacial tension. Unless we have perfect homeotropic alignment we do need, however, to take two separate such anisotropies into account as we are dealing with an interface in three-dimensional space. On the one hand, we need one interfacial tension to determine how much favorable a planar interface is compared to a homeotropic, or vice versa (also intermediate states can represent the global free energy minimum, a situation that is referred to as 'non-zero pretilt'). We may call this the polar anchoring energy density W_p or W_θ, as it defines the equilibrium value of the polar angle θ.

The second anisotropy refers to which direction in the plane of the interface that represents the free energy minimum in case of planar alignment. In case of a pre-tilted interface, the same consideration holds for the projection of **n** onto the interface. This in-plane direction is defined by the azimuthal angle φ and the corresponding interfacial tension is thus referred to as the azimuthal anchoring energy density W_a or W_φ. In case of a degenerate planar (or degenerate pretilted) interface this direction has no importance, i.e. any value of φ is as good as any other, hence W_φ =constant. But for many applications, including displays, this is not sufficient, and we thus need to ensure that one direction becomes the 'easy direction', representing the global energy minimum in the absence of field. In the case of thermotropic liquid crystal cells, this is the purpose of the rubbing or photoalignment process.

For a full treatment of the quantitative analysis of surface anchoring of liquid crystals, the reader is referred to standard liquid crystal textbooks, e.g. Ref. 50. Here we will only consider a simple special case, following de Gennes and Prost,[22] which serves to introduce the concept of the **extrapolation length**. This is a convenient way of comparing anchoring strength and elasticity of the liquid crystal. We consider a nematic in contact with a substrate in the xy plane located at $z = 0$, neglecting the possibility of variation of the polar angle. Instead we assume fully planar alignment (i.e. $\theta = 90°$, defining the polar angle with respect to the surface normal $\hat{z}$), at the substrate and in the bulk, and we consider only the azimuthal anchoring energy density, i.e. the energy cost of azimuthal deviation of the director at the substrate away from the easy direction $\mathbf{n}_0$. Moreover, we assume that a pure twist deformation has been induced, i.e., although the director is parallel to the bounding surface throughout the bulk of the liquid crystal, it rotates in the xy plane as we move away from the substrate, such that at a distance $z = L$ it points along $\mathbf{n}(L) \neq \mathbf{n}_0$. This twist may for instance be a result of another bounding surface or a localized electric or magnetic field that promotes a different orientation.

If the anchoring strength had been infinite the director at the substrate would be locked to $\mathbf{n}_0$ regardless of what goes on in the bulk, but for a real case there will be a slight deviation from this orientation, even at the substrate ($z = 0$), because we have a balance between the surface anchoring, promoting $\mathbf{n}_0$, and the nematic elasticity, which tries to minimize the twist and thus get $\mathbf{n}(L)$ and $\mathbf{n}_0$ as close to each other as possible. If we for instance define the azimuthal angle such that $\varphi(\mathbf{n}_0) = 0$ and assume a $90°$ twist between the two unequal preferred orientations at $z = 0$ and $z = L$, i.e. $\varphi(z = L) = 90°$, we will have a situation as in Fig. 23. In a first approximation φ decreases roughly linearly from $90°$ at $z = L$ to a small positive and non-zero value at $z = 0$.

To actually reach $\varphi = 0$, i.e. the orientation $\mathbf{n}_0$ promoted by the surface treatment, we would have to extrapolate the $\varphi(z)$ curve *outside* the cell. The distance ξ that we have to move into this virtual regime is what we call the extrapolation length, and it can be used as a measure of how strong the surface anchoring is in comparison to the twist elastic constant of the nematic (and analogous extrapolation lengths can be defined for other deformations and other anchoring geometries). If the anchoring energy dominates over the elastic distortion energy, which for our case is proportional to K_2, then the deviation from $\varphi = 0$ at $z = 0$ is small, and consequently ξ is small (strong anchoring). On the other hand, if the anchoring energy

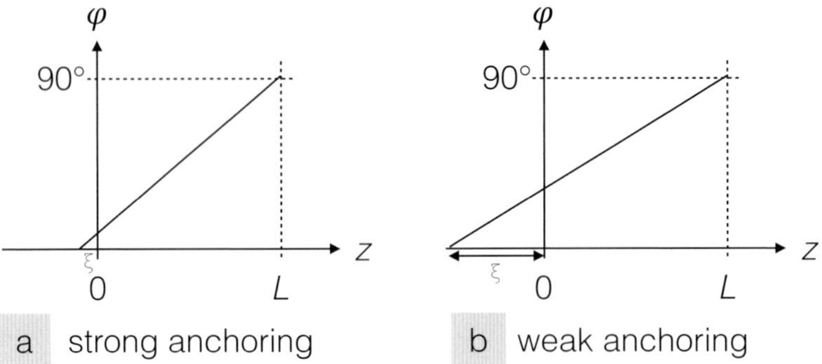

Fig. 23. The extrapolation length ξ for strong (a) and weak (b) anchoring, respectively, to a substrate at $z = 0$, for the case of a 90° twist from the substrate to a distance L into the bulk.

density is low compared to the twist energy density, then we need to extrapolate far beyond the substrate to reach a virtual $\varphi = 0$ state, i.e. ξ is large. Quantitatively, we can define the extrapolation length as:[22]

$$\xi = \frac{K_2}{W_\varphi} \tag{8}$$

with the relevant alternative elastic constants and anchoring energy densities taking the places of K_2 and W_φ, respectively, for other anchoring and deformation situations. Given the material parameters that we have, ξ is the only natural length scale. Strong anchoring means that ξ is on the order of the molecule size, i.e. a few nanometers. In case of weak anchoring ξ can easily take values on the order of several microns.

When we consider liquid crystals with inclusions, the extrapolation length that interests us the most is the distance that we would have to move *into* the inclusion in order to achieve the preferred interfacial director orientation (as a virtual state). If ξ is large compared to the scale of an anisometric inclusion the anchoring is weak and we may expect either little impact on the orientation of the inclusion (low anchoring energy) or particle aggregation due to the director field distortion that the particle induces (in case of high elastic constant, also yielding large ξ). But if ξ is on the order of the inclusion size or smaller, then we either have very weak elasticity, which may not be very helpful, or we have strong anchoring of **n** at the interface to the inclusion, such that we may achieve alignment of the inclusion by the liquid crystal.

7. Dielectric, conductive and magnetic anisotropy and the response to electric and magnetic fields

While the optical anisotropy is responsible for the function of a liquid crystal in a device in its bright state, it is normally the dielectric anisotropy that allows us to change the state; to 'switch' the director field between different defined geometries, giving different transmission. This dynamic aspect is a requirement for the operation of displays or related electrooptic devices. It is highly useful also when doing research on liquid crystals.

If an electric field $\mathbf{E}$ is applied over a dielectric medium such as a liquid crystal, the field will polarize the medium, i.e. an electric dipole moment will be induced, proportional to the field strength and to the dimensionless electrical susceptibility tensor χ^e of the medium:

$$\mathbf{P} = \epsilon_0 \chi^e \cdot \mathbf{E} \tag{9}$$

The vacuum permittivity $\epsilon_0 \approx 8.85 \cdot 10^{-12}$ C/Vm is required to get the dimension of a polarization. In an isotropic medium χ^e is independent of direction and can be represented by a scalar, and the induced polarization will be parallel to $\mathbf{E}$. In anisotropic media, in contrast, the susceptibility depends on the direction of the field and its full description requires the tensorial χ^e. We will here consider only the simplest uniaxial nematic case, for which we only require the two scalar susceptibility values $\chi^e_{||}$ parallel and $\chi^e_\perp$ perpendicular to $\mathbf{n}$. Analogously to the optical anisotropy we can now define the susceptibility anisotropy as $\Delta\chi^e = \chi^e_{||} - \chi^e_\perp$.

The very important consequence of the susceptibility being anisotropic is that the induced polarization $\mathbf{P}$ is not necessarily directed along $\mathbf{E}$. Field application thus generally results in a local torque $\mathbf{\Gamma}_\epsilon = \mathbf{P} \times \mathbf{E}$ on the director, acting to align $\mathbf{n}$ along ($\Delta\chi^e > 0$) or perpendicular ($\Delta\chi^e < 0$) to the field, allowing us to quickly and easily modulate the director orientation with the field. The electrical susceptibility is rarely considered in practice, as the quantity that is typically known (or measured) is the dielectric permittivity $\epsilon = \chi^e + 1$. However, as the one quantity is just the other rescaled, their anisotropies are numerically identical, $\Delta\epsilon = \epsilon_{||} - \epsilon_\perp = \Delta\chi^e$.

Consider the situation depicted in Fig. 24: an electric field $\mathbf{E}$ is applied vertically (in $-\hat{x}$ direction as defined in the figure) over a uniaxial nematic with positive $\Delta\epsilon$, the director of which is inclined an angle ϕ from the vertical direction. The anisotropic permittivity is represented graphically by a rotationally symmetric ellipsoid, the distance between its center and its surface in each point being equal to ϵ in that particular radial direction.

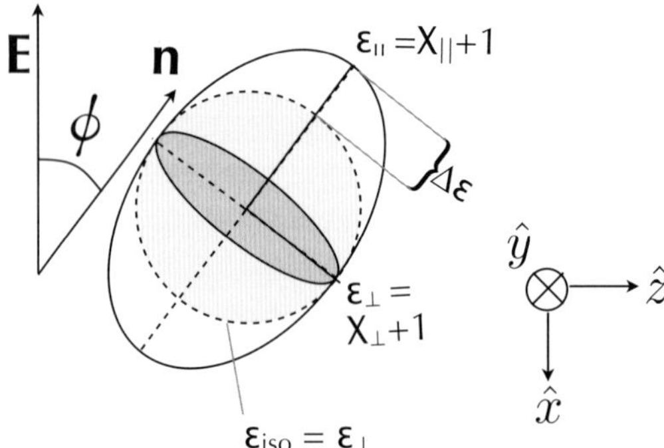

Fig. 24. When an electric field is applied over an anisotropic dielectric medium like a liquid crystal, a polarization is induced that may be non-parallel to the field. This results in a torque which, in case of the highly fluid nematic, reorients the director until the induced polarization is along the electric field. From Ref. 32.

It is convenient to separate the permittivity in an isotropic component $\epsilon_{iso} = \epsilon_\perp$ (graphically represented by the dotted sphere) and an anisotropic addition $\Delta\epsilon$. The former component can be analyzed as for any isotropic system, i.e. the resulting polarization is parallel to the field and has the magnitude $P_{iso} = \epsilon_0 \chi_\perp^e E = \epsilon_0(\epsilon_\perp - 1)E$. More interesting is the anisotropic component, which generates a polarization along the director, driven by the component of the field along $\mathbf{n}$, i.e. $E_{||} = E\cos\phi$.

We can now calculate the dielectric torque $\mathbf{\Gamma}_\epsilon = \mathbf{P} \times \mathbf{E}$ imposed on the nematic director by the electric field. Since the isotropic permittivity leads to a polarization parallel to $\mathbf{E}$, it yields no torque, and we need to consider only the anisotropic addition (we remind that the anisotropic addition of the susceptibility is $\Delta\chi^e = \Delta\epsilon$):

$$\mathbf{\Gamma}_\epsilon = \epsilon_0 \Delta\epsilon E \cos\phi(\mathbf{n} \times \mathbf{E}) = -\epsilon_0 \Delta\epsilon E^2 \cos\phi \sin\phi \hat{y} \tag{10}$$

In the last step we have evaluated the cross product between the director and field, amounting to $|\mathbf{n} \times \mathbf{E}| = E\sin\phi$ and directed out of the paper, i.e. in the $-\hat{y}$ direction. We can finally rewrite (10) to get a compact final expression:

$$\mathbf{\Gamma}_\epsilon = -\frac{1}{2}\epsilon_0 \Delta\epsilon E^2 \sin 2\phi \hat{y} \tag{11}$$

Applying this expression to our situation we see that the torque turns the director into the field direction, i.e. the field rotates $\mathbf{n}$ until it lines up with the electric field. At that point $\phi = 0$ and the torque disappears.

A curious thing is that in display devices the starting alignment is often planar, i.e. $\mathbf{n}\|\hat{z}$ in Fig. 24 and $\phi = 90°$. If you enter $\phi = 90°$ into Eq. (11) you will obtain the result that there is no torque at all on the director. What the equation does not show is that $\phi = 90°$ is an unstable state of maximum energy in the presence of the field. The situation is analogous to Euler buckling in mechanics, where a force is applied along e.g. a column or rod. While no response is seen for weak forces, above a threshold value of the force the column becomes unstable and will buckle in some direction perpendicular to the column. In both cases it is a fluctuation that initiates the response. Although the zero-field display ground state is planar (a situation ensured by adequate substrate treatment, cf. Sec. 6) thermal fluctuations constantly turn the local director out of the display plane, by randomly varying small amounts $\delta\phi$. The angle ϕ thus fluctuates around $90°$, any deviation resulting in a non-zero dielectric torque from the applied field, trying to enhance the fluctuation and turn the director away from the electrostatically energy-maximizing planar state. The operation of displays thus relies not only on our ability to control the steady-state alignment and to apply electric fields at will, but also on the spontaneous thermal fluctuations in the director field.

Had there been no influence on the director except the electric field we would be able to reorient $\mathbf{n}$ with an almost arbitrarily weak field, the only requirement being to overcome thermal fluctuations. In a display there is, however, a strong influence from the sample substrates, for instance imposing planar anchoring, i.e. the director is, in the absence of field, kept in an orientation parallel to the sample plane. When an electric field is applied we get a competition between the dielectric contribution to the free energy, promoting a reorientation of the director, and the combination of surface anchoring and nematic elasticity, counteracting any change from the initial planar-aligned state. At weak fields anchoring and elasticity 'win' and the director remains unaffected by the field, at strong fields it is the other way around and the sample is switched. The borderline case is called the **Frederiks threshold** after the Polish-Russian physicist Vsevolod Frederiks,[q] who was the first to study the switching phenomenon in detail. The switching process is nowadays called the **Frederiks transition**.

By equating the driving dielectric torque Eq. (11) with the counteracting viscous and elastic torques at the onset of switching, for simplicity assuming

---

[q]A much more awkward alternative spelling of this name is sometimes seen but our choice is promoted,[1] as it is in fact the direct transcription of the original cyrillic spelling.

infinitely strong surface anchoring (the situation can be modeled as a small splay-like deformation, the elastic torque of which is achieved by taking the negative functional derivative of the splay elastic energy[51]), the Frederiks threshold voltage can be calculated as:

$$V_F = \sqrt{\frac{\pi^2 K_1}{\epsilon_0 \Delta \epsilon}} \qquad (12)$$

At the onset of switching (small times and small angular deviation Φ from the planar ground state; $\Phi = \phi - 90°$) the induced director reorientation as a function of time t is:[51]

$$\Phi = \Phi_0 e^{t/\tau} \qquad (13)$$

with the switching time τ given by:

$$\tau = \frac{\gamma_1 d^2}{\epsilon_0 \Delta \epsilon V^2 - \pi^2 K_1} \qquad (14)$$

where d is the sample thickness, V is the voltage applied over the sample and γ_1 is the rotational viscosity, defined by Eq. (5). Equation (13) reflects the fact discussed above, that a fluctuation is needed to initiate switching: without a fluctuation, $\Phi_0 = 0$ and there would be no switching regardless how long time t we wait.

The anisotropy of liquid crystals is also reflected in their magnetic and conductive properties. As for the former, the diamagnetic anisotropy $\Delta \chi^m = \chi^m_{||} - \chi^m_{\perp}$ of a thermotropic liquid crystal most often has the same sign as its dielectric anisotropy, i.e. it is positive for calamitic and negative for discotic mesogens. In lyotropics, on the other hand, this relation as well as the reverse one occurs and lyotropic nematic phases are therefore often denoted with one of the shorthands N_C^+, N_C^-, N_D^+ or N_D^-. The index C or D refers to calamitic (or cylindrical) and discotic micelle or particle shape, respectively, and the + or - superscript to the sign of the diamagnetic anisotropy.

As with dielectric anisotropy and electric fields, the non-zero diamagnetic anisotropy means that we can exert a torque on the director by applying a magnetic field. The same type of analysis as done above for electric fields yields analogous results, including the definition of a (magnetic) Frederiks threshold. While it is thus perfectly possible to build a magnetically controlled liquid crystal device (a magnetooptic device) this is rarely done, mainly because of the greater practical ease in using electric fields to control the orientation of a thermotropic liquid crystal. The influence of magnetic fields on the director orientation can be quite important in research on lyotropics, however, since water, being the most common solvent, greatly complicates the use of electric fields for reorienting the director. The diamagnetic anisotropy is however often not large enough to allow a reorientation of higher-ordered lyotropic phases like the lamellar and columnar phases, hence field alignment in lyotropics is a realistic option essentially only when working with nematic phases.

Just like the optical anisotropy, the dielectric and diamagnetic anisotropies depend on the orientational order and anisotropy in the molecular origins of the susceptibilities, and the type of behavior sketched in Fig. 13 for Δn is seen also for these parameters. The numerical relations are however somewhat more complex than Eq. (3) since we are here considering electric and magnetic fields of frequencies much lower than those of light, extending down to the static case. At optical frequencies, the electronic polarizability (the field-induced temporary distortion of the electron cloud within the molecule) is the only contribution to the polarization of the material, hence it is the only molecular property appearing in Eq. (3). But if the field is static, or oscillating with a relatively low frequency (kHz - MHz), permanent dipoles in the molecules contribute strongly, as they are (partially) aligned by the applied field, resulting in a much stronger induced macroscopic dipole than what would result from the electronic polarization alone (corresponding to α). Thus, while the dielectric and diamagnetic susceptibility anisotropies will still be linearly proportional to the order parameter, becoming exactly zero for $S = 0$ in the isotropic phase, there is also a considerable dependence on frequency, even to the extent that reversal of the anisotropy upon crossing a threshold frequency is possible.[52]

The molecular origin of the macroscopic dielectric susceptibility anisotropy is thus the molecular polarizability anisotropy and the molecular dipole moment. Among most thermotropics, the latter is in fact the dominating factor. This dipole moment (as well as the molecular polarizability anisotropy) is present whether or not we have a liquid crystal phase, so, we might expect that we can align the molecules by applying an electric field over a sample even if it is in its isotropic state. A typical mesogen dipole moment is on the order of 5 D or about $17 \cdot 10^{-30}$Cm so the energy of interaction with a typical applied electric field (say 10 V/μm = 10 MV/m) is on the order of $-\mathbf{p} \cdot \mathbf{E} \approx 2 \cdot 10^{-22}$J. This should be compared to the thermal energy, $k_B T$, which at room temperature is about $4 \cdot 10^{-21}$J, thus about an order of magnitude larger than the electrical interaction energy. Hence, it is clear that the alignment induced by a reasonable electric field applied over a mesogenic compound in its isotropic phase is negligible. Only because of the long-range order prevailing in the liquid crystalline phases, resulting in some 10^{23} molecules responding together in unison to applied fields, do we get the strong response to relatively weak electric fields that is the hallmark of liquid crystals. While this example was worked out for the case of electric fields, an analogous estimation for the magnetic field response yields the same results, see e.g. Ref. 22.

While the dielectric and diamagnetic anisotropies are not too much affected by an inter-liquid crystal phase transition, the situation can be radically different for the electrical conductivity anisotropy $\Delta\sigma$, which typically changes sign at the transition between a nematic and a smectic phase. This is because the appearance of long-range positional order greatly influences the charge carrier mobility μ, the smectic structure increasing μ along the layers but decreasing it perpendicular to them. Also in columnar phases the translational order greatly affects the conductivity σ, the greatest value appearing along the columns. In most cases, this direction coincides with the director, hence there would be no change in sign of $\Delta\sigma$ expected in case of a nematic-columnar phase transition. The high conductivity along $\mathbf{n}$ in discotic columnar phases has rendered these phases particularly interesting for organic electronics.[18]

8. Some special properties of chiral liquid crystals

As mentioned in Sec. 1.6 the N* and SmC* phases feature helical modulations of $\mathbf{n}$ and $\mathbf{c}$ in their respective ground states. Both helical structures are incompatible with Eq. (6) which predicts a totally uniform ground state director field. As was pointed out by Frank in 1958 the expression for the elastic contribution in the free energy density must thus be modified for the case of a chiral nematic (we discuss only this case here, referring readers interested in the analogous but slightly more complex SmC* case, the helix of which involves twist as well as bend, to other liquid crystal textbooks). The standard achiral twist term is replaced by an extended term that expresses the spontaneous twist:

$$g^{N*}_{twist} = \frac{1}{2} K_2 \left(\mathbf{n} \cdot (\nabla \times \mathbf{n}) + q_0 \right)^2 \tag{15}$$

The addition $q_0 = 2\pi/p_0$ is the wave vector of the cholesteric helix, p_0 being its natural pitch. It is a straight-forward exercise to show that (15) indeed gives a minimum for the helical ground state. By parametrizing a cholesteric director field with an arbitrary helical wave vector q as $\mathbf{n} =$

$(\cos qz, \sin qz, 0)$, where we have taken the $\hat{z}$ direction as the helix axis, we find that the curl of the director, $\nabla \times \mathbf{n}$, becomes simply $-q\mathbf{n}$. Since the director is a unit vector, $\mathbf{n} \cdot \mathbf{n} = 1$, hence the content of the parenthesis in Eq. (15) becomes $-q + q_0$ and the equation can alternatively be written:

$$g_{twist}^{N*} = \frac{1}{2} K_2 (q - q_0)^2 \tag{16}$$

In other words, the twist term of the free energy density is minimized not by a uniform director field but by a twisted one, for which q is equal to the natural wave vector q_0. When the natural twist is very weak, q_0 is small and the term in Eq. (15) does not add significantly to the non-chiral elastic energy density described by Eq. (6). For strong natural twist, however, typically with the pitch on the same order as the wavelength of visible light or smaller, the added term in Eq. (15) or Eq. (16) means a new contribution to the elastic energy density that can be dominant. As Eq. (16) shows, if we compress or dilate the helix, the elastic energy is a quadratic function of the deviation from the natural wave vector. This means that the cholesteric helix acts as an elastic spring trying to keep the pitch equal to p_0. Indeed, Eq. (16) is nothing else than Hooke's law for cholesterics, analogous to the well known equation in mechanics.

Chirality has several important consequences for the physical properties of liquid crystal phases, sometimes related to the helical modulation, sometimes simply to the loss of mirror symmetry. The chiral SmA* phase for instance shows a totally different response to electric fields than an achiral SmA phase,[53] although structurally the two phases are identical since a helical modulation is not allowed. And in the chiral SmC* phase the chirality leads to an even more dramatic effect: the appearance of a spontaneous polarization.[53] Among helix-related effects in chiral nematics can be mentioned strong optical activity, an apparent viscosity that for short-pitch cholesterics may be several orders of magnitude higher than that of an achiral nematic, and that the characteristic textures and defects of the non-chiral phases are replaced by other defects characteristic of the helical structure. If the helix pitch is short, on the order of 300 nm, the optical anisotropy of the phase reverses compared to the non-helical analog, the helix axis becoming the effective optic axis. Moreover, the substance may show so-called **selective reflection** of visible light, a striking phenomenon that is both useful and beautiful. In this introduction we cannot go through all the phenomena mentioned but we will say a few words about the optical activity and selective reflection.

8.1. *Optical activity and selective reflection*

Few liquid crystals are as immediately fascinating as a short-pitch cholesteric. Placed on a dark background and observed by the naked eye, it can exhibit striking iridescent colors, ranging from deep violet to dark red. If the observer tilts the sample, s/he will notice that the color changes with the angle at which the sample is observed, shifting towards shorter wavelengths (more towards the violet) for more oblique angles. In thermotropics, the color will often change also as a result of variations in temperature, generally towards longer wavelengths on cooling, allowing them to be used as thermometers. The origin of the colors is selective reflection. A somewhat more elaborate examination will reveal that the selectively reflected light is circularly polarized if the sample is viewed at normal incidence, elliptically polarized if it is tilted. Sometimes the cholesteric will not be colored because it is so strongly twisted that the reflected wavelength is in the UV region, or the twist may be too weak, giving selective reflection of IR light. A careful investigator might then find, however, that plane polarized light sent through the sample along the helix axis gets its polarization plane strongly rotated: the cholesteric is optically active, in some cases extremely strongly so.

Cholesterics have not been much studied as hosts for inclusions yet, some exceptions being discussed by Torsten Hegmann and co-workers in Chap. 14. There are many indications that they will play a more prominent role in the future, however, and thus we feel it worthwhile to give a brief primer of the peculiar optical properties of cholesterics in this introduction. This is also motivated by the fact that these properties are central to the interest in dried films derived from cholesteric liquid crystalline cellulose nanocrystal suspensions, discussed in Chap. 27.

The complete derivation of the optical properties of cholesterics is a rather advanced optics exercise, involving the solution of Maxwell's equations in the helically modulated medium. As it is outside the scope of this book we refer the interested reader to e.g. chapter 11 of the *Introduction to Liquid Crystals* by Priestley and Wojtowicz,[54] where a very readable account of the procedure can be found. We will here simply state the results of this derivation, summarized graphically in Fig. 25. We distinguish three regimes of different behavior, depending on the ratio of the pitch of the cholesteric helix, p_0, and the light wavelength inside the cholesteric, $\lambda_{N*} = \lambda_0/\bar{n}$, where λ_0 is the vacuum wavelength and $\bar{n}$ is the average refractive index of the cholesteric:

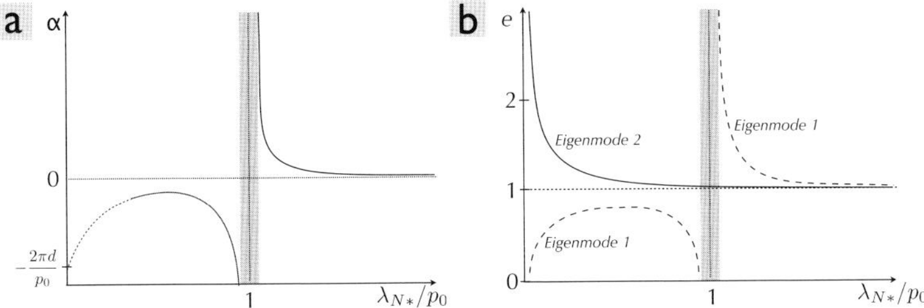

Fig. 25. Generic sketches of the optical rotatory power α (left; $\alpha > 0$ defined as right-handed rotation) and the ellipticity e of the eigenmodes (right) of light propagating along the helix axis of a left-handed cholesteric liquid crystal, as a function of the ratio of the light wavelength in the cholesteric medium to its helix pitch, λ_{N*}/p_0. The handedness in eigenmode 1 is the same as in the helix, in mode 2 it is opposite. From Ref. 32.

- **$p_0 \gg \lambda_{N*}$ (*Mauguin limit*):**
  For very long helix pitch, light propagates along the N* helix essentially as two orthogonal linearly polarized eigenmodes (they are slightly elliptic), their planes of polarization following the rotation of the local optical indicatrix in the structure. In the $p_0/\lambda_{N*} \to \infty$ limit the formal optical 'rotatory power' $|\alpha|$ (the magnitude of the polarization plane rotation) for each mode is simply equal to $2\pi d/p_0$ (see Fig. 25a), where d is the sample thickness. Thus, for a sample of thickness $d = p_0$ the polarization plane is rotated one full turn. This is not optical activity in the normal sense, since the rotation is just given by the helix and is independent of λ. It is thus *achromatic* (a useful property) but requires that the incident light is polarized according to one of the eigenmodes of the cholesteric structure in order to work. This long-pitch regime is often called the Mauguin limit, in recognition of the first analysis of the situation by Charles Mauguin.[1]

- **$p_0 \approx \lambda_{N*}$:**
  As λ_{N*} approaches p_0 from the short-wavelength side the ellipticity e of eigenmode 1 grows from zero (vertical linear polarization) to near one (circular polarization) and then back to zero at the edge of the selective reflection band, cf. Fig. 25b. At the same time eigenmode 2 goes from horizontal linear polarization (infinite ellipticity) to circular. The medium becomes truly optically active, with a rotatory power that diverges, $|\alpha|$ becoming extremely high in the direct vicinity of the selective reflection band, cf. Fig. 25a.

Since optical activity can be regarded as birefringence of a medium with circularly polarized eigenmodes ('circular birefringence') the process can alternatively be described as the refractive index of one circular mode diverging, i.e. this circular polarization experiences increasing difficulties to propagate through the medium. The point of divergence is the edge of the reflection band, defined by $\lambda_{N*} = p_0 \pm \frac{1}{2}\Delta n p_0$, where Δn is the birefringence the sample would have had if the helix were unwound. Within the reflection band the light is truly separated into two circularly polarized components, the one with the same handedness as the cholesteric helix no longer being accepted by the medium and thus fully reflected, the other one fully transmitted. The attribute 'selective' refers to the rather narrow width of the reflection band. In modern terminology, the cholesteric liquid crystal has a natural *photonic band gap*. On the long-wavelength side of the selective reflection band the cholesteric is again strongly optically active, just as on the short-wavelength side, but the sign of the optical rotation has changed. While the rotation of the polarization plane was in the same sense as the helix for $\lambda_{N*} < p_0$, it is now in the opposite sense.

- **$p_0 << \lambda_{N*}$:**
  All light is again transmitted through the sample but both eigenmodes are now very nearly circularly polarized. In this regime the optical rotatory power decreases with increasing wavelength as $\alpha \sim \lambda_{N*}^{-2}$, like in other common optically active media, e.g. quartz.

The origin of the selective reflection is the optically periodic structure resulting from the helical modulation. Although the periodicity of the helix is p_0 the optical periodicity is half of this, since already a 180° turn of the director takes us back to an optically equivalent situation. Based on this periodicity we can apply Bragg's geometrical method well known from the analysis of x-ray diffraction from crystals to, in a simple way, obtain an expression for the relation between the selectively reflected color and the viewing angle. Not surprisingly, we will thereby obtain a result that is identical to Bragg's law, but for cholesterics we must add some restrictions.

Consider the schematic cholesteric structure drawn in the left part of Fig. 26. The sample is aligned with its helix axis vertical and it is illuminated by light coming from the left in the picture at some arbitrary angle θ. Just as in the analysis of Bragg scattering in crystals the rays entering the cholesteric can be considered reflected at a periodic set of planes, the

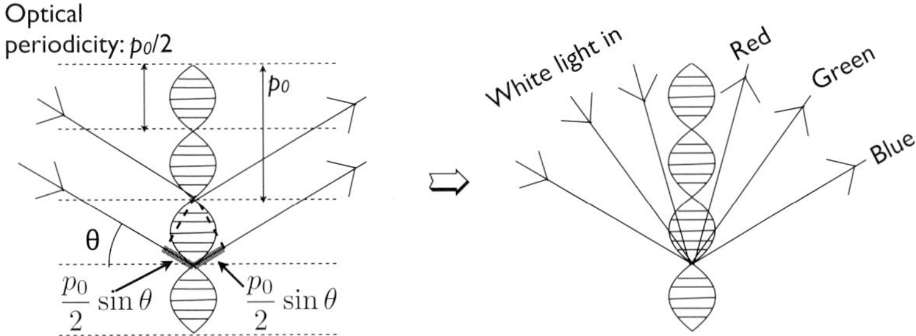

Fig. 26. The viewing angle dependence of the color of a cholesteric liquid crystal, summarized to the right, can be understood following a simple graphical procedure analogous to Bragg's law for x-ray diffraction, sketched to the left. See text for further explanations. From Ref. 32.

spacing here being the optical period $p_0/2$. These virtual planes are defined by the local director having the same (arbitrarily chosen) orientation with respect to the plane of incidence (the paper plane in Fig. 26). Basic optics tells us that the reflection angle is equal to the angle of incidence. Looking at the figure we see that, when the light exits the figure area, the lower of the two depicted reflected rays has gone a slightly longer path than the upper one, the difference being exactly $2 \cdot (p_0/2)\sin\theta = p_0\sin\theta$. These two rays will interfere to produce the effective reflected light and we know (again from basic optics) that the interference will be constructive if the path difference is equal to a multiple of a full wavelength. In other words, we obtain for the reflected light the result:

$$p_0 \sin\theta = m\lambda_{N*} \tag{17}$$

where m is an integer. We recognize this from crystallography as Bragg's law. In cholesterics Eq. (17) is however correct only for oblique incidence ($\theta \neq 90°$). For normal incidence (along the helix) all higher-order reflections are absent, i.e. only the fundamental reflection ($m = 1$) is present. Basically, the reason is the perfectly sinusoidal modulation in the N* phase: higher-order reflections would be the result of higher harmonics of the periodic structure but a sinusoidal modulation has no harmonics, only the fundamental. For oblique incidence the modulation is no longer perfectly sinusoidal since we are not following the helix, hence higher harmonics are present in the structure and we get higher-order reflections (albeit very weak).

For the normal incidence case, $\theta = 90°$ and $m = 1$, Eq. (17) gives us the result stated previously, namely that the selectively reflected light has a wavelength equal to the cholesteric pitch. The light wavelength in the medium is shortened with respect to the wavelength in vacuum (which is basically the wavelength in air) by a factor equal to the average refractive index. For typical liquid crystals this is about 1.5, so we can immediately estimate the helix pitch of a cholesteric that looks, for instance, green ($\sim$550 nm wavelength in air) when we observe it straight on as roughly 370 nm. A decrease in the angle of incidence θ of the light leads, according to Eq. (17), to a reduced wavelength of the selectively reflected light. This immediately explains the observation that the color changes towards shorter wavelengths (in the direction from red to blue) if we tilt a cholesteric sample away from us, as schematically summarized in the right part of Fig. 26.

Since the helical modulation imposed on **n** in cholesterics applies to **c** in chiral smectic-C-type liquid crystals, also these chiral phases exhibit the special optical properties described above, including the optical activity (with sign and magnitude depending on the relation between light wavelength and helix pitch) and selective reflection. For the basic SmC* phase the quantitative results derived above regarding the selective reflection—Eq. (17) complemented with the restriction that $m = 1$ for normal incidence—are directly valid. For more complex chiral smectic-C-type structures the situation may be slightly different.

9. Typical molecular structures of liquid crystals

Very often in the discussion of liquid crystals the building blocks of the phases are approximated with full cylindrical symmetry around the long axis (rods) or short axis (discs). In graphical representations of mesophases, one frequently encounters cigar- or plate-like shapes that should represent molecules, micelles or particles. This approximate approach is indeed very useful in most situations—in fact often necessary—but one should still be aware of what the true molecular structure may look like, and how its details can influence the properties of the macroscopic phase. For our purposes the chemical structure of the mesogens is of particular importance as it can have great impact on how they interact with the inclusions that we introduce into the liquid crystal.

There are today tens of thousands of substances known to form liquid crystal phases, some thermotropic, some lyotropic, some belonging to both categories (these are called **amphitropic**). We will here give only a few characteristic examples of molecular structures giving rise to either main class of liquid crystal, discussing the design of rod-shaped mesogens in somewhat more detail since calamitic thermotropics are by far the most commonly employed hosts for liquid crystal inclusion studies. Readers with a deeper interest in mesogen chemistry are referred to more specialized texts, e.g. Chapter 3.2 of the text book by Collings and Hird.[55] Particles forming liquid crystals are the topic of the final chapters of this book where they are discussed in detail.

9.1. *Rod-shaped mesogens*

The first great synthetic chemist in the field of liquid crystals was Daniel Vorländer in Halle, Germany. Based on his work around the turn from the 19th to the 20th century he formulated a number of fundamental rules about how the chemical structure should be to promote liquid crystal formation:

- the molecule should exhibit a linear rigid core,[56]
- this core should contain aromatic rings,
- the core should be as flat as possible,
- anisometry is of essence, molecules with a too small length-to-width ratio being non-mesogenic.[56]

Each individual rule has eventually been broken in rare cases, but overall the rules give an excellent idea of what gives rise to mesogenicity.

We can define a highly schematic generic template of a rod-shaped mesogen as in Fig. 27, in many respects a graphical equivalent to (some of) the Vorländer rules. During the following discussion it can be compared with the representative examples of real mesogen structures shown in Fig. 28. We have in Fig. 27 drawn a more or less linear and rigid, and most often aromatic, core surrounded by terminal aliphatic chains (also referred to as tails) R and R'. The combination of rigid aromatic core and flexible aliphatic terminal chains often leads to a certain degree of microphase segregation, the cores preferentially packing with other cores and chains with other chains. Such a segregation, if occurring on large scale, corresponds to

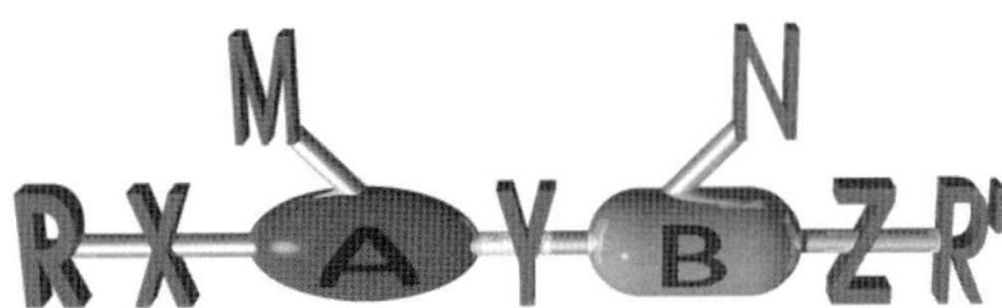

Fig. 27. A highly schematic generic 'template' for typical rod-shaped mesogens (redrawn from Ref. 55). See text for explanations.

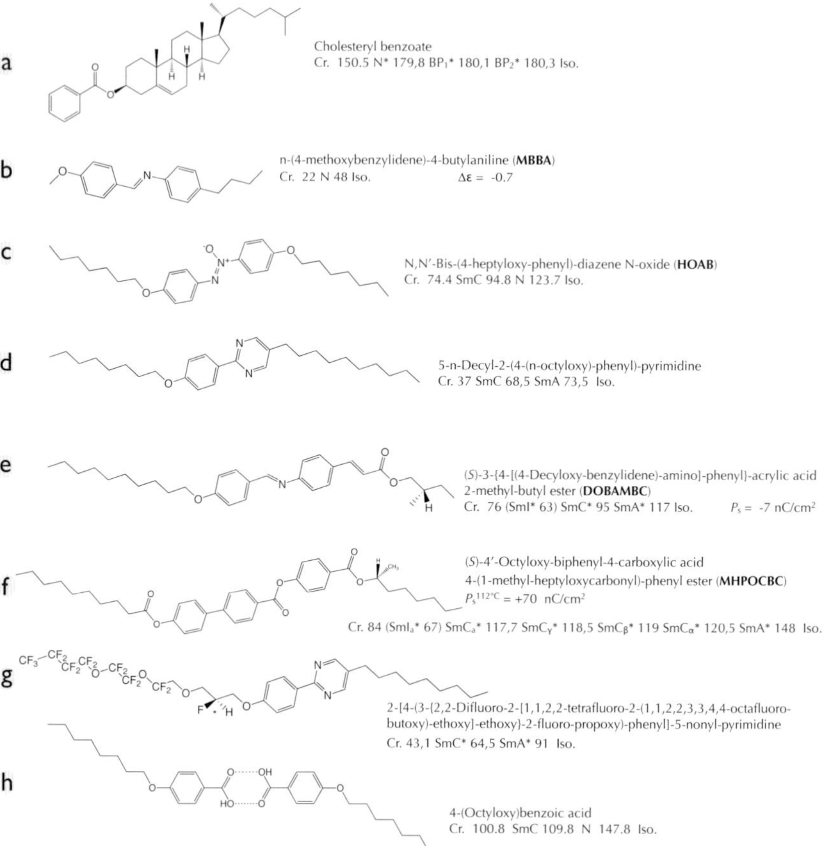

Fig. 28. Some representative examples of rod-shaped mesogens. Transition temperatures are in °C.

a smectic organization. Molecules that are roughly symmetric, with tails of similar length, promote the lateral intermolecular interactions giving rise to this effect, and are thus particularly suitable for the generation of smectic phases. Figure 28d is a typical example. Even stronger microphase segregation effects can be achieved by making the mesogens lightly amphiphilic (not in the usual hydrophobic/hydrophilic sense, though), e.g. using perfluorinated or oligosiloxane terminal chains, cf. the example in Fig. 28g. These chains mix poorly with ordinary hydrocarbons and thus strongly prefer their own environment, rendering the microphase-segregated molecule arrangement energetically favorable.

However, the director sign invariance $\mathbf{n} = -\mathbf{n}$ means that there are as many molecules directed with a certain tail R pointing upwards as there are with R pointing downwards. This means that the core-core and tail-tail interactions can be suppressed by making one tail R much longer than the other tail R', rendering such a design a good choice if a nematic phase is desired, see e.g. the classic mesogen MBBA in Fig. 28b. It also turns out that a broad core or one which is long compared to the flexible tails favors the formation of the nematic phase at the cost of smectic order (the cholesterol benzoate in Fig. 28a is a good example). Long end chains, in contrast, tend to entangle from molecule to molecule, promoting a stratified structure, thus smectic order. Tails of intermediate length (e.g. C_6H_{13}) often yield nematic as well as smectic phases in the phase sequence (Fig. 28c is an example, the nematic order being expressed as a cholesteric phase with this chiral mesogen).

While filling the purpose of providing the required flexibility at the molecule ends, the chains R and R' (which normally are unbranched or branched aliphatic chains) are however far from completely flexible. This is illustrated for instance by the so-called 'odd-even effect', referring to a certain physical property, e.g. the clearing temperature, changing back and fourth within a homologous series as a terminal chain is extended in length. Also the melting point often oscillates within a homologous series although it does not necessarily follow a strict odd-even relation. Disregarding the local oscillations, we can state that short terminal chains often yield high melting points, a lengthening of the chain quickly decreasing the melting temperature towards a minimum found for intermediate lengths. Further extension of the chains tends to raise the melting point again.

The terminal chains can be connected directly to the core, or via linking groups (X and Z in Fig. 27). With for instance a carbonyl as linking group, one can introduce a strong lateral dipole into the structure, generally enhancing smectic organization, in particular the tilted ones. On the other hand, such linking groups may increase the lateral size of the molecule, thereby disrupting lamellar packing and thus favoring nematic organization at the cost of smectic. A danger in incorporating linking groups (regardless of their location in the mesogen) is that they are often sources of chemical instability. A famous example is DOBAMBC (Fig. 28e), the very first SmC* liquid crystal synthesized, which due to an imine group linking the two core phenyl rings has a notorious tendency to decompose when illuminated by visible or UV light. The same holds for MBBA (Fig. 28b), as it has the same imine linking group.

                    J. P. F. Lagerwall

For achieving chiral mesogens the stereogenic center can be placed in various places of the molecule, but most often it is located in one of the terminal chains, cf. Figs. 28e–g. This choice often means that the chain is branched, the resulting steric effect in principle disrupting the liquid crystal phase stability. To minimize this adverse effect the branch can be located towards the end of the chain (see e.g. DOBAMBC, Fig. 28e) where the chain is maximally flexible, resulting in a kind of 'dilution' of the negative effects of the branch. However, this solution also facilitates rotation of the stereogenic center around the long axis of the molecule, thereby decreasing the power in transferring the molecular chirality to a phase chirality (the helical twisting power (HTP) in case of a cholesteric phase or spontaneous polarization of a SmC* phase; indeed, DOBAMBC has a very small magnitude of polarization). This effect can in turn be reduced somewhat by making one of the chiral center branches extended in length, but with a risk of reducing mesophase stability.

The rigidity of the mesogen is given by the core, consisting of a system of linked rings (symbolized by A and B in Fig. 27) such as phenyls, cyclohexyls or pyrimidines. In Fig. 29 one of the most commonly used thermotropic compounds, '5CB' (or, more properly, 4-Cyano-4′-n-pentylbiphenyl) is shown, together with four closely related analogs differing from 5CB only in the core structure. The replacement of an aromatic phenyl ring by a non-aromatic cyclohexyl, or the extension of the core by a third phenyl ring,

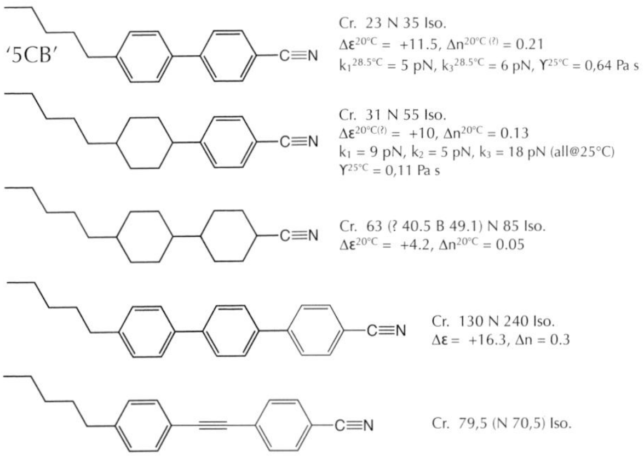

Fig. 29. Variations of the commonly employed nematogen '5CB' (top), illustrating how the most important properties change as the core structure is systematically varied. Transition temperatures are in °C.

clearly has dramatic effects on the physical properties. While the impact on the phase sequence is not always easy to predict, the birefringence and dielectric anisotropy—both dependent on the longitudinal polarizability of the mesogen core—are directly dependent on the amount of continuous aromatic structures along the length of the core. The more aromatic moieties in series, the longer is the resulting non-localized π-electron system, responsible for the polarizability of the molecule. In this context one should remember that also the cyano group contributes delocalized n-electrons.

We used the 5CB theme in this example because of its widespread use and because of the many variations around the basic structure that have been made, not because it is a particularly representative structure of mesogens. In fact, it is a relatively special design, its strong end chain asymmetry with one side being strongly polar due to the cyano group resulting in spontaneous dynamic 'dimerization' of the molecules, each 'dimer' consisting of two antiparallely oriented 5CB (or analog) molecules.

The optical and dielectric properties of the liquid crystal are thus mainly dictated by the core structure, but long end chains can 'dilute' the influence of the core somewhat, resulting e.g. in decreased birefringence. As the core is far from cylindrically symmetric, mesogens are always inherently biaxial, i.e. the core is actually more 'brick-like' than 'cigar-like'. In general, however, most or all of the biaxiality is averaged out through fluctuations and molecular rotations, leading to the macroscopic phase being uniaxial (nematic or SmA) or only weakly biaxial (SmC).

Two rings can be regarded as a practical minimum for mesophase formation. Mesogens with only one ring exist, but they then generally owe their mesogenicity to e.g. a hydrogen bond-capable end group that leads to dimerization into building blocks that are clearly rod-shaped and effectively have two rings, cf. Fig. 28h. Liquid crystals with more than two rings, on the other hand, are common, particularly among smectics. In general, the increased length to breadth ratio resulting from the linear addition of a ring to the core stabilizes liquid crystal phases, the smectic microsegregated organization being the most promoted. The rings can be directly connected, as in biphenyl or naphthalene (the former very common, the latter rather rare among mesogens), or they can be linked via a linking group (Y in Fig. 27). If a linking group is used, this should generally maintain the linearity of the core, though a slight bend can help to promote tilting in smectic phases when this is desired. Tilt is also promoted by strong lateral dipoles, and it is therefore common in particular in chiral smectics to place an ester linking group at position Y in a molecule with two long terminal alkoxy chains.

Linking groups, or their absence, can also influence the flatness of the core. A very important examples is the commonly employed biphenyl moiety, which in fact has an energy minimum for a twisted conformation (this is because the hydrogens of each ring that are directed towards the center interfere with each other sterically) and therefore does *not* take on the flat structure that standard drawings as in Figs. 28–29 may seem to suggest. This is frequently ignored when considering how 5CB interacts with aromatic inclusions like e.g. carbon nanotubes.[57] Likewise, one should remember that cyclohexyl rings are not flat. When a flat core structures is required, this can be achieved by moving the phenyl rings apart, e.g. by introducing a C≡C triple bond linking group (a tolane), cf. the final example in Fig. 29.

Lateral substituents (M and N in Fig. 27), i.e. atoms or groups of atoms attached off the linear axis of the molecule, most often to the core units, have a tendency to counteract mesophase formation, as recognized already by Vorländer. They are particularly detrimental to the stability of smectic phases. Lateral substitution is thus often avoided, but it can be useful for tailoring certain physical properties for specific applications. The most common choice is the fluoro substituent because of its combination of small size and high electronegativity, resulting in a minimal steric effect (undesired) but a maximized influence on properties such as dielectric anisotropy or non-linear optical coefficients (desired).

9.2. *Discotic and bow-shaped mesogens*

Until the end of the 1970's Vorländer's paradigm that a mesogen should be rod-shaped prevailed. In 1977, however, the Indian physicist Sivaramakrishna Chandrasekhar and his co-workers reported investigations of a homologous series of disc-shaped compounds, including the mesogen shown in Fig. 30a. They found that they formed liquid crystal phases of a new type.[58] Via x-ray investigations they could conclude that the phases had columnar hexagonal geometry, at that time well known from lyotropic but not from thermotropic liquid crystals.

Chandrasekhar's discovery inspired a great number of synthetic chemists around the world to create new discotic mesogens and by now quite a few thermotropic liquid crystals with disc-like molecules have been found, most developing columnar phases, a few of them forming nematic phases, and a very limited number surprisingly showing smectic mesomorphism.[18] Discotic mesogens generally have a more or less circular flat disc-like rigid

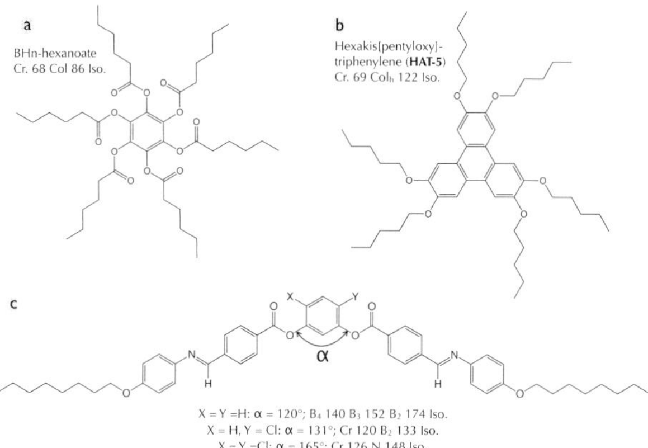

Fig. 30. While rod-shaped mesogens dominate among thermotropic liquid crystals, the last thirty years has seen the birth of other approaches, the two most important of which are disc-shaped (a, b) and bow-shaped mesogens (c). Transition temperatures are in °C. For an explanation of the B_x phases formed by bow-shaped mesogens, see e.g. Refs. 59–61.

and aromatic core, with between four and eight terminal chains attached symmetrically around the core circumference. It is difficult to define any 'standard' discotic mesogen but one that is relatively commonly studied, and that is also commercially available, is HAT-5, depicted in Fig. 30b.

The development of the research on discotic liquid crystals, as well as their application possibilities, has been well covered in a review by Sabine Laschat and co-workers,[18] and we refer the reader to that paper for more details on the topic. Most work on inclusions in thermotropic liquid crystals has been done using calamitic hosts, but some nice studies with discotic hosts have been reported.[62] Sandeep Kumar covers this body of work in Chap. 13.

Some twenty years after the discovery of discotic liquid crystals the next big change to the mesogen shape paradigm was made, as the first reports of liquid crystals from molecules with a distinctly bent core appeared. Such mesogens are nowadays often referred to as bow- or 'banana'-shaped. This was a revolutionary discovery not just because it was the first example of clearly non-axially symmetric mesogens, thus really going beyond Vorländer's initial ideas of requirements for mesogenicity, but also because the smectic phases formed by the *achiral* molecule in Fig. 30c (the X=Y=H version) turned out to exhibit a spontaneous polarization,[63] allowing the director to be switched by an electric field. This property is known to require a chiral tilted smectic and previously seen only in smectic-C-type phases and other tilted smectic phases containing chiral molecules. The tilted smectic phases formed by bow-shaped mesogens are indeed locally chiral, despite the non-chirality of the mesogens themselves.

This discovery created a whole new sub-field of academic liquid crystal research and hundreds of new bent-core mesogens have been synthesized in various academic research groups, allowing some generic conclusions to be drawn about how they should be designed. The core should normally consist of at least five rings and the bending angle turns out to be very important for the resulting phase sequence. The three examples depicted in Fig. 30c show how a tuning of the bending angle via small substitutions to the center ring allows the phase sequence to be systematically modified. An angle of about 120° seems to be quite ideal for a maximum 'bent-core smectic' mesomorphology, whereas nematic phases appear as the bending is made less pronounced (making the mesogen more 'calamitic-like').

With time the mesomorphology of bow-shaped mesogens has broadened, with nematic, SmA-like and columnar phases being added to the initial tilted smectic phases.[64] In this respect bow-shaped mesogens are in a way an intermediate between calamitics and discotics, columnar phases being almost as important as smectics in their phase diagrams. We know of no works where the effects of inclusions have been studied in liquid crystals from bent-core mesogens and they will thus play no further role in this book. This does not rule out, however, that they may enter the topic in the future. For more information on liquid crystals from bent-core mesogens, a number of reviews can be recommended.[59–61]

Among recent new developments in mesogen design, a very interesting addition is the concept of polyphilic molecules (comprising more than two chemically incompatible segments), resulting in quite complex self-assembly with interesting possibilities for tailoring for specific purposes. They have a clear potential for combining with particles, which may well segregate to certain volumes of the overall structure as a result of the polyphilism of the mesogens, but experiments of this kind are until now lacking. For more information, see the review by Tschierske.[65]

9.3. *Amphiphilic molecules*

Low molar mass amphiphilic molecules may be subdivided according to different schemes. For instance, one can focus on the uses/natural appearance of the amphiphiles and distinguish two major classes: artificial, technical surfactants and biological amphiphilic lipids, the most important of the latter being phospholipids. Another alternative is to group amphiphiles according to their non-polar part, e.g. single-chain, double-chain, aromatic etc. Biological amphiphiles often have twin non-polar end chains whereas most technical surfactants have a single chain. Amphiphiles with aromatic non-polar chains are—although highly interesting[66,67]—rarely employed and generally not commercially available. The most common classification scheme is, however, to group amphiphiles according to the type of polar head group, resulting in four main classes: cationic, anionic, zwitterionic, and nonionic.

The polar, and thus hydrophilic, head group is particularly important to the phase sequence generated by the amphiphile in water, because its effective size can be greatly varied. This can be achieved either by simply increasing the amphiphile concentration until the head group is no longer fully hydrated, resulting in an effective head group size that continuously decreases as more amphiphile is added. As a result, the liquid crystal phase changes according to the generic lyotropic phase diagram depicted in Fig. 2. The reason is the change in preferred aggregate curvature as the head group size is decreased at essentially constant size of the nonpolar chain.[68] In case of ionic amphiphiles, one can alternatively add electrolytes (salts) to the mixture, the added ions affecting the head group size in two ways. First, they screen out the electrostatic interactions, thereby reducing the repulsion between adjacent (equally charged) head groups. Second, as the electrolytes use up water for their own hydration the surfactant head groups may be less hydrated at a specific amphiphile concentration than they would be without the presence of the electrolytes. Both phenomena result in smaller effective polar head group, again without affecting the nonpolar end chain size, rendering a different aggregate curvature energetically favored. With nonionic surfactants the first effect is absent, whereas the reduced hydration of the head group can arise at high salt concentration. In general nonionic surfactants are much less sensitive to salt addition.

9.3.1. *Anionic amphiphiles*

One of the most commonly employed amphiphiles in lyotropic liquid crystal science is sodium dodecyl sulfate (Fig. 31), often abbreviated SDS. It is a surfactant that is commonly used in many commercial soaps and detergents. It has been extensively investigated, in simple aqueous solutions as well as in mixtures with other surfactants, salts etc., and it can be acquired at

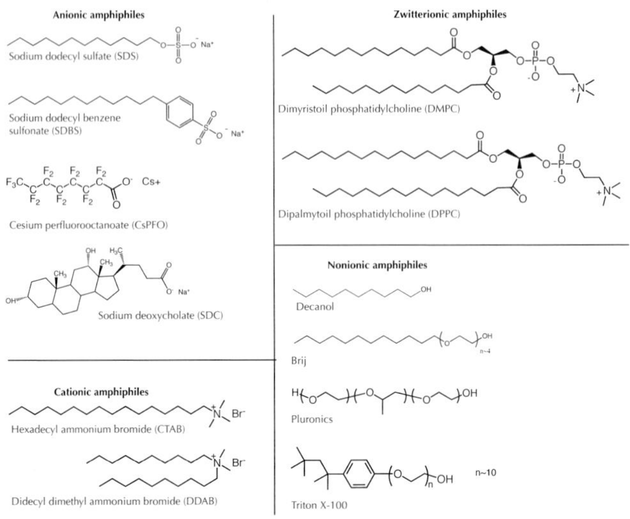

Fig. 31.   Examples of ionic and nonionic amphiphilic molecules, many of them commonly appearing in lyotropic liquid crystalline systems.

low cost and high purity in large quantities. It displays a quite rich phase diagram as a function of its concentration in water, albeit without any nematic phase.[69]

A nematic phase can be achieved by the addition of a co-surfactant, often a long-chain alcohol such as decanol, cf. Fig. 31. This can be regarded as a nonionic surfactant with an extremely small head group. The starting point is a relatively saturated but still isotropic (surfactant concentration around 20-30 wt.-%) aqueous solution of SDS or a related surfactant. When decanol is added, we introduce a small amount of new amphiphiles which, due to their much smaller head group, prefer a lower degree of curvature. The easiest way for both surfactant species to be accommodated in micelles is if these are disc- or rod-shaped, the decanol molecules preferably being situated at the less curved central parts. The first nematic phase formed upon decanol addition is a rod-micelle phase, changing into a disc micelle nematic when the molar ratio of decanol to SDS exceeds about 0.4.[70,71] The SDS-decanol combination is thus a very versatile system for anyone looking for a lyotropic nematic liquid crystal mixture. Interestingly, preparing a nematic mixture at the borderline regime between the two micelle shapes results in a biaxial nematic phase.[2,3] An alternative approach to achieving nematic lyotropic phases is to add electrolytes rather than a co-surfactant, a strategy that works with some surfactants.[72,73]

A related surfactant which is popular (and effective) in particle dispersion is sodium dodecyl benzene sulfonate (SDBS, Fig. 31), the main difference being the introduction of an aromatic phenyl ring between the polar head group and the apolar end chain. While the phase diagram of SDBS has been poorly investigated (this may be due to the rather low purity, often ∼80%, at which it is commercially available but also because its primary use is in fact not liquid crystal formation) it is a surfactant with technological importance and it has been used in some work on inclusions in liquid crystals.[74] A slightly similar situation holds for the structurally very different anionic amphiphile sodium deoxycholate (Fig. 31), a bile salt that can be effectively used for nanoparticle dispersion.[75] The apolar part is basically a steroid moiety, making it a rather unusual surfactant. Nevertheless, this and related bile salts have been shown to form lyotropic liquid crystal phases.[76,77]

The third anionic surfactant listed in Fig. 31 is cesium perfluorooctanoate (CsPFO), with a relatively short but fully perfluorinated apolar chain. It is interesting because it is one of few amphiphiles that form nematic lyotropic phases in aqueous solution without the need of a co-surfactant or salt addition.[78] This has been used extensively also as a basis for investigating the formation of lyotropic cholesteric phases, resulting from the addition of chiral dopants.[79]

9.3.2. *Cationic amphiphiles*

Also cationic surfactants, i.e. amphiphiles with a positively charged ionic head group and (consequently) negative counter ions, can be very effectively used in lyotropic liquid crystal research, as well as for particle dispersion, detergency etc. The standard head group is based on the ammonium ion, allowing single-chain primary salt surfactants such as the commonly employed surfactant hexadecyl trimethylammonium bromide (CTAB; the 'C' standing for 'cetyl', an older name for hexadecyl), cf. Fig. 31. But one can also replace one, two or even all three hydrogens of the ammonium head group with aliphatic chains, resulting in surfactants with two, three and four chains, respectively, cf. the double-chain examle DDAB in Fig. 31. The ammonium head group surfactant model is thus very versatile in terms of tuning the effective amphiphile shape over a broad range.

9.3.3. *Zwitterionic amphiphiles*

The most important example of zwitterionic amphiphiles are the biologically crucial amphiphilic lipids building up our cell membranes, in particular phospholipids. Two commonly studied examples, DMPC and DPPC, are drawn in Fig. 31. The term '**zwitterionic**' (coming from German 'der Zwitter' = hybrid) means that the molecule can be anionic, cationic as well as neutral, all depending on the pH of the solution. At low pH (excess of H^+) the negative charge at the phosphate moiety is neutralized and the head group is effectively cationic. At high pH (excess of OH^-) it is the ammonium ion that is neutralized and the head group appears negatively charged, i.e. the molecule is an anionic amphiphile. In between there is a particular pH-value, different for different zwitterions, where the head group is effectively uncharged. This pH is called the 'isoelectric point'.

Phospholipids do not form micelles; the first type of phospholipid aggregate encountered as the concentration is raised is a **vesicle** (also called 'liposome'), a (normally) spherical aggregate with water inside (in contrast to micelles) as well as outside, the wall of which consists of one or several phospholipid bilayer(s). The vesicle is thus a very small sample of a lamellar phase curved up onto itself. Note that the diameter of the vesicle is at least an order of magnitude greater (often much more) than that of a micelle, hence the curvature of the wall is much weaker than that of a micelle perimeter. The twin apolar chains of phospholipids would not allow the very high curvature of a normal micellar structure.

With increasing amount of phospholipid, bulk lamellar phases typically form. The resulting phase and aggregate geometry depends on the exact phospholipid type as well as on its concentration. While the biological relevance of phospholipids makes their study extremely interesting, we are not aware of any work where bulk liquid crystal phases formed by phospholipids have been studied from the viewpoint of inclusions in liquid crystals (although there is plenty of work on particles dispersed in dilute phospholipid solutions, including vesicular systems). Considering the increasing interest in biology among physicists and chemists, including those working with liquid crystals, it seems likely that such studies will come in the near future. Temperature plays a larger role for lamellar phases from double-chain zwitterionic amphiphiles than for the lamellar phases formed by many standard technical surfactants, the L_α-$L_{\beta'}$ transition being ubiquitous among phospholipids.

9.3.4. *Nonionic amphiphiles*

All amphiphiles considered so far owe the hydrophilicity of the head group to its ionic nature. The final subclass of amphiphiles considered is non-ionic, the hydrophilicity of the head group instead being ensured by e.g. oligooxyethylene chains or hydroxyl groups, cf. the examples in Fig. 31. In some respects the absence of ionic species makes the analysis of the liquid crystal phases formed by nonionic amphiphiles a bit simpler (electrostatic interactions play no role) but there are other aspects that can complicate the phase diagrams instead. Systematic investigations of liquid crystal formation from nonionic surfactants were carried out e.g. by Kratzat and Finkelmann.[80,81] German speaking readers will find a very good treatise with emphasis on the chemistry in Ref. 82.

10. Why do liquid crystal phases form?

There is no space in this book to go into the explanation of liquid crystalline order in detail, but we will summarize the key ideas and main outcomes of two important and commonly employed models, the Maier–Saupe model for the thermotropic nematic state and the Onsager approach for modelling the lyotropic hard rod colloidal nematic phase. This choice is based primarily on the fact that later chapters in the book refer to these two models. We make no claim of completeness and encourage the interested reader to learn more about these theoretical tools (and others) in some of the many excellent general liquid crystal text books.

10.1. *The Maier-Saupe theory*

The German physicists Wilhelm Maier and his student Alfred Saupe developed the first theory of the thermotropic nematic state that became widely known in the end of the 1950's[1] The theory proved to be a very successful framework capable of describing the thermotropic nematic-isotropic transition in a quantitative way. It is a molecular field (or mean field) theory, meaning that the actual intermolecular interactions are modeled by considering a single molecule surrounded by a 'nematic continuum'. All other molecules are thus replaced by their effect on the probe molecule, a 'molecular field' that this molecule experiences.

The approach can be summarized as follows. After having established an expression for the orientation-dependent potential resulting from the molecular field we can use Boltzmann statistics to formulate an expression for an ***orientational distribution function*** (ODF), a function that gives the probability that our probe molecule has a certain orientation at a certain moment in time (a probability that is identical to the fraction of all molecules that have this orientation). Armed with the ODF we can formulate an expression for *any* variable that depends on the distribution of molecular orientations, for instance the orientational order parameter S. We do exactly this, thereby formulating a self-consistent equation effectively giving S as a function of an assumed value of S. For each temperature of interest the values of S satisfying the equation are established, the true value finally being identified by minimizing the free energy. One ends up with an $S(T)$ curve that has an excellent general agreement with experimental data. However, because molecular field theories ignore fluctuations they all fail in the direct vicinity of a phase transition where fluctuations become important, the Maier-Saupe theory being no exception. Nevertheless its predictions about the transition state capture the essential physics.

10.1.1. *The molecular potential*

Maier and Saupe ruled out the role of permanent molecular dipole moments for the formation of the nematic phase. This would yield a spontaneously polarized nematic,[1] breaking the $\mathbf{n} = $ -$\mathbf{n}$ symmetry. In fact, the molecules in the nematic phase orient on the average with their dipoles antiparallel to those of their neighbors, canceling out the effect of permanent dipoles. They identified that the potential should exhibit a maximum if the probe molecule is perpendicular to $\mathbf{n}$ and a minimum if it is parallel. The interaction filling their needs is the London-type van der Waals attraction (induced dipole-induced dipole) between adjacent mesogens, which can be very strong and highly anisotropic due to the large and directed polarizability of the linear multiple-ring aromatic core structures typical of mesogens.

Consider two nearby rod-shaped mesogens inclined by an angle β with respect to each other. The essence of London interactions is that spontaneously occurring fluctuations in the electron distribution within molecules lead to an induced dipole moment in one molecule, producing an electric field that in turn induces an oppositely directed dipole moment in the neighbor molecule. The resulting attractive interaction decreases the free energy of the system, the maximum reduction occurring for tightly packed equally oriented molecules. If the molecules are instead perpendicular to each other the effective distance increases, reducing the attraction strength since London interactions are strongly dependent on the distance between interacting molecules. In addition, the attraction strength of two parallel molecules is proportional to the longitudinal polarizability α_l squared, whereas it for perpendicular molecule alignment is proportional to $\alpha_l\alpha_t$, where α_t is the much smaller transverse polarizability.

To formalize, in a generic phenomenological way, the dependence of the London attraction-based potential on the orientation of the probe molecule (defined by the angle β), a convenient choice—because it has the right nematic symmetry: cylindrical and inversion—is to use the second Legendre polynomial, just like in the definition of S:

$$U(\beta) \propto -P_2(\cos\beta) = -\frac{1}{2}(3\cos^2\beta - 1) \tag{18}$$

Because we are considering a statistical distribution of reference molecules we must weight the orientation dependence of the potential accordingly, the natural weighting factor being the orientational order parameter S. If the molecules of the surrounding nematic responsible for the molecular field are not ordered at all ($S = 0$) it makes no difference how our probe molecule is aligned, whereas if they are perfectly ordered ($S = 1$) we must have the maximum possible orientation dependence. This dependence of the potential on the probe molecule orientation and on the orientational order of the surrounding nematic is illustrated graphically in Fig. 32. Maier and Saupe finally introduced a prefactor, multiplying by a constant A, reflecting the London interaction strength, and dividing by the molar volume V_m squared.

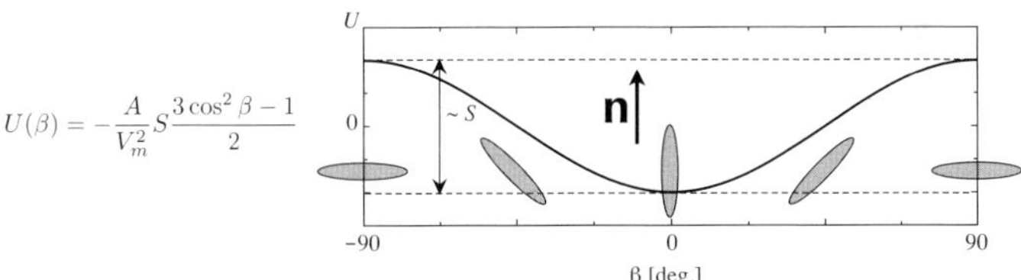

$$U(\beta) = -\frac{A}{V_m^2}S\frac{3\cos^2\beta - 1}{2}$$

Fig. 32.   The dependence of the molecular field potential U on the angle β of the probe molecule (grey ellipsoid) with respect to the director $\mathbf{n}$ (vertical), and on the orientational order S of the nematic surrounding.

10.1.2. *The orientational distribution function*

Now that we have an expression for the orientation-dependent potential experienced by the molecule, we can insert this into a Boltzmann statistics expression to get our orientational distribution function (ODF), telling the probability that our probe molecule takes a certain angle β with respect to the director:

$$f(\beta) = \frac{e^{-\frac{U(\beta)}{k_B T}}}{Z} = \frac{e^{\frac{A}{2V_m^2 k_B T} S(3\cos^2\beta - 1)}}{\int_0^\pi e^{\frac{A}{2V_m^2 k_B T} S(3\cos^2\beta - 1)} 2\pi \sin\beta d\beta} \tag{19}$$

When calculating the partition function Z we have integrated over all possible orientations, effectively amounting to an integration over all tilt angles β from 0 to π, remembering to weight the result by the factor $2\pi \sin\beta$ in order to take the degeneracy corresponding to all possible molecule tilting *directions* into account.

10.1.3. *The self-consistent equation*

The next step in our strategy is to use our ODF $f(\beta)$ to determine the order parameter S. A problem seems to be, however, that S itself appears in the expression for $f(\beta)$: if we need S to calculate the ODF, how can we then use the latter to determine S? The trick is to formulate a self-consistent equation, i.e. we *assume* a value for S and then use this, inserted in our ODF, to calculate the expectation value of P_2, which by definition should be identical to the order parameter:

$$\langle P_2 \rangle = \frac{1}{Z} \int_0^\pi \frac{3\cos^2\beta - 1}{2} e^{\frac{cS}{T}(3\cos^2\beta - 1)} 2\pi \sin\beta d\beta = S \tag{20}$$

where we for convenience have collected the material parameters and the Boltzmann constant in the constant c defined by:

$$c = \frac{A}{2V_m^2 k_B} \tag{21}$$

For most assumed S values we will end up with a different calculated value $\langle P_2 \rangle$, i.e. the last equality in Eq. (20) does not hold. This result simply means that the initial assumption was wrong. But for some values the calculated expectation value will agree with the assumption, confirming that this is a plausible value of the order parameter. This rather painstaking process must be done for a single temperature at a time since T appears in the Boltzmann statistics expression.

    The process is best illustrated graphically, cf. Fig. 33, by plotting Eq. (20) as a function of assumed S-values for a selected temperature, together with the trivial line $\langle P_2 \rangle = S$ in the same diagram and looking for points where they cross. We will then find two different regimes, both

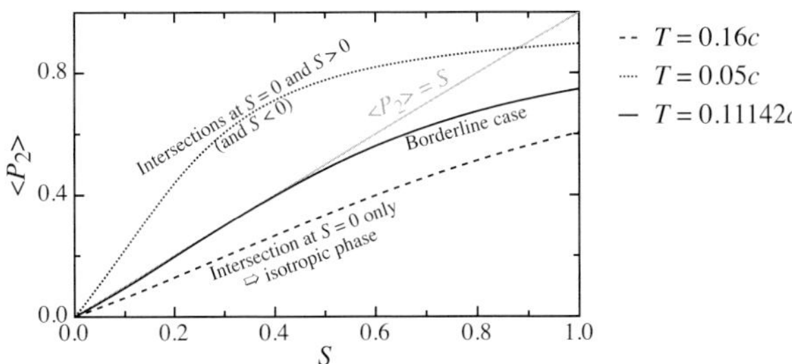

Fig. 33. The self consistent equation resulting from the Maier-Saupe approach can be solved graphically by plotting the expectation value of $\langle P_2 \rangle$, as calculated using the ODF $f(\beta)$, as a function of the order parameter S, together with the trivial line $\langle P_2 \rangle = S$ (grey line). Where the calculated curve and the trivial line cross we have solutions. Here this is illustrated for three different temperatures: one in the isotropic phase where there is only one intersection at $S = 0$, one in the temperature range where nematic order is possible, an intersection at $S > 0$ appearing in addition to the one at $S = 0$, and for the temperature at the border between the two regimes.

exemplified in the figure together with the border line case $T = 0.11142c$. For higher temperatures the two curves cross only at $S = 0$, i.e. this corresponds to an isotropic state. In the low-temperature regime, on the other hand, the self-consistent equation has a solution for $S = 0$ as well as for one positive and one negative value of S. (The latter is not shown in Fig. 33 since $S < 0$ is physically irrelevant.) To understand which solution corresponds to a real (thermodynamically stable) nematic state we must, in a first approximation, determine the thermodynamic potential for $S = 0$ and $S > 0$ (also this is done using the ODF, Eq. (19); for details see one of the more complete liquid crystal text books), identifying the physically correct value as the one that minimizes the energy. This yields a temperature of the isotropic-nematic transition equal to $T = 0.1101c$ at which the order parameter discontinuously jumps from $S = 0$ to $S = 0.43$. The experimentally well-established first-order nature of the isotropic-nematic transition is thus well reproduced by the Maier-Saupe theory and the predicted value of the order parameter at the transition is in surprisingly good agreement with the data.

10.1.4. *The Maier-Saupe model predictions*

The results of the Maier-Saupe approach are depicted qualitatively in Fig. 34. Not only is the first-order phase transition reproduced but the

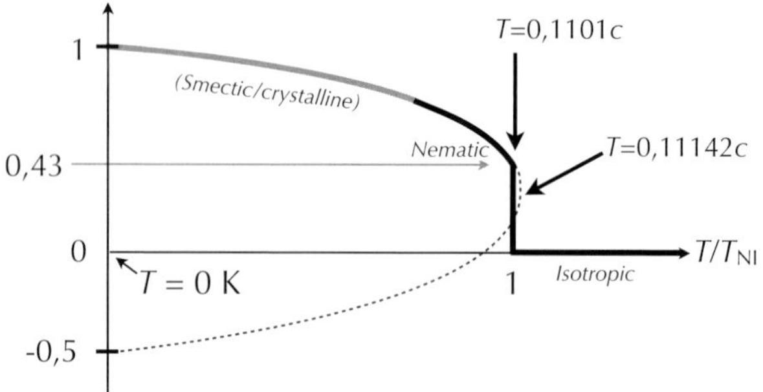

Fig. 34. The Maier-Saupe procedure yields a single solution $S = 0$ for absolute temperatures above $T = 0.11142c$ but three solutions, including $S = 0$ and one physically irrelevant solution $S < 0$, for temperatures below this value. Minimization of the thermodynamic potential yields the true $S(T)$ behavior, indicated here with the thick curve. The phase transition temperature T_{NI} corresponds to $T = 0.1101c$ and the order parameter of the nematic phase at the clearing point is obtained as $S = 0.43$. The part of the thick curve for values $S \gtrsim 0.7$ is drawn grey, reflecting the fact that such values are hardly reached in reality. A phase transition to smectic or crystalline phases would take place before S could increase further. Note that this graph is only qualitatively correct.

temperature dependence of the order parameter in the nematic phase predicted by the model fits excellently with experimental data. It is important that the results are universal; *any* thermotropic nematic exhibits roughly the $S(T)$ behavior sketched in Fig. 34, with reasonable accuracy even quantitatively. The material parameters A and V_m hidden in the constant c only determine what the transition temperature will be (note that the temperature (absolute, i.e. in Kelvin, not Celcius degrees) in Fig. 34 is rescaled on the x-axis with respect to the transition temperature T_{NI}).

The value of S at the actual phase transition temperature has been experimentally found to vary somewhat, but it is indeed around the predicted value $S_{NI} = 0.43$ (for instance, published data from order parameter measurements yield $S_{NI} \approx 0.31$ for MBBA (Fig. 28b)[22] and $S_{NI} \approx 0.5$ for p,p'-Azoxyanisole, 'PAA'[83]).

10.2. *The Onsager approach*

The Maier-Saupe model has had a considerable impact in the thermotropic liquid crystal community, by virtue of its concrete approach to specifically model the isotropic-nematic transition of thermotropics and its relative ease in grasping even for experimentalists. With the additional fine-tuning that with time has been done by subsequent researchers it could be applied successfully to essentially all thermotropic nematics. It may not work so well for lyotropic nematics, however, the main reason being that the Maier-Saupe potential often is not necessarily suited for describing lyotropics. First, London interactions are not nearly as important since the surfactants forming micelles as well as many nanoparticles are generally non-aromatic.[r] Second, the repulsive interactions ignored by Maier and Saupe are of considerable importance in lyotropics. The anisometry of nematic-forming micelles is considerably larger than that of thermotropic mesogens and it gets extreme in many non-micellar lyotropic systems formed by e.g. viruses or carbon nanotubes. In such cases steric repulsion, which can be adequately described in terms of excluded volume effects, plays a central role.

Moreover, lyotropic systems are very often electrically charged, hence electrostatic repulsion between building blocks may also become important. In case of nonionic surfactants, the electrostatic repulsion is replaced by an entropically driven repulsion due to steric constraints on surfactant chains when micelles get too close. In fact, entropic effects are generally key to understanding lyotropic liquid crystallinity. The first, and still most widely used, entropic model to address the question was that of the Norwegian-American theoretical chemist Lars Onsager, which we will now briefly describe in a highly simplified manner. It is actually some ten years older than the Maier-Saupe model but it was explicitly derived for colloidal systems developing lyotropic liquid crystal phases and did not work well for thermotropics, giving the two Germans a good reason to work out their own model. Onsager's inspiration was not micellar lyotropics (the first micellar nematics were found much later, in the 1960s) but probably mainly a 1936 *Nature* paper reporting the observation of liquid crystal phases in aqueous suspensions of the rod-like tobacco mosaic virus (TMV).[84]

Just like Maier and Saupe, Onsager was forced to do some rather drastic simplifications regarding the molecular interactions. While the former team ignored steric repulsion, this was the only type of interaction that Onsager kept throughout his treatment, discussed in terms of the excluded volume that it gives rise to. In other words, the Onsager model is a strictly repulsive model, attractive van der Waals interactions being considered

---

[r]An example of a lyotropic nematic where van der Waals attraction might be very important is suspensions of carbon nanotubes. As discussed in Chapters 17 and 18 their completely aromatic structure results in extremely strong London van der Waals attraction between adjacent CNTs. However, in order to be able to prepare a CNT suspension at all, this attraction must be counteracted, e.g. by surfactant coating, and the complex interplay of interactions that results is non-trivial to analyze.

insignificant. The electrostatic repulsion due to the ionic nature of many lyotropic building blocks was remodelled by Onsager as an effective increase of block size.[1] (This was rectified later on by Odijk and others.) Onsager furthermore restricted his treatment to systems of monodisperse perfectly rigid rods of length L much greater than their diameter D. The restrictions in terms of perfect rigidity and monodispersity have later on been released by extensions of the model by other researchers[85] while the case of disc-shaped building blocks with $D >> L$ can be treated analogously to Onsager's original treatment,[22] at least in an approximative manner.

The key issue in Onsager's approach is thus that of excluded volume and the resulting entropy penalty: a rod approaching another one is blocked in its translational motion from a certain volume around the second rod due to the steric impossibility to overlap with the other rod, cf. Fig. 35. This excluded volume gets larger with increasing rod size, but also the angle γ between their symmetry axes plays a crucial role: the leading term in the excluded volume is proportional to $\sin \gamma$, i.e. it vanishes if the rods are parallel, leaving only terms that are at least a factor D/L smaller than the leading term.[85] Thus, although parallel alignment clearly has a penalty in *orientational* entropy, the gain in *translational* entropy is so much greater that the free energy of the system can be lower for an orientationally ordered than for an isotropic state. This will only happen if there is a sufficient concentration of rods, such that the steric interactions really play an important role, and if the rods are sufficiently anisometric: spheres will block each others' paths equally regardless of how you 'reorient' them.

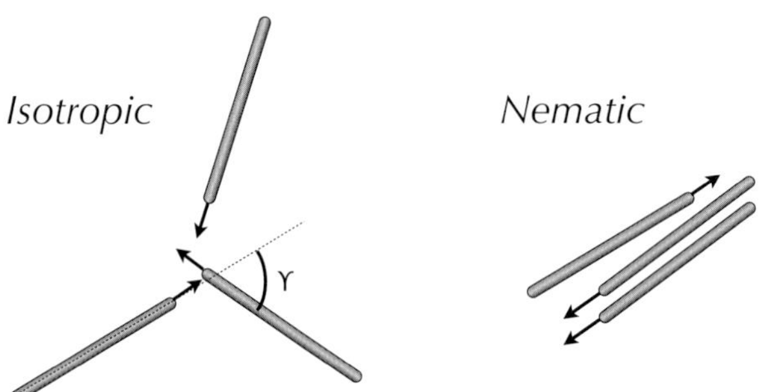

Fig. 35.   The excluded volume of an orientationally ordered system of anisometric objects, e.g. rods, is much lower than in an orientationally disordered one, explaining why such a system may exhibit a transition from an isotropic (left) to a nematic state (right) at a certain critical concentration.

In strong contrast to the Maier-Saupe model Onsager's treatment of liquid crystallinity is athermal, i.e. temperature never enters the equations, the only thermodynamic control variable being the particle concentration. Indeed, as already mentioned above (see also Fig. 2) the concentration is the primary control variable in lyotropics, but temperature does enter as a secondary parameter at least when treating micellar systems. This weak temperature dependence can be introduced by extensions of Onsager's results but for anisotropic colloidal systems like nematic virus or nanotube suspensions this is often not necessary: most of them *are* in fact athermal for all practical purposes. If one speaks of a 'clearing point' for such systems one would thus not refer to any particular temperature but to the minimum volume fraction Φ_c of the whole system taken up by the particles. Formulated in the simplest possible way, the Onsager theory predicts for this critical volume fraction, the largest particle volume fraction that the system can exhibit and still remain isotropic (i):[22]

$$\Phi_c^i = 3.3\frac{D}{L} \tag{22}$$

Once the particle volume fraction reaches Φ_c^i a first order phase transition takes place, dividing the system into coexisting isotropic and nematic phases. Incidentally, the particle volume fraction in the nematic phase (n) is higher than in the isotropic phase:[22]

$$\Phi_c^n = 4.5\frac{D}{L} \tag{23}$$

The resulting difference in density between the nematic and isotropic phases is most fortunate from a practical point of view, because it allows us to separate the ordered phase from the disordered one by means of centrifugation.[86] As should be expected, the critical volume fraction depends directly on the anisometry L/D of the particles, long and thin rods forming anisotropic phases at lower concentration than short and thick ones.

Just like the Maier-Saupe theory the Onsager results are universal. Although Onsager did not work this out in his original paper, his model results in a discrete jump of the orientational order parameter from $S = 0$ to $S \approx 0.84$ in the nematic phase once the critical particle concentration Φ_c^i is reached. While subsequent extensions of Onsager's model have come to slightly different values for the critical volume fraction as well as for the order parameter at the phase transition, the result that the orientational order parameter is extremely high in *athermal* nematic lyotropic phases, like those formed by viruses, remains valid. However, as mentioned in Sec. 2

the nematic micellar phases that were later on discovered turned out to be quite different, exhibiting a strongly temperature dependent order parameter that furthermore can reach very low values, even lower than that of typical thermotropics at T_{NI}. Such nematic phases can clearly not be understood by the bare Onsager approach but require substantial modifications.

Acknowledgments

I am indebted to Paul van der Schoot for a careful reading of the manuscript for this chapter, with many valuable suggestions for improvements.

References

1. T. J. Sluckin, D. A. Dunmur, and H. Stegemeyer, *Crystals that flow: Classic papers from the history of liquid crystals*. Taylor and Francis, London (2004).
2. P. Boonbrahm and A. Saupe, Critical-behavior of uniaxial biaxial nematic phase-transitions in amphiphilic systems, *J. Chem. Phys.* **81**(4), 2076–2081 (1984).
3. L. J. Yu and A. Saupe, Observation of a biaxial nematic phase in potassium laurate-1-decanol-water mixtures, *Phys. Rev. Lett.* **45**(12), 1000–1003 (1980).
4. D. Chandler, Interfaces and the driving force of hydrophobic assembly, *Nature.* **437**(7059), 640–647 (2005).
5. J. N. Israelachvili, *Intermolecular and Surface Forces, Third Edition*. Academic Press, Burlington, MA, USA (2010).
6. F. Keber, E. Loiseau, T. Sanchez, S. DeCamp, L. Giomi, M. J. Bowick, M. C. Marchetti, Z. Dogic, and A. R. Bausch, Topology and dynamics of active nematic vesicles, *Science* (2014).
7. P. Sharma, A. Ward, T. Gibaud, M. Hagan, and Z. Dogic, Hierarchical organization of chiral rafts in colloidal membranes, *Nature.* **513**(7516), 77–80 (2014).
8. J. P. F. Lagerwall, C. Schütz, M. Salajkova, J. Noh, J. H. Park, G. Scalia, and L. Bergström, Cellulose nanocrystal-based materials: from liquid crystal self-assembly and glass formation to multifunctional thin films, *NPG Asia Mater.* **6**(1), e80 (2014).
9. N. Puech, M. Dennison, C. Blanc, P. van der Schoot, M. Dijkstra, R. van, Roij, P. Poulin, and E. Grelet, Orientational order of carbon nanotube guests in a nematic host suspension of colloidal viral rods, *Phys. Rev. Lett.* **108**(24), 247801 (2012).
10. T. Gibaud, E. Barry, M. Zakhary, M. Henglin, A. Ward, Y. Yang, C. Berciu, R. Oldenbourg, M. Hagan, D. Nicastro, R. Meyer, and Z. Dogic, Reconfigurable self-assembly through chiral control of interfacial tension, *Nature.* **481**(7381), 348–351 (2012).

11. D. Kleshchanok, P. Holmqvist, J.-M. Meijer, and N. W. Lekkerkerker, Henk, Lyotropic smectic b phase formed in suspensions of charged colloidal platelets, *J. Am. Chem. Soc.* **134**(13), 5985–5990 (2012).

12. S. H. Aboutalebi, M. M. Gudarzi, Q. B. Zheng, and J.-K. Kim, Spontaneous formation of liquid crystals in ultralarge graphene oxide dispersions, *Adv. Funct. Mater.* **21**(15), 2978–2988 (2011).

13. S. Zhang, I. Pelligra, Candice, G. Keskar, W. Majewski, Pawel, F. Ren, D. Pfefferle, Lisa, and O. Osuji, Chinedum, Liquid crystalline order and magnetocrystalline anisotropy in magnetically doped semiconducting zno nanowires, *ACS Nano.* **5**(10), 8357–8364 (2011).

14. P. van der Schoot, The hexagonal phase of wormlike micelles, *J. Chem. Phys.* **104**, 1130 (1996).

15. G. Zanchetta, M. Nakata, M. Buscaglia, T. Bellini, and N. A. Clark, Phase separation and liquid crystallization of complementary sequences in mixtures of nanoDNA oligomers, *Proc. Natl. Acad. Sci. U.S.A.* **105**(4), 1111–1117 (2008).

16. M. Nakata, G. Zanchetta, B. D. Chapman, C. D. Jones, J. O. Cross, R. Pindak, T. Bellini, and N. A. Clark, End-to-end stacking and liquid crystal condensation of 6 to 20 base pair DNA duplexes, *Science.* **318**(5854), 1276–1279 (2007).

17. J. Lydon, Chromonic mesophases, *Curr. Opin. Colloid Interface Sci.* **8**(6), 480–490 (2004).

18. S. Laschat, A. Baro, N. Steinke, F. Giesselmann, C. Hägele, G. Scalia, R. Judele, E. Kapatsina, S. Sauer, A. Schreivogel, and M. Tosoni, Discotic liquid crystals: From tailor-made synthesis to plastic electronics, *Angew. Chem. (Int. Ed.).* **46**(26), 4832–4887 (2007).

19. X. H. Cheng, M. K. Das, S. Diele, and C. Tschierske, Novel liquid-crystalline phases with layerlike organization, *Angew. Chem.* **114**(21), 4203–4207 (2002).

20. C. Tschierske, Micro-segregation, molecular shape and molecular topology partners for the design of liquid crystalline materials with complex mesophase morphologies, *J. Mater. Chem.* **11**(11), 2647–2671 (2001).

21. J. P. F. Lagerwall and F. Giesselmann, Current topics in smectic liquid crystal research, *ChemPhysChem.* **7**(1), 20–45 (2006).

22. P.-G. de Gennes and J. Prost, *The Physics of Liquid Crystals*. Clarendon Press, Oxford, UK (1993).

23. M. Barón, Definitions of basic terms relating to low-molar-mass and polymer liquid crystals, *Pure Appl. Chem.* **73**(5), 845–895 (2001).

24. A. M. F. Neto and S. R. A. Salinas, *The Physics of Lyotropic Liquid Crystals: Phase Transitions and Structural Properties (Monographs on the Physics and Chemistry of Materials)*. Oxford University Press, USA, New York, NY, USA (2005).

25. P. H. Hermans and P. Platzek, *Kolloid Z.* **88**, 68 (1939).

26. V. Tsvetkov, Über die molekularordnung in der anisotrop-flussigen phase, *Acta Physiochim. (USSR).* **16**, 132–147 (1942).

27. P. O. Quist, B. Halle, and I. Furo, Nuclear-spin relaxation in a hexagonal lyotropic liquid-crystal, *J. Chem. Phys.* **95**(9), 6945–6961 (1991).

28. T. Beica, R. Moldovan, M. Tintaru, I. Enache, and S. Frunza, Measurements of optical anisotropy of a calamitic lyotropic liquid crystal, *Cryst. Res. Technol.* **39**(2), 151–156 (2004).

29. H. Johannesson, I. Furo, and B. Halle, Orientational order and micelle size in the nematic phase of the cesium pentadecafluorooctanoate-water system from the anisotropic self-diffusion of water, *Phys. Rev. E.* **53**(5), 4904–4917 (1996).

30. N. Boden, J. Clements, K. A. Dawson, K. W. Jolley, and D. Parker, Universal nature of the nematic-to-isotropic transition in solutions of discotic micelles, *Phys. Rev. Lett.* **66**(22), 2883–2886 (1991).

31. J. P. McClymer and M. M. Labes, Simultaneous measurement of guest and host ordering in a nematic lyophase via fluorescence spectroscopy, *Mol. Cryst. Liq. Cryst.* **195**, 39–44 (1991).

32. J. P. F. Lagerwall, Three facets of modern liquid crystal science, *Habilitation thesis, Martin-Luther-Universität Halle-Wittenberg* (2010).

33. M. Miesowicz, The three coefficients of viscosity of anisotropic liquids, *Nature.* **158**, 27 (1946).

34. A. Fernandez-Nieves, V. Vitelli, A. Utada, D. R. Link, M. Marquez, D. R. Nelson, and D. A. Weitz, Novel defect structures in nematic liquid crystal shells, *Phys. Rev. Lett.* **99**(15), 157801 (2007).

35. O. Thiebaut, H. Bock, and E. Grelet, Face-on oriented bilayer of two discotic columnar liquid crystals for organic donor-acceptor heterojunction, *J. Am. Chem. Soc.* **132**(20), 6886–6887 (2010).

36. P. Morales, J. Lagerwall, P. Vacca, S. Laschat, and G. Scalia, Self-assembled ordered structures in thin films of HAT5 discotic liquid crystal, *Beilstein J. Org. Chem.* **6**(51), doi:10.3762/bjoc.6.51 (2010).

37. E. Charlet, E. Grelet, P. Brettes, H. Bock, H. Saadaoui, L. Cisse, P. Destruel, N. Gherardi, and I. Seguy, Ultrathin films of homeotropically aligned columnar liquid crystals on indium tin oxide electrodes, *Appl. Phys. Lett.* **92**(2), 024107 (2008).

38. M. Cavallini, A. Calo, P. Stoliar, J. C. Kengne, S. Martins, F. C. Matacotta, F. Quist, G. Gbabode, N. Dumont, H. Geerts, Yves, and F. Biscarini, Lithographic alignment of discotic liquid crystals: A new time-temperature integrating framework, *Adv. Mater.* **21**(46), 4688 (2009).

39. A. A. Sonin, *Freely Suspended Liquid Crystalline Films.* Wiley (1999).

40. G. S. Smith, E. B. Sirota, C. R. Safinya, R. J. Plano, and N. A. Clark, X-ray structural studies of freely suspended ordered hydrated DMPC multimembrane films, *J. Chem. Phys.* **92**(7), 4519–4529 (1990).

41. R. Stannarius, C. Cramer, and H. Schuring, Self-supporting smectic bubbles (vol 350, pg 297, 2000), *Mol. Cryst. Liq. Cryst.* **350**, 297–305 (2000).

42. R. Stannarius and C. Cramer, Self-supporting bubbles of thermotropic smectic liquid crystals, *Europhys. Lett.* **42**(1), 43–48 (1998).

43. H. Liang, J. Noh, R. Zentel, P. Rudquist, and J. Lagerwall, Tuning the defect configurations in nematic and smectic liquid crystalline shells., *Philos. Transact. A Math. Phys. Eng. Sci.* **371**(1988), 20120258 (2013).

44. Y. Uchida, Y. Takanishi, and J. Yamamoto, Controlled fabrication and pho-

tonic structure of cholesteric liquid crystalline shells, *Adv. Mater.* **25**(23), 3234–3237 (2013).

45. H.-L. Liang, R. Zentel, P. Rudquist, and J. Lagerwall, Towards tunable defect arrangements in smectic liquid crystal shells utilizing the nematic-smectic transition in hybrid-aligned geometries, *Soft Matter.* **8**(20), 5443–5450 (2012).

46. H.-L. Liang, S. Schymura, P. Rudquist, and J. Lagerwall, Nematic-smectic transition under confinement in liquid crystalline colloidal shells, *Phys. Rev. Lett.* **106**(24), 247801 (2011).

47. T. Lopez-Leon and A. Fernandez-Nieves, Drops and shells of liquid crystal, *Colloid Polym. Sci.* **289**(4), 345–359 (2011).

48. E.-K. Fleischmann, H.-L. Liang, N. Kapernaum, F. Giesselmann, J. P. F. Lagerwall, and R. Zentel, One-piece micropumps from liquid crystalline core-shell particles, *Nat. Commun.* **3**, ARTN: 1178 (2012).

49. N. Lockwood, J. Mohr, L. Ji, C. Murphy, S. Palecek, J. De Pablo, and N. Abbott, Thermotropic liquid crystals as substrates for imaging the reorganization of matrigel by human embryonic stem cells, *Adv. Funct. Mater.* **16**(5), 618–624 (2006).

50. D. Demus, J. W. Goodby, G. Gray, H.-W. Spiess, and V. Vill, eds., *Handbook of liquid crystals.* Wiley-VCH, Weinheim (1998).

51. S. T. Lagerwall, G. Rudquist, Per, and D. S. Hermann. Liquid crystals - optical properties and basic devices. In *Encyclopedia of Optical Engineering*, pp. 1159 –11176. Marcel Dekker Inc. (2003).

52. H. Xianyu, S.-T. Wu, and C.-L. Lin, Dual frequency liquid crystals: a review, *Liq. Cryst.* **36**(6-7), 717–726 (2009).

53. S. T. Lagerwall, *Ferroelectric and antiferroelectric liquid crystals.* Wiley-VCH, Weinheim (1999).

54. E. B. Preistley and P. J. Wojtowicz, *Introduction to Liquid Crystals.* Plenum Pub Corp, New York, NY, USA (1976).

55. P. J. Collings and M. Hird, *Introduction to liquid crystals.* The Liquid Crystal Books Series Taylor & Francis, London (1997).

56. D. Vorländer, Einfluß der molekularen gestalt auf den krystallinisch-flüssigen zustand, *Ber. Bunsen Phys. Chem.* **40**, 1970–1972 (1907).

57. S. Schymura, M. Kühnast, V. Lutz, S. Jagiella, U. Dettlaff-Weglikowska, S. Roth, F. Giesselmann, C. Tschierske, G. Scalia, and J. Lagerwall, Towards efficient dispersion of carbon nanotubes in thermotropic liquid crystals, *Adv. Funct. Mater.* **20**(19), 3350–3357 (2010).

58. S. Chandrasekhar, B. K. Sadashiva, and K. A. Suresh, Liquid-crystals of disc-like molecules, *Pramana.* **9**(5), 471–480 (1977).

59. R. A. Reddy and C. Tschierske, Bent-core liquid crystals: polar order, superstructural chirality and spontaneous desymmetrisation in soft matter systems, *J. Mater. Chem.* **16**(10), 907–961 (2006).

60. H. Takezoe and Y. Takanishi, Bent-core liquid crystals: Their mysterious and attractive world, *Jpn. J. Appl. Phys. 1.* **45**(2A), 597–625 (2006).

61. G. Pelzl, S. Diele, and W. Weissflog, Banana-shaped compounds - a new field of liquid crystals, *Adv. Mater.* **11**(9), 707–724 (1999).

62. H. K. Bisoyi and S. Kumar, Carbon nanotubes in triphenylene and rufigallol-

based room temperature monomeric and polymeric discotic liquid crystals, *J. Mater. Chem.* **18**(25), 3032–3039 (2008).

63. T. Niori, T. Sekine, J. Watanabe, T. Furukawa, and H. Takezoe, Distinct ferroelectric smectic liquid crystals consisting of banana shaped achiral molecules, *J. Mater. Chem.* **6**(7), 1231–1233 (1996).

64. D. Shen, A. Pegenau, S. Diele, I. Wirth, and C. Tschierske, Molecular design of nonchiral bent-core liquid crystals with antiferroelectric properties, *J. Am. Chem. Soc.* **122**(8), 1593–1601 (2000).

65. C. Tschierske, Liquid crystal engineering - new complex mesophase structures and their relations to polymer morphologies, nanoscale patterning and crystal engineering, *Chem. Soc. Rev.* **36**(12), 1930–1970 (2007).

66. T. Kunitake, Y. Okahata, M. Shimomura, S. I. Yasunami, and K. Takarabe, Formation of stable bilayer assemblies in water from single-chain amphiphiles - relationship between the amphiphile structure and the aggregate morphology, *J. Am. Chem. Soc.* **103**(18), 5401–5413 (1981).

67. T. Kunitake, Synthetic bilayer-membranes - molecular design, self-organization, and application, *Angew. Chem. (Int. Ed.).* **31**(6), 709–726 (1992).

68. D. F. Evans and H. Wennerström, *The Colloidal Domain: Where Physics, Chemistry, Biology, and Technology Meet (Advances in Interfacial Engineering).* Wiley-VCH, New York, NY, USA (1999).

69. P. Kekicheff, C. Grabiellemadelmont, and M. Ollivon, Phase-diagram of sodium dodecyl-sulfate water-system.1. a calorimetric study, *J. Colloid Interface Sci.* **131**(1), 112–132 (1989).

70. L. J. Yu and A. Saupe, Liquid-crystalline phases of the sodium decyl sulfate-decanol-water system - nematic-nematic and cholesteric-cholesteric phase-transitions, *J. Am. Chem. Soc.* **102**(15), 4879–4883 (1980).

71. L. Q. Amaral and M. E. Marcondes Helene, Nematic domain in the sodium lauryl sulfate water decanol system, *J. Phys. Chem.* **92**(21), 6094–6098 (1988).

72. T. Haven, D. Armitage, and A. Saupe, Bend and splay elastic-constants and the rotational viscosity of nematic decylammonium chloride and ammonium-chloride water mixtures, *J. Chem. Phys.* **75**(1), 352–364 (1981).

73. P. K. Mukherjee, J. P. F. Lagerwall, and F. Giesselmann, Electrolyte effects on the nematic-isotropic phase transition in lyotropic liquid crystals, *Liq. Cryst.* **32**(10), 1301–1306 (2005).

74. G. Scalia, C. von Bühler, C. Hägele, S. Roth, F. Giesselmann, and J. P. F. Lagerwall, Spontaneous macroscopic carbon nanotube alignment via colloidal suspension in hexagonal columnar lyotropic liquid crystals, *Soft Matter.* **4**(3), 570–576 (2008).

75. W. Wenseleers, I. I. Vlasov, E. Goovaerts, E. D. Obraztsova, A. S. Lobach, and A. Bouwen, Efficient isolation and solubilization of pristine single-walled nanotubes in bile salt micelles, *Adv. Funct. Mater.* **14**(11), 1105–1112 (2004).

76. H. Amenitsch, H. Edlund, A. Khan, E. F. Marques, and C. La Mesa, Bile salts form lyotropic liquid crystals, *Colloid Surf. A-Physicochem. Eng. Asp.* **213**(1), 79–92 (2003).

77. E. F. Marques, H. Edlund, C. La Mesa, and A. Khan, Liquid crystals and phase equilibria binary bile salt-water systems, *Langmuir.* **16**(11), 5178–5186 (2000).

78. C. S. Rosenblatt, S. Kumar, and J. D. Litster, Approach to a second-order nematic-isotropic phase-transition in a lyotropic liquid-crystal, *Phys. Rev. A.* **29**(2), 1010–1012 (1984).

79. E. Figgemeier and K. Hiltrop, Quantified chirality, molecular similarity, and helical twisting power in lyotropic chiral nematic guest/ host systems, *Liq. Cryst.* **26**(9), 1301 – 1305 (1999).

80. K. Kratzat and H. Finkelmann, Branched nonionic oligo-oxyethylene v-amphiphiles effect of molecular-geometry on lc-phase behavior.2., *Colloid Polym. Sci.* **272**(4), 400–408 (1994).

81. K. Kratzat, C. Stubenrauch, and H. Finkelmann, Mixtures of branched nonionic oligo-oxyethylene surfactants in aqueous-solutions.4. the effect of molecular-geometry on lc phase-behavior, *Colloid Polym. Sci.* **273**(3), 257–262 (1995).

82. H. Stegemeyer, *Lyotrope Flüssigkristalle. Grundlagen - Entwicklung - Anwendung.* Steinkopff Verlag (1999).

83. G. Luckhurst and G. Gray, *Molecular Physics of Liquid Crystals.* Academic Press Inc.,U.S. (1979).

84. F. C. Bawden, N. W. Pirie, J. D. Bernal, and I. Fankuchen, Liquid crystalline substances from virus-infected plants, *Nature.* **138**(3503), 1051–1052 (1936).

85. G.-J. Vroege and H. N. W. Lekkerkerker, Phase-transitions in lyotropic colloidal and polymer liquid-crystals, *Rep. Prog. Phys.* **55**(8), 1241–1309 (1992).

86. S. J. Zhang, I. A. Kinloch, and A. H. Windle, Mesogenicity drives fractionation in lyotropic aqueous suspensions of multiwall carbon nanotubes, *Nano. Lett.* **6**(3), 568–572 (2006).

Chapter 3

Nanoparticle dispersions:
A colloid and polymer solution perspective

Paul van der Schoot[*]

Theory of Polymers and Soft Matter,
Eindhoven University of Technology, Eindhoven, The Netherlands
p.vanderschoot@phys.tue.nl

For most solid nanoparticles there are no true solvents in the sense that
a powder or crystal of these nanoparticles would spontaneously dissolve
when immersed in them. There are exceptions but these typically in-
volve unusual solvents such as super acids or chemical modification of
the particles to make particles and solvent compatible. Conventional
fluids, including water, are generally poor solvents or dispersants and in
them the nanoparticles need to be stabilised against aggregation. Indeed,
nanoparticles dispersed or dissolved in a liquid behave very much like
polymers and colloidal particles do. The properties of such dispersions
can thus be understood in terms of what is known about the behaviour of
colloids and polymer solutions. Important aspects are Van der Waals and
Coulomb interactions, steric interactions, the impact of depletion agents,
phase separation and the tendency of elongated colloidal particles and
stiff polymers to form nematic and other types of liquid-crystalline phase.
For this book a question of particular interest is how the nanoparticles
behave if they are present in a liquid crystalline host fluid, and what kind
of medium-induced interaction operates between these particles. However, most types of interaction are also present in isotropic host fluids,
so the attention of this chapter will primarily be directed towards conventional dispersions. I shall give an overview of the physico-chemical
principles most relevant to understanding the behaviour of fluid dispersions and solutions of nanoparticles, using spherical, cylindrical and flat,
plate-like nanoparticles as illustrative examples.

Contents

---

[*]Also at Institute for Theoretical Physics, Utrecht University, Utrecht, The Netherlands.

1. Introduction

Solid particles are not easily uniformly dispersed in any kind of liquid. There are, in essence, two main reasons for this. The first has to do with a difference in density between particle and solvent, and the second with a difference in optical properties between the two components. The former causes the particles to either sediment to the bottom or to cream to the top of the fluid in the container, depending on which is the most dense.[1] The latter causes attractive Van der Waals interactions between the particles,[2] and makes the dispersion phase separate into co-existing dilute and dense phases, or, if strong enough, form fractal aggregates or, if these aggregates become large enough, even a rigid gel.[3,4] In all of these cases of phase separation, aggregation and gelation, the homogeneous fluid dispersion is thermodynamically unstable.

If thermodynamically stable, nanoparticles dispersed in a fluid will sediment or cream, unless sufficiently small so that thermal fluctuations are able to overcome the force of gravity. A crude estimate for how small particles have to be to not appreciably cream or sediment is straightforward to obtain. Let us presume the particles are more or less spherical with a diameter σ [m], and let the mass density difference between particle and fluid be $\Delta\rho$ [kg m^{-3}]. Ignoring unimportant numerical prefactors, the gravitational force working on each particle is then approximately equal to $\sigma^3 \Delta\rho g$ [N], with $g \approx 9.8$ [m s^{-2}] the gravitational acceleration. The thermal energy is equal to $k_B T$ [J], with k_B [J K^{-1}] Boltzmann's constant and T [K] the absolute temperature, so thermal forces must be of the order of magnitude $k_B T / \sigma$ [N] as σ is the only available length scale.[4]

We conclude that if $\sigma^3 |\Delta\rho| g \ll k_B T / \sigma$, or, equivalently, if $\sigma < (k_B T / |\Delta\rho| g)^{1/4}$, the influence of gravity should be unimportant. For density differences $|\Delta\rho|$ of the order of one gram per milliliter, this corresponds to $\sigma < 10^{-6}$ [m], in other words, for particles of submicron size. If the particle is not spherical and has at least one linear dimension in the nanometre range, which constitutes an informal definition of nanoparticles, then we are in this limit and we can ignore the effects of gravity. From now on, we shall presume this to be the case. Colloidal particles larger than, say, a few micrometres require the specific consideration of the role of gravity, unless of course appropriate solvent mixtures are used that are density matched with the particles.

Differences in optical properties between host fluid and particles dispersed in it cause the particles to attract each other.[2] The reason is that differences in optical properties reflect differences in the refractive index and hence in their polarisability. This causes spontaneous fluctuations in the electro-magnetic fields in the fluid being influenced by the presence of the particles, giving rise to an attractive force between them. In effect, spontaneous fluctuations in the distribution of the electrons in one particle produce electro-magnetic fields that perturb the fluctuations in the electron density in another particle, which in turn couple back to the original particle.[5] This is not very different from how the Casimir force causes metallic plates to be drawn to each other, even in a vacuum.[4] In any event, a way to diminish these so-called London or dispersion interactions between particles is to index match particles and host fluid over a frequency domain around the optical and adsorption frequencies from $10^{14} - 10^{16}$ s^{-1}, again by choosing appropriate fluid mixtures.

Apart from London (dispersion) interactions between "induced" dipoles, there are also attractive interactions between freely rotating permanent dipoles called Keesom interactions and between permanent and induced dipoles known as Debye interactions. The combined effect of London, Keesom and Debye interactions between particles are called Van der Waals interactions.[2] Not only Van der Waals interactions tend to destabilise particulate dispersions. There are also other forces that conspire against nanoparticles remaining uniformly distributed in a fluid. These include what one may call structural forces because they find their origin in the "graininess" of fluids, that is, the fact that all matter is particulate.[4] A well-known example is that of hydrophobic interactions acting between apolar particles in aqueous solution.[5,6] The presence of a third component in the dispersion, e.g., dissolved polymers or surfactant micelles, can give rise to so-called depletion interactions purely for entropy reasons.[7]

It does not end there. If dispersed in liquid-crystalline solvents, there are additional sources of interaction that as a rule are very complex and highly anisotropic, and depend on the relative orientation of the particles. This is caused by the coupling of the particles to the broken symmetry.[8] In uniaxial nematic liquid crystals these include perturbations of the local degree or order of the fluid molecules, perturbations of the local axis of symmetry (the director) and perturbations of the fluctuations of that local axis. The latter are sometimes referred to as pseudo-Casimir forces.[9]

It is evident that to keep nanoparticles in solution or in dispersion in any appreciable concentration, special measures have to be taken. For instance, one may somehow put charges on the surfaces of the particles, which in particular is relevant if the solvent is water. This can be done chemically or physically, e.g., by somehow adsorbing charged molecules onto them. Another way is to cause steric repulsion between the particles, e.g., by adsorbing or chemically grafting polymers onto them, polymers for which the fluid host acts as a good solvent. Once stabilised, kinetic or otherwise, solution conditions may for some reason change, e.g., because of a change in temperature, acidity or ionic strength, and the stabilisation may fail and becomes too weak to overcome the Van der Waals or other types of attraction between the nanoparticles. In that case the particles will drop out of the solvent.[3]

Even if the particles are stabilised against falling out of suspension, other types of phase transition may occur too, in particular if the concentration of the particles is sufficiently large. Interestingly, driven by volume exclusion alone, spherical particles may spontaneously crystallise, whilst rod-like and disk-like particles may on top of that form a host of symmetry-broken, liquid-crystalline states.[1,4] What kind of phases present themselves depends on factors such as precise particle shape but also on how polydisperse the particles are. A second type of particle dispersed into these will also order in one way or another. For instance, carbon nanotubes dispersed in a nematic phase of flexuous fd virus particles will align to a lesser or greater degree, depending on whether they are longer or shorter than the particles of the host phase they are dispersed in,[10] whilst spherical particles dispersed in such a phase may self-assemble into strings that are aligned along the nematic director.[11]

It has become clear that inserting small particles into liquid crystals gives rise to interesting and complex behaviour, the understanding of which remains sketchy.[12] This is true for both thermotropic and lyotropic liquid crystals, that is, molecular liquid crystals and liquid crystal colloids. In the following, I will highlight important basic aspects of the physics of nanoparticles in fluids, focusing mainly on isotropic fluids, but will in addition address a few issues relating to anisotropic fluids not covered by other chapters in this book. In Sec. 2, I first review the basics of Van der Waals interactions between differently shaped particles, and highlight their sticky nature. Repulsive electrostatic interactions are covered in Sec. 3 and in particular the effects of screening by mobile salt ions also present in the solvent. Section 4 deals with the balance between repulsion and attraction, and how we can estimate what effects predominate the thermodynamics of colloidal dispersions. Other sources of interaction are discussed in Sec. 5, including hydrophobic interactions and depletion interactions. Simple rules of thumb for estimating under what conditions dispersions may undergo phase transitions of various kind are presented in Sec. 6.

I end this Chapter by considering particles dispersed in nematic liquid crystals in Sec. 7.

2. Van der Waals interactions

Van der Waals interactions between particles in vacuum or in an isotropic fluid medium is a topic that has long drawn the interest of physicists and chemists alike, and the field has witnessed a renewed interest not least because of their importance to nanomaterials. The calculation of Van der Waals forces is very much a non-trivial, quantum-mechanical problem that is outside the scope of this book. Hence, I refer to the textbook by Parsegian[2] for a near complete description of the state of affairs until its publication in 2006, and will make use of a more pedestrian account in which I choose to ignore what is known as "retardation". Retardation stems from the finite speed of light and the concomitant delay in information transfer from one particle to another. It modifies the functional dependence of interaction potentials at distances larger than, say, a micrometer, in general making them weaker. I will also ignore any effects of anisotropy of the liquid medium, which is relevant if it is liquid crystalline, not least because much less is known about them.[13]

A phenomenological potential that describes interactions between small molecules is the well-known Lennard-Jones potential. It has the following simple form,[15]

$$U_{LJ}(r) = 4\epsilon \left[\left(\frac{\sigma}{r} \right)^{12} - \left(\frac{\sigma}{r} \right)^{6} \right]. \tag{1}$$

Here, r is the distance between the centres of mass of the molecules, presumed to be spherical, σ is a measure for their diameter and ϵ the strength of the Van der Waals interaction energy. The first term accounts for the repulsive interaction between the molecules on account of the Pauli exclusion of the electrons in overlapping electron clouds. The second describes the result of attractive Van der Waals interactions, recalling that we usually distinguish between contributions from Keesom, Debye and London types of interaction.[5] The first is due to the presence of permanent dipoles, the second is due to the interaction between a permanent dipole and the dipole it induces in the electron cloud of another molecule, and the third is due to the coupling between spontaneous fluctuations in the electron clouds that produce temporary dipoles. The values of σ and ϵ for a great many compounds have been deduced from the thermodynamic properties of gases and liquids. Figure 1 shows the universal shape of the Lennard-Jones potential, if plotted in terms of the dimensionless strength of the potential U/ϵ and the dimensionless distance r/σ.[14]

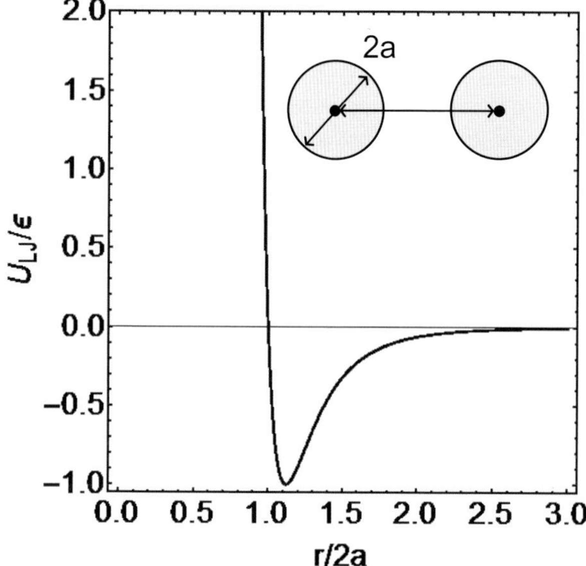

Fig. 1.   Dimensionless Lennard-Jones potential U_{LJ}/ϵ as a function of the dimensionless distance between the centres of mass of two particles $r/2a$. Here, ϵ is the strength of the potential and a the "radius" of the particles.

If we wish to know what the Van der Waals interaction energy is between two identical nanoparticles made up of very many molecules, we could pretend that interactions are pair-wise additive and simply calculate the sum over all pairs of molecule between two nanoparticles. This approximation was first proposed by H. C. Hamaker.[2] If we do this for the attractive part of the Lennard-Jones potential, we get a specific form that crucially depends on the shape of the nanoparticles involved. For two spherical nanoparticles of diameter σ, we get a form that can be cast in the form

$$U_{vdW}(r) = -\frac{A_H}{24}\left(\frac{\sigma}{r-\sigma}\right), \tag{2}$$

at least for very short surface-to-surface distances $0 < r - \sigma \ll \sigma$. Here, r is the distance between the centres of mass of the nanoparticles and A_H is the Hamaker constant that in our prescription is some function of ϵ and the (square of the) number density of the molecules that make up these particles. For large distances $r \gg \sigma$, the Hamaker approximation reproduces, as expected, the $1/r^6$ form with $U_{vdW}(r) = -A_H\sigma^6/36r^6$, because then the nanoparticles behave as if they are just big atoms.[2] It transpires that for distances smaller than about their diameter the attraction can become much stronger and it is in this sense that particles behave as if they are sticky.

A few things need to be noted, however. The first is that expression (2) diverges for zero surface-to-surface separation, as $r \to \sigma$. This is due to the continuum limit that we have tacitly taken in a coarse-grained description of the particle, in which we lose information about the graininess of matter. This should break down for distances comparable to the size of the molecules (or atoms) that make up the particles. In fact, it breaks down earlier than that, so for larger distances, because particles are typically not smooth but rough on much larger than microscopic length scales.

Second point, of course, is that in the limit $r \to \sigma$ we should also start to feel the repulsive part of the potential. As it is much steeper than the soft attractive part, it becomes large and positive once the (electron clouds of the) particles start to overlap. A useful model potential that describes what is known as "volume exclusion" or steric interactions, is the so-called hard core potential. To model this, we often write

$$U_{hc}(r) = +\infty, \tag{3}$$

for all centre-to-centre distances $r \leq \sigma$. Colloidal particles can indeed be made to approximately interact via a hard-core potential alone, in which case they are called hard particles.[1] I shall return to hard particles when describing ordering transitions in nanoparticulate dispersions in Sec. 6.

Third, if the Hamaker constant is not very much smaller than the thermal energy, $k_B T$, and the particles do not behave as hard particles, then we often take it to be a phenomenological parameter, that is, a parameter we obtain experimentally rather than calculate it from first principles. The reason is that interactions are generally not pair-wise additive. This does not essentially change the fundamental form of the potential but does affect the value of Hamaker constant. Quantum-mechanical calculations, based on a continuum description of matter, show that it becomes an integral of a function proportional to the square of the difference between the frequency-dependent dielectric constants of the particles and the medium. The predictive power of the method, known as Lifshitz theory, is rather good.[16] I refer again to Parsegian's book for details of how to calculate Hamaker constants from the optical properties of the particles and the medium.[2]

It is important to realise that the Hamaker constant, A_H, is very different in vacuum from that in any fluid medium and usually much larger in the former. For instance, for particles consisting of hydrocarbons the Hamaker constant across vacuum is about 12 times the thermal energy $k_B T$ at room temperature, whilst in water it is only about one $k_B T$. For gold particles we have $A \approx 49\ k_B T$ across vacuum *versus* $A_H \approx 29\ k_B T$ across water, again both at room temperature.[2] The reason why in a fluid the Hamaker constant is lower than in vacuum is because we need to subtract the dielectric properties of the fluid medium. Matter is always more polarisable than vacuum. Loosely speaking, we need to subtract from the attraction between a particle and another particle, that of the particle and the fluid the second particle displaces. A fact not always appreciated, Van der Waals interactions between charged nanoparticles, e.g., in water, depend also on the concentration of mobile salt ions that screen electrostatic interactions in the aqueous medium. I will return to this briefly in the following section.

To see how particle shape changes the functional form of the interaction potential, let us consider two rod-like particles of length L and width σ inclined at some angle γ. This would be a model for, say, carbon nanotubes, filamentous viruses or very stiff polymer molecules. Let us for simplicity focus on surface-to-surface distances larger than the width of the cylinders yet smaller than their length: $L \gg r - \sigma \gg \sigma$ where r now refers to the shortest distance between the main axes of two cylinders. See also Fig. 2. In this case, the cylinders behave as if they are line particles and the integrations give us an expression of the form[2]

$$U_{vdW}(r) = -\frac{\pi}{32} A_H \frac{1}{|\sin\gamma|} \left(\frac{\sigma}{r}\right)^4, \tag{4}$$

at least if the angle γ between the main axes is larger than the "internal angle" σ/L.[a] The fourth power dependence on the distance is easily un-

---

[a]For perfectly parallel particles the form of the Van der Waals potential is lightly different, $U_{vdW} = -\frac{3\pi}{128\sigma} A_H z \left(\frac{\sigma}{r}\right)^5$, where $0 \leq z \leq L$ is the overlap length between the rods.[2]

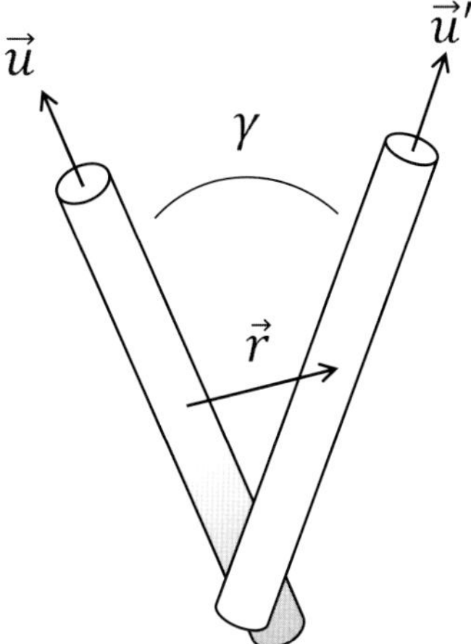

Fig. 2. Configuration of two rod-shaped particles of orientations $\vec{u}$ and $\vec{u}'$. The vector connecting the centres of mass is denoted $\vec{r}$, and the angle between the centre lines γ.

derstood to arise because in effect we integrate over the lengths of two line particles. Here, we have presumed the polarisability along and perpendicular to the main body axis vector of the cylinder to be equal.

The $1/\sin\gamma$ dependence is also relatively straightforward to understand, because the number of points along the lines in the region around the distance of closest approach that contribute to the total interaction scales with this factor. This $1/\sin\gamma$ dependence of the interaction energy tends to align rods and explains why elongated molecules tend to form liquid crystalline phases. These are the thermotropic liquid crystals discussed in the preceding Chapter.[b] In fact, the $1/\sin\gamma$ dependence of the Van der Waals attraction also explains why long, rod-like macromolecules are difficult to dissolve or disperse at all in fluid media. Even if the attraction energy of two rods near contact and at right angles is much lower than the thermal energy, if rotated to assume a parallel orientation this energy increases by a factor of L/σ. For carbon nanotubes, for example, aspect ratios L/σ of one thousand are not uncommon and as-produced carbon nanotubes, which come in large bundles, dissolve in very few solvents exactly for this reason.[17,18] The solvents they do dissolve in put charges on them and sta-

---

[b]To translate the Van der Waals potential into a potential of the Maier-Saupe form discussed in the preceding Chapter, one must integrate it over the spatial co-ordinate, and make use of an expansion of the $|\sin\gamma|$ in spherical harmonics of the solid angles of the orientations of the two cylinders.

bilise the dispersed state electrostatically, which is the topic of the next section.[19] And, as to be discussed in Sec. 6, if properly stabilised, the particles for entropy reasons may form (lyotropic) liquid crystalline states at sufficiently high concentrations.

The Van der Waals interaction potential for perfectly flat nanoparticles, which may be seen as a model for clay particles or graphene, is an extremely complex function of the centre-to-centre distance r and angle γ between the main body axis vectors, even within the Hamaker approximation. (See also Fig. 2.) If the platelets are perfectly parallel with $\gamma = 0$, and if their centres co-align so that we have maximum overlap between the particles, we have[2]

$$U_{vdW}(r) = -\frac{A_H}{12\pi} \left(\frac{\sqrt{A}}{r - \sigma} \right)^2, \tag{5}$$

if their thickness $\sigma \ll \sqrt{A}$ is much smaller than their width $\sqrt{A}$, and then only for very small separations $r - \sigma \ll \sigma$. For larger but still relatively small distances $\sqrt{A} \gg r \gg \sigma$, this becomes[2]

$$U_{vdW}(r) = -\frac{A_H}{2\pi} \frac{A}{\sigma^2} \left(\frac{\sigma}{r} \right)^4, \tag{6}$$

where the fourth power comes from integrating over the surface of the other particle, which behaves as if it were infinitely thin.[2]

In both cases the interaction energy scales with the area, and again we find a very strong increase in interaction strength for shorter separations: flat particles are also sticky and have an inherent propensity to form stacks. Not surprisingly, flat particles such as clay particles and graphene flakes are also difficult to disperse in fluids and need to be stabilised, say, in water, by oxidising their surface (graphene) or letting them acquire an electrical charge (clay).[20,21] The latter is the topic of the next section. Note that the entropy associated with the thermal flexing motion of semi-flexible surfaces does oppose stacking but cannot suppress it.[22]

3. Electrostatic interactions

Nanoparticles dispersed in water are often stabilised electrostatically not dissimilar to how in a biological context macromolecules, including proteins, viruses and DNA, are stabilised. Charges can be put on nanoparticles by chemically grafting ionisable moieties onto their surfaces or by physisorption of ionic surfactants or ionic polymers.[3] Indeed, carbon nanotubes have been made to disperse homogeneously in water by adsorption of charged surfactant molecules,[23] bile salts[10] and single-stranded DNA.[24] In principle, polymers need not be charged to be able to stabilise nanoparticles for reasons that have to do with steric repulsion between adsorbed polymer layers. This will be discussed in a following Section.

Like charges repel each other and charging up nanoparticles should reasonably counter the effects of Van der Waals attraction between them. This turns out to be the case, but as we shall see not quite in the manner that might naïvely be expected. The reason is that there are always mobile ions in fluids, sometimes, but not always, due to the presence of dissociated salts. Water, for instance, dissociates in small part into the oppositely charged ions H_3O^+ and OH^-. It is almost impossible to prevent other small ions to be also present in water, including Na^+ and Cl^-. The presence of mobile ions drastically changes how like-charge repulsion works in practice. A large part of electrostatic repulsion in fluid media turns out not to be energetic in nature but due to entropy.[3]

The interaction between charged nanoparticles in aqueous solution also containing mobile ions is described by Poisson-Boltzmann theory, the basic ingredients of which we only briefly mention.[3] For an extensive review the interested reader is referred to the textbook of Fennell Evans and Håkan Wennerström. The first ingredient, the Poisson equation, describes how the electrical potential responds to the presence of mobile and fixed charges in the solution. The second ingredient, the Boltzmann equation, describes how the distribution of mobile charges responds to the local electrostatic potential. This set of equations has to be solved self-consistently, giving rise to the Poisson-Boltzmann equation for the self-consistent electrical potential that is a function of the ionic strength of the solution. If there are only monovalent mobile ions in the solution, the ionic strength is given by the number density of salt in it. The fact that the Poisson-Boltzmann equation is a self-consistent field equation implies that it is a mean-field theory.[20]

The Poisson-Boltzmann equation is a non-linear differential equation that has to be supplemented with appropriate boundary conditions. These boundary conditions depend on whether one has (i) a fixed surface charge, (ii) a fixed surface potential, or (iii) a surface that is "charge regulated" implying that the charged state of ionisable moieties respond to the acidity, the ionic strength and the local electrical potential.[20] All of this in turn depends on the surface properties (and chemistry) of the nanoparticles.

The Poisson-Boltzmann equation has been solved exactly for a few particle geometries and in a few limits.[3,27] Usually, it is solved numerically. Solving the Poisson-Boltzmann equation is necessary but not sufficient, however, to calculate the interaction potential between the charged nanoparticles. Indeed, one must in addition either apply thermodynamic integration or apply statistical mechanical theory to the problem in hand.[25] In the end, the interaction potential acting between nanoparticles is not a proper interaction potential, but what is known as a "potential of mean force". It means that it contains information on the free energy of the mobile ions that surround the charged nanoparticles. These include the counterions of the charged groups on the surface but also the co- and counterions of the salt present in the solution. Counterions accumulate in a region near the charged surface of the particles while co-ions are expelled from it. See Fig. 3.

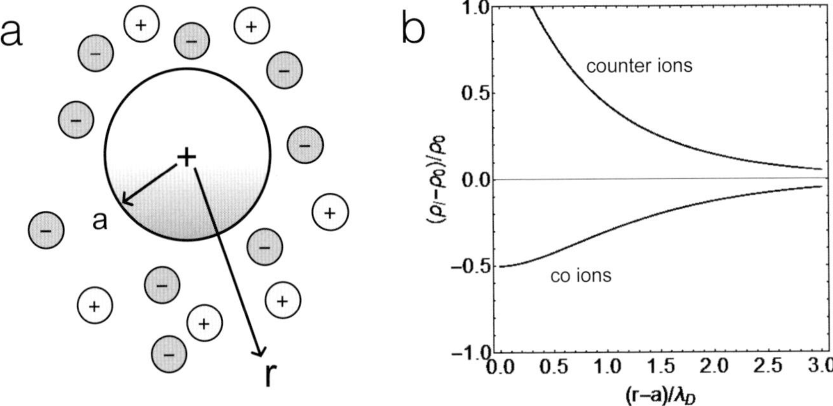

Fig. 3. a) Positively charged nanoparticle of radius a has an ion cloud dominated by negatively charged counter ions. The positively charged co ions are expelled from near the surface of the nanoparticle. b) In a solution of background salt density ρ_0 [m^{-3}], the density of ionic species ρ_i deviates from its background value for distances $r - a$ within a few times the Debye screening lengths λ_D. For counter ions, the density is larger whilst for co ions it is lower. Notice the asymmetry of the ion profiles due to the presence of the oppositely charged ions dissociated from the chargeable groups on the particle surface.

Overall, the local concentration of ions near the surface of the nanoparticle, within a distance known as the *Debye length* to be defined in the next paragraph, is larger than that in bulk solution, far from the surface of the nanoparticles. This means that if these zones of increased overall salt concentration, which are called "double layers", overlap in the gap between the particles, this in effect increases the local osmotic pressure and drives the particles away from each other. It is in this sense that the Coulomb interaction between charged particles is in part entropic in nature, for osmotic pressure is in essence an entropy phenomenon. Of course, the Coulomb interaction between nanoparticle and ions sets up this imbalance in osmotic pressure and hence screened Coulomb interaction potentials are potentials of mean force, i.e., are free energies rather than enthalpies.

The electrostatic energy that a unit charge experiences near a charged surface is smaller than the thermal energy $k_B T$ (at room temperature) if the surface potential is below 25 [mV]. If that is the case we can linearise the Poisson-Boltzmann equation and obtain, e.g., via thermodynamic integration, the Debye-Hückel approximation to the potential of mean force acting between two charged spheres of diameter σ.[3] It reads

$$U_C(r) = +k_B T q^2 \left(\frac{\exp \sigma/2\lambda_D}{1 + \sigma/2\lambda_D} \right)^2 \frac{\lambda_B}{r} \exp\left(-r/\lambda_D\right). \tag{7}$$

The subscript 'C' refers to the Coulomb origin of the interaction, q to the (fixed) number of charges on each nanoparticle, $\lambda_B = e^2/4\pi\varepsilon k_B T$ [m] to the Bjerrum length and $\lambda_D = 1/\sqrt{8\pi\lambda_B\rho_s}$ [m] to the Debye length. Here, e [C] denotes the elementary charge, ε [F m^{-1}] the permittivity of the liquid medium and ρ_s [m^{-3}] the number density of monovalent salt in the solution.[c] The Bjerrum length measures the distance beyond which thermal energy predominates over the (unscreened) Coulomb interaction. From Eq. (7) it is evident that the Debye length must be the distance over which the presence of mobile ions in the solution suppresses ("screens") electrostatic interactions between any pair of charged species. In water at room temperature we have $\lambda_B \approx 0.7$ [nm] and $\lambda_D \approx 0.3/\sqrt{c_s}$ [nm] with c_s [M] the concentration of salt in moles per litre.

So, the presence of mobile ions screens Coulomb interactions beyond about one Debye length, which for that reason is also called the "screening length". The range of the interaction decreases with increasing concentration of salt. The strength of the interaction of two touching particles at the contact distance $r = \sigma$, $U_C(\sigma)$, is equal to $k_B T \lambda_B q^2/(1 + \sigma/2\lambda_D)^2 \sigma$ and hence also decreases with increasing concentration of salt. See Fig. 4. It can also be seen from Eq. (7) that in the limit where the particles are much larger than the Debye length $\sigma \gg \lambda_D$ the interaction free energy for two touching particles reduces to $U_C(\sigma) \sim 4k_B T \lambda_B \lambda_D^2 q^2/\sigma^3 = k_B T q^2/2\pi\rho_s\sigma^3$. This implies that the contact potential increases with increasing temperature, showing that ion entropy indeed contributes to the interaction and

---

[c]If multivalent ions are present, then ρ_s is replaced by the ionic strength in terms of the valencies and concentrations of all ionic species.[27]

                    P. van der Schoot

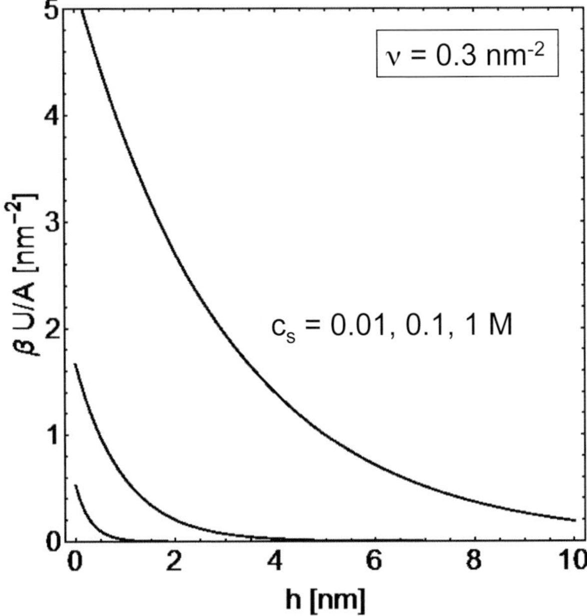

Fig. 4. Calculated electrostatic potential of mean force U per unit area A and per unit thermal energy ($\beta = 1/k_B T$) as a function of the surface-to-surface distance h for two flat surfaces at different concentrations of monovalent salt, c_s. The surface charge density was set at 0.3 [nm^{-2}] and the prediction is based on the Debye-Hückel approximation. See the main text.

in fact enhances it! The descreasing range and strength of the repulsion with increasing salt concentration has important consequences for colloid stability, as we shall see below.

For rod-like particles, such as stiff charged polymers and filamentous viruses, the interaction energy becomes more complicated and exact solutions are hard to come by even in the Debye-Hückel approximation of low surface charges. If we focus on shortest distances $L \gg r \gg \sigma$ between the main body axis vectors of cylinders of length L and width σ, that is, in the limit where they can be seen as line charges, we have[26]

$$U_C(r) = +k_B T 2\pi\nu^2 \lambda_B \lambda_D \frac{\exp\left(-r/\lambda_D\right)}{|\sin\gamma|}. \tag{8}$$

This expression is valid within the Debye-Hückel approximation, so for low linear charge density $\nu < \lambda_B^{-1}$ [m^{-1}], defined as the number of elementary charges per unit length, and for angles γ between the main-body axes larger than the "internal" angle of a cylinder σ/L. See Fig. 2. Again, the strength and range of the interaction reduces with increasing concentration of salt. Notice also that for long thin rods the angular dependence of the repulsive screened Coulomb potential is identical to that of the attractive Van der Waals attraction. Hence, whilst the latter drive pairs of rod to take on parallel orientations, the former do the opposite and favour perpendicular orientations.

For our last example of perfectly parallel flat particles of thickness σ and area A, the potential of mean force, again within the Debye-Hückel approximation for weak surface potentials, reads[1,3,25]

$$U_C(r) = +k_B T 8\pi A \nu^2 \lambda_B \lambda_D \exp\left(-r/\lambda_D\right) \tag{9}$$

for distances $\sqrt{A} \gg r \gg \sigma$ where the particles can be treated as two-dimensional objects, and ν $[\mathrm{m}^{-2}]$ is the number of elementary charges per unit area on the particles. This has a rather complicated temperature dependence, signalling again the combination of energetic and entropic contributions to the potential of mean force. As regards the angular dependence of the electrostatic interactions between flat particles, this turns out to be a complicated function of their relative orientation to the centre-to-centre vector.[21] If the particles are nearly parallel, then the repulsion increases with the angle between the surface normals, γ, for a fixed distance between the centres of mass. This implies that charged disks would statistically prefer parallel orientations.[28]

Finally, as particles usually need to be highly charged for electrostatic repulsion to be strong enough to overcome Van der Waals attraction, the Debye-Hückel theory that we have focused attention on breaks down. On the other hand, the trends remain the same and Debye-Hückel theory has the advantage of analytical treatment and providing insight. Still, an accurate prediction of electrostatic interaction between particles requires solving the non-linear Poisson-Boltzmann equation, which for most systems requires numerical evaluation outside of the scope of this chapter. It is also important to point out that Poisson-Boltzmann theory has issues because it is a mean-field theory, which become apparent in particular in the presence of multivalent ions where it breaks down.[29]

4. Attraction versus repulsion

What should be clear now is that the Van der Waals attraction and the electrostatic repulsion have a very different dependence on the inter-particle separation. First, for very small distances the former if not diverges then certainly becomes very large and negative. Electrostatic interactions never become very large at short separation, implying that Van der Waals interactions always win out for particles at short enough distance from each other. Electrostatic interactions also decay faster with distance (exponential) than Van der Waals interactions do (algebraic). This in turn means that for larger distances, Van der Waals interactions win out too. In conclusion, if electrostatics are to do anything, it is at intermediate distances. This teaches us that charged particles must be kinetically stabilised, not thermodynamically.[25] This is true for all particle shapes, in principle.

In this kind of reasoning, we tacitly and naturally presume that we can simply add up all potentials discussed so far, to give

$$U(r) = U_{hc}(r) + U_{vdW}(r) + U_C(r) \tag{10}$$

to describe the combined effect of hard-core (hc), Van der Waals (vdW) and Coulomb (C) interactions. This is known as DLVO theory, after Derjaguin, Landau, Verwey and Overbeek who first formulated it in the 1940s.[25,27] DLVO theory not only ignores any ionic screening of Van der Waals interactions, in particular the contribution from low frequency charge density fluctuations, but also Van der Waals interactions between ions and nanoparticles.[30] The low-frequency charge density fluctuations are due to the presence of permanent dipoles, quadrupoles, etc., on the particles. It is straightforward to show that the interaction free energy between two freely rotating dipolar particles of size σ, which scales as $1/r^6$ with distance r provided $r \gg \sigma$, is screened by the presence of mobile ions by a factor $\exp\left(-2r/\lambda_D\right)$. The factor of 2 stems from the fact that the orientation of one dipole influences that of another dipole, which in turn influences that of the first dipole. Extensions of DLVO theory that deal with issues like this one have been put forward but are outside the scope of this Chapter.[30]

If for simplicity we follow classical DLVO theory, and for example insert the Van der Waals potential Eq. (2) and the Debye-Hückel potential Eq. (7) for spherical particles in Eq. (10), then depending on the number of charges, the value of the Hamaker constant and the Debye length, we find in essence three regimes as a function of particle separation, illustrated in Figs. 5(a) and (b): (i) a monotonically increasing potential dominated by a primary minimum at near zero surface-to-surface separation,[d] (ii) a non-monotonic potential dominated by the primary minimum but that in addition has a

---

[d]Of course, at and below zero separation, we have the hard-core steric repulsion between the particles.

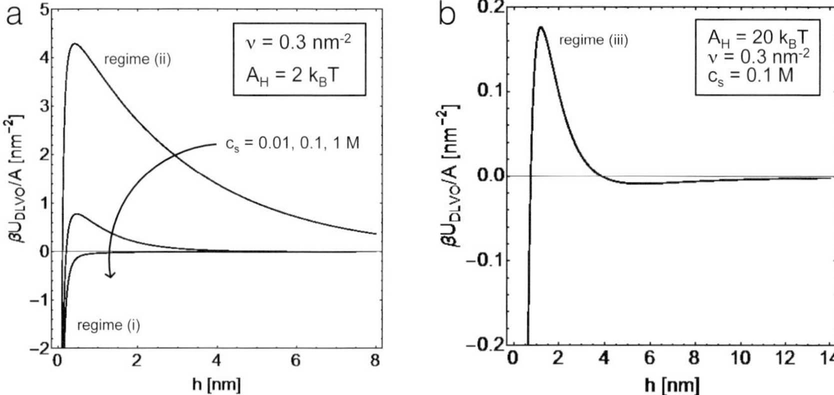

Fig. 5.   a) Calculated DLVO-type potential of mean force per unit area U_{DLVO}/A between flat surfaces as a function of the surface-to-surface separation h, for different concentrations of salt c_s. The potential is scaled to the thermal energy $k_B T = \beta^{-1}$. The surface charge density was put at $\nu = 0.3$ [m^{-2}] and the Hamaker constant of the Van der Waals interaction at $A_H = 2$ times the thermal energy $k_B T$. b) DLVO potential of mean force for a salt concentration of $c_s = 0.1$ [M], surface charge density of $\nu = 0.3$ [m^{-2}] and Hamaker constant $A_H = 20 k_B T$. In regime (i) the potential is a monotonically increasing function of the separation of the surfaces, while in regime (ii) it is non-monotonic and has a distinct maximum. Regime (iii) is characterised by the existence of a secondary minimum.

maximum that may be negative or weakly positive, and (iii) potential that is strongly positive at intermediate surface-to-surface distances, strongly negative at short separations and weakly negative at large separations. The last one has a discernable secondary minimum at relatively large separations that under certain conditions may trap particles into so-called flocks.[3,27]

Clearly, the primary minimum at zero separation is the state of lowest free energy and should be the preferred state of any pair of particles. However, if the particles are initially at a large distance from each other and the barrier is large enough compared to the thermal energy, it will take a very long time before the state of lowest free energy will actually be reached. The reason is of course that it requires nucleation, that is, the crossing of the barrier for the particles to be able to come in close proximity of each other. The time required for that to happen is proportional to the exponent of the ratio of the barrier energy and the thermal energy.[25] For all intents and purposes, however, we can treat charge-stabilised particles as if they are in thermal equilibrium and apply the principles of (statistical) thermodynamics. The same is true for particles that have been stabilised by adsorbing polymers onto them, because once adsorbed the desorption of polymers from particles that approach each other is a very slow process indeed.[31]

In principle, the conditions under which particles may be considered stable on the time-scale of the experiment require the evaluation of the coagulation kinetics. A crude estimate may be provided, e.g., for spherical particles for the case that they are large on the scale of the Debye length, which is typically true in water. Kinetic stability requires the maximum in the interaction potential to be positive and much larger than $k_B T$. For our purposes Debye-Hückel theory is sufficiently accurate, so we obtain from Eqs. (2) and (7) the condition that to secure kinetic stability, the surface charge density (the number of elementary charges per unit area) should be larger than approximately $(A_H/k_B T)^{1/2}\lambda_D^{-3/2}\lambda_B^{-1/2}$ [m^{-2}]. Similar conditions can be straightforwardly derived for cylindrical and flat particles. So, the larger the Hamaker constant and the larger the amount of salt in the solution, the larger the number of charges per unit area of the particles is required to obtain effective charge stabilisation. On the other hand, each added surface charge comes with an added counter ion in the solution thereby increasing its ionic strength. This implies that it often is actually more effective to reduce the salt concentration than to increase the surface charge of the particles if they are to be charge stabilised.

If we ignore this for simplicity, and wish to get an order-of-magnitude estimate of surface charge densities needed to get charge stabilisation, then we need to consider typical values for the Hamaker constant. The Hamaker constant A_H for organic nanoparticles across water at room temperature is in the range $0.5 - 3$ times the thermal energy $k_B T$, for non-metallic inorganic materials this increases to $1 - 20$, and for metallic particles to a whopping $20 - 100$.[2] Hence, under conditions of physiological salt, equal to about 0.15 moles per litre of monovalent salt, we conclude that for most non-metallic nanoparticles about one charge per square nanometer suffices, but that for metallic ones much more than that is required. To achieve the latter is not so straightforward because of the effects of counter ion condensation that happens when the surface charge density increases to in excess of roughly one charge per Bjerrum length squared.[20] This leads to counter ions accumulating near the surface of the particles in effect reducing their net surface charge density.

Treated as thermodynamically stable, what electrostatic interactions do is (in a sense) "renormalise" the hard cores of the nanoparticles. To illustrate this, and for later reference, it is useful to introduce the second virial co-efficient, B [m^3], of the particles. The second virial co-efficient is associated with the first-order correction in powers of the number density ρ [m^{-3}] of the particles to the Van't Hoff law for the osmotic pressure, $\Pi = k_B T \rho$ [N m²], of dilute solutions and dispersions,[15]

$$\Pi = k_B T \rho \left[1 + B\rho + ...\right]. \tag{11}$$

Here, $k_B T$ is as usual the thermal energy. We read off from Eq. (11) that if $B > 0$ the net interaction between the particles must be repulsive and if $B < 0$ it must be attractive: the osmotic pressure is in these cases larger and smaller, respectively, than expected from the ideal Van't Hoff law. The virial expansion was first introduced by Heike Kamerlingh-Onnes to generalise the ideal gas law. Near-ideal conditions occur in non-ideal gases and solutions if $B = 0$, called the Boyle point for gases and the θ-point for polymer solutions.[32]

The second virial co-efficient of particles can be calculated from statistical mechanics. For spatially uniform and orientationally isotropic distributions of particles it can be expressed as[15]

$$B = -\frac{1}{2} \int d\mathbf{1} \left(\exp\left[-U(\mathbf{0}, \mathbf{1})/k_B T\right] - 1\right), \tag{12}$$

where $\mathbf{0}$ represents the generalised co-ordinates of a reference particle and $\mathbf{1}$ that of a second particle, relative to the reference particle. For spherical particles we would replace $\mathbf{0}$ by the position of the reference particle at the origin of a Cartesian co-ordinate system and let the second be at position $\mathbf{1} \equiv \mathbf{r}$. See Fig. 6, in which we show the calculated second virial co-efficient of Lennard-Jones particles.

If we ignore Van der Waals interactions and presume interactions to be dominated by the hard-core and the electrostatic repulsion, we obtain for weakly charged spherical particles within the Debye-Hückel approximation

$$B = \frac{2\pi}{3}\sigma^3 \left[1 + q^2 \frac{3\lambda_B \lambda_D^2}{\sigma^3} \frac{(1 + \sigma/\lambda_D)}{(1 + \sigma/2\lambda_D)^2}\right] \equiv \frac{2\pi}{3}\sigma_{\text{eff}}^3. \tag{13}$$

where as before σ [m] is the particle diameter, q the (fixed) number of charges on each nanoparticle, λ_B [m] the Bjerrum length and λ_D [m] the Debye length. Here, we have defined an effective diameter σ_{eff} [m] that is a function of the actual diameter σ and the number of charges on the particles, the concentration of salt and so on. Notice that the first term is half the excluded volume of a hard spherical particle. For particles much larger than the Debye screening length with $\sigma \gg \lambda_D$, we have $\sigma_{\text{eff}} \approx \sigma(1 + 12\pi^2 \lambda_B \lambda_D^3 \nu^2)$ if we let $\nu = q/\pi\sigma^2$ [m^{-2}] be the surface charge

                                    P. van der Schoot

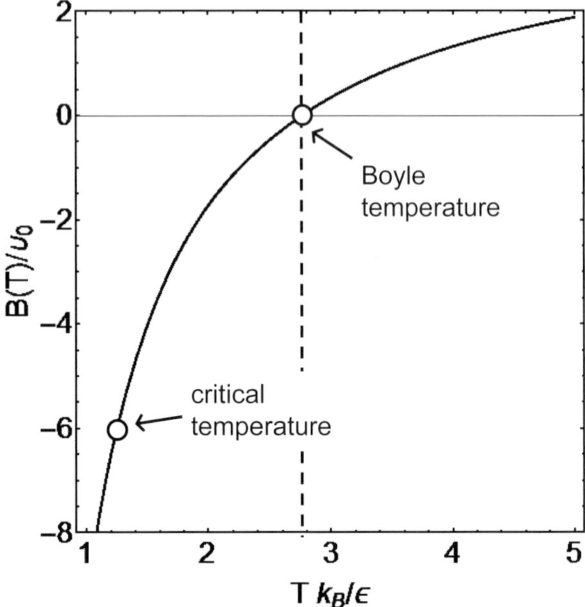

Fig. 6. Second virial co-efficient B of spherical particles interacting via a Lennard-Jones potential as a function of the temperature T. The second virial co-efficient is scaled to the effective hard-core volume $\nu_0 = \pi\sigma^3/6$ in terms of the "diameter" σ [m] of the particles, and the temperature to the strength of the Lennard-Jones potential ϵ [J]. Indicated are the Boyle temperature and an estimate of the critical temperature.[44]

density of the particles, that is, the number of elementary charges per unit area. So, the particles behave, in a way, as if they are hard particles, but with a larger diameter due to the electrostatic interaction between them. Their effective size increases with surface charge density but decreases with increasing concentration of salt in the solution. This, of course, is due to the weakening and diminishing range of the electrostatic interactions with increased effectiveness of the screening of the interaction by the mobile ions in the solution.

Something similar happens to charged rod-like particles. Let the co-ordinate **0** now refer to the centre of mass of the reference particle that co-incides with the centre of a Cartesian co-ordinate system and that defines the z-axis along the main body axis vector of this reference particle. The co-ordinate **1** now refers to the position of the centre of mass as well as the orientation vector of the second particle. For cylindrical particles of length

L much longer then their width σ, and inserting Eq. (8) that is valid in the limit where the particles can be seen as line charges with low linear charge density, gives[26]

$$B = \frac{\pi}{4}L^2\sigma\left[1 + \frac{\lambda_D}{\sigma}\left(\ln\left[2\pi\nu^2\lambda_B\lambda_D\right] + \gamma_E + \ln 2 - \frac{1}{2}\right)\right] \equiv \frac{\pi}{4}L^2\sigma_{\text{eff}}, \quad (14)$$

where $\gamma_E = 0.5772\ldots$ denotes Euler's constant and ν $[\text{m}^{-1}]$ the linear charge density. Beyond this approximation, only the logarithmic term is modified but the renormalisation of the diameter survives. So, a charged rod behaves like a hard one, but with a diameter larger by about a Debye length. Note that a simple interpretation like this one does not, so to speak, hold water for spherical particles, as can be seen from the more intricate Eq. (13).

Attractive interactions reduce the second virial co-efficient and hence the effective excluded volume between the particles. Because of the (spurious) divergence of the Van der Waals interaction potential within the continuum approximation and the complicated expressions involved, simplified versions are usually employed. An often-employed model potential, in particular in the context of the thermodynamic behaviour of protein solutions, is the "sticky" square-well potential, where the Van der Waals potential $U_{vdW}(r)$ is replaced by a constant value $-\epsilon$ for distances $\sigma < r \leq \sigma + h$ where ϵ is the potential well depth and h the range of the interaction.[1] For spheres, an alternative for the square-well potential is $U_B(\sigma < r \leq \sigma+h) = -k_BT\ln\left[(\sigma + h)/12\tau h\right]$, with τ the "stickiness parameter". It is a sensible way of taking the limit $h/\sigma \to 0$ and $\epsilon \to \infty$, and reducing the number of free parameters from two to one. It is known as the Baxter potential.[33]

For charged hard spheres that also interact via the short-range Baxter potential, we obtain for the second virial co-efficient

$$B = \frac{2\pi}{3}\sigma^3\left[1 + q^2\frac{3\lambda_B\lambda_D^2}{\sigma^3}\frac{(1 + \sigma/\lambda_D)}{(1 + \sigma/2\lambda_D)^2} - \frac{1}{4\tau}\right], \quad (15)$$

if we presume the Debye-Hückel approximation to hold, so for low surface potentials, and we take the formal limit $h/\sigma \to 0$. We see that B can become negative if τ is sufficiently small. This will have consequences for the thermodynamic stability of the homogeneous solution. We will return to this point in Sec. 6.

Finally, for cylindrical particles the square-well and other approximate potentials have also been invoked to model Van der Waals interactions between them. Calculations show that as soon as the Hamaker constant

A_H is larger than $k_B T \sigma / L$, which for long thin rods with aspect ratio $L/\sigma \gg 1$ is very small indeed, parallel configurations are strongly biased.[17] This is not surprising, of course. For hard rods that also interact via a Van der Waals model potential such as that of Eq. (4) extrapolated to all distances, the second virial co-efficient becomes negative if the Hamaker constant A_H is larger than approximately $128\pi^{-1}(\sigma/L)\ln(L/\sigma)$.[17] This confirms once again that rod-like particles are very difficult to disperse in fluids unless properly stabilised.

5. Other sources of interaction

In water, as in other types of solvent, sources of attractive interaction other than those that give rise to Van der Waals interactions may also present themselves and even predominate. These include solvation, structural and hydration forces, and are associated with the "graininess" of matter. Fluids are not homogeneous continua but consist of molecules that themselves have a chemical structure and hence have internal or "conformational" degrees of freedom. The interactions that this gives rise to can be attractive or repulsive, depending on the combination of solvent and particle properties, and on the distance and orientation (if the fluid is symmetry-broken). The presence of other components in the fluid such as surfactants or polymers induces so-called depletion interactions between the nanoparticles dispersed in it. Finally, if the host fluid is not isotropic but liquid-crystalline, additional interactions arise due to the elastic deformation that the particles induce in the liquid crystal.

In water, hydrophobic interactions may predominate over van der Waals forces between apolar molecules and particles dispersed in it.[5] There is a heated debate about their precise origin but the consensus view is that hydrophobic interactions are due to water molecules forming transient, fluctuating networks because of their ability to engage in hydrogen bonding.[34,35] Particles inserted in water that perturb this transient network structure experience an attractive interaction. It is entropy-dominated for particles in the nanometer size range or below, but acquires an energetic component that is predicted to take over for particles larger than this and is linked with cavitation.[34] For macroscopic surfaces, the distance dependence seems to be exponential with a decay length on the order of a few nanometers.[35]

Theoretically, an approximately exponential decay can be understood from a simple phenomenological, coarse-grained Landau model in which one defines some local order parameter $\eta = \eta(\mathbf{r})$ in a volume large compared to the size of the fluid molecules but small on the scale of the nanoparticles, centred around the position $\mathbf{r}$.[4] It describes deviations away from optimal local ordering for which by definition $\eta = 0$. A simple free energy functional that describes the penalty on variations of the order parameter, induced by the coupling of the order parameter to surfaces introduced in the fluid, would be $F = \int d\mathbf{r}[\frac{1}{2}W\eta^2 + \frac{1}{2}K(\nabla\eta)^2]$.[29] Here, W is the strength of the free energy penalty of the order parameter attaining a value away from the equilibrium value, and K the strength of the free energy penalty due to gradients in the order parameter. For flat macroscopic surfaces we may invoke boundary conditions on the surface at $\mathbf{r} = 0$ and $\mathbf{r} = r$, so $\eta(0) = \eta(r)$, and (functionally) minimise the free energy with respect to η.

If we calculate the equilibrium free energy of a fluid with two flat surfaces of area A at distance r from each other, and subtract from that the equilibrium free energy for the case $r \to \infty$, we obtain an approximately exponential potential of mean force (a free energy). It can be written as[36]

$$U_s(r) \simeq -2\gamma A \exp\left(-r/\xi\right), \tag{16}$$

where the subscript "s" indicates that we are considering solvation forces, and where we define an interfacial tension given by $\gamma \equiv \sqrt{WK}\eta(0)^2/2$ and a decay length $\xi \equiv \sqrt{K/W}$.[29] See Fig. 7. Note that the form of the constant of proportionality makes intuitive sense. Removing two surfaces from contact with the solution liberates two times the interfacial area times the interfacial tension. This, of course, is the total interfacial free energy or solvation free energy of inserting two surfaces into the fluid.[34] Interestingly, if we set $\eta(0) = -\eta(r)$, we get Eq. (16) with a positive sign: these surfaces repel each other, showing that it depends on the surface properties of the particle whether the solvation interaction is attractive or repulsive.[4,29,37]

Note that this type of argument, even though it is based on a coarse-grained model in which all molecular detail has been lost, applies to any type of fluid. Indeed, if the host fluid is isotropic but has a nematic liquid crystalline state below the clearing temperature, then even above this clearing temperature the interaction with the surface of a nanoparticle inserted into it will induce a nematic order parameter S that is non-zero near it. (I refer to the preceding Chapter of this book for a definition of the nematic order parameter.) We only need to replace the order parameter η by S in the expressions given in the preceding paragraph. If the surface is conducive to the nematic state, the nematic phase will wet this surface above the clearing temperature. Overlapping wetting layers induce an attraction between the particles of the same kind as the solvation interaction

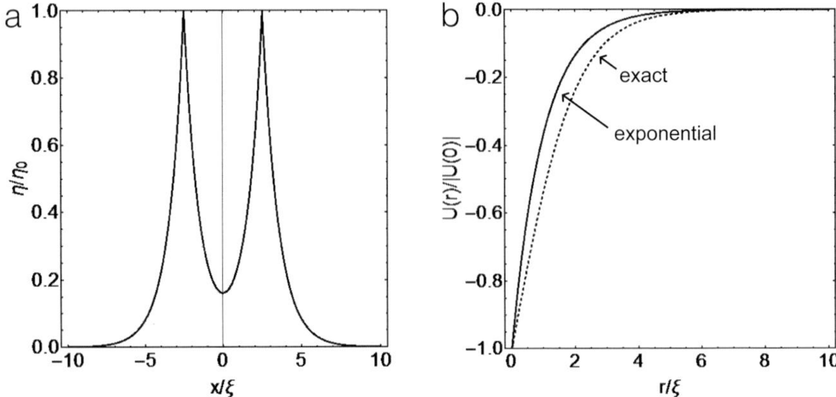

Fig. 7.   a) Order parameter profile $\eta(x)$ as function of the distance x near two flat surfaces inserted in a fluid at a distance h [m] of five times the correlation length ξ of the order parameter η. The order parameter at the particle surface is fixed at a value of η_0. b) Resulting potential of mean force, $w(r)$, scaled to the absolute value at contact $|w(0)|$ between the two flat plates as function of their distance r relative to the correlation length ξ. Exact and exponential results are shown. See the main text.

discussed earlier.[38] In fact, near critical mixtures of binary solvents will do the same if the surfaces of particles are preferentially wetted by one of the two components.[39] Additional attraction arises from interference of the particles with fluctuations in the relevant order parameter, giving rise to Van der Waals-like forces also referred to as pseudo-Casimir forces.[9]

Structural interactions between nanoparticles are due to the graininess of matter and are not only relevant in simple liquids. These are also important, and perhaps more so, if the nanoparticles are embedded in a fluid that has other types of colloidal particle dispersed in it as well.[7] These potentially give rise to long-ranged interaction because they are much larger than the solvent molecules are. For instance, if surfactants are added to a solution to stabilise nanoparticles by adsorption and if their concentration is larger than a critical value, then micelles form.[5] Micelles are self-assembled aggregates that, if spherical, are three to five nanometers in diameter, but if cylindrical can be very long and polymer-like. The presence of micelles has been shown to affect the stability of, for instance, surfactant-stabilised carbon nanotubes.[40] The presence of polymer coils, which for concentrations below the overlap threshold may be treated as more or less hard spherical particles, are also known to drive phase separation in colloidal suspensions.[7,41]

In essence, the reason for this is the additional loss of translational entropy by volume exclusion between species that differ in shape and/or size. This is usually translated into a potential of mean force acting between the larger species due to the presence of the smaller species, which in a manner of speaking are "integrated out" of the description. Let us consider the case where the smaller species of nanoparticle are spherical and interact with the larger species only via a hard-core repulsion. Then the centres of mass of the smaller species are excluded from a volume given by the volume of the larger particles plus that of a depletion zone, the width of which equals the radius of the smaller particles. If these depletion zones overlap there are no small particles in the overlap region and hence an imbalance in the osmotic pressure arises that pushes the larger particles together. See Fig. 8.

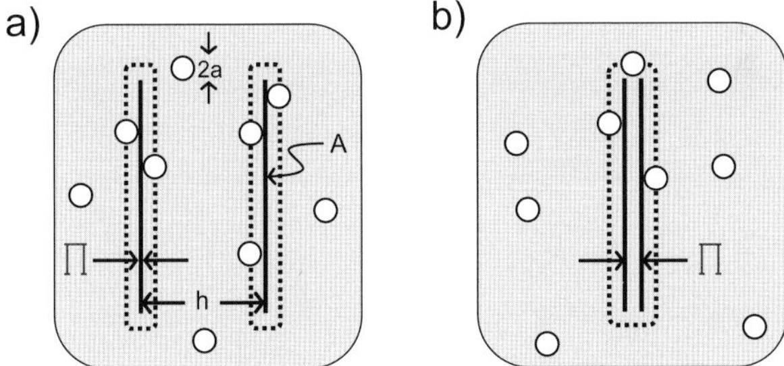

Fig. 8. Depletion interactions arise because the centres of mass of small particles cannot get closer to a surface than twice their radius, a. This defines a depletion zone around the larger particles, here modeled as flat surfaces of area A. If two depletion zones overlap, so when the distance between the parallel plates obeys $h \leq 2a$, an imbalance in the osmotic pressure Π pushes the plates toward each other.

Thermodynamically, one expects the depletion potential, U_d, to obey[7]

$$U_d(\mathbf{0}, \mathbf{1}) = -\Pi \Delta V(\mathbf{0}, \mathbf{1}), \tag{17}$$

where Π is the osmotic pressure imparted by the smaller species, and ΔV the overlap volume of the depletion zones. The depletion potential depends on the generalised co-ordinates $\mathbf{0}$ and $\mathbf{1}$ of two nanoparticles. For non-spherical particles these of course include their orientations. Within this *Ansatz*, for surface-to-surface distances larger than the diameter of the "depletion agents" or "deplesons", the depletion potential is zero.[7] So, the range and strength of the depletion potential depends on the size of the depletion agents and the osmotic pressure and hence on their concentration.[e]

____

[e]Actually, because the smaller particles interact via the larger ones, the density of the

Within this perhaps somewhat naïve description, the contribution B_d of the depletion interactions to the effective second virial co-efficient B would read

$$B_d = -\frac{1}{2}\int d\mathbf{1}\left(\exp\left[-\frac{U_d\left(\mathbf{0},\mathbf{1}\right)}{k_BT}\right]-1\right) \approx -\frac{\Pi}{2k_BT}\int d\mathbf{1}\Delta V_d(\mathbf{0},\mathbf{1}), \quad (18)$$

provided the dispersion is isotropic. It is a result that may also be obtained from more formal statistical mechanical calculations in the limit where the smaller particles do not interact strongly among themselves.[42] The second virial co-efficient becomes negative at high enough density of the depletion agents, indicating that the mixture tends towards phase separation. Note that this is a phase separation that is entropy rather than enthalpy driven!

For the simple case of perfectly parallel flat plates of area A $[\text{m}^2]$ in a dilute suspension of spherical depletion agents of radius σ $[\text{m}]$ and number density ρ $[\text{m}^3]$, the depletion potential has a particularly simple form[7]

$$U_d(r) = -k_BT\rho A\left(\sigma - r\right), \quad (19)$$

for surface-to-surface distance $r \leq \sigma$ $[\text{m}]$ and $U_d(r) = 0$ $[\text{J}]$ for $r \geq \sigma$. Here, we tacitly presume the Van't Hoff law, $\Pi = k_BT\rho$ $[\text{N m}^{-2}]$, to apply to the suspension of depletion agents, and the plates to be much bigger than the depletion agents, so $A \gg \sigma^2$. This of course implies that the depletion agents behave ideally and do not interact. If we identify with the amount of work done to vacate the centres of mass of the particles from a depletion zone $\sigma/2$ wide as the interfacial free energy, we find that the contribution by the depletion agents to the surface tension γ_d of the flat surfaces must be $\gamma_d = \rho k_BT\sigma/2$ $[\text{N m}^2]$.[f] This means that the depletion potential can be written as $U_d(r) = -2\gamma_dA\left(1 - r/\sigma\right)$ for $r \leq \sigma$, so attains a form consistent with the solvation potential Eq. (16).

Things become rather more complicated once the nanoparticles are not perfectly parallel flat plates and the depletion agents not ideal and/or not spherical. Indeed, interactions between the depletion agents lead to a depletion potential between the guest particles that is attractive at short distances but repulsive at larger ones, in essence due to the presence of solvation or co-ordination layers.[7] If spherical nanoparticles are inserted in a host dispersion consisting of a lyotropic nematic of hard cylindrical

---

larger particles impacts on the depletion potential too.[7]

[f]This follows also from the Gibbs isotherm $d\gamma = -\Gamma d\mu$, where Γ $[\text{m}^{-2}]$ is the number of particles adsorbed per unit area. For ideal solutions $d\mu = k_BT d\rho/\rho$, so $d\gamma = -\Gamma k_BT d\rho/\rho = +\Gamma k_BT$ because $d\rho = +\rho$ across the depletion zone. Since $\Gamma = -\rho\sigma/2$ on account of the particles not approaching the surface for distances smaller than $\sigma/2$, this gives $\gamma_d = k_BT\rho\sigma/2$.

colloids, then the depletion interaction between pairs of nanoparticle induced by the presence of the rod-like colloids depends not only on their separation but also on their orientation relative to the nematic director.[43] It turns out that in that case the depletion interaction is much stronger along the director than perpendicular to it, but also much longer ranged in particular if the nanoparticles are smaller than the length of the cylindrical particles. This strongly anisotropic depletion potential induces the particles to self-assemble into long chains along the nematic director.[11]

6. Phase transitions

Attractive and repulsive interactions are both known to drive phase transitions. Clearly, proper statistical mechanical theory is required to predict what kind of state of aggregation of a nanoparticle dispersion is thermodynamically stable and under what conditions.[15] Of course, this depends also on whether the solvent is an isotropic host fluid or a liquid crystalline one. Crude estimates may nonetheless be given by considering the magnitude and sign of the second virial co-efficient, B, in particular for particles in isotropic solvents. Hence, we will focus on these.

For spherical particles of diameter σ, it appears that if B is more negative than roughly six times their volume, $\pi\sigma^3/6$, a homogeneous dispersion is not thermodynamically stable for all densities.[44] In other words, if

$$B \lesssim -\pi\sigma^3, \tag{20}$$

there is a range of concentrations (the "miscibility gap") in which a homogeneous mixture phase separates into dense and dilute dispersions. This happens either below or above a critical temperature T_c, depending on whether we are dealing with an upper critical solution temperature or with a lower critical solution temperature. These are usually abbreviated UCST and LCST, respectively, and differentiate between endothermic and exothermic interactions.[32] Exactly at the critical temperature, the miscibility gap is zero: there is in that case no difference in concentration between the phase-separated phases that hence are identical. See Fig. 9.

Within mean-field lattice theory,[1] we find for the density difference between the co-existing dense and dilute phases, $\Delta\rho$ [m^3], the following expression

$$\frac{\Delta\rho}{\rho_c} \sim \left[3\left(\frac{h_c}{\epsilon_c}\right)\frac{T_c - T}{T_c} \right]^{1/2} + \cdots, \tag{21}$$

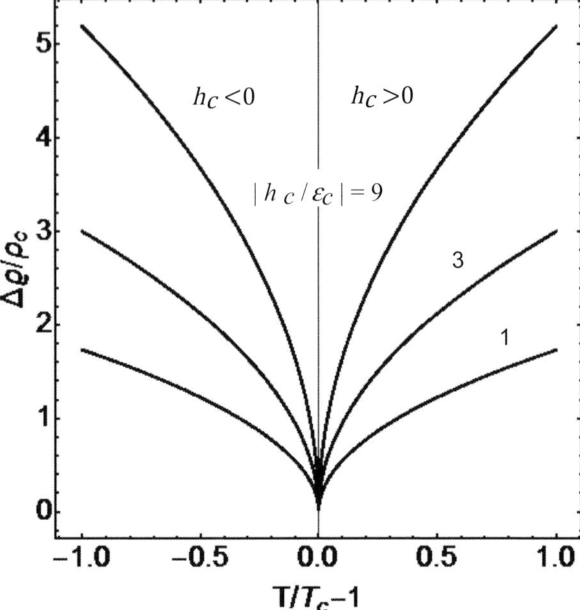

Fig. 9. Calculated scaled density difference $\Delta\rho/\rho_c$ between phase separated dispersions of nanoparticles, as a function of the scaled temperature T/T_c. Here, ρ_c [m^{-3}] is the critical density and T_c the critical temperature. At the critical temperature the density difference is zero. For exothermic interactions, i.e., a negative enthalpy of interaction $h_c < 0$, phase separation occurs for $T < T_c$. For endothermic interactions, i.e., a positive enthalpy of interaction $h_c > 0$, phase separation occurs for $T > T_c$. This makes the critical points upper and lower critical solution temperatures, respectively. The width of the biphasic gap also depends on the ratio of the enthalpy and free energy of the interaction, h_c/ϵ_c, at the critical temperature.

by Taylor expanding the interaction free energy $\epsilon/k_B T$ around the critical temperature, T_c [K], so it holds for temperatures T [K] near that critical temperature. Here, ρ_c [m^{-3}] is the density at the critical point, $\epsilon_c < 0$ [J] the strength of the attractive part of the potential of mean force acting between the particles at contact at the temperature $T = T_c$, and h_c [J] the corresponding enthalpy. For instance, curve fitting of Eq. (21) to data on aqueous solutions of a protein known as γ_{II} crystallin gives $h_c/\epsilon_c \approx 9$, implying that $T_c s_c = h_c - \epsilon_c = 8\epsilon_c < 0$.[45] This in turn implies that whilst phase separation is in this case driven by enthalpy gains, the entropy losses are very significant!

If $h_c < 0$, the inter-particle interaction is exothermic, and phase separation occurs for $T \leq T_c$ whilst that if $h_c > 0$ this happens for $T \geq T_c$ in which case the interaction is endothermic.[32] The enthalpy h_c and the free energy ϵ_c can be related to the second virial co-efficient through the approximate identity

$$B \sim \frac{\pi \sigma^3}{6} \left(-6 + \frac{2h_c \left(T - T_c \right)}{\epsilon_c T_c} + \cdots \right), \tag{22}$$

which, again, is valid near the critical point.[g] Notice that at the critical point we indeed find $B(T_c) = -6 \times \pi \sigma^3/6$, and that even under conditions where phase separation does not take place the second virial co-efficient can be negative.[44] From Eq. (22) we find that for our spherical nanoparticles we must have the equivalent of the Boyle or θ temperature, $T_{B=0} \simeq T_c(1 + 3\epsilon_c/h_c + \cdots)$ at which $B = 0$.

Four remarks are in order at this point. First, the mean-field exponent of one-half of Eq. (21) is expected to apply close but not too close to the critical point and is close to one-third nearer it.[15] Second, if the range of the attractive interactions is sufficiently short then the liquid-liquid phase separation occurs at concentrations above the solubility limit of the particles. The solubility limit is the concentration at which crystals appear in the solution. This does not mean that liquid-liquid phase separation does not occur, only that it is meta-stable.[45] This is often the case in protein solutions. Third, as soon as the particles are not spherical and/or they interact through not spherically symmetric potentials, for instance if dispersed in liquid-crystalline fluids or if they are polydisperse, matters become much more complex and theoretical descriptions are fraught with difficulty.

For instance, many liquid-state theories of particulate dispersions tacitly treat attractive interactions perturbatively, that is, presume these to be in some sense weak.[1] Hard-core volume repulsion then predominates the structure and correlations between the particles, which for spherical particles at least seems not unreasonable. However, for non-spherical particles and in particular long cylindrical ones, this approximation is highly inaccurate due to the coupling of translational and rotational degrees of freedom.[17] Indeed, for thin rods attractive and repulsive interactions cannot be separated into, say, an entropic and an enthalpic contribution to the free energy of the dispersion, exactly because they are so strongly coupled.

Whilst for hard cylindrical particles a prescription in which interactions enter only through the second virial co-efficient is believed to be exact in the

---

[g]To obtain this, one needs to identify the cell volume of the lattice to hard-core virial co-efficient of hard spheres to get the correct virial.

limit of infinite aspect ratio, this approximation breaks down once attractive interactions come into play. This happens even if they are relatively weak and not strongly impact the value of B away from the hard-core value. We have seen in the preceding section that unless vanishingly small, attractive interactions are highly directional and favour parallel configurations. Once that happens, the second virial co-efficient is still near its positive and hard-core value, while the third virial co-efficient (probing three-particle collisions) becomes large and negative.[17] As far as I am aware, there are no treatments that satisfactorily deal with this problem, and arguably one has to take recourse to computer simulation to sort things out.

Let us now focus attention on particles that, statistically, interact purely repulsively, implying that the second virial co-efficient $B > 0$. These, too, can undergo phase transitions, which in essence are now driven by entropy not enthalpy. Realising that for repulsive particles for which the solvent quality by definition is good, B is a measure of their excluded volume, we expect something to happen when

$$B\rho \gtrsim 1 \tag{23}$$

because the uniform dispersion then runs out of free volume. The only way out for the dispersion is to somehow make B smaller. It can only do that by ordering particles. This leads to a loss of what one might call "configurational entropy" but a gain in translational entropy.[1,4] Here, the term configurational entropy refers not only to the entropy associated with a uniform positional and orientational distribution of the particles, but also to internal conformational degrees of freedom of the particles that may couple to the transition.[26,46]

Hard spheres of diameter σ, for instance, would be able to reduce B by forming a colloidal crystal phase. Localising the particles on a lattice diminishes the importance of inter-particle collisions and hence lowers B. Our crude estimate Eq. (22) would tell us that this happens if the volume fraction of particles $\phi \equiv \pi\sigma^3/6$ becomes larger than $1/4$. That hard spheres do crystallise is an experimental fact, but our simple estimate is off by a factor of two: monodisperse hard spheres crystalise if $\phi \geq 0.49$, creating a phase gap at volume fraction of 0.49 in the fluid phase and 0.54 in the crystalline phase.[1] Of course, a second virial estimate that only deals with two-body interactions cannot be expected to be accurate at such large volume fractions, but it does actually predict the hard-sphere transition![47]

Clearly, if the particles are charge-stabilised, we can replace σ by an effective value that depends on the concentration of salt as we saw in Section

4. This effective size is larger than the physical size, so crystallisation may occur at very small actual volume fractions in particular if there is little salt in the solution to screen the electrostatic interactions. On the other hand, if the particles are not rigid but can be deformed elastically, the phase gap moves to higher concentrations and becomes less wide.[46] This is not surprising, as excitations away from the spherical shape will be penalised by interactions with neighbouring molecules.

For hard cylindrical particles of length L and width σ, the second virial coefficient B is an average over the solid angles of the two test particles $B = \langle\langle B(\gamma)\rangle\rangle'$. Here, $B(\gamma)$ is the second virial co-efficient of two cylinders inclined at an angle γ, and $\langle\cdots\rangle$ denotes an averaging over the solid angle of one particle and $\langle\cdots\rangle'$ that over the other. For cylinders of aspect ratio $L/\sigma \gg 1$ we have $B(\gamma) \sim L^2\sigma|\sin\gamma|$, whilst for cylinders of aspect ratio $L/\sigma \ll 1$ this changes to $B(\gamma) \sim \pi\sigma^3|\sin\gamma|/4$.[26,49,h] The former describes long thin rods, the latter thin disks. Again, σ and L may represent effective values if the particles are charge stabilised.

We see that by reducing the angle γ between the main axes of the particles, B becomes smaller. This implies that by spontaneous alignment to a uniaxial nematic phase, the average excluded volume between the particles reduces, and hence the free volume and with it the translational entropy increases albeit at the expense of orientational entropy. For isotropic solutions, $\langle\langle|\sin\gamma|\rangle\rangle' = \pi/4$, so we expect a dispersion of long rods to crossover to the nematic phase if $\phi > \sigma/L$ because in that case $B\rho \simeq B\phi/(4\pi L\sigma^2/4) > 1$. A more accurate analysis based on Onsager theory[49] gives co-existence at $\phi = 3.3\sigma/L$ in the isotropic phase and $\phi = 4.2\sigma/L$ in the nematic phase, valid in the limit $L/\sigma \to \infty$.[26] So, the nematic phase appears at rather small volume fractions if the rods are sufficiently thin, such as is the case for carbon nanotubes.

Applying our condition Eq. (22) to thin disks, and inserting the volume of a disk $\pi L\sigma^2/4$ and the second virial $B \simeq \pi^2\sigma^3/16$ into Eq. (23), we expect the isotropic-nematic transition to occur if $\phi > \pi L/4\sigma$. This can also be very small for very thin disks, that is, if $L \ll \sigma$. Simulations show that at co-existence the phase gap is minute if $L/\sigma \to 0$ and that the transition occurs if $\phi \approx \pi L/\sigma$, quite close to our estimate.[48] This is surprising because, unlike for long thin hard rods, the second virial approximation is not all that

---

[h] Apart from numerical prefactors, this is easy to understand for rods and disks alike. Let us take two hard rods of length L and width $\sigma \ll L$ inclined at an angle γ. The volume they exclude each other is the product of the area of the parallellepipedum $L^2|\sin\gamma|$ and the width 2σ. See Fig. 2. For thin disks $L \ll \sigma$ one only needs to replace L with σ.

accurate for thin hard disks. Still, our estimate is only off by a numerical factor of order unity, as in fact for all cases discussed in this Chapter.

As already mentioned, the fact than in experimental reality not all particles in the dispersion are of the same size, and hence are polydisperse, complicates matters further. The most significant effect at least for rod-like particles is to shift the transition to lower densities and to significantly widen the phase gap.[50] This is due to fractionation: the longer rods prefer the nematic phase leaving the isotropic phase to the shorter ones.[51] Weak attractive interactions seem to do the same for rod-like particles,[19] although accurate theories do not seem to exist yet for reasons explained earlier. Another issue is bending flexibility, which is relevant to rod-like and disk-like particles alike.[52,53] For rods, bending flexibility increases the concentration at which the transition to the nematic phase takes place, and in fact also that from the nematic to the smectic phase where the particles are arranged and aligned in layers.[54]

The quantity of interest is the persistence length, P, which measures the distance along a semi-flexible object, such as a stiff polymer, over which it loses its directional memory.[32] The persistence length is a function of the bending stiffness of the particle, which depends on the thickness σ, and for single-wall carbon nanotubes has been shown to scale as σ^3 and to be in excess of 20 μm.[55] Naively, one would presume that for most cases these would behave like rigid rods, but a very slight flexibility significantly influences the transition to the nematic phase.[53] The reason is that for the nematic phase the persistence length is not the relevant length scale, but a much smaller length known as the Odijk or deflection length.[26] It is proportional to the persistence length and measures the distance over which nematic interactions redirect the flexing rods towards the preferred direction of the nematic.

In the limit of very long semi-flexible polymers, for which $L \gg P \gg \sigma$, the nematic phase sets in for $\phi > \sigma/P$ rather than $\phi > \sigma/L$, so at much larger concentrations.[53] Much less is known about semi-flexible surfaces, except that provided their cross section is much larger than the persistence length P, the nematic phase is unstable within a second virial theory and must be stabilised by higher than two-body contacts.[52] Nematic dispersions of graphene and graphene oxide sheets have indeed been reported in the literature[56] albeit that these are often thought to behave like rigid platelets. On the other hand, here too a small degree of flexibility might have a large impact. At present, this remains largely unexplored territory.

7. Remarks on nanoparticles in nematic fluids

Dispersing nanoparticles in liquid-crystalline rather than isotropic fluids gives rise to completely new physics. This, of course, is due to the symmetry-broken character of liquid crystals.[57] To date, most experimental work relates to particles dispersed in nematic liquid crystalline host fluids, lyotropic and thermotropic.[8,12] Because nematic liquid crystals obey uniaxial symmetry, i.e., cylindrical and inversion symmetry, this has consequences for collections of particles dispersed into them as will become clear in a number of contributions to this book. We end this chapter with touching upon a few aspects that largely, but not exclusively, relate to how large the inclusions are relative to a number of length scales relevant to the problem in hand.

It is important to realise that due to their uniaxial symmetry nematics have properties that differ along the symmetry axis, the director, from that perpendicular to it.[57] For instance, the dielectric properties of nematics are different along and perpendicular to the director. This implies that particles with anisotropic dielectric properties because of their shape or internal structure will experience a torque on them in effect due to Van der Waals interactions from the surrounding fluid. Little is known about the strength of this torque in actual experimental systems.[13] An important reason is that it is hard to separate these from other causes that also tend to align particles in nematics. Indeed, non-spherical particles will align for other reasons as well but it depends on their size whether this is due to surface or elastic forces induced by contact with the medium.[57–59]

If a surface is brought into contact with a nematic liquid crystal, then this gives rise to a surface tension that depends on the angle between the director and the surface normal. One usually distinguishes two extreme cases, representing a preference for the director to lie along the surface and one where the director prefers to align perpendicular to the surface, that is, along the surface normal. This preference for a given alignment is called anchoring, and expresses itself in a difference in the surface tension along and perpendicular to the surface. This difference can be quantified in an anchoring (free) energy, w [N m^{-2}].[57] Whether a nematic prefers planar or perpendicular (homeotropic) alignment depends on the details of the interactions of the nematogens with the surface. If there are no strong specific interactions, then disk-like nematogens prefer homeotropic and rod-like nematogens planar alignment, purely for entropy reasons because of the magnitude of the depletion zone near the surface excluding the centres of mass of the nematogens.[60] See Fig. 10.

Whether the anchoring of the director field to the surface actually leads to the deformation of the director field depends on the elastic properties of the nematic. Let K [N] be some average of the elastic constants of a nematic. The director field will accommodate its preference for a particular kind of anchoring provided the size of the particle, σ, is larger than a length scale K/w known as the extrapolation length.[57] For spherical particles, σ is the diameter, while for rod-like ones it is the width and for disk-like particles it is thickness or width depending on their orientation.[58,59] If $\sigma \ll K/w$ the director field is weakly perturbed by the presence of the particles, while if $\sigma \gg K/w$ the opposite is true. This may ultimately lead to the emergence of different kinds of topological defect in the nematic, depending on the type of anchoring and shape of the particle.[8] In both cases, rod- and disk-shaped nanoparticles will orient, in the former case to minimise the surface energy and in the latter in order to minimise the elastic energy.

If the nanoparticles are dispersed in a lyotropic nematic, then they need not be larger than the nematogens in all of the particle dimensions. For instance, single-wall carbon nanotubes dispersed in a lyotropic nematic of elongated virus particles or of cylindrical or discoidal surfactant micelles are thinner than the relevant molecular dimensions of the host fluid.[10,12] In that case one cannot invoke a continuum description, and a particle-based description such as that provided by excluded-volume or depletion theory

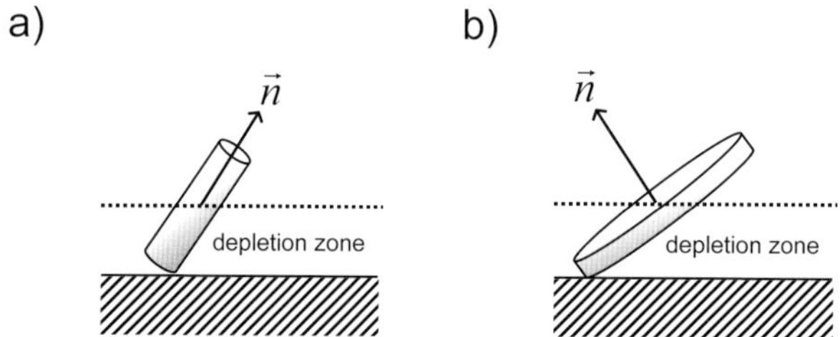

Fig. 10.   Entropy-driven anchoring of rod- and disk-like particles. The centres of mass of hard particles are excluded from a volume (the "depletion zone") near a hard wall that depends on their orientation and shape. The smaller the depletion zone, the larger the accessible volume of the particles and hence the larger their translational entropy. For nematics of rod-like particles this leads to the director $\vec{n}$ to prefer planar alignment, whilst for plate-like particles homeotropic alignment is preferred. This is only true if other types of interaction between particles and surface are weak.

is required.[43,61] In any event, the hard-core type of interaction between the embedded nanoparticles and nematogens leads to the alignment of the former if they are not spherical.[10,50]

That this must be so can be illustrated by considering hard "tracer" cylinders of length L_t and width $\sigma_t \ll L_t$, dispersed in a host nematic of hard cylinders of length L_h and width $\sigma_h \ll L_h$. These two species experience an excluded volume equal to twice the cross virial coefficient $B_{th} = L_t L_h (\sigma_t + \sigma_h) \langle \langle | \sin \gamma_{th} | \rangle_t \rangle_h / 2$.[49] Here, γ_{th} is the angle between a tracer particle and a host particle, and $\langle \langle \cdots \rangle_t \rangle_h$ indicates an average over the orientations of the tracer (subscript t) and host particles (subscript h). The interaction free energy with the host particles a tracer particle experiences is proportional to B_{th}.

This has to be compared with interaction free energy of a single particle of the host fluid with the remainder of the host fluid, which (to leading order in the aspect ratio of the rods) is proportional to $B_{hh} = L_h^2 \sigma_h \langle \langle | \sin \gamma_{hh} | \rangle_h \rangle_h$, where the subscripts should be self explainatory. Arguably, the tracer particle optimises its interaction with the host to match that of a test particle from the host fluid, suggesting that for highly ordered nematics $\langle \langle | \gamma_{th} | \rangle_t \rangle_h / \langle \langle | \gamma_{hh} | \rangle_h \rangle_h \approx L_h \sigma_h / L_t (\sigma_h + \sigma_t)$. It shows that if $L_t > L_h$ the tracer particles must be more strongly ordered than the host particles, whilst if $L_t < L_h$ the reverse is true. More accurate calculations confirm this.[10,50,51]

Particles inserted in the nematic interact at non-vanishing concentrations, either because of Van der Waals interactions or because they perturb the host fluid. As to the former, not much quantitative is known about the anisotropic Van der Waals interactions between particles in a nematic, not for spherical nor non-spherical particles.[13] Regarding the latter, the particles not only perturb the local host fluid structure, but also the degree of local orientational order of the nematogens and the director field to a larger or smaller degree as we have just put forward. In fact, the presence of particles in the nematic host fluid also influence director fluctuations, giving rise to what are known as pseudo-Casimir interactions already alluded to in Section 5.[8,38] All of this gives rise to medium-induced interactions between the particles that are complex and inherently anisotropic. Aspects of these will be discussed in other Chapters in this volume.

All in all, what can be said in conclusion is that all these phenomena conspire against the long-term homogeneous dispersion of large amounts of guest particles in liquid crystals. This does not mean that materials cannot be made that are based on dispersing nanoparticles in liquid crystals, if structures can be frozen in quickly enough after preparation, e.g., by polymerising the host fluid.[62]

Acknowledgments

I am grateful to Jan Lagerwall, Epifanio Virga and Charley Schaefer for a critical reading of the manuscript. I am also indebted to Holger Stark for his hospitality when on leave at TU Berlin, allowing me to write this chapter.

References

1. Jean-Louis Barrat and Jean-Pierre Hansen, *Basic Concepts for Simple and Complex Liquids* (CUP, Cambridge, 2003).
2. V. Adrian Parsegian, *Van der Waals Forces: a Handbook for Biologists, Chemists, Engineers, and Physicists* (CUP, Cambridge, 2006).
3. D. Fennell Evans and Håkan Wennerström , *The Colloidal Domain: Where Physics, Chemistry, Biology, and Technology Meet, 2nd edition* (Wiley VCH, Hoboken, NJ, 1999).
4. Thomas A. Witten and Philip A. Pincus, *Structured fluids* (OUP, Oxford, 2010).
5. Jacob N. Israelachvili, *Intermolecular and surface forces, 3rd edition* (Academic Press, Burlington, MA, 2011).
6. Ken A. Dill and Sarina Bromberg, *Molecular Driving Forces* (Garland Science, New York, 2003).
7. Henk N.W. Lekkerkerker and Remco Tuinier, *Colloids and the Depletion Interaction* (Springer, Dordrecht 2011).
8. Holger Stark, *Physics of colloidal dispersions in nematic liquid crystals*, Physics Reports **351** (2001), 387.
9. A. Ajdari, B. Duplantier, D. Hone, L. Peliti, J. Prost, *"Pseudo-Casimir" effect in liquid crystals*, J. Phys. France II **2** (1992), 487.
10. Nicolas Puech, Matthew Dennison, Christophe Blanc, Paul van der Schoot, Marjolein Dijkstra, RenÈ van Roij, Philippe Poulin, and Eric Grelet, *Orientational Order of Carbon Nanotube Guests in a Nematic Host Suspension of Colloidal Viral Rods*, Phys. Rev. Lett. **108** (2012), 247801.
11. Frédéric Mondiot, Robert Botet, Patrick Snabre, Olivier Mondain-Monval, and Jean-Christophe Loudet, *Colloidal aggregation and dynamics in anisotropic fluids*, Proc. Nat. Acad. Sci. USA **111** (2014), 5831.
12. Jan Lagerwall, Giusy Scalia, Miroslav Haluska, Ursula Dettlaff-Weglikowska, Siegmar Roth, and Frank Giesselmann, *Nanotube alignment using lyotropic liquid crystals*, Adv. Mater. **19** (2007), 359.
13. Pavel E. Kornilovitch, *Van der Waals interaction in uniaxial anisotropic media*, J. Phys.: Condens. Matter **25** (2013), 035102.

14. F. Cuadros, I. Cachadiña, W. Ahumada, *Determination of Lennard-Jones interaction parameters using a new procedure*, Mech. Eng. **6** (1996), 319.

15. L.E. Reichl, *A modern course in statistical physics* (Edward Arnold, London, 1980).

16. G. L. Klimchiskaya, U. Mohideen, V. M. Mostepanenko, *The Casimir force between real materials: experiment and theory*, Rev. Mod. Phys. **81** (2009), 1827.

17. Paul van der Schoot and Theo Odijk, *Statistical theory and structure factor of a semidilute solution of rodlike macromolecules interacting by van der Waals forces*, J. Chem. Phys. **97** (1992), 515.

18. Micah J. Green, A. Nicholas G. Parra-Vasquez, Natnael Behabtu and Matteo Pasquali, *Modeling the phase behavior of polydisperse rigid rods with attractive interactions with applications to single-walled carbon nanotubes in superacids*, J. Chem. Phys. **131** (2009), 084901.

19. Micah J. Green, Natnael Behabtu, Matteo Pasquali, W. Wade Adams, *Nanotubes as polymers*, Polymer **50** (2009), 4979.

20. H. Boroudjerdi, Y.-W. Kim, A. Naji, R. R. Netz, X. Schlagberger, A. Serr, *Statics and dynamics of strongly charged soft matter*, Physics Reports **416** (2005), 129.

21. Sara Jabbari-Farouji, Jean-Jacques Weis, Patrick Davidson, Pierre Levitz and Emmanuel Trizac, *On phase behavior and dynamical signatures of charged colloidal platelets*, Sci. Rep. **3** (2013), 3559.

22. Christin Hiergeist, Michael Lassig, Reinhard Liposwky, *Bundels of interacting strings in 2 dimensions*, Europhys. Lett. **28** (1994), 103.

23. B. Vigolo, C. Coulon, M. Maugey, C. Zakri, P. Poulin, *Macroscopic fibers and ribbons of oriented carbon nanotubes* Science **309** (2005), 920.

24. Nicolas Puech, Christophe Blanc, Eric Grelet, Camilo Zamora-Ledezma, Maryse Maugey, Cécile Zakri, Eric Anglaret, and Philippe Poulin, *Highly ordered carbon nanotubes in nematic liquid crystals*, J. Phys. Chem. C **115** (2011), 3272.

25. E. J. W. Verweij and J. Th. G. Overbeek, *Theory of the Stability of Lyotropic Colloids* (Elsevier, New York, 1948).

26. G. J. Vroege and H. N. W. Lekkerkerker, *Phase transitions in lyotropic colloidal and polymer liquid crystals*, Rep. Prog. Phys. **55** (1992), 1241.

27. J. Lyklema (ed.), *Fundamentals of Interface and Colloid Science, Volume IV: Particulate Colloids* (Elsevier, Amsterdam, 2005).

28. R. Agra, E. Trizac and L. Bocquet, *The interplay between screening properties and colloid anisotropy: Towards a reliable pair potential for disc-like charged particles*, Eur. Phys. J. E **15** (2004), 345.

29. Matej Kanduè, Alexander Schlaich, Emanuel Schneck, Roland R. Netz, *Hydration repulsion between membranes and polar surfaces: Simulation approaches versus continuum theories*, Advances in Colloid and Interface Science **208** (2014), 142.

30. M. Boström, V. Deniz, G.V. Franks, B.W. Ninham, *Extended DLVO theory: Electrostatic and non-electrostatic forces in oxide suspensions*, Advances in Colloid and Interface Science **123ñ126** (2006), 5.

31. G. J. Fleer, M. A. Cohen Stuart, J. M. H. M. Scheutjens, T. Cosgrove, B. Vincent, *Polymers at interfaces* (Chapman and Hall, London, 1993).
32. Michael Rubinstein and Ralph C. Colby, *Polymer physics* (Oxford University Press, Oxford, 2003).
33. Peter Prinsen and Theo Odijk, *Optimized Baxter model of protein solutions: electrostatics versus adhesion*, J. Chem. Phys. **121** (2004), 6525.
34. David Chandler, *Interfaces and the driving force of hydrophobic assembly*, Nature **437** (2005), 640.
35. Emily E. Meyer, Kenneth J. Rosenberg, and Jacob Israelachvili, *Recent progress in understanding hydrophobic interactions*, Proc. Nat. Acad. Sci. USA **103** (2006), 15739.
36. Stephen H. Donaldson, Jr., Anja Royne, Kai Kristiansen, Michael V. Rapp, Saurabh Das, Matthew A. Gebbie, Dong Woog Lee, Philipp Stock, Markus Valtiner, and Jacob Israelachvili, *Developing a general interaction potential for hydrophobic and hydrophilic interactions*, Langmuir **31** (2015), 2051.
37. Yuncheng Liang, Nidal Hilal, Paul Langston, Victor Starov, *Interaction forces between colloidal particles in liquid: Theory and experiment*, Advances in Colloid and Interface Science **134** (2007), 151.
38. P. Ziherl, R. Podgornik, and S. Žumer, *Wetting driven Casimir force in nematic liquid crystals*, Phys. Rev. Lett. **82** (1999), 1192.
39. Daniel Bonn, Jens Eggers, Joseph Indekeu, Jacques Meunier, and Etienne Rolley, *Wetting and spreading*, Rev. Mod. Phys. **81** (2009), 739.
40. Brigitte Vigolo, Alain Pénicaud, Claude Coulon, Cédric Sauder, René Pailler, Catherine Journet, Patrick Bernier, Philippe Poulin, *Macroscopic fibers and ribbons of oriented carbon nanotubes*, Science **209** (2000), 1331.
41. Marjolein Dijkstra, René van Roij, and Robert Evans, *Phase diagram of highly asymmetric binary hard-sphere mixtures*, Phys. Rev. E **59** (1999), 5744.
42. Paul van der Schoot, *Protein-induced collapse of polymer chains*, Macromolecules **31** (1998), 4635.
43. Paul van der Schoot, *Depletion interactions in lyotropic nematics*, J. Chem. Phys. **112** (2000), 9132.
44. G. A. Vliegenthart and H. N. W. Lekkerkerker, *Predicting the gas-liquid critical point from the second virial coefficient*, J. Chem. Phys. **112** (2000), 5364.
45. J. A. Thomson, P. Schurtenberger, G. M. Thurston, and G. B. Benedek, *Binary liquid phase separation and critical phenomena in a protein/water solution*, Proc Natl Acad Sci U S A. Oct **84** (1987), 7079.
46. Vera M. O. Batista and Mark A. Miller, *Crystallization of deformable spherical colloids*, Phys. Rev. Lett. **105** (2010), 088305.
47. Benito Groh and Bela Mulder, *Why all crystals need not be bcc: Symmetry breaking at the liquid-solid transition revisited*, PRE **59** (1999), 5613.
48. H. H. Wensink and H. N. W. Lekkerkerker, *Phase diagram of hard colloidal platelets: a theoretical account*, Molecular Physics, **107** (2009), 2111.
49. Lars Onsager, *The effects of shape on the interaction of colloidal particles*, Ann. N. Y. Acad. Sci. **51** (1949), 627.
50. H. H. Wensink and G. J. Vroege, *Isotropic nematic phase behavior of length*

polydisperse hard rods, J. Chem. Phys. **119** (2003), 6868.

51. H. N. W. Lekkerkerker, Ph. Coulon, R. Van Der Haegen, R. Deblieck, *On the isotropic-liquid crystalline phase separation in solutions of rodlike particles of different length*, J. Chem. Phys. 80 (1984), 3427.

52. Theo Odijk, *Analysis of the stability of the nematic phase consisting of semi-flexible surfaces*, J. Chem. Phys. **88** (1988), 7167.

53. Zheng Yu Chen, *Nematic Ordering in Semiflexible Polymer Chains*, Macromolecules **26** (1993), 3419.

54. Saber Naderi and Paul van der Schoot, *Effect of bending flexibility on the phase behavior and dynamics of rods*, J. Chem. Phys. **141** (2014), 124901.

55. Nikta Fakhri, Dmitri A. Tsyboulski, Laurent Cognet, R. Bruce Weisman, and Matteo Pasquali, *Diameter-dependent bending dynamicsof single-walled carbon nanotubes in liquids*, Proc. Natl. Acad. Sci. USA **106** (2009), 14219.

56. Alain Pénicaud, Carlos Drummond, *Deconstructing Graphite: Graphenide Solutions*, Acc. Chem. Res. **46** (2013), 129.

57. P. G. de Gennes and J. Prost, *The Physics of Liquid Crystals*, Second Edition (OUP, Oxford, 1995).

58. Paul van der Schoot, V. Popa-Nita, and S. Kralj, *Alignment of Carbon Nanotubes in Nematic Liquid Crystals*, J. Phys. Chem. B **112** (2008), 4512.

59. C. Lapointe, A. Hultgren, D. M. Silevitch, E. J. Felton, D. H. Reich, R. L. Leheny, *Elastic torque and the levitation of metal wires by a nematic liquid crystal*, Science **303** (2004), 652.

60. Paul van der Schoot, *Remarks on the interfacial tension in colloidal systems*, J. Phys. Chem. B **103** (1999), 8804.

61. Muataz S. Al-Barwani, Gregory S. Sutcliffe and Michael P. Allen, *Forces between two colloidal particles in a nematic solvent*, J. Phys. Chem. B **108** (2004), 6663.

62. Blaž Tašič, Aleš Mrzel, Miro Huskič, Xinzheng Zhang, Irena Drevenšek - Olenik, *Alignment of MoS_2 nanotubes in a photopolymerizable liquid-crystalline material*, J. Phys. Chem. C **118** (2014), 26396.

Chapter 4

Nematic liquid crystals doped with nanoparticles: Phase behavior and dielectric properties

Mikhail A. Osipov

*Department of Mathematics, University of Strathclyde,
Glasgow G1 1XH, United Kingdom
2 Topchiev Institute of Petrochemical Synthesis,
Russian Academy of Sciences,
Leninsky Prosp. 29, 119991 Moscow, Russia
m.osipov@strath.ac.uk*

Maxim V. Gorkunov

*Shubnikov Institute of Crystallography of Federal Scientific Research
Centre "Crystallography and Photonics" of Russian Academy of Sciences,
119333 Moscow, Russia*

Thermodynamics and dielectric properties of nematic liquid crystals doped with various nanoparticles have been studied in the framework of a molecular mean-field theory. It is shown that spherically isotropic nanoparticles effectively dilute the liquid crystal material and cause a decrease of the nematic-isotropic transition temperature, while anisotropic nanoparticles are aligned by the nematic host and, in turn, may significantly improve the liquid crystal alignment. In the case of strong interaction between spherical nanoparticles and mesogenic molecules, the nanocomposite possesses a number of unexpected properties: The nematic-isotropic co-existence region appears to be very broad, and the system either undergoes a direct transition from the isotropic phase into the phase-separated state, or undergoes first a transition into the homogeneous nematic phase and then phase-separates at a lower temperature. The phase separation does not occur for sufficiently low nanoparticle concentrations, and, in certain cases, the separation takes place only within a finite region of the nanoparticle concentration. For nematics doped with strongly polar nanoparticles, the theory predicts the nanoparticle aggregation in linear chains that make a substantial contribution to the static dielectric anisotropy and optical birefringence of the nematic composite. The theory clarifies the microscopic origin of im-

portant phenomena observed in nematic composites including a shift of
the isotropic-nematic phase transition and improvement of the nematic
order; a considerable softening of the first order nematic-isotropic transition; a complex phase-separation behavior; and a significant increase
of the dielectric anisotropy and the birefringence.

Contents

1. Introduction

Liquid crystal nanocomposites are considered to be extremely promising
materials in which the properties of a liquid crystal (LC), used, for example, in display applications, are modified/improved by the presence of
various nanoparticles (NPs). There are many reports showing that doping
of a nematic LC with even a small amount of NPs affects nearly all important properties of nematic materials, resulting in a decrease of threshold
and switching voltages and reducing the switching times of LC displays
(see, for example, Refs. 1–5). Suspensions of metal, dielectric and semiconductor NPs in various nematic LCs have been investigated by many
authors and, in particular, doping of nematics with ferroelectric NPs is
known to enhance dielectric and optical anisotropy, increase the electro-
optic response[6,7] and improve the photorefractive properties.[8] Suspensions

of para- and ferromagnetic particles in nematics are promising candidates for magnetically tunable structures, and doping of ferroelectric LCs with metal and silica nanoparticles enables one to improve the spontaneous polarization and dielectric permittivity and to decrease switching times.[9–11] Metal NPs have been also used to widen the temperature range of LC blue phases,[12] which are important for applications, and enhance random lasing in the dye-doped LC medium.[13] Finally, distributing semiconductor quantum dots in smectic LC-polymers enables one to achieve the positional ordering of nanosize particles.[14,15]

At the same time, LC-NP composites are also considered as the building blocks of novel metamaterials. Metamaterials, i.e., arrays of sub-wavelength metallic/semiconductor particles, offer a new degree of freedom in controlling light: they enable tailoring the optical response, achieving very high, very low and negative values of refractive index, permittivity and/or permeability.[16] Combining emerging optical metamaterials with LCs provides a new important quality – tunability, which is of key importance for emerging applications including tunable photonic materials, optically addressed spatial light modulators and dynamic holography. Upon immersing a metamaterial into a nematic LC one can switch the LC alignment by external voltages and modify the overall optical properties of the composite.[17] For instance, the localized plasmon resonance of gold NPs can be tuned by changing the refractive index and, in particular, the birefringence of the surrounding LC medium.[18–20]

Many applications of LC nanocomposites require an understanding of how the NPs affect the orientational order in the LC medium and the thermodynamic stability of the LC phase. Recently it has been shown[10,11] that the dipolar induction interaction between ferroelectric NPs and the surrounding nematic LC medium may result in a substantial decrease of the nematic-isotropic (N-I) transition temperature. It has also been shown experimentally that the N-I transition temperature can be significantly affected by the presence of other types of NPs. For example, a decrease of the N-I transition temperature is observed in nematics doped with approximately isotropic silver,[21] gold[22] or aerosil particles,[23,24] while the N-I transition temperature increases if the nematic LC is doped with strongly anisotropic NPs including nanotubes,[25] magnetic nanorods[26] and ferroelectric particles.[9,10] Recently a detailed mean-field molecular theory of nematic LCs doped with both isotropic and anisotropic NPs has been developed.[27] The effect of isotropic NPs has also been considered in Ref. 28, while the effect of the external electric field on the nematic nano-composites has been studied in Ref. 29.

In the case of spherical or weakly anisotropic NPs, the N-I transition temperature decreases with the increasing concentration of NPs and as a result the nematic phase is partially destabilized. In such a system the total free energy may be minimized if the system separates into the isotropic phase with an increased concentration of NPs and the nematic phase with lower concentration of NPs. One notes that such a phase separation is very much different from an ordinary demixing, which takes place already in the isotropic phase and does not require the system to undergo a phase transition. Experimentally such a demixing can be suppressed by attaching appropriate organic groups to the surface of the NPs which makes them more compatible with the surrounding fluid. In contrast, the origin of the nematic-isotropic phase separation is intimately related to the phase transition thermodynamics, and we find such a phase separation to be very interesting from both the fundamental and the applications point of view.

It should be noted that a similar phase separation occurs around the N-I transition point in mixtures of different LCs and, in particular, in nematics doped with nonmesogenic molecules (see e.g. Refs. 30,31). The corresponding two-phase region around the N-I transition, however, is usually very narrow. This is related to the fact that properties of the dopant molecules do not differ much from those of the host ones. In contrast, the properties of metal or semiconductor NPs may differ very significantly from those of typical mesogenic molecules, and, as a result, the region of coexistence of the isotropic and the nematic phase may be much wider.[32] The first molecular theory of the nematic-isotropic phase separation in nematic nano-composites has recently been developed by the authors.[33]

Strong interaction between NPs may also lead to their aggregation including the formation of chains of NPs when the interaction is strongly anisotropic. Aggregates of NPs in general, and polar chains in particular, are expected to modify all major properties of nematic nano-composites, including their dielectric and optical properties. Nematic LCs with polar chains should also be very sensitive to external electric fields which may be used for alignment and switching at very low applied voltage.

It has been shown experimentally (see, for example, Refs. 9,34) that the dielectric anisotropy of nematic LCs doped with strongly polar (ferroelectric) NPs is dramatically increased. Indeed, a very small molar fraction of ferroelectric NPs (of the order of 10^{-3}) accounts for a contribution of the order of $5-6$ to the anisotropy of the dielectric constant, which is comparable with the anisotropy of the nematic host. Preliminary estimates indicate that the increase is too strong to be explained without taking into account possible aggregation of NPs and formation of polar chains. There exists some experimental evidence that quantum dots may also form long chains in nematic LCs[35] even though such NPs are nonpolar.

Aggregation of NPs in the nematic phase may occur if the inter-particle interaction potential is not strong enough to induce demixing but is still much stronger than the interaction between mesogenic molecules. Strongly anisotropic interaction between NPs, including in particular dipole-dipole one, will lead to the formation of polar chains. It has been shown[36] that the equilibrium chain length strongly depends on the contact interaction potential normalized by the temperature. Long chains of NPs may occur only if the contact interaction is of the order of $10k_BT$[36] which is satisfied, for example, for ferroelectric NPs.[9,34] Polar chains should make a significant contribution to the dielectric anisotropy of nematic composites.

In this chapter we summarize the results of a molecular-field theory of nematic LCs doped with NPs. In Sec. 2 we consider the effect of both isotropic and anisotropic NPs on the nematic-isotropic phase transition temperature and discuss a softening of the N-I phase transition. In Sec. 3 the isotropic-nematic phase separation caused by isotropic NPs is studied in detail and the corresponding phase diagrams are presented. Finally, in Sec. 4 we describe the effect of chains of polar NPs on the dielectric anisotropy and the birefringence of nematic composites.

2. Effect of nano-particles on the nematic-isotropic phase transition

2.1. *Mean-field theory of nematic composites*

Consider a composite material formed by N_m highly anisotropic identical LC molecules and N_p NPs with possible deviations in physical properties or shape, size and surface structure. To take into account this NP diversity we assume that there are L different types of NPs in the composite and the number of the NPs of the type l is N_l such that $N_1 + N_2 + ...N_L = N_p$.

Now let V_{mol} be the part of the total volume V occupied by the LC molecules, while the volume $V_p = V - V_{\mathrm{mol}}$ is occupied by NPs. Then $\phi = V_p/V$ is the volume fraction of NPs and the number density of NPs $\rho_p = \phi/v_p$, where v_p is the average particle volume. Assuming that the number density of LC molecules in the pure LC is ρ_0, one may express the number density of LC molecules in the composite as $\rho = \rho_0(1 - \phi)$.

Following the classical Maier-Saupe theory of nematic ordering, we specify the orientation of a LC molecule by the unit vector $\mathbf{a}$ in the direction of its long axis and express the microscopic pair intermolecular interaction potential as $u_{\mathrm{mol}}(\mathbf{a}_1, \mathbf{a}_2, \mathbf{r})$, i.e., as depending on the intermolecular vector $\mathbf{r}$ and the long axes of the two molecules $\mathbf{a}_1$ and $\mathbf{a}_2$.

Macroscopically, the orientational nematic order of the LC is described by the tensor order parameter $\mathbf{Q} = S(\mathbf{n} \otimes \mathbf{n} - 1/3)$, which is the macroscopic average of the microscopic molecular tensor $\mathbf{Q}^M = (\mathbf{a} \otimes \mathbf{a} - 1/3)$. The conventional scalar nematic order parameter is defined as $S = \langle 3/2(\mathbf{n} \cdot \mathbf{a})^2 - 1/2 \rangle$, where $\langle ... \rangle$ denotes the statistical average, and $\mathbf{n}$ is the nematic director, i.e., a unit vector parallel to the nematic symmetry axis.

Generally, the orientation of the anisotropic NP can be characterized by three orthogonal unit vectors: the "primary" axis $\mathbf{A}_l$, and the two secondary orthogonal axes $\mathbf{B}_l$ and $\mathbf{C}_l$. In the statistical theory, the orientational ordering of the NPs can be described in a way similar to that established for the orientational ordering of biaxial molecules.[37]

In this Section, we assume that the NP concentration is relatively low and thus we neglect the direct interaction between NPs. In this case, the orientational order of NPs is induced by the uniaxial LC medium and the NPs possess tensor order parameters of the same uniaxial symmetry, i.e., $\mathbf{Q}_l = S_l(\mathbf{n} \otimes \mathbf{n} - 1/3)$ and $\mathbf{D}_l = D_l(\mathbf{n} \otimes \mathbf{n} - 1/3)$. Here $S_l = \langle 3/2(\mathbf{n} \cdot \mathbf{A}_l)^2 - 1/2 \rangle$ is the nematic order parameter of the primary axis of l-th type NP and D_l is the additional order parameter which describes uniaxial ordering of short axes of the NPs of the type l.

The order parameter D_l is usually much smaller than S_l and thus it may be neglected. This is equivalent to the assumption that short axes of the particles are distributed randomly in the uniaxial nematic phase and hence the particle may be considered as effectively uniaxial. As a result, one may introduce the uniaxial microscopic pair interaction potential $u_l(\mathbf{a}, \mathbf{A}_l, \mathbf{r})$ between an LC molecule, which orientation is specified by the long axis $\mathbf{a}$, and a uniaxial NP with the axis $\mathbf{A}_l$.

Then in the mean-field approximation, the free energy of the composite

LC-NP medium reads:

$$F = \frac{1}{2V} \sum_{m=1}^{N_m} \sum_{m'=1}^{N_m} \int f(\mathbf{a}_m) u_{\mathrm{mol}}(\mathbf{a}_m, \mathbf{a}_{m'}, \mathbf{r}) f(\mathbf{a}_{m'}) d\mathbf{r} \, d\mathbf{a}_m d\mathbf{a}_{m'}$$

$$+ N_m k_B T \int f(\mathbf{a}) \ln f(\mathbf{a}) \, d\mathbf{a}$$

$$+ \frac{1}{V} \sum_{m=1}^{N_m} \sum_{l=1}^{L} \sum_{n=1}^{N_l} \int f(\mathbf{a}_m) u_n(\mathbf{a}_m, \mathbf{A}_n, \mathbf{r}) f_l(\mathbf{A}_n) d\mathbf{r} \, d\mathbf{a}_m \, d\mathbf{A}_n$$

$$+ k_B T \sum_{l=1}^{L} \sum_{n=1}^{N_l} \int f_l(\mathbf{A}_n) \ln f_l(\mathbf{A}_n) \, d\mathbf{A}_n, \tag{1}$$

where $m' \neq m$ in the first term, $f(\mathbf{a})$ is the orientational distribution function of the LC molecules and where $f_l(\mathbf{A})$ is the orientational distribution function of the NPs of type l.

Due to the lack of positional order, the free energy of the nematic phase is determined by the so-called effective orientational pair potentials which are obtained by the integration of the corresponding microscopic pair potentials over the intermolecular vector or the vector between a molecule and a NP. In the mean-field theory of uniaxial nematics, the effective interaction potential is expressed, in the first approximation, as a sum of the isotropic part and the anisotropic potential $w(\mathbf{a}_m \cdot \mathbf{a}_{m'})^2$ which is a simplest bilinear coupling between the molecular tensors $(\mathbf{a}_{ml} \otimes \mathbf{a}_{ml} - 1/3)$ and $(\mathbf{a}_{m2} \otimes \mathbf{a}_{m2} - 1/3)$ which are composed from the components of the molecular long axes $\mathbf{a}_m$ and $\mathbf{a}_{m'}$:

$$U_{\mathrm{mol}}(\mathbf{a}_m, \mathbf{a}_{m'}) = \int d\mathbf{r} \, u_{\mathrm{mol}}(\mathbf{a}_m, \mathbf{a}_{m'}, \mathbf{r}) = const + w(\mathbf{a}_m \cdot \mathbf{a}_{m'})^2, \tag{2}$$

The latter term is obviously invariant under the molecular permutation $m \leftrightarrow m'$ and the head-tail transformations $\mathbf{a} \leftrightarrow -\mathbf{a}$. The nematic phase is stable in the pure LC when the constant w is negative.

Similarly, one can express the effective interaction potential between a NP and an LC molecule as:

$$U_n(\mathbf{a}_m, \mathbf{A}_n) = \int d\mathbf{r} \, u_n(\mathbf{a}_m, \mathbf{A}_n, \mathbf{r}) = const + W_n(\mathbf{a}_m \cdot \mathbf{A}_n)^2. \tag{3}$$

Note that this potential is also determined by a coupling between nonpolar molecular tensors of a LC molecule and a NP. Even if NPs are polar, i.e. there is no $\mathbf{A} \leftrightarrow -\mathbf{A}$ symmetry, the lowest-order anisotropic term in the interaction potential has exactly the same form as in Eq. (2).

In the context of various models of the dominant anisotropic LC-NP interaction, it is possible to obtain particular expressions for the interaction constants W. For example, according to Ref. 11, dipole-dipole induction interaction between a spherical ferroelectric NP and the nematic LC matrix corresponds to the following constant W

$$W = \frac{\Delta \alpha p^2}{90 \varepsilon_0 \varepsilon^2 v_p},\tag{4}$$

where p is the absolute value of ferroelectric NP permanent dipole, $\Delta \alpha$ is the dielectric anisotropy of a LC molecule and ε is the static LC permittivity. Some expressions for the constants W determined by the NPs shape anisotropy have been obtained in Ref. 27.

Since all LC molecules are identical, the sums over m and m' in the free energy (1) reduce to a multiplication by N_m. Similarly, summations over the NPs of the same type reduces to the multiplication by the numbers N_l. Minimizing the free energy one obtains from the Euler-Lagrange equations the following expression for the LC orientational distribution function

$$f(\mathbf{a}) = \frac{1}{Z} \exp \left[-\frac{U_{\text{mol}}^{MF}(\mathbf{a})}{k_B T} \right],\tag{5}$$

where the molecular partition function Z is also the normalization constant

$$Z = \int \exp \left[-\frac{U_{\text{mol}}^{MF}(\mathbf{a})}{k_B T} \right] d\mathbf{a}.\tag{6}$$

The orientational distribution function of the NPs of the l-th type NPs is similarly given by

$$f_l(\mathbf{A}) = \frac{1}{Z_l} \exp \left[-\frac{U_l^{MF}(\mathbf{A})}{k_B T} \right],\tag{7}$$

where Z_l is expressed as

$$Z_l = \int \exp \left[-\frac{U_l^{MF}(\mathbf{A})}{k_B T} \right] d\mathbf{A}.\tag{8}$$

The mean-field potential for the LC molecules is given by:

$$U_{\text{mol}}^{MF}(\mathbf{a}) = \rho \int f(\mathbf{a}') \, U_{\text{mol}}(\mathbf{a}, \mathbf{a}') \, d\mathbf{a}' + \rho_p \sum_{l=1}^{L} \frac{N_l}{N_p} \int f_l(\mathbf{A}) \, U_l(\mathbf{a}, \mathbf{A}) \, d\mathbf{A},\tag{9}$$

and the mean field potential for the NPs of the l-th type is expressed as

$$U_l^{MF}(\mathbf{A}) = \rho \int f(\mathbf{a}) \, U_l(\mathbf{a}, \mathbf{A}) \, d\mathbf{a}.\tag{10}$$

Using the effective interaction potentials given by (2) and (3) one can express the mean-field potential (9) as

$$U_{\text{mol}}^{MF}(\mathbf{a}) = \rho w(\mathbf{Q}^M : \mathbf{Q}) + \rho_p \sum_{l=1}^{L} \frac{N_l}{N_p} W_l(\mathbf{Q}^M : \mathbf{Q}_l), \qquad (11)$$

while the potential (10) reads

$$U_l^{MF}(\mathbf{A}) = \rho W_l(\mathbf{Q}_l^M : \mathbf{Q}), \qquad (12)$$

where the irrelevant isotropic constant terms has been omitted.

Substituting the distribution functions (5) and (7) together with the above expressions for the mean-field potentials into Eq. (1) one can express the free energy of the nematic phase as a function of the scalar nematic order parameters of the LC and NPs:

$$\frac{1}{V}F(S, S_1, ..., S_L) = -\frac{1}{3}\rho^2 w S^2 - \frac{2}{3}\rho\rho_p S \sum_{l=1}^{L} \frac{N_l}{N_p} W_l S_l$$

$$- \rho k_B T \ln Z - \rho_p k_B T \sum_{l=1}^{L} \frac{N_l}{N_p} \ln Z_l, \qquad (13)$$

The partition functions can be expressed in terms of the integrals over the polar angles between the long axes of the particles and the director:

$$Z = \int_0^{\pi} \sin\gamma \, d\gamma \exp\left[-\frac{2}{3k_B T}\left(\rho w S + \rho_p \sum_{l=1}^{L} \frac{N_l}{N_p} W_l S_l\right) P_2(\cos\gamma)\right], \qquad (14)$$

$$Z_l = \int_0^{\pi} \sin\gamma \, d\gamma \exp\left[-\frac{2}{3k_B T}\rho W_l S P_2(\cos\gamma)\right], \qquad (15)$$

where P_2 is the second Legendre polynomial.

The free energy (13) formally depends on a macroscopic number of variables. Direct numerical minimization of the free energy is possible in the case of identical particles or in a more general case of a reasonable finite number of types of particles.

Alternatively, one may find the extremum of Eq. (13) by differentiating it with respect to S and $S_{1,...,L}$. This yields the system of self-consistent equations:

$$S = \frac{1}{Z} \int_0^{\pi} d\gamma \, P_2(\cos\gamma) \sin\gamma$$

$$\times \exp\left[-\frac{2}{3k_B T}\left(\rho w S + \rho_p \sum_{l=1}^{L} \frac{N_l}{N_p} W_l S_l\right) P_2(\cos\gamma)\right], \qquad (16)$$

$$S_l = \frac{1}{Z_l} \int_0^{\pi} d\gamma \, P_2(\cos\gamma) \sin\gamma \, \exp\left[-\frac{2}{3k_B T}\rho W_l S P_2(\cos\gamma)\right], \qquad (17)$$

which can also be solved numerically for a finite number of particle types.

2.2. *Shift of the nematic-isotropic transition temperature caused by nano-particles*

In this subsection we first present a general analytical consideration of the mixture of LC with nonidentical particles which is possible in the limit of weak particle anisotropy.

According to the Maier-Saupe mean-field theory of one-component LCs the nematic order parameter satisfies the following equation:

$$S = \frac{1}{Z} \int_0^\pi d\gamma \, P_2(\cos\gamma) \sin\gamma \, \exp\left[-\frac{2\rho_0 w}{3k_B T} S P_2(\cos\gamma) \right], \qquad (18)$$

which is known to describe the first order isotropic-nematic phase transition, which occurs at the following transition temperature

$$T_0 \simeq 0.149 \frac{\rho_0 |w|}{k_B}. \qquad (19)$$

If the nematic is doped by isotropic spherical NPs, the interaction constants W_n vanish identically. In this case, Eq. (16) is reduced to the form (18) with ρ instead of ρ_0, i.e., in the case of spherical NPs the effective interaction constant w is renormalized by the factor $(1 - \phi)$. Thus the composite LC material with spherical inclusions undergoes the isotropic-nematic phase transition at the lower temperature

$$T_{\mathrm{NI}} = (1 - \phi)T_0. \qquad (20)$$

The decrease of the transition temperature by the factor $(1 - \phi)$ clearly describes the so-called effect of dilution of LC by isotropic particles.

For weakly anisotropic particles, the constants W_l are small compared to w. Then in the nematic temperature range one also obtains $W_l \rho_0 \ll k_B T$ and therefore the exponent in Eq. (17) can be expanded. As a result, the induced order parameter of NPs appears to be linearly related to the LC order parameter:

$$S_l \simeq -\frac{2}{15} \frac{\rho_0(1 - \phi)W_l}{k_B T} S. \qquad (21)$$

Substituting these small induced parameters S_l into Eq. (16) one again obtains the self-consistent equation of the form (18), where the interaction constant w is renormalized by the following factor

$$\left[1 - \phi + \phi(1 - \phi) \frac{2\langle W^2 \rangle}{15|w|k_B T v_p} \right], \qquad (22)$$

and where $\langle W^2 \rangle = \sum_{l=1}^{L} W_l^2 N_l/N_p$ is an average square of LC-NP anisotropic interaction constant.

One can readily see that due to the particle anisotropy, the effective nematic interaction constant increases and becomes slightly temperature dependent. This promotes the nematic ordering of the LC matrix and, in the first approximation, this describes the positive feedback from the orientation ordering of anisotropic NPs.

Accordingly, in the case of weakly anisotropic NPs, the transition temperature undergoes the following shift:

$$T_{\mathrm{NI}} \simeq T_0 \left[1 - \phi + \phi(1 - \phi) \frac{2\langle W^2 \rangle}{15|w|k_B T_0 v_p} \right],\tag{23}$$

where the terms linear in concentration ϕ contain also a positive contribution from the NP anisotropy and can therefore compensate the dilution effect of the LC matrix by NPs. An exact compensation occurs at $\langle W^2 \rangle = 1.12 w^2 v_p \rho_0$. The terms quadratic in ϕ give rise to a weakly parabolic concentration dependence of the transition temperature $T_{\mathrm{NI}}(\phi)$. The sign of the quadratic term is negative in line with the experimental results for nematic LC polymers doped with silver NPs.[21]

2.3. *Numerical results in the case of strong NP anisotropy*

In order to clarify the effects of anisotropic NPs on the nematic-isotropic transition in the general case one has to solve numerically the system of equations (16) and (17). For simplicity, we assume that there is only one type of NPs in the composite. Then the system of simultaneous equations for the nematic order parameters can be conveniently reduced to the nondimensional form:

$$S = \frac{1}{Z} \int_{-1}^{1} dx\, P_2(x) \exp\left[\frac{2}{3\tau} \left[(1 - \phi)S + \phi\xi\omega S_p \right] P_2(x) \right],\tag{24}$$

$$S_p = \frac{1}{Z_p} \int_{-1}^{1} dx\, P_2(x) \exp\left[\frac{2}{3\tau} (1 - \phi)\omega S P_2(x) \right],\tag{25}$$

where the partition functions reads:

$$Z = \int_{-1}^{1} dx\, \exp\left[\frac{2}{3\tau} \left[(1 - \phi)S + \phi\xi\omega S_p \right] P_2(x) \right],\tag{26}$$

$$Z_p = \int_{-1}^{1} dx\, \exp\left[\frac{2}{3\tau} (1 - \phi)\omega S P_2(x) \right],\tag{27}$$

and where the following dimensionless parameters have been introduced: $\tau = k_B T / (\rho_0 |w|)$ is the dimensionless temperature; $\omega = W/w$ describes the relative strength of LC-NP anisotropic interaction; and $\xi = v_m/v_p$,which is the ratio of the LC molecular volume to the NP volume, characterizes the relative NP size.

Equations (24) and (25) have been solved iteratively and the numerical results for the orientational order parameters as functions of temperature and the N-I transition temperature have been obtained.[27]

We first analyze the effect of NPs on the isotropic-nematic transition temperature. Typical profiles of the calculated transition temperatures as functions of the NP volume fraction are presented in Fig. 1 for $\xi = 0.5$, i.e., the NP volume is twice larger than the LC molecular volume. Note that the transition temperatures for particles with negative and positive anisotropy are presented on the left and on the right hand side of the chart, respectively. One can readily see that the $T_{NI}(\phi)$ variations are almost linear, which is very similar to the experimental results in Ref. 21 and the analytical Eq. (23). For smaller ω, the addition of NP results in a decrease of the transition temperature, i.e., the effect of LC dilution prevails. For the values $\omega \simeq -2$ and $\omega \simeq 1.5$ the transition temperature remains almost constant due to the compensation of the dilution by the effect of NP anisotropy. For stronger anisotropy, the transition occurs at temperatures higher than in the pure LC, and the otherwise hardly noticeable parabolic shape of the curves becomes clearer.

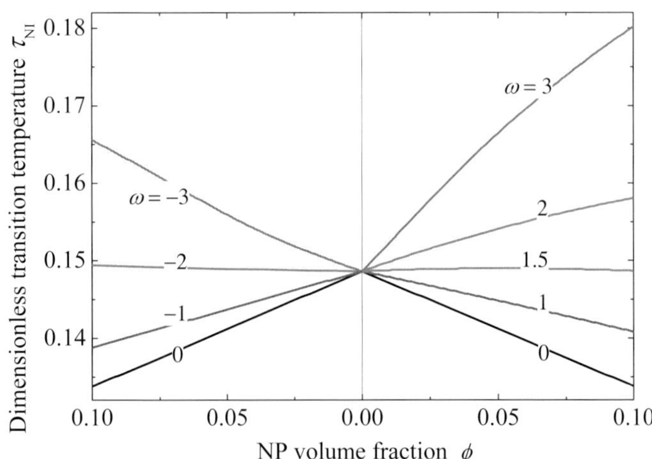

Fig. 1.   Isotropic-nematic transition temperature as a function of the NP volume fraction for several negative (on the left) and positive (on the right) values of the NP anisotropy ω. Note the reversed direction of the ϕ-axis on the left.

Typical variations of the transition temperature as functions of the NP anisotropy are presented in Fig. 2. It can be seen that even far beyond the limit of the weak NP anisotropy, the curves still correspond to the approximately parabolic dependence on W of Eq. (23). For larger NP concentrations the effect of NPs is more pronounced. According to Fig. 1, in the region of small ω the NPs again effectively dilute the LC. At stronger anisotropy, the NPs make a positive effect on the nematic and increase its temperature range. The intersections of different curves take place at the points, which correspond to the lines $\omega = -2$ and $\omega = 1.5$ in Fig. 1. The points on these lines correspond to the values of parameters for which the effect of dilution is compensated by that of the anisotropy and as a result the transition temperature is practically independent of ϕ.

In summary, both analytic and numerical results demonstrate the two main mechanisms of the effect of randomly distributed NPs on the nematic LC. Firstly, in the presence of NPs the average separation between mesogenic molecules of the LC matrix is increased, i.e., the LC matrix is effectively diluted. This decreases the average strength of intermolecular interactions, reduces the nematic ordering and decreases the temperature of the transition into the nematic phase. In contrast, partial orientation of NPs along the LC director appears to be an aligning factor for the surrounding LC molecules and provides a positive feedback for the nematic ordering.

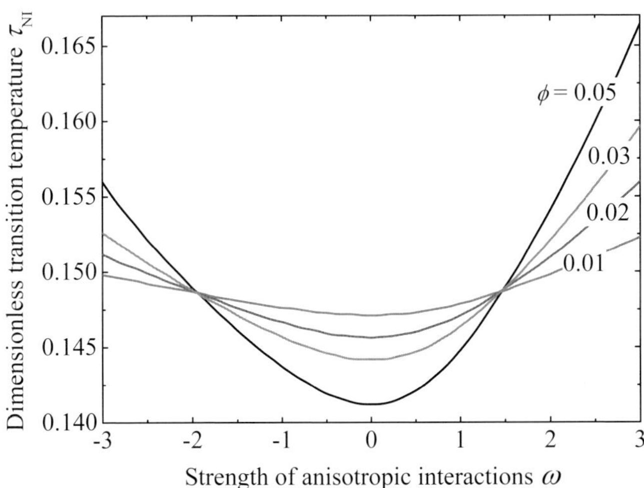

Fig. 2. Isotropic-nematic transition temperature as function of nanoparticle anisotropy for several values of nanoparticle concentration ϕ.

Therefore the nematic ordering improves and the transition temperature increases. At certain values of the NP anisotropy this effect can compensate the negative "dilution" effect, and then the main LC thermodynamic properties remain almost constant independently of the NP concentration. In general, the behavior of a particular composite material is determined by the competition of "dilution" and "orientation" effects.

2.4. *Softening of the first order N-I transition*

Let us now consider the temperature profiles of the LC order parameter S and NP order parameter S_p. As shown in the previous subsection, for small anisotropy, the presence of NPs mainly results in a renormalization of the transition temperature, while the nematic order parameter S does not experience any qualitative changes. In contrast, for stronger NP anisotropy, NPs may significantly affect the transition scenario. Several examples of such behavior are shown in Figs. 3 and 4, where the profiles are presented for $\omega = 3$ and $\omega = -3$, respectively, and for several values of the concentration ϕ between 0 to 0.1. For an easier comparison, we plot the order parameters as functions of the relative temperature measured from the phase transition point. Clearly, the presence of strongly anisotropic NPs considerably softens the first order phase transition, and at larger NP concentration and anisotropy the profile $S(T)$ becomes very similar to that characteristic for a second order phase transition.

Comparing the behavior of S and S_p one concludes that they tend to follow qualitatively the proportionality given by Eq. (21). The latter cannot be applied here directly, but the main features remain valid: larger S corresponds to larger $|S_p|$, and sign reversal of ω reverses the sign of S_p.

A considerable softening of the first-order nematic-isotropic transition, in the presence of anisotropic NPs, predicted by the theory can be considered as fingerprint of the orientation order effect of such NPs on the LC matrix. One notes that this softening remarkably resembles the softening due to alignment of short molecular axes which has been predicted recently in the theory of biaxial nematics.[38] Therefore one expects that this may be a general feature of the nematic-isotropic phase transition in systems with additional degrees of freedom, which can be modified/ordered by the conventional uniaxial nematic ordering. Such a softening of the nematic-isotropic transition has not been described in Ref. 11 because the phenomenological theory developed there accounts for the orientational order of the NPs only to the lowest order.

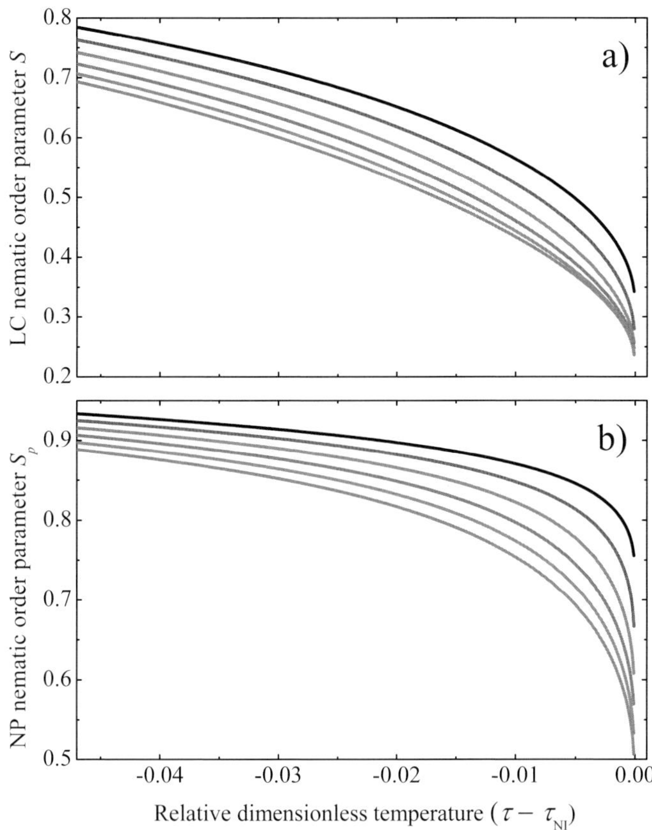

Fig. 3.   Temperature dependencies of the nematic order parameters of LC (a) and NP (b) for $\xi = 0.5$, $\omega = 3$ and $\phi = 0, 0.02, 0.04, 0.06, 0.08, 0.1$ (from the upper to lower curves respectively).

2.5.   *Comparison with existing experimental data*

Although there exist relatively few experimental studies of the effect of NPs on the phase behavior of LCs, we believe that our results are in line with the main established facts. For example, the "dilution"-type decrease of the transition temperature has been found in nematic LC polymers doped with isotropic (at least on average) silver NPs (see Fig. 3 of Ref. 21), in a typical nematic LC doped with gold NPs with the diameter of 3–5 nm and volume fraction of $10^{-4} - 10^{-3}$ (see Table of Ref. 22), in LCs doped with spherical aerosil particles[23,24] and in dye doped nematics and polymer dispersed nematic LCs (see Table 1 of Ref. 39).

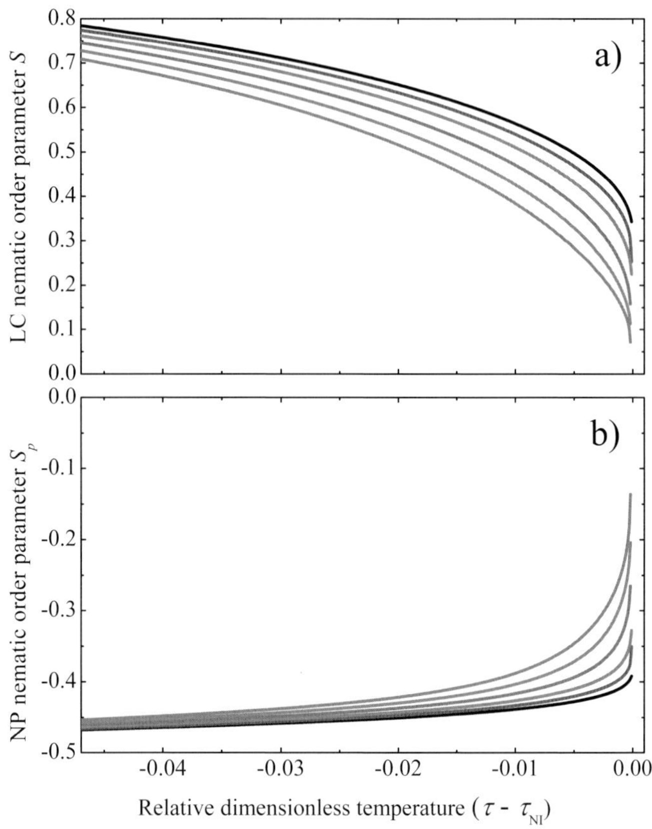

Fig. 4.   The same as in Fig. 3 for the negative NP anisotropy $\omega = -3$.

An example of substantially anisotropic NPs are carbon nanotubes which are known to promote the nematic order and increase the transition temperature.[25]   The increase of the N-I transition temperature by 3-4 degrees has also been observed in nematics doped with large magnetic nanorods of the average diameter of 40 nm and the average aspect ratio of 10 (see Table 1 of Ref. 26). Also it has been shown experimentally that ferroelectric $Sn_2P_2S_6$ or $BaTiO_3$ nanoparticles at low concentration ($< 1\%$) enhance the orientational order parameter of the host liquid crystal and increase the transition temperature by about 5 K.[9,10]

Very recently a detailed experimental study of the effect of the shape anisotropy of magnetic NPs on the N-I phase transition has been undertaken[40] inspired by the theoretical results presented in Ref. 27. The LC was doped with spherical and rod-like magnetic particles of different size and the measurements have been made for different volume concentrations of NPs. It has been shown that the variation of the phase transition temperature with the increasing the NP concentration depends significantly on the NP shape anisotropy. In full agreement with the theoretical conclusions presented above, ferronematics doped with rod-like magnetic NPs are characterized by a higher N_I transition temperature T_{NI} in comparison with the host nematic or the same nematic LC doped with spherical NPs.

In Ref. 41, the effects of the cis and trans forms of 4-OMephenylazobenzene at 1% and 7% mole fraction on the order and stability of the nematic phase of the 5CB LC were studied using the ESR spin probe technique. One notes that in the trans form the dye has approximately the same dimension as the 5CB molecule, and does not influence significantly the nematic ordering of the host. In contrast, the cis isomer is plate-like, i.e. it is characterized by negative anisotropy, using the terminology adopted here. As shown in Fig. 4 of Ref. 41, the jump of the nematic order parameter at the N-I transition point is decreasing with the increasing concentration of cis isomers, and the order parameter becomes more temperature dependent. This behavior corresponds to the results presented in this section which demonstrate a similar softening of the transition.

3. Nematic-isotropic separation in liquid crystals doped with spherical nanoparticles

3.1. *Simple molecular theory*

Let us consider a nematic LC doped with small amount of spherical NPs. In the appropriate molecular theory one has to take into account both isotropic and anisotropic interactions between LC molecules, isotropic interactions between LC molecules and spherical NPs, and also isotropic interactions between NPs themselves.[33] Then the system can be characterized by the following total interaction potential averaged over all molecule/particle positions:

$$H = \frac{1}{2}\sum_{ij}[V_{mm}(\mathbf{a}_i \cdot \mathbf{a}_j) + U_{nn} + U_{nm} + U_{mm}], \tag{28}$$

where U_{nn}, U_{mm} and U_{nm} are the average isotropic interaction potential between NPs , LC molecules and between a NP and a LC molecule, respectively. $V_{mm}(\mathbf{a}_i \cdot \mathbf{a}_j)$ is the anisotropic interaction potential between LC molecules which depends on the unit vectors $\mathbf{a}_i$ and $\mathbf{a}_j$ in the direction of the primary axis of the molecules i and j, respectively.

In the mean field approximation, the free energy of the nematic phase can be written in the form (see, for example, Ref. 42).

$$\frac{1}{V}F_{\mathrm{N}} = k_B T \rho_n (\ln \rho_n - 1) + k_B T \rho_m (\ln \rho_m - 1)$$
$$- \frac{1}{2}\rho_n^2 U_{nn} - \frac{1}{2}\rho_m^2 U_{mm} + \rho_m \rho_n U_{mn}$$
$$+ \frac{1}{2}\rho_m^2 \int V_{mm}(\mathbf{a}_i \cdot \mathbf{a}_j) f_m(\mathbf{a}_i) f_m(\mathbf{a}_j) d\mathbf{a}_i d\mathbf{a}_j$$
$$+ k_B T \int f_m(\mathbf{a}) \ln f_m(\mathbf{a}) d\mathbf{a}, \tag{29}$$

where $f_m(\mathbf{a})$ is the orientational distribution function of the mesogenic molecules, and ρ_m and ρ_n are the number densities of the mesogenic molecules and NPs correspondingly.

The function $V_{mm}(\mathbf{a}_i \cdot \mathbf{a}_j)$ can be expanded in Legendre polynomials $P_n(\mathbf{a}_i \cdot \mathbf{a}_j)$ taking into account the first nonpolar term which is responsible for the nematic ordering:

$$V_{mm}(\mathbf{a}_i \cdot \mathbf{a}_j) \approx U_0 + J P_2(\mathbf{a}_i \cdot \mathbf{a}_j). \tag{30}$$

Here $P_2(x) = 3x^2/2 - 1/3$ is the second Legendre polynomial.

Substituting this expansion into Eq. (29) one obtains the following Maier-Saupe type free energy of the nematic composite:

$$\frac{1}{V}F_{\mathrm{N}} = k_B T \rho_n (\ln \rho_n - 1) + k_B T \rho_m (\ln \rho_m - 1)$$
$$- \frac{1}{2}\rho_n^2 U_{nn} - \frac{1}{2}\rho_m^2 U_{mm} + \rho_m \rho_n U_{mn}$$
$$+ \frac{1}{2}\rho_m^2 J S^2 k_B T \int f_m(\mathbf{a}) \ln f_m(\mathbf{a}) d\mathbf{a}, \tag{31}$$

where S is the nematic order parameter of the mesogenic molecules which is expressed as:

$$S = \int P_2(\mathbf{a} \cdot \mathbf{n}) f_m(\mathbf{a}) d\mathbf{a}, \tag{32}$$

where $\mathbf{n}$ is the nematic director. Minimizing the free energy (31) with respect to the orientational distribution function $f_m(\mathbf{a})$ and substituting the equilibrium expression for $f_m(\mathbf{a})$ back into Eq. (31) one obtains:

$$\frac{1}{V}F_{\mathrm{N}} = k_B T \rho_n (\ln \rho_n - 1) + k_B T \rho_m (\ln \rho_m - 1)$$
$$- \frac{1}{2}\rho_n^2 U_{nn} - \frac{1}{2}\rho_m^2 U_{mm} + \rho_m \rho_n U_{mn} - \frac{1}{2}\rho_m^2 J S^2 - k_B T \ln Z, \tag{33}$$

where

$$Z_N = \int_0^\pi \exp[-\beta\rho_m JSP_2(\cos\gamma)]\sin\gamma d\gamma, \tag{34}$$

and where the nematic order parameter S satisfies the following self-consistent equation:

$$S = \frac{1}{Z_N}\int_0^\pi P_2(\cos\gamma)\exp[-\beta\rho_m JSP_2(\cos\gamma)]\sin\gamma d\gamma, \tag{35}$$

The free energy of the isotropic phase is obtained by setting $S = 0$:

$$\frac{1}{V}F_{\mathrm{I}} = k_B T\rho_n(\ln\rho_n - 1) + k_B T\rho_m(\ln\rho_m - 1)$$
$$- \frac{1}{2}\rho_n^2 U_{nn} - \frac{1}{2}\rho_m^2 U_{mm} + \rho_m\rho_n U_{mn}. \tag{36}$$

3.2. *Nematic-isotropic phase separation*

One notes that the concentration of NPs in the nematic phase is generally different from that in the coexisting isotropic phase, and may be strongly temperature dependent. The coexistence between the nematic and the isotropic phases in the system under consideration is possible only if the chemical potentials of both NPs and mesogenic molecules are the same in the two phases. The pressure must also be the same in the two phases. However, for incompressible LCs only the equations for the chemical potentials are relevant that is $\mu_{nI} = \mu_{nN}$ and $\mu_{mI} = \mu_{mN}$ where μ_{nI} and μ_{nN} are the chemical potentials of the NPs in the isotropic and in the nematic phase, respectively, and μ_{mI} and μ_{mN} are the corresponding chemical potentials of the mesogenic molecules.

Using the well known general equation for the chemical potential one obtains the following system of two simultaneous equations

$$\frac{1}{V_I}\frac{\partial F_I}{\partial\rho_n} = \frac{1}{V_N}\frac{\partial F_N}{\partial\rho_n}, \quad \frac{1}{V_I}\frac{\partial F_I}{\partial\rho_m} = \frac{1}{V_N}\frac{\partial F_N}{\partial\rho_m}. \tag{37}$$

Substituting Eqs. (36) and (33) for the free energies of the isotropic and the nematic phase into (72) one obtains the following equations:

$$\ln\frac{\rho_{mN}}{\rho_{mI}} = U_1(\rho_{mN} - \rho_{mI}) + U_{12}(\rho_{nN} - \rho_{nB}) + \ln Z_N, \tag{38}$$

and

$$\ln\frac{\rho_{nN}}{\rho_{nI}} = U_2(\rho_{nN} - \rho_{nI}) + U_{12}(\rho_{mN} - \rho_{mI}), \tag{39}$$

where we have introduced the non dimensional interaction constants $U_1 = U_{mm}/(kT_B)$, $U_2 = U_{nn}^{\mathrm{eff}}/(kT_B)$, $U_{12} = U_{nm}^{\mathrm{eff}}/(kT_B)$ and the number densities of the mesogenic molecules, ρ_{mI} and ρ_{mN}, and NPs, ρ_{nI} and ρ_{nN}, in the isotropic and nematic phases correspondingly.

Neglecting a small density change at the transition, the number densities of both NPs and mesogenic groups in the nematic and in the isotropic phase can be expressed in terms of the volume fraction ϕ_i of NPs in the corresponding phase i:

$$\rho_{ni} = \rho_{n0}\phi_i, \quad \rho_{mi} = \rho_{m0}(1 - \phi_i), \tag{40}$$

where $i = N, I$, ρ_{m0} is approximately equal to the number density of the mesogenic groups in the pure LC and ρ_{n0} can be estimated as $\rho_{n0} \sim 1/v_p$ where v_p is the NP volume.

Now Eq. (38) and Eq. (39) can be expressed in terms of the two variables ϕ_N and ϕ_I:

$$\ln \frac{1 - \phi_N}{1 - \phi_I} = w_1(\phi_I - \phi_N) + \ln Z_N, \tag{41}$$

$$\ln \frac{\phi_I}{\phi_N} = w_2(\phi_I - \phi_N), \tag{42}$$

where

$$w_1 = (\rho_{m0}U_1 - \rho_{n0}U_{12}), \quad w_2 = (\rho_{n0}U_2 - \rho_{m0}U_{12}). \tag{43}$$

One notes that Eq. (41) contain only two constants w_1, w_2, and it can readily be shown that the phase coexistence is possible only if $w_2 > 1$. If the isotropic attraction between NPs and mesogenic molecules is much stronger than that between the mesogenic molecules, the inequality $\rho_{n0}U_{12} > \rho_{m0}U_1$ is satisfied and hence $w_1 < 0$.

Numerical solution of Eqs. (41, 42) together with Eq. (34) and the self-consistent Eq. (35) for the nematic order parameter is significantly simplified if the volume fraction of NPs is sufficiently small in both phases, that is $\phi_I \ll 1$ and $\phi_N \ll 1$. In this case Eq. (41) is simplified as:

$$(1 - w_1)(\phi_I - \phi_N) = \ln Z_N, \tag{44}$$

One notes also that the partition function Z_N is independent of ϕ_I, and therefore ϕ_I can be excluded from the system of simultaneous equations for $\phi_I \ll 1$ and $\phi_N \ll 1$ which results in a single equation for ϕ_N:

$$Z_N^{w_2/(1-w_1)} = 1 + \frac{\ln Z_N}{\phi_N(1 - w_1)} \tag{45}$$

Now ϕ_N can be found by solving Eq. (45) numerically, and ϕ_I can then be evaluated in terms of ϕ_N as:

$$\phi_I = \phi_N + \frac{\ln Z_N}{1 - w_1} \tag{46}$$

Naturally, the volume fractions of NPs in the nematic and the isotropic phases are not completely independent. Indeed, in the experiment one normally controls the total number of NPs N_n in the volume V which yields the average volume fraction of NPs ϕ. It follows from the conservation of the total number of NPs that $\phi V = \phi_I V_I + \phi_N V_N$ where $V = V_I + V_N$ is the total volume of the system. On the other hand, solutions of the Eqs. (41) and (42) are independent of ϕ. From these equations one obtains the following expressions for the volumes V_N and V_I:

$$V_I = V\frac{\phi - \phi_I}{\phi_I - \phi_N}, \qquad V_N = V\frac{\phi_N - \phi}{\phi_I - \phi_N}. \tag{47}$$

One can readily see from Eq. (47) that the phase coexistence is possible only if $\phi_N < \phi < \phi_I$ as $\phi_N < \phi_I$. Taking into account that ϕ_N and ϕ_I are independent of ϕ, one concludes that if ϕ is outside the interval (ϕ_N, ϕ_I), the phase coexistence is impossible and only one phase may be stable at a given temperature. This condition should be used as an additional constraint imposed on the solutions of the Eqs. (41) and (42).

Finally, coexisting nematic and isotropic phases are globally stable only if the total free energy of the phase-separated system is lower than the free energy of both isotropic and nematic homogeneous phases. This is the second independent condition which should be taken into account in the consideration of the physical meaning of the formal solutions of the Eqs. (41) and (42) This condition can be expressed as:

$$\frac{F_{NI}^{\text{sep}} - F_{\text{hom}}}{V k_B T} = \frac{1}{V k_B T}\left[\frac{V_I}{V}F_I(\phi_I) + \frac{V_N}{V}F_N(\phi_N) - F_{I,N}(\phi)\right] < 0, \tag{48}$$

where V_I and V_N are given by Eq. (47) and the free energy densities $F_I(\phi)$ and $F_N(\phi)$ can be expressed using Eqs. (33, 36, 40):

$$F_I(\phi)/V k_B T = \rho_{n0}\phi \ln\phi + \rho_{m0}(1 - \phi)\ln(1 - \phi)$$
$$- \frac{1}{2}\rho_{n0}^2\phi^2 U_2 - \frac{1}{2}\rho_{m0}^2(1 - \phi)^2 U_1 + \rho_{m0}\rho_{n0}\phi(1 - \phi)U_{12}, \tag{49}$$

$$F_N(\phi)/V k_B T = F_I(\phi)/V k_B T$$
$$- \frac{1}{2}\rho_{m0}^2(1 - \phi)^2 J^* S_m^2 - \rho_{m0}(1 - \phi)\ln Z_N, \tag{50}$$

where $J^* = J/k_B T$. Note that for the separated state in Eq. (48) the nematic order parameter is $S(\phi_N)$ in the nematic phase, which coexists with the isotropic one, and is given by Eq. (35) with $\rho_m = \rho_{m0}(1 - \phi_N)$ and $Z_N = Z_N(\phi_N)$. At the same time, the order parameter of the homogeneous nematic phase $S(\phi)$ is given by the same equation with $\rho_m = \rho_{m0}(1 - \phi)$ and $Z_N = Z_N(\phi)$.

3.3. *Phase diagrams*

Let us first consider Eqs. (41) and (42) which enable one to determine the molar fractions of NPs in coexisting phases as functions of temperature. A typical numerical solution of these equations for moderately strong interactions between NPs and mesogenic molecules is presented in Fig. 5. One notes that there exists a bifurcation point which corresponds to a critical temperature T_c. At higher temperatures there is no solution, that is the phase separation is impossible, and directly below the critical temperature the difference between molar fractions of NPs in the two phases is fairly small.

It should be noted, however, that in the general case only part of this solution corresponds to an actual physical state of the system. As discussed in the previous subsection, Eqs. (41) and (42) do not depend on the average molar fraction of NPs ϕ which can be actually controlled in experiments. At the same time, the value of ϕ must lie between the two branches in Fig. 5, as $\phi_N < \phi < \phi_I$. If ϕ is different from the critical value of ϕ_c at the bifurcation point, the system separates into the nematic and the isotropic phases with finite difference of NP molar fractions and finite volumes of both phases. In this general case the separation occurs at some temperature T_{sep} which

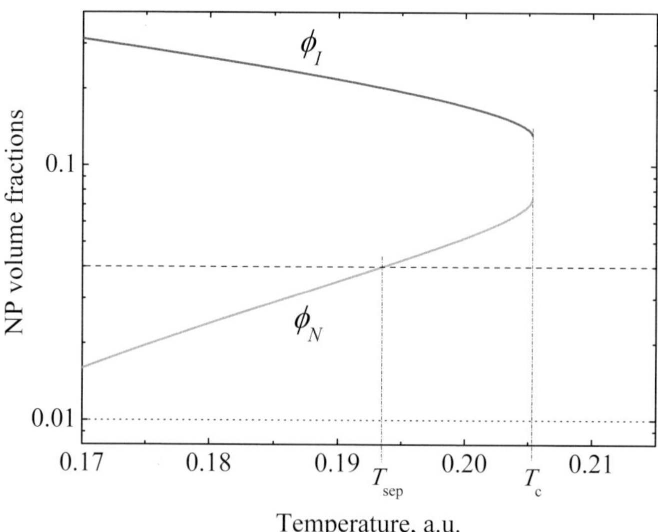

Fig. 5. Nanoparticle volume fractions in coexisting isotropic (upper curve) and nematic (lower curve) phases of the composites with $w_1 = -5$, $w_2 = 10$.

is below the bifurcation temperature T_c, and which is an intersection of the horizontal line ϕ and one of the curves representing $\phi_N(T)$ or $\phi_I(T)$ (see the intersection of $\phi_N(T)$ and the horizontal dashed line $\phi = 0.04$ in Fig. 5).

In principle, even if $T < T_{sep}$ one cannot finally conclude that the system phase separates, because the separated state is globally stable only if the total free energy of the separated system is lower than that of any homogeneous phase at the same temperature and NP concentration (see Eq. (48)). One notes also that if the value of ϕ is too small or too large (see the dotted line $\phi = 0.01$ in Fig. 5), there may be no intersection at all, that is the condition $\phi_N < \phi < \phi_I$ is not satisfied at any temperature and, therefore, the system never phase separates.

The solutions for ϕ_N and ϕ_I together with Eq. (48) have been used to compose the temperature-concentration phase diagram presented in Fig. 6 for the same values of the interaction constants w_1 and w_2 as in Fig. 5. One notes that there is no phase separation at sufficiently low concentration of NPs. In this domain, the N-I transition temperature decreases with the increasing ϕ due to the "dilution" effect considered in Sec. 2. Above a certain critical concentration, the N-T phase transition is accompanied by the separation between the isotropic and the nematic phase, and the two

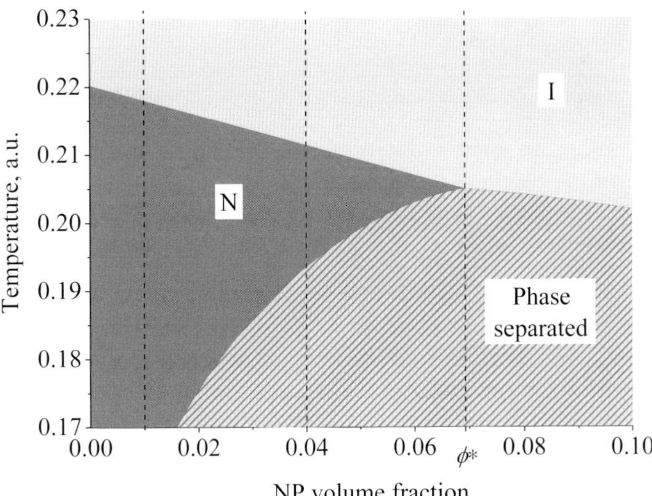

Fig. 6. Phase diagram of the composite calculated from the mean-field theory with interaction constants $w_1 = -5$ and $w_2 = 10$.

phases coexist over a significant temperature interval. In this region the transition temperature into the phase-separated state decreases more slowly than the N-I transition temperature at low concentrations. It is interesting to note also, that in this case there exists another critical value ϕ^* of the NP molar fraction shown in Fig. 6. When $\phi > \phi^*$, the system undergoes a direct transition from the isotropic into the the phase separated state in which the isotropic and the nematic phases coexist. In contrast, when $\phi < \phi^*$, the system first undergoes a transition into the homogeneous nematic phase and then phase separates at some lower temperature.

The solution of Eqs. (41) and (42) and the corresponding phase diagram for a nematic composite with very strong interaction between NPs and the mesogenic molecules are presented in Fig. 7 and Fig. 8 correspondingly. In this case the temperature range of the coexistence between the nematic and the isotropic phase is more narrow, and there is only a relatively small window of NP concentration when the separation takes place at all. One notes also, that in this case a reentrant homogeneous nematic phase may occur within a narrow interval of NP molar fraction.

On the other hand, for weaker interactions between NPs and meso-genic molecules (smaller absolute values of w_1), the region of phase sep-arated state expands considerably (compare Figs. 6 and 9). Decreasing

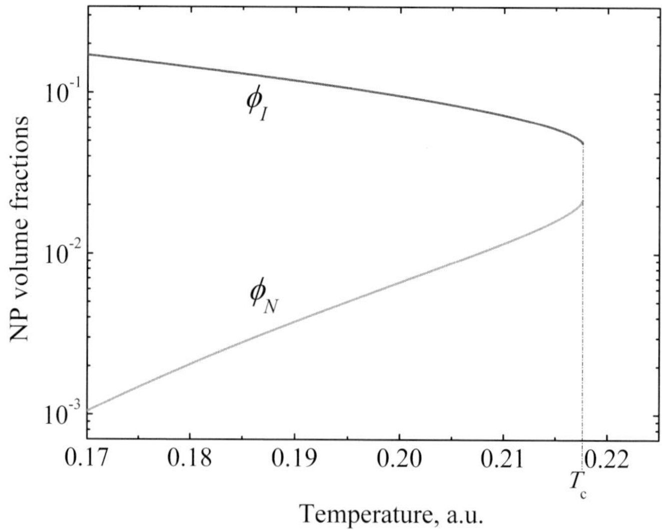

Fig. 7.   The same as in Fig. 5 with $w_1 = -10$ and $w_2 = 30$.

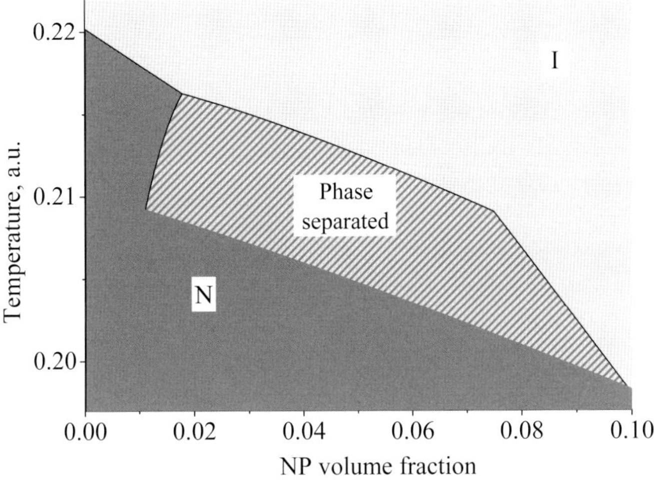

Fig. 8.   The same as in Fig. 6 with $w_1 = -10$ and $w_2 = 30$.

$|w_1|$ results in a proportionate decrease of the critical total concentration ϕ^*. Additionally, in this case the phase separated state dominates over the low-temperature part of the phase diagram and even at small total NP concentrations ϕ the homogeneous nematic phase exists only in a finite temperature range as illustrated by Fig. 9.

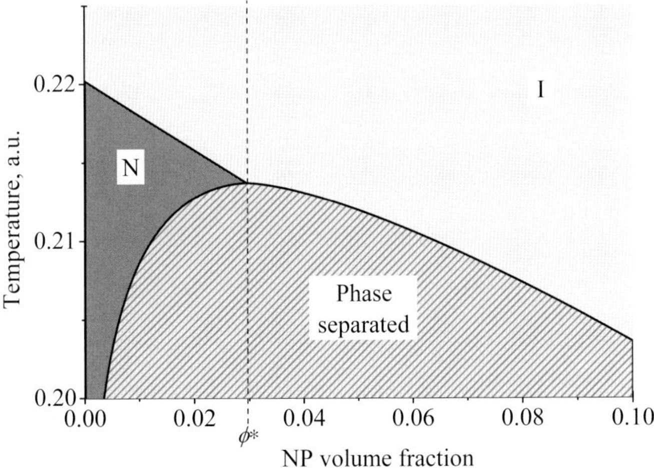

Fig. 9.   The same as in Fig. 6 with $w_1 = -1$ and $w_2 = 10$.

These results appear to be rather unusual and are different from what one may expect from the behavior of nematics doped with small nonmesogenic dopants. In particular, the temperature range of the coexisting nematic and isotropic phases may be very large. It is well known, that in mixtures of LCs the N-I coexistence region is typically of the order of 1-2 degrees and can often be neglected. In contrast, the theory indicates that in nematic nano-composites the coexistence region may be as broad as the nematic phase itself. Secondly, the phase separation does not occur at sufficiently low concentration of NPs because the entropy of mixing dominates the behavior of the system. Moreover, within a certain range of concentrations of NPs the composite may undergo a direct transition from the isotropic phase into the phase separated state, while at other concentrations of NPs the system first undergoes a transition into the homogeneous nematic phase and then into the phase separated state at lower temperature.

This unexpected behavior of nematic nano-composites is related to the fact that the properties of NPs differ very much from those of typical mesogenic molecules. In particular, the isotropic interaction between NPs and mesogenic groups (and between NPs themselves) is expected to be significantly stronger than that between mesogenic molecules. This is mainly due to the large effective volume of a typical spherical NP which includes also organic chains attached to the surface of metal or semiconductor core.

Isotropic-nematic phase separation has been observed in a few anisotropic soft matter systems[43,44] but it has not been studied in detail experimentally so far. Very recently, however, a two-step decrease of both the N-I transition temperature and the transition heat in few polymer and low molecular weight LCs doped with quantum dots[32] has been interpreted assuming that the system separated into the isotropic and the nematic phase with different concentrations of quantum dots. A different type of phase separation has recently been observed in Refs. 45 and 46. It has been shown experimentally that gold NPs with mesogenic coatings form reversible networks composed of nematic droplets accompanied by disclination lines and loops as a result of a specific phase separation which results in an enrichment of the NPs at the nematic-isotropic liquid interfaces.

Finally it should be noted that the theory of phase separation in LC nano-composites is at its rudimentary stage and there is much to be done here. Recently phase separation effects in nematics doped with large colloidal particles have been studied theoretically in Refs. 47–49. In particular, very broad N-I coexistence region has been found in Refs. 47 and 48 using simple mean-field theory of mixtures. This theory, however, is based on a different (and rather oversimplified) model interaction potential which is more suitable for large colloidal particles.

4. Chain formation and dielectric anisotropy of nematic nanocomposites

4.1. *Simple theory of chain formation*

Nano-particles may form dimers and even long chains in a solution if the interparticle interaction potential is sufficiently anisotropic and strong. In this section we assume that spherical NPs possess relatively large permanent electric dipoles. In this case the minimum of the dipole-dipole interaction energy is achieved when the dipoles of the two adjacent NPs and parallel to each other and to the interparticle vector $\mathbf{r}_{12}$. If this potential minimum is sufficiently deep, the NPs form polar chains which may significantly contribute to the dielectric anisotropy of the nematic composite.

The nematic composite with chains of NPs is characterized by the distribution of chain lengths which can be evaluated using the existing theory of chain formation in the system of polar spheres presented, for example, in Ref. 36. According to this theory, the number density of chains of length l (i.e. composed of l NPs) is expressed as:

$$\phi_l = v_p \rho_l = e^{l(U_0 + \Lambda)} e^{-U_0}, \tag{51}$$

where ϕ_l is the volume fraction of chains of length l, v_p is the NP volume and U_0 is the contact energy determined by the dipole-dipole interaction between NPs:

$$U_0 = \ln\left(\frac{\pi\sigma^3 e^{2\lambda}}{18v\lambda^3}\right). \tag{52}$$

Here $\lambda = \mu^2/k_B T \sigma^3$ and σ is the NP diameter and the NP volume v has been introduced for dimensional correctness.

In Eq. (51), Λ is the Lagrange multiplier (chemical potential) which is determined from the conservation rule for NPs:

$$\rho_p = \sum_{l=1}^{\infty} l\rho_l, \tag{53}$$

where, as above, ρ_p is the total NP number density which is controlled experimentally.

Substituting Eq. (51) into Eq. (53) and performing the summation one obtains:

$$\rho_p = v_p^{-1} \frac{e^{\Lambda}}{(1 - e^{U_0 + \Lambda})^2}. \tag{54}$$

Accordingly,

$$1 - e^{U_0 + \Lambda} = \frac{-1 + \sqrt{1 + 4\eta}}{2\eta}, \tag{55}$$

where $\eta = v_p \rho_p e^{U_0}$. Thus the value of the chemical potential Λ is mainly determined by the order of η.

Finally, one can readily obtain the following expression for the number density of chains of length l:

$$\rho_l = v_p^{-1} e^{-U_0} \left(1 - \frac{-1 + \sqrt{1 + 4\eta}}{2\eta}\right)^l. \tag{56}$$

4.2. *High frequency permittivity of a nematic composite*

At sufficiently high (optical) frequencies the polarization is mainly determined by induced dipoles created by the electric field. Orientational fluctuations of permanent dipoles make a minor contribution because the characteristic times of such fluctuations are much larger than the inverse optical frequency.[50] Relatively simple explicit expressions for the dielectric constant can be obtained in the molecular field approximation in the form of generalized Clausius-Mossotti relation[51] assuming that the composite nematic phase contains mesogenic molecules, NPs and chains of NPs of various lengths l:

$$(\hat{\epsilon} - 1)(\hat{\epsilon} + 2)^{-1} = \frac{4\pi}{3} \left(\langle \hat{\beta}_m \rangle \rho_m + \langle \hat{\beta}_{np} \rangle \rho_{np} + \sum_{l=2}^{\infty} \langle \hat{\beta}_l \rangle \rho_l \right), \tag{57}$$

where $\langle \hat{\beta}_m \rangle$, $\langle \hat{\beta}_{np} \rangle$ and $\langle \hat{\beta}_l \rangle$ are the average polarizabilities of mesogenic molecules, single NPs and chains of NPs of length l, respectively, and ρ_m, ρ_{np} and ρ_l are the corresponding number densities.

Introducing the long axes of the molecules $\mathbf{a}_m$ and the unit vectors of the chain directions $\mathbf{a}_l$, and using the corresponding scalar nematic order parameters S_α one obtains the following expressions for the averaged polarizability tensors:

$$\langle \hat{\beta}_\alpha \rangle = \bar{\beta}_\alpha \hat{I} + S_\alpha \Delta \beta_\alpha \mathbf{n} \otimes \mathbf{n}, \tag{58}$$

where the isotropic polarizabilities are expressed as $\bar{\beta}_\alpha = \beta_{\alpha\perp} + \Delta\beta_\alpha(1 - S_\alpha)/3$.

Assuming that moderate dielectric anisotropies $\Delta\beta_\alpha$ give rise to a relatively small anisotropy of the composite permittivity $\Delta\varepsilon$, Eq. (57) can be expanded and simplified as follows:

$$\Delta\varepsilon = \frac{4\pi}{9}(\varepsilon_\perp + 2)^2 \left(\Delta\beta_m \rho_m S_m + \sum_{l=2}^{\infty} \langle\Delta\beta_l\rangle \rho_l \right), \tag{59}$$

while the isotropic part of the composite permittivity satisfies the scalar Clausius-Mossotti relation

$$\frac{\varepsilon_\perp - 1}{\varepsilon_\perp + 2} = \frac{4\pi}{3} \left(\beta_{m\perp}\rho_m + \beta_{np}\rho_{np} + \sum_{l=2}^{\infty} \beta_{l\perp}\rho_l \right), \tag{60}$$

which includes also the contribution from the isotropic non-aggregated NPs.

One notes that Eqs. (59) and (60) are not expected to be quantitatively precise but they can be used to estimate the dependence of the refractive indices of the nematic composite on the concentration of NPs, their aggregation and ordering provided that the effective polarizability of a NP in the nematic solvent is known.

4.3. *Polarizability of a single chain*

Generally, the NP contribution to the composite permittivity (59) and (60) is twofold: both aggregated and non-aggregated NPs affect $\varepsilon_\perp$ while only those NPs which are aggregated into chains contribute to $\Delta\varepsilon$.

To sum over chains of different lengths in Eq. (59) one needs to know the quantity $\langle\Delta\beta_l\rangle$ which can be evaluated as the average dielectric anisotropy of a chain of l spheres (with the permittivity ε_{np}) immersed into a medium with the permittivity $\varepsilon_\perp$. Although the exact solution of such a problems can be obtained only numerically, one can obtain useful analytical estimates[52] using a few realistic approximations. Thus taking into account the strongest dipole interactions between NPs and restricting the calculations to the nearest-neighbor contributions (already the next-nearest neighbor ones are at least eight times smaller) and introducing the single NP dielectric polarizability $\beta_1 = 1/8 \, \sigma^3(\varepsilon_{np} - \varepsilon_\perp)/(\varepsilon_{np} + 2\varepsilon_\perp)$ one can express the dipole moment of the k-th NP in the chain of the total length l as

$$\mathbf{p}_k = \beta_1 \mathbf{E} + \beta_1 \hat{T}_{k,k-1}\mathbf{p}_{k-1} + \beta_1 \hat{T}_{k,k+1}\mathbf{p}_{k+1}, \tag{61}$$

where

$$\hat{T}_{k,k\pm1} = (3\mathbf{u}_{k,k\pm1} \otimes \mathbf{u}_{k,k\pm1} - \mathbf{1}) \, \sigma^{-3}, \tag{62}$$

is the non-singular part of the dipole-dipole propagator, $\mathbf{u}_{k,k\pm 1}$ are the unit vectors between the centers of the adjacent NPs and the following natural condition is satisfied $\hat{T}_{1,0} = \hat{T}_{l,l+1} = 0$ at the chain ends.

As shown below, the effect of chain formation on high-frequency permittivity is rather moderate, and one can solve the system (61) by iterations. While in the zeroth order (neglecting the NP interactions) one obtains merely $\mathbf{p}_k = \beta_1 \mathbf{E}$ and the chain remains dielectrically isotropic, the next iteration yields:

$$\mathbf{p}_k = \beta_1 \left(1 + \beta_1 \hat{T}_{k,k-1} + \beta_1 \hat{T}_{k,k+1}\right) \mathbf{E}. \tag{63}$$

Since the average chain direction is controlled by the overall composite nematic director $\mathbf{n}$, the averaged nearest-neighbor propagator reads

$$\langle \hat{T}_{k,k\pm 1} \rangle = S(3\mathbf{n} \otimes \mathbf{n} - \mathbf{1}) \, \sigma^{-3}, \tag{64}$$

where we have again assumed that all the scalar nematic order parameters in the composite are equal.

Evaluating the average chain dipole moment as $\langle \mathbf{P}_l \rangle = \sum_{k=1}^{l} \langle \mathbf{p}_k \rangle$ one obtains the following expression for the overall average chain polarizability tensor

$$\langle \hat{\beta}_l \rangle = l\beta_1 \mathbf{1} + \frac{2}{\sigma^3}(l-1)\beta_1^2 S(3\mathbf{n} \otimes \mathbf{n} - \mathbf{1}). \tag{65}$$

The anisotropy of this polarizability is given by:

$$\langle \Delta \beta_l \rangle = \frac{6}{\sigma^3}(l-1)\beta_1^2 S. \tag{66}$$

4.4. *Contribution of polar chains to the dielectric anisotropy of the nematic composite*

Accordingly, the chain contribution to the composite permittivity anisotropy (59) is given by

$$\Delta \varepsilon_{\mathrm{ch}} = \frac{\pi}{24} \left[\frac{(\varepsilon_\perp + 2)(\varepsilon_{np} - \varepsilon_\perp)}{\varepsilon_{np} + 2\varepsilon_\perp} \right]^2 S\sigma^3 \sum_{l=2}^{\infty}(l-1)\rho_l. \tag{67}$$

Substituting the number densities (56) an using the summation rule

$$\sum_{l=2}^{\infty}(l-1)x^l = \frac{x^2}{(1-x)^2} \tag{68}$$

one can express the dielectric anisotropy in terms of the dimensionless NP density $\rho^* = \rho\sigma^3$ and the parameter λ:

$$\Delta \varepsilon_{\mathrm{ch}} = \frac{\pi}{24} \left[\frac{(\varepsilon_\perp + 2)(\varepsilon_{np} - \varepsilon_\perp)}{\varepsilon_{np} + 2\varepsilon_\perp} \right]^2 S\rho^* \delta_\eta. \tag{69}$$

where the function

$$\delta_\eta = 2 + \frac{1}{\eta} - \frac{4\eta}{(\sqrt{1+4\eta}-1)^2} \tag{70}$$

effectively describes the dependence on the NP chain formation as η is also expressed in terms of the non-dimensional parameters as $\eta = \pi\rho^* e^{2\lambda}/(18\lambda^3)$.

Representative profiles of the factor δ_η as functions of the NP coupling strength, which controls the chain formation, are presented in Fig. 10. One notes that for weaker coupling this factor is very small, as most of the NPs remain single here and do not contribute to the anisotropy. For stronger coupling, the average chain length increases which leads to a pronounced increase of the anisotropy. The saturation at $\delta_\eta \approx 1$ for strongly interacting NPs means that in this limit practically all NPs belong to long chains and contribute equally to the anisotropy. Evidently, for higher total NP concentrations this saturation occurs at smaller λ.

The variation of the high frequency dielectric anisotropy as a function of the NP concentration is illustrated by Fig. 11 for different values of the dipole-dipole interaction strength. One notes that this variation is approximately linear when the NP coupling is strong enough, i.e., when all the NPs are aggregated in long chains.

Generally, the high-frequency anisotropy is weak as the factor $\delta_\eta < 1$ is multiplied in Eq. (69) by a number of other small factors. Thus for the dielectric NPs with ε_{np} of the same sign and order of magnitude as $\varepsilon_\perp$ the

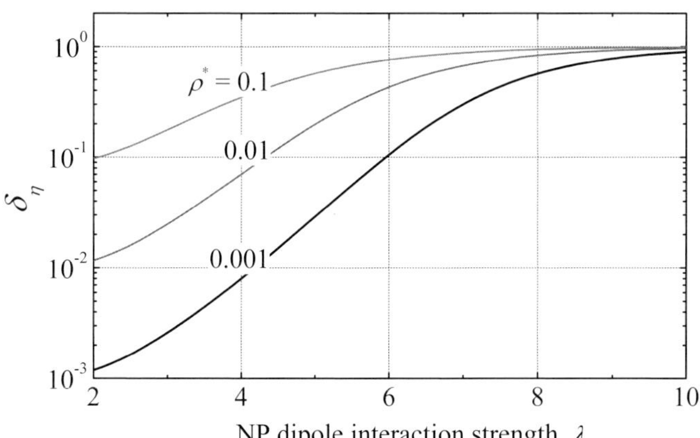

Fig. 10. The effect of chain formation on the high-frequency dielectric anisotropy of the composite: dependences of the factor δ_α given by Eq. (70) on the NP coupling strength for NP densities $\rho^* = 0.1$, 0.01 and 0.001 as indicated on the lines.

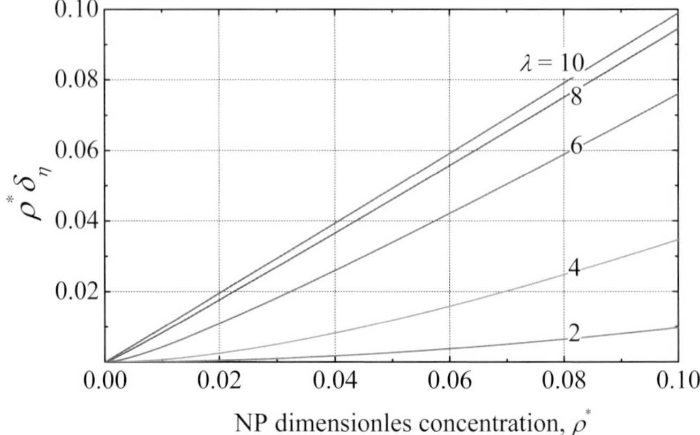

Fig. 11.   The effect of chain formation on the high-frequency dielectric anisotropy of the composite: dependences of the factor $\rho^*\delta_\eta$ in Eq. (69) on the NP concentration for the coupling strength λ varying from 2 to 10 as indicated on the lines.

factors in the square brackets are of the order of unity, while $S < 1$ and $\rho^* \ll 1$. On the other hand, the variation of δ_η by three orders of magnitude for low $\rho^* = 0.001$ in Fig. 10 suggests that this anisotropy can be employed as a sensitive tool for quantitative assessment of the NP chain formation in nematic composites.

4.5. *Low frequency dielectric constant of a strongly polar nematic composite*

Low frequency dielectric constant of the nematic phase composed of strongly polar molecules is mainly determined by the orientational fluctuations of permanent molecular dipoles while the molecular polarizability gives a much smaller contribution. Indeed, the static dielectric constant of a strongly polar nematic can be of the order of 100 while a typical contribution from the molecular polarizability is of the order of $3.$[50] In this case, the macroscopic polarization can be expressed as a sum of averaged molecular dipoles of all components α of the mixture in the unit volume:

$$\mathbf{P} = \sum_\alpha \rho_\alpha \langle \boldsymbol{\mu}_\alpha \rangle, \tag{71}$$

where $\boldsymbol{\mu}_\alpha$ is the permanent molecule/particle dipole of the component α.

In the static case, the average dipole can be expressed as:

$$\langle \boldsymbol{\mu}_\alpha \rangle = \int \boldsymbol{\mu}_\alpha f_\alpha(\theta) d\theta, \tag{72}$$

where $f_\alpha(\theta)$ is the one-particle distribution function which can be written in the following form in the mean-field approximation

$$f_\alpha(\theta) = Z^{-1} \exp\left[-(U_{\mathrm{MF},\alpha}(\theta) + (\boldsymbol{\mu}_\alpha \cdot \mathbf{E}))/(k_B T)\right]. \tag{73}$$

Here $U_{\mathrm{MF},\alpha}(\theta)$ is the mean-field potential for the component α, θ specifies the orientation of the particle/molecule and $\mathbf{E}$ is the external electric field.

The mean-field potential can be written in the form:

$$U_{\mathrm{MF},\alpha}(\theta_1) = \sum_\beta \int V_{\alpha,\beta}(\theta_1, \theta_2) f_\beta(\theta_2) d\theta_2, \tag{74}$$

where $V_{\alpha,\beta}(\theta_1, \theta_2)$ is the pair interaction potential between the components α and β.

Let us now assume that both mesogenic molecules and NPs are uniaxial and their permanent dipoles are parallel to the corresponding long axes. This is also valid for rigid chains of spherical dipolar NPs. In this case, the pair interaction potential V depends on the unit vectors $\mathbf{a}_1$ and $\mathbf{a}_2$ in the direction of the long axes of the molecules "1" and "2", respectively, and on the intermolecular vector $\mathbf{r}_{12}$, i.e. $V(1,2) = V(\mathbf{a}_1, \mathbf{r}_{12}, \mathbf{a}_2)$. The pair potential can now be written as a sum of the nonpolar and the polar parts, $V(1,2) = V_{np}(1,2) + V_{dd}(1,2)$, where the nonpolar potential $V_{np}(1,2)$ is an even function of $\mathbf{a}_1$ and $\mathbf{a}_2$ and where the polar potential $V_{dd}(1,2)$ is the electrostatic dipole-dipole interaction potential which can be expressed as:

$$V_{dd}(1,2) = \boldsymbol{\mu}_1 \cdot \hat{F}(\mathbf{r}_{12}) \cdot \boldsymbol{\mu}_2, \tag{75}$$

where the dipole-dipole propagator can be written in the form:

$$\hat{F}(\mathbf{r}_{12}) = \frac{4\pi}{3}\delta(\mathbf{r}_{12}) + \Theta(r_{12} - D)(\hat{I} - 3\mathbf{u} \otimes \mathbf{u})r_{12}^{-3}, \tag{76}$$

where $\mathbf{u} = \mathbf{r}_{12}/r_{12}$ and where $\Theta(r_{12} - D)$ is a step function which is equal to unity if $r_{12} > D$ and vanishes otherwise. One notes that the first term in Eq. (76) takes into account a singularity of the dipole-dipole potential at the origin (see a detailed discussion of the averaging of the dipole-dipole potential in Refs. 36 and 53).

Substituting Eq. (76) into Eqs. (75) and (74) and taking into account that the second term in Eq. (76) vanishes after integration over all $\mathbf{u}$, one obtains the final expression for the mean-field potential:

$$U_{\mathrm{MF},\alpha}(\theta) = U_\alpha^{(0)}(\theta) + \frac{4\pi}{3}(\boldsymbol{\mu}_\alpha \cdot \mathbf{P}), \tag{77}$$

Finally this mean-field potential can be substituted into the orientational distribution function (73) and expanding it in powers of the small electric field $\mathbf{E}$ and filed-induced polarization $\mathbf{P}$ one obtains:

$$f_\alpha(\theta) \approx f_\alpha^{(0)}\left(1 + \frac{4\pi}{3}\frac{\boldsymbol{\mu}_\alpha \cdot \mathbf{P}}{k_B T} - \frac{\boldsymbol{\mu}_\alpha \cdot \mathbf{E}}{k_B T}\right), \tag{78}$$

where the nonpolar distribution function $f_\alpha^{(0)}$ is determined by the nonpolar part $U_\alpha^{(0)}(\theta)$ of the mean field potential, that is $f_{0,\alpha} = Z_0^{-1} \exp\left[-U_\alpha^{(0)}(\theta)/(k_B T)\right]$.

Substituting Eq. (78) into Eqs. (72) and (71) one obtains the following linear equation for the macroscopic polarization $\mathbf{P}$:

$$P_i = \sum_\alpha \frac{\rho_\alpha}{k_B T} \langle \mu_{\alpha,i}\mu_{\alpha,j}\rangle_0 \left(\frac{4\pi}{3} P_j + E_j\right), \tag{79}$$

where the averaging $\langle \mu_{\alpha,i}\mu_{\alpha,j}\rangle_0$ is performed with the nonpolar orientational distribution function $f_\alpha^{(0)}$. As a result, one obtains the following expression for the dielectric polarizability tensor $\hat{\chi}$:

$$\hat{\chi} = \frac{\hat{\chi}_0}{1 - \frac{4\pi}{3}\hat{\chi}_0} \tag{80}$$

where

$$\hat{\chi}_0 = \sum_\alpha \frac{\rho_\alpha}{k_B T} \langle \boldsymbol{\mu}_\alpha \otimes \boldsymbol{\mu}_\alpha\rangle_0. \tag{81}$$

Taking into account that the dipole $\boldsymbol{\mu}_\alpha$ is parallel to the long axis $\mathbf{a}$ of the corresponding molecule one obtains:

$$\hat{\chi}_0 = \sum_\alpha \frac{\rho_\alpha\mu_\alpha^2}{k_B T} \langle \mathbf{a} \otimes \mathbf{a}\rangle_0 = \sum_\alpha \frac{\rho_\alpha\mu_\alpha^2}{k_B T} \left[S_\alpha(\mathbf{n} \otimes \mathbf{n} - 1/3) + 1/3\right]. \tag{82}$$

Here S_α is the nematic order parameter of the compound α in the mixture.

Let us consider the nematic composite in which the permanent dipoles of NPs are sufficiently large and larger than those of the mesogenic molecules. Then the main contribution to the low frequency dielectric constant of the nano-composite stems from the NPs and their chains and can be written using Eq. (81) as:

$$\hat{\varepsilon} \approx 1 + 4\pi\hat{\chi}_0 = 1 + 4\pi \sum_{l=1}^{\infty} \frac{\rho_l\mu_l^2}{k_B T} \left[S_l(\mathbf{n} \otimes \mathbf{n} - 1/3) + 1/3\right], \tag{83}$$

where μ_l is the total dipole of the chain of length l, ρ_l is the number density of chains of length l and S_l is the corresponding nematic order parameter.

One may assume that for short rigid chains of polar NPs the total dipole $\mu_l = l\mu$ where μ is the permanent dipole of a single NP. This assumption is obviously not valid for long flexible chains. However, the concentration of such chains is exponentially small and we will see below that for realistic values of the NP dipole only short chains ($l = 1 - 4$) make a significant contribution to the dielectric constant of the composite. In this approximation Eq. (83) yields the dielectric susceptibility anisotropy:

$$\Delta\chi = \frac{\mu^2}{k_B T} \sum_{l=1} l^2 \rho_l S_l.$$ (84)

By setting $S_l = S$ and substituting the number densities (56) one can perform the summation over chains of all lengths in Eq. (84). Indeed, using the summation rule

$$\sum_{l=1}^{\infty} l^2 x^l = \frac{x(1+x)}{(1-x)^3}$$ (85)

the low-frequency dielectric anisotropy can be expressed explicitly in terms ρ^* and λ:

$$\Delta\chi = 4\rho^* \lambda S \frac{4\eta^2 + 5\eta + 1 - (3\eta + 1)\sqrt{1 + 4\eta}}{\left(-1 + \sqrt{1 + 4\eta}\right)^3}.$$ (86)

In Fig. 12 the dielectric anisotropy given by Eq. (86) is presented for different NP molar fractions as a function of the parameter λ which describes the strength of the dipole-dipole interaction between NPs. For comparison we also present the corresponding variation $\Delta\tilde{\chi} = \lambda S \rho^*$ of the dielectric anisotropy of the composite without any chains, as well as the results of the partial summation in Eq. (84) which show the relative scale of contributions from chains of different lengths. One can see that the chain formation can modify the dielectric properties by orders of magnitude when the NP interaction (determined by the permanent dipole) is sufficiently strong. At the same time, for weak interaction, the effect of chains is practically negligible and the NPs respond to the electric field independently. For moderate interactions, there exists a noticeable area of λ, where the formation of short chains (dimers and trimers) contributes to $\Delta\chi$ considerably, while the effect of longer chains is practically absent.

One can readily see in Fig. 12 that the contributions from monomers and dimers (similar to that from monomers and l-mers for $l = 3, 4, 5$) first increases with the increasing dipolar strength λ, then reaches a maximum and finally begins to decrease. The decreasing stage corresponds to the range of λ which correspond to the formation of longer chains which make a predominant contribution to the dielectric anisotropy. In this range the contribution from dimers, trimers etc. decreases due to a decrease of the corresponding number densities. The increasing stage corresponds to the

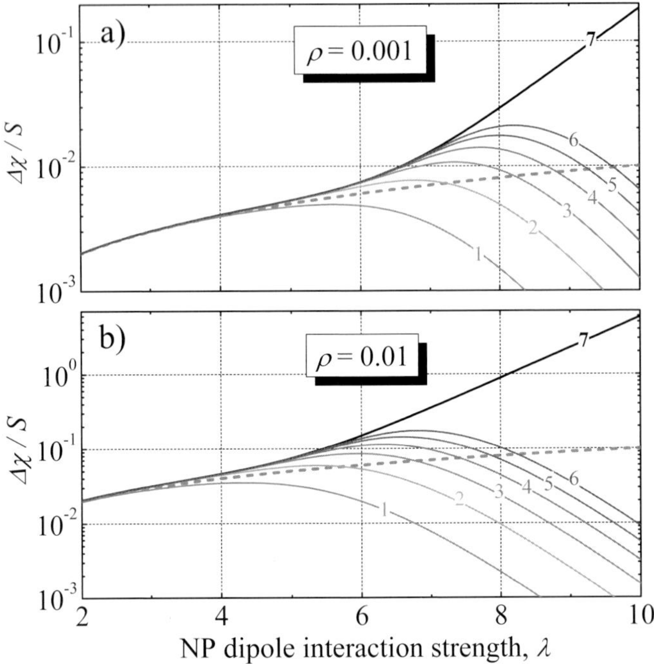

Fig. 12. Anisotropy of the low-frequency composite dielectric susceptibility as a function of NP coupling strength for NP densities $\rho^* = 0.001$ (a) and $\rho^* = 0.01$ (b). Solid lines $1 - 6$ depict results of partial summation in Eq. (84) neglecting chains with l higher than $1 - 6$ correspondingly. Solid line 7 represents the dependence (86), and the dashed line shows the anisotropy in the absence of chain formation.

range of smaller λ where the corresponding short chains make a predominant contribution.

Finally, the variation of the dielectric anisotropy as a function of the NP concentration for different values of the dipole-dipole interaction strength is presented in Fig. 13. Evidently, the increase of the NP concentration by an order of magnitude results in the increase of the dielectric anisotropy by several orders of magnitude depending on the value of the parameter λ. Thus one can readily see (compare also with Figs. 12a and 12b) that the experimentally observed increase of the dielectric constant[9,34] at very low NP number density $\rho = 10^{-2} - 10^{-3}$ can be explained by the effect of chain formation only if the dipole-dipole interaction strength is sufficiently high which is the case for ferroelectric NPs with large spontaneous polarization.

One notes that at present there is no direct experimental evidence of the existence of chains of NPs in nematic composites although a number of ex-

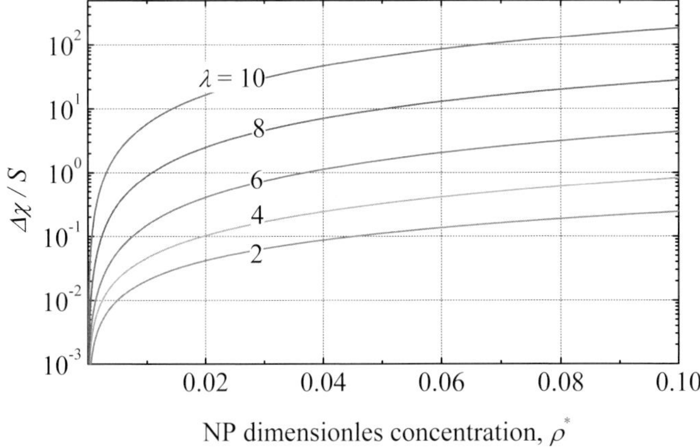

Fig. 13.   Anisotropy of the low-frequency composite dielectric susceptibility as a function of the NP concentration for the NP interaction strength λ varying from 2 to 10 as indicated on the lines.

perimental data cannot be explained without assuming that such chains are actually formed. Recently, however, it has been shown experimentally that in an isotropic fluid doped with an extremely low concentration of magnetic dipolar spherical NPs some birefringence can be induced by the external magnetic field.[54] In such a fluid, the macroscopic magnetic anisotropy can only be determined by the orientational ordering of dimers of magnetic NPs induced by the external field, and theoretical estimates of dimer concentration can be used to explain the experimentally observed dependence of the birefringence on the external magnetic field.[54]

5. Conclusions

Molecular theory of nematic nano-composites is at its early stage but, on the other hand, there is a number of interesting theoretical results obtained recently in this area and presented in this review. This includes, in particular, stabilization of the nematic order in the presence of anisotropic NPs, softening of the nematic-isotropic phase transition and peculiar phase diagrams which contain isotropic and nematic phases with different concentration of NPs coexisting over a very broad temperature range. It seems that there is sufficient experimental and theoretical evidence that strongly polar NPs should form at least dimers (but possibly also longer chains) in a nematic host. On the other hand, it is difficult to evaluate the anisotropy of the particle interaction potential and thus the results remain mainly qualitative. In general, there is a significant shortage of systematic experimental studies of the physical properties of LC nano-composites despite the growing interest attracted by these systems. Further development of the molecular theory would strongly benefit from the detailed experimental studies of the shift of the N-I transition temperature as a function of NP concentration, on the measurements of orientational order parameter of anisotropic NPs and, in particular, on the experimental studies of phase separation effects for different molar fractions of NPs. Finally, some experimental methods should be found to study directly the chain formation in strongly polar nematic nano-composites.

Acknowledgments

The authors are grateful to J. Goodby, R. Richardson, N. Vaupotich, Yu. Reznikov, T. J. Sluckin, N. Tomasovicova, R. V. Talroze, A. A. Ezhov, A. S. Merekalov and Ya. V. Kudryavtsev for interesting discussions.

References

1. H. Qi, B. Kinkead, and T. Hegmann, Effects of functionalized metal and semiconductor nanoparticles in nematic liquid crystal phases, *Proc. SPIE.* **6911**, 691106 (2008).
2. H. Qi and T. Hegmann, Formation of periodic stripe patterns in nematic liquid crystals doped with functionalized gold nanoparticles, *J. Mater. Chem.* **16**, 4197–4205 (2006).
3. Y. Shiraishi, N. Toshima, H. Maeds, K.and Yoshikawa, J. Xu, and S. Kobayashi, Frequency modulation response of a liquid-crystal electro-optic device doped with nanoparticles, *Appl. Phys. Lett.* **81**(15), 2845–2847 (2002).
4. S. Kobayashi and N. Toshima, Nanoparticles and lcds: It's a surprising world, *Information Display.* **23**, 26 (2007).
5. H. Yoshida, K. Kawamoto, H. Kubo, A. Tsuda, T.and Fujii, S. Kuwabata, and M. Ozaki, Nanoparticle-dispersed liquid crystals fabricated by sputter doping, *Adv. Mater.* **22**, 622–626 (2010).
6. S. Kaur, S. P. Singh, A. M. Biradar, A. Choudhary, and K. Sreeniva, Enhanced electro-optical properties in gold nanoparticles doped ferroelectric liquid crystals, *Appl. Phys. Lett.* **91**, 023120 (2007).
7. A. Kumar, J. Prakash, A. M. Mehta, D. S.and Biradar, and W. Haase, Enhanced photoluminescence in gold nanoparticles doped ferroelectric liquid crystals, *Appl. Phys. Lett.* **95**, 023117 (2009).
8. O. Buchnev, A. Dyadyusha, M. Kaczmarek, V. Reshetnyak, and Y. Reznikov,

Enhanced two-beam coupling in colloids of ferroelectric nanoparticles in liquid crystals, *J. Opt. Soc. Am. B.* **24**(7), 1512–1516 (2007).

9. Y. Reznikov, O. Buchnev, O. Tereshchenko, V. Reshetnyak, A. Glushchenko, and J. West, Ferroelectric nematic suspension, *Appl. Phys. Lett.* **82**(12), 1917–1919 (2003).

10. F. Li, C. Buchnev, O.and Cheon, A. Glushchenko, V. Reshetnyak, Y. Reznikov, T. Sluckin, and J. West, Orientational coupling amplification in ferroelectric nematic colloids, *Physical Review Letters.* **97**, 147801 (2006).

11. L. Lopatina and J. Selinger, Theory of ferroelectric nanoparticles in nematic liquid crystals, *Physical Review Letters.* **102**, 197802 (2009).

12. H. Yoshida, Y. Tanaka, H. T. T. Kawamoto, K.and Kubo, A. Fujii, S. Kuwabata, H. Kikuchi, and M. Ozaki, Nanoparticle-stabilized cholesteric blue phases, *Applied Physics Express.* **2**, 121501 (2009).

13. S. Wiersma, The physics and applications of random lasers, *Nature Physics.* **4**, 359–367 (2008).

14. G. A. Shandryuk, E. V. Matukhina, A. Vasil'ev, R. B.and Rebrov, A. Bondarenko, G.N.and Merekalov, A. Gas'kov, and R. Talroze, Effect of h-bonded liquid crystal polymers on cdse quantum dot alignment within nanocomposite, *Macromolecules.* **41**, 2178–2185 (2008).

15. G. A. Tal'roze, R.V.and Shandryuk, A. S. Merekalov, A. M. Shatalova, and O. A. Otmakhova, Alignment of nanoparticles in polymer matrices, *Polymer Science Ser. A.* **51**(12), 1194–1203 (2009).

16. W. Cai and V. Shalaev, *Optical Metamaterials: Fundamentals and Applications.* Springer (2009).

17. M. Gorkunov and M. Osipov, Tunability of wire-grid metamaterial immersed into nematic liquid crystal, *Journa of Applied Physics.* **103**, 036101 (2008).

18. R. Pratibha, K. Park, I. Smalyukh, and W. Park, Tunable optical metamaterial based on liquid crystal-gold nanosphere composite, *Optics Express.* **17**(22), 19459–19469 (2009).

19. A. Kossyrev, P. A.and Yin, S. G. Cloutier, D. A. Cardimona, D. Huang, P. M. Alsing, and J. M. Xu, Electric field tuning of plasmonic response of nanodot array in liquid crystal matrix, *Nano Letters.* **5**(10), 1978–1981 (2005).

20. C. Y. Chu, K. C.and Chao, Y. F. Chen, Y. C. Wu, and C. C. Chen, Electrically controlled surface plasmon resonance frequency of gold nanorods, *Appl. Phys. Lett.* **89**, 103107 (2006).

21. E. B. Barmatov, D. A. Pebalk, and M. V. Barmatova, Influence of silver nanoparticles on the order parameter of liquid crystalline polymers, *Liq. Cryst.* **33**(9), 1059–1063 (2006).

22. P. Kopcansky, N. Tomasovicova, M. Koneracka, M. Timko, Z. Mitroova, V. Zavisova, N. Eber, K. Fodor-Csorba, T. Toth-Katona, A. Vajda, E. Jadzyn, J.and Beaugnon, and X. Chaudd, Structural phase transition in liquid crystal doped with gold nanoparticles, *Acta Phys. Polonica A.* **118**(5), 988–989 (2010).

23. G. Sinha, C. Glorieux, and J. Thoen, Broadband dielectric spectroscopy study of molecular dynamics in the glass-forming liquid crystal isopentylcyanobiphenyl dispersed with aerosils, *Phys. Rev. E.* **69**, 031707 (2004).

24. T. Bellini, M. Buscaglia, C. Chiccoli, F. Mantegazza, P. Pasini, and C. Zannoni, Nematics with quenched disorder: What is left when long range order is disrupted?, *Phys. Rev. Lett.* **85**, 1008–1011 (2000).

25. H. Duran, B. Gazdecki, A. Yamashita, and T. Kyu, Effect of carbon nanotubes on phase transitions of nematic liquid crystals, *Liq. Cryst.* **32**(7), 815–821 (2005).

26. P. Kopcansky, N. Tomasovicova, M. Koneracka, M. Timko, V. Zavisova, A. Dzarova, J. Jadzyn, E. Beaugnon, and X. Chaud, Phase Transitions in Liquid Crystal Doped with Magnetic Particles of Different Shapes, *Int. J. Thermophys.* **32**(4), 807–817 (2011).

27. M. V. Gorkunov and M. A. Osipov, Mean-field theory of a nematic liquid crystal doped with anisotropic nanoparticles, *Soft Matt.* **7**(9), 4348–4356 (2011).

28. L. M. Lopatina and J. V. Selinger, Maier-saupe-type theory of ferroelectric nanoparticles in nematic liquid crystals, *Phys. Rev. E.* **84**, 041703 (2011).

29. Y. L. Raikher, V. I. Stepanov, and A. N. Zakhlevnykh, Mean-field description of the order-disorder phase transition in ferronematics, *Soft Matter.* **9**, 177–184 (2013).

30. G. Gray, *Molecular structure and the properties of liquid crystals*. New York: Academic (1962).

31. H. Peterson and D. Martire, Thermodynamics of solutions with liquid crystal solvents. viii. solute induced nematicisotropic transitions, *Mol. Cryst. Liq. Cryst.* **25**, 89–103 (1974).

32. M. V. Gorkunov, G. A. Shandryuk, A. M. Shatalova, I. Y. Kutergina, A. S. Merekalov, Y. V. Kudryavtsev, R. V. Talroze, and M. A. Osipov, Phase separation effects and the nematic-isotropic transition in polymer and low molecular weight liquid crystals doped with nanoparticles, *Soft Matt.* **9**(13), 3578–3588 (2013).

33. M. A. Osipov and M. V. Gorkunov, Molecular Theory of Phase Separation in Nematic Liquid Crystals Doped with Spherical Nanoparticles, *ChenPhysChem.* **15**(7, SI), 1496–1501 (2014).

34. E. Ouskova, O. Buchnev, V. Reshetnyak, Y. Reznikov, and H. Kresse, Dielectric relaxation spectroscopy of a nematic liquid crystal doped with ferroelectric $Sn_2P_2S_6$ nanoparticles, *Liq. Cryst.* **30**(10), 1235–1239 (2003).

35. R. Basu and G. S. Iannacchione, Evidence for directed self-assembly of quantum dots in a nematic liquid crystal, *Phys. Rev. E.* **80**, 010701 (2009).

36. M. A. Osipov, P. I. C. Teixeira, and M. M. Telo da Gama, Structure of strongly dipolar fluids at low densities, *Phys. Rev. E.* **54**, 2597–2609 (1996).

37. J. P. Straley, Ordered phases of a liquid of biaxial particles, *Phys. Rev. A.* **10**, 1881–1887 (1974).

38. M. V. Gorkunov, M. A. Osipov, A. Kocot, and J. K. Vij, Molecular model of biaxial ordering in nematic liquid crystals composed of flat molecules with four mesogenic groups, *Phys. Rev. E.* **81**, 061702 (2010).

39. K. K. Raina, P. Kumar, and P. Malik, Morphological control and polarization switching in polymer dispersed liquid crystal materials and devices, *Bull. Mat. Sc.* **29**(6), 599–603 (2006).

40. V. Gdovinova, N. Tomasovicova, N. Eber, T. Toth-Katona, V. Zavisova, M. Timko, and P. Kopcansky, Influence of the anisometry of magnetic particles on the isotropic-nematic phase transition, *Liq. Cryst.* **41**(12), 1773–1777 (2014).

41. I. Vecchi, A. Arcioni, C. Bacchiocchi, G. Tiberio, C. Zannoni, and P. Zanirato, A non-standard temperature dependence of the order parameter of the 5cb liquid crystal doped with an azo-derivative, *Mol. Cryst. Liq. Cryst.* **465**(1), 271–281 (2007).

42. M. A. Osipov, *Molecular Theories of Liquid Crystals*, In eds. D. Demus, J. Goodby, G. W. Gray, H.-W. Spies, and V. Vill, *Handbook of Liquid Crystals*, vol. 1. Wiley-VCH, Weinheim (1998).

43. H. Qi and T. Hegmann, Formation of periodic stripe patterns in nematic liquid crystals doped with functionalized gold nanoparticles, *J. Mater. Chem.* **16**, 4197–4205 (2006).

44. J. Yamamoto and H. Tanaka, Transparent nematic phase in a liquid-crystal-based microemulsion, *Nature.* **409**(6818), 321–325 (2001).

45. J. Milette, S. J. Cowling, V. Toader, C. Lavigne, I. M. Saez, R. B. Lennox, J. W. Goodby, and L. Reven, Reversible long range network formation in gold nanoparticle-nematic liquid crystal composites, *Soft Matter.* **8**(1), 173–179 (2012).

46. J. Milette, S. Relaix, C. Lavigne, V. Toader, S. J. Cowling, I. M. Saez, R. B. Lennox, J. W. Goodby, and L. Reven, Reversible long-range patterning of gold nanoparticles by smectic liquid crystals, *Soft Matter.* **8**(24), 6593–6598 (2012).

47. A. Matsuyama and R. Hirashima, Phase separations in liquid crystal-colloid mixtures, *The Journal of chemical physics.* **128**(4), 044907 (2008).

48. A. Matsuyama, Phase separations in mixtures of a liquid crystal and a nanocolloidal particle., *The Journal of chemical physics.* **131**(20), 204904 (2009).

49. V. Popa-Nita, P. van der Schoot, and S. Kralj, Influence of a random field on particle fractionation and solidification in liquid-crystal colloid mixtures, *The European Physical Journal E.* **21**(3), 189–197 (2006).

50. W. De Jeu and P. Bordewijk, Physical studies of nematic azoxybenzenes. ii. refractive indices and the internal field, *J. Chem. Phys.* **68**(1), 109–115 (1978).

51. M. A. Osipov and M. V. Gorkunov, Effect of nanoparticle chain formation on dielectric anisotropy of nematic composites, *Phys. Rev. E.* **92**, 032501 (2015).

52. M. Quinten, *Optical Properties of Nanoparticle Systems, Mie and Beyond.* Wiley-VCH (2011).

53. M. A. Osipov and G. Pajak, Molecular theory of proper ferroelectricity in bent-core liquid crystals, *Eur. Phys. J. E.* **37**(9), 1–7 (2014).

54. J. Szczytko, N. c. v. Vaupotič, M. A. Osipov, K. Madrak, and E. Górecka, Effect of dimerization on the field-induced birefringence in ferrofluids, *Phys. Rev. E.* **87**, 062322 (2013).

Part 2

Methods for studying liquid crystals and their inclusions

Chapter 5

Conventional and nonlinear optical microscopy
of liquid crystal colloids

Taewoo Lee[a] and Ivan I. Smalyukh[a,b,c,*]

[a]*Department of Physics and Liquid Crystal Materials Research Center,
University of Colorado, Boulder, Colorado 80309, USA*
[b]*Department of Electrical, Computer, and Energy Engineering and
Materials Science and Engineering Program, University of Colorado,
Boulder, CO 80309*
[c]*Renewable and Sustainable Energy Institute, National Renewable Energy
Laboratory and University of Colorado, Boulder, Colorado 80309, USA*
**Ivan.Smalyukh@colorado.edu*

The fast-growing field of liquid crystal colloids requires increasingly so-
phisticated optical microscopy tools for experimental studies. Recent
technological advances have resulted in a vast body of new imaging
modalities, such as nonlinear optical microscopy techniques, that were
developed to achieve high resolution while probing director structures
and material composition at length scales ranging from hundreds of
nanometers to macroscopic. These techniques are ideally suited for experimental exploration of liquid crystal colloids.

The goal of this chapter is to introduce a variety of optical microscopy
techniques available to researchers in the field, starting from basic principles and finishing with a discussion of the most advanced microscopy
systems. We describe traditional imaging tools, such as bright field and
polarizing optical microscopy, along with state-of-the-art orientation-
sensitive three-dimensional imaging techniques, such as various nonlinear
optical microscopies. Applications of these different imaging approaches
are illustrated by providing specific examples of imaging of liquid crystal
colloids and other soft matter systems.

Contents

1. Introduction

In fields of liquid crystals and colloids, optical microscopy is perhaps the most widely used experimental tool throughout history. This is not surprising as the optical microscopy has been equally extensively used in many other scientific research fields since the current form of a compound microscope was invented in the 17th century.[1] Its younger counterpart imaging techniques, such as electron and scanning probe microscopies, have enabled spatial resolution down to the atomic scale, which is often key to understanding both synthetic and natural materials. However, optical microscopy is much less invasive and thus maintains its important role in the ongoing development of fast growing fields of soft matter research, such as liquid crystal (LC) colloids. The developments of new technology, such as digital imaging and analysis, not only expanded the experimental capabilities of optical microscopy, but also led to significant breakthroughs. Recently new optical microscopic techniques, such as nonlinear and super-resolution optical microscopies, have revolutionized the three-dimensional (3D) imaging with far-field optical resolution down to the nanometer scales, resulting in a vast body of new experimental discoveries in both biological and synthetic systems.[2,3] As new microscopy approaches continue emerging, their uses in experimental explorations of LC colloids are expected to continue growing, posing the need of an overview of the state of the art in this field.

This chapter will introduce a broad variety of optical microscopy techniques useful in LC colloids research, starting from basic principles and traditional imaging techniques, such as bright/dark field and polarizing microscopy, continuing with 3D imaging techniques, such as fluorescence confocal and nonlinear optical microscopies, and then finishing with a state-of-the-art 3D super-resolution optical microscopy approaches. Along with a brief overview of different approaches, each section provides typical experimental examples emerging from the LC colloids research. Researchers who seek a more detailed description of techniques and samples studied in different imaging modes, which we use as demonstration examples, should refer to original works.[2-25] The introductory optical imaging basics and a detailed description of optical imaging techniques can be also found in recent books and reviews.[1,26-34]

The chapter is organized as follows: Sections 2–4 deal with basic principles and parameters important to all optical microscopy modalities as well as overview the simplest imaging modalities. Fluorescence and confocal microscopies are discussed in Secs. 5–6. Section 7 provides an extended account of nonlinear optical microscopy techniques. Since many experiments in the field of LC colloids require simultaneous non-contact optical manipulation and 3D imaging, integration of these techniques is immensely useful and is discussed in the Sec. 8. The time-resolved transient absorption microscopy, which is capable of revealing excited-state phenomena, and newly emerged sub-diffraction-limited super-resolution imaging techniques are discussed in Secs. 9 and 10, respectively. We conclude our review on optical microscopy by discussing future prospects of its uses in the study of LC colloidal systems in the Sec. 11.

2. Basic principles of optical microscopy

The simplest type of an optical imaging system is composed of two converging lenses, illumination light, and light collection optics, such as the retina of the observer's eyes. In the modern optical microscopes, owing to advances in optical technology, various types of light detecting devices are nowadays widely used to reconstruct an optical image, including charge-coupled device cameras, avalanche photodiodes, photomultiplier tubes, and other optical sensors. The transmitted light after passing through a sample in the case of transmission-mode imaging or the light reflected by a sample in the case of epi-illumination and reflection-mode imaging, is collected by the objective lens and transferred to the eyepiece to form an image. Hence the objective lenses are essential optical components, which are characterized by parameters like numerical aperture (NA) and working distance. The NA of the objective determines the range of acceptance angles of light and is defined as $NA = n\sin\theta$ where n is the refractive index of the medium between the objective lens and the sample, and θ is the half-cone angle of light accessible for collection/emission by the objective shown in Fig. 1a.

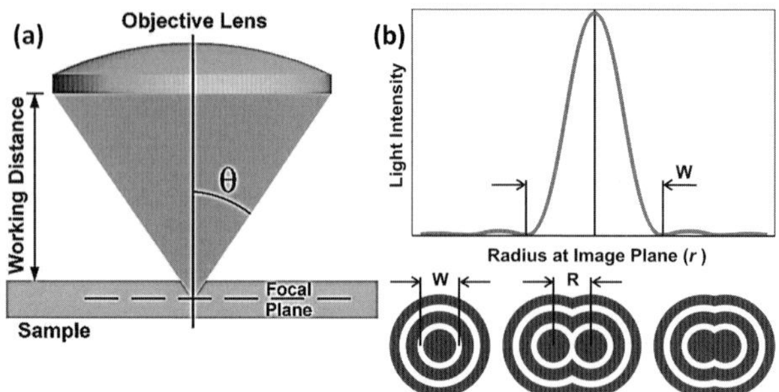

Fig. 1. (a) Definition of numerical aperture and working distance of an objective lens. (b) Overlapping of Airy disks in relation to the optical resolution: the PSF with the first minimum at distance from the center of the peak in light intensity $r = W/2$ and Airy patterns on the image plane when the two Airy disks are close to each other, where R is the separation distance between the central spots of Airy disks.

Hence the NA is used as a measure of the light collecting capabilities of an objective lens. In practice, it is difficult to achieve the NA above 0.95 when using dry objectives, but higher NA close to 1.5 can be obtained by increasing n of medium between the sample and the objective front lens by using immersion fluids, such as water ($n = 1.33$) and immersion oil ($n = 1.51$). The working distance is another practically important parameter of an objective lens, which is determined by the linear distance of the objective front lens to the closest sample surface (such as the confining glass plate's surface of a liquid crystal cell), as presented in Fig. 1a, when the focal plane is within the sample. In general, the working distance of objectives decreases as both the magnification and NA increase and immersion type objectives are typically restricted to relatively low working distance lengths.

Optical resolution is one of the most important microscope characteristics, which is dependent on the NA of objectives. The objectives project the light from point sources onto the image plane of the eyepiece and form circular diffraction patterns, the so-called Airy disks, which are described by the point spread function (PSF)[27,33] of width W shown in Fig. 1b. The Rayleigh equation, describing the case when two Airy disks separated by the distance between their centers $R \geq W/2$ can still be resolved, defines the lateral optical resolution, i.e., the resolution in the plane orthogonal to the microscope's optical axis given by:[27,33]

$$r_{lateral} = \frac{1.22\lambda}{2\mathrm{NA}_{obj}} = \frac{0.61\lambda}{\mathrm{NA}_{obj}} \tag{1}$$

where λ is the wavelength of imaging light. According to Eq. (1), higher-

NA objectives yield better diffraction-limited resolution as compared to low-NA objectives. Modern optical techniques for 3D imaging, such as confocal and nonlinear optical microscopies, can additionally provide high axial resolution along the optical axis of the microscope, which will be discussed in Sections 5.6 and 5.7 later in the chapter. Recently emerged super-resolution optical imaging techniques allow one to circumvent the diffraction limit for both lateral and axial directions, as we will discuss in the Sec. 5.10.

3. Bright field and dark field microscopies

Bright field microscopy was historically the first optical imaging modality. The contrast of brightness in the image arises usually from different degrees of transmission at different positions in the sample caused by the direct interaction of illuminated light (usually unpolarized white light) with the sample, such as absorption, scattering, reflection, and refraction. The experimental setting of a simple transmission-mode bright field microscopy is shown in Fig. 2a. The illumination light from an incandescent bulb or other sources is focused onto the sample by a condenser lens with numerical aperture NA_{cond} and, after passing through the sample, is then collected by an objective lens with the numerical aperture NA_{obj}, finally forming an image when viewed by the eyes through eyepieces. In order to get high image quality, a proper illumination is crucial and is part of all types of microscopic techniques. Most bright field microscopes adopt the Köhler illumination,[32] which has been broadly utilized since the end of the 19th century, as a method of achieving the uniform bright illumination on the sample plane. The contrast and resolution of an image are also affected by the ratio of NA_{cond} and NA_{obj}, and the optimal image quality is typically obtained by using condenser and objective lenses with similar NAs. On the other hand, depending on experimental needs, these NAs can be varied as using NA_{obj} higher than NA_{cond} usually decreases the resolution while increasing the image contrast and vice versa.[32,33]

Images depicted in the Figs. 2b and c show a scanning electron microscopy and a bright field micrographs of a trefoil knot colloidal microparticle, which was fabricated by the two-photon photo-polymerization process.[14] In the bright field image (Fig. 2c), the contrast emerges mostly from refraction and scattering of light at the boundaries of the polymer-based colloidal knot having refractive index different from that of the surrounding LC medium, as can be concluded from its direct comparison with the scan-

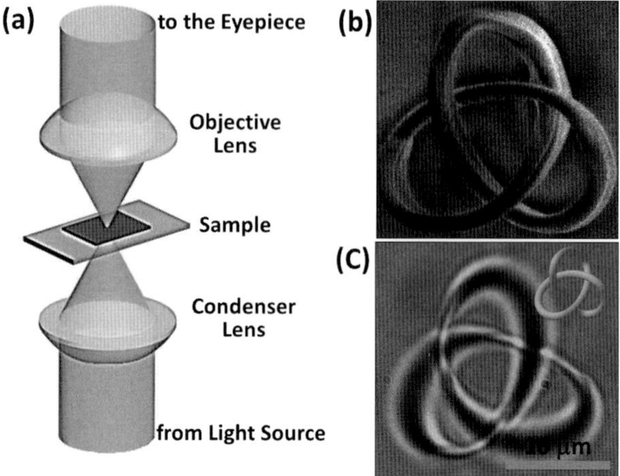

Fig. 2. (a) A schematic diagram of bright field microscopy and (b-c) images of a tre-foil knot colloidal particle: (b) Scanning electron microscopy image of an as-fabricated particle and (c) bright field micrograph of the knot-shaped particle in a nematic LC; the inset shows a computer model for comparison (images courtesy of Dr. Angel Martinez). See Ref. 14 for more details.

ning electron microscopy image (Fig. 2b). One of the main limitations of bright field imaging is that samples with weak spatial variation of the refractive index or absorption produce poor-contrast images. In order to enhance the contrast in transparent non-birefringent samples, the differential interference contrast and phase contrast techniques are commonly used, being implemented by supplementing the bright field microscope with additional optical elements, such as polarizers, beam splitters, and prisms.[26,27,29,31,32] Dark-field microscopy uses a special illumination technique, which allows collecting only the scattered, diffracted, or refracted light by the objects while the direct light is excluded. This allows enhancing contrast in the sample that is not imaged well under normal bright field illumination conditions. In a typical implementation shown in Fig. 3a, a hollow cone of light passes from a special condenser through the specimen after the direct light is blocked by an opaque light stop in the condenser, so that only the sample-scattered light reaches the objective, forming a bright image of the objects on the dark background. For optimized imaging in this optical arrangement, NA_{obj} should be smaller than NA_{cond}.[32] This technique is especially useful for imaging of samples with small scattering objects, such as colloidal particles of size below the diffraction limit, dispersed within a

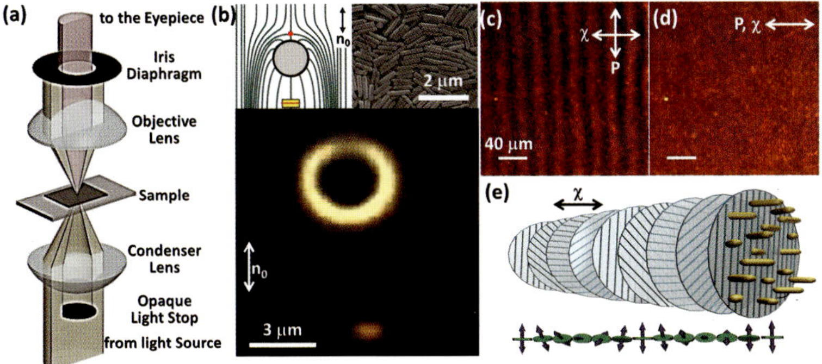

Fig. 3. (a) Dark field microscopy diagram. (b) Dark field imaging of a mixed colloidal system exhibiting elastic interactions between gold rod-like nanocolloids and silica microspheres dispersed in a nematic LC cell (image courtesy of Dr. Bohdan Senyuk): the top-left is a schematic of the system, with the green lines showing the director field **n** and the double arrow and n_0 marking the far-field director, yellow rectangle with a red line depicting the rod-like gold nanoparticle with a defect loop around it, and the red dot showing the hedgehog point defect; the top-right micrograph is a transmission electron microscopy image of gold rod-like nanoparticles (image courtesy of Nanopartz Inc.); the bottom dark field image depicts the microparticle visualized by a doughnut of light coming from its interface with the LC within the focal plane and the rod-like gold nanoparticle next to it as a small anisotropic scattering object. (c, d) Dark field images visualizing the helicoidal orientationally ordered structure of gold nanorods when dispersed in a micellar-based lyotropic discotic cholesteric LC at two polarizations (P) relative to the helical axis (χ): (c) perpendicular and (d) parallel to the helical axis. (e) A schematic diagram of the gold nanorods self-aligned perpendicular to the spatially-varying helicoidal director, depicted by blue lines and double arrows, and green disc-like micelles. (c - e images and schematics courtesy of Dr. Qingkun Liu). See Refs. 11, 12, 18 and 19 for more details.

non-scattering medium.[11] To demonstrate that dark field imaging approach can be used to visualize individual micro- and nanocolloids, we show an example of a dark field image in Fig. 3b. It depicts a single rod-like colloidal gold nanoparticle and a silica microsphere dispersed in a thermotropic nematic LC. The color and contrast in the image are due to scattering of dark-field illumination light by the particles and their interfaces with the LC.[18,19] To demonstrate that dark field microscopy is also useful in probing orientationally ordered structural organization of concentrated dispersions of nanocolloids in LCs, we also show a micrograph depicting a helicoidal structures of gold nanorods dispersed in a cholesteric lyotropic LC, Figs. 3c and d. The images are obtained for two orthogonal polarizations of imaging light, revealing orientational ordering of the nanoparticles, which is illustrated in a schematic diagram in Fig. 3e.[12]

4. Polarizing optical microscopy

Polarized light can be effectively used to probe optical properties of bire-fringent materials, such as minerals, crystals, and LCs. The experimental study is done by generating contrast via the differential interaction of the linearly polarized light with the LC sample having spatially-varying optical axis orientation. The optical microscope is supplemented by a 'polarizer' and 'analyzer' that are usually aligned either orthogonal or parallel to each other, with the sample placed in-between.[32] The basic idea is that the LC sample changes the linear polarization of light initially set by the orienta-tion of a polarizer, which is then probed by an analyzer. The polarizing optical microscopy (POM) setup shown in Fig. 4a can have the two crossed polarizers additionally supplemented by various compensators, phase retar-dation plates, and a Bertrand lens, which allow for a variety of different means for probing the interaction of polarized light with the LC colloidal systems.

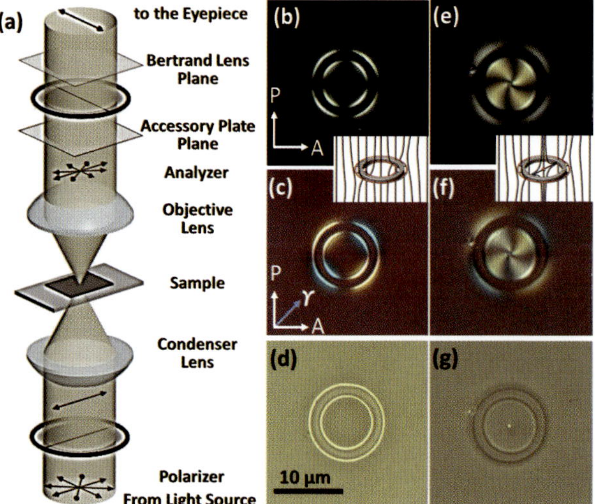

Fig. 4. (a) A typical POM setup. (b-g) A colloidal ring aligned with its plane orthogonal to the far-field director in a homeotropic nematic LC cell: optical micrographs without (b, e) and with (c, f) a red 530 nm retardation plate, and the corresponding bright field images (d, g). The insets in (b, c and e, f) show the director field around the colloidal particle. (Images courtesy of Dr. Bohdan Senyuk). The arrows marked by 'P', 'A' and 'γ' show orientations of the polarizer, analyzer and the slow axis of the 530 nm retardation plate, respectively. See Ref. 20 for more details.

When a birefringent LC colloidal material is placed between two crossed polarizers, linearly polarized incident light is split into two components, i.e. the ordinary and extraordinary waves that propagate at different speeds within the sample, introducing phase difference of $2\pi \cdot \Delta n_{\mathrm{eff}} \cdot d/\lambda$ where d is uniform thickness, λ is wavelength of incident light, and n_{eff} is the effective birefringence, i.e. the difference between refractive indices seen by the extraordinary and ordinary waves in the LC. The transmitted-light intensity depends on the angle β between the polarization of incident light and the optic axis:[26]

$$I = I_0 \sin^2 (2\beta) \sin^2 (\pi \Delta n_{\mathrm{eff}} \cdot d/\lambda) \tag{2}$$

where I and I_0 are the intensities of light after and before the sample, respectively. When the incident linearly polarized light propagates along the optic axis of the LC, one observes a dark background. This is also the case when the optical axis (uniaxial LC director) across the entire sample thickness is orthogonal to the direction of light propagation but aligned parallel to the polarizer or analyzer. In LC colloidal systems, the director is typically a function of spatial coordinates, which causes spatial variations of β and Δn_{eff} and thus also complex POM images $I(x, y)$ of LC colloidal samples. For example, the POM images in Figs. 4b and e, acquired between two crossed polarizers, show the texture around a colloidal ring in a nematic LC cell with homeotropic alignment.[20,35] The variation of transmitted intensity provides insights into the orientation of the optic axis (director) in the lateral plane of an optically anisotropic sample, Figs. 4b and e. As a result of interference, when the phase retardation of visible light is of the order of 2π, vivid color patterns often emerge and are also utilized to deduce the values of optical anisotropy, director orientation, and cell thickness.[32]

Accessory birefringent plates, such as compensators and retardation plates, Fig. 4a, are immensely useful in probing the LC director fields. For example, shown in Figs. 4c and f are POM images obtained when introducing a 530 nm retardation plate into the optical path in-between the crossed polarizers. In these images, the in-plane orientation of the local LC optic axis is parallel to the 'slow axis' of the plate in the bluish regions and perpendicular to it in the yellowish regions, where the phase retardations within the sample and the plate are mutually adding and subtracting, respectively. In addition to the patterns of director orientation, when the variation of the director across the sample thickness are negligible or well-known, the effective birefringence of the LC material and its spatial changes can also be determined by using a quartz wedge, a quarter-wave retardation plate (Sénarmont method), or a Berek compensator.[26,32]

5. Fluorescence microscopy

While the discussed above optical microscopy techniques rely on light-matter interactions related to absorption, refraction, or scattering of light, fluorescence phenomena from dyes or fluorophores can also be used to provide the needed contrast mechanism. The basic principle of a fluorescence microscope's function is to excite the fluorescent molecules in the sample with light at a specific wavelength, and then to separate the information-carrying fluorescence emission signal from the excitation light.[28,29] The fluorescence microscopy setup, such as the one shown in Fig. 5a, requires an excitation light source, such as a mercury lamp, and a special fluorescence filter cube set, which contains a dichroic mirror, an excitation filter, and an emission filter. When light is absorbed by fluorescent dye molecules, an electronic transition from the ground state to the excited state of the molecule occurs. Then, within a short time period (typically in the range of nanoseconds), the molecules transition back to the initial ground state, which is accompanied by the emission of light at a wavelength longer than that of the excitation light, Fig. 5b. This red shift, also known as Stokes shift, is caused by losses of the absorbed energy due to non-radiative processes and is instrumental in enabling imaging as the emission light can be spectrally separated from the excitation light using optical filters and

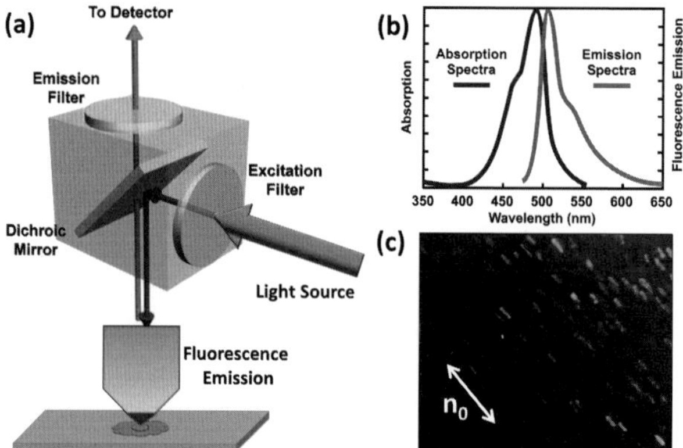

Fig. 5.   Fluorescence microscopy: (a) A schematic diagram of a fluorescence microscope with a filter cube set; (b) a typical example of absorption and emission spectra of a fluorescent dye used in fluorescence microscopy; (c) a fluorescence image of unidirectionally oriented P. aeruginosa cells (the fluorescence signals come from the green fluorescent protein within the bacteria cells) in an aligned lyotropic LC matrix of concentrated, flow-extended DNA chains. See Ref. 22 for more details.

then collected by a photodetector, such as a charge-coupled device camera. As an example, the fluorescence micrograph in Fig. 5c shows an active biologically derived LC colloidal system in which unidirectionally oriented P. aeruginosa cells exhibit unidirectional active motion in an aligned LC matrix of concentrated DNA. The fluorescence imaging is enabled by the green fluorescent protein incorporated within the cells.[22] Since the fluorescence emission maximum is well separated from the absorption maximum, the fluorescence collected in the epi-detection mode depicts locations of the aligned cells (Fig. 5c).

6. Fluorescence confocal polarizing microscopy

While the optical imaging techniques discussed so far are two-dimensional (2D) in nature, lacking resolution in the direction of the optical axis of the microscope, fluorescence confocal microscopy can offer depth-resolved 3D imaging capabilities. In the confocal microscope, the main new feature is the use of spatial filtering to exclude the out-of-focus light from the image formation. This can be implemented by, for example, using the detection pinhole at the position right before the detector that is confocal to the focal plane of the objective, as depicted in Fig. 6a. The only detected signal is arising from the inspected small volume (voxel) of interest and the signal from the adjacent regions is prevented from detection, since the pinhole and the inspected voxel are confocal. This enables diffraction-limited imaging along the optical axis, in addition to that in the lateral plane.[33] To obtain a full 3D high-quality image in the fluorescence confocal microscopy, the tightly focused imaging beam is spatially translated, voxel-by-voxel across the sample. This scanning is usually achieved by using galvano-mirrors or acousto-optic deflectors for raster scanning in the lateral xy-directions and then by moving the objective or the sample along the optical axis, in the z-direction, using a stepper motor, as shown in Fig. 6a.[33] The resultant reconstructed 3D image consists of a stack of computer-assembled 2D optical slices. The fluorescence confocal technique enables the following lateral and axial resolution:

$$r_{\text{lateral-confocal}} = 0.44\lambda/\text{NA}_{\text{obj}} \tag{3}$$

$$r_{\text{axial-confocal}} = 1.55n\lambda/(\text{NA}_{\text{obj}})^2 \tag{4}$$

Different factors can degrade spatial resolution as compared to the above theoretical estimates, including light scattering, optical aberrations, refractive index mismatch at interfaces, light defocusing due to the studied medium's birefringence and spatial inhomogeneity etc.[33]

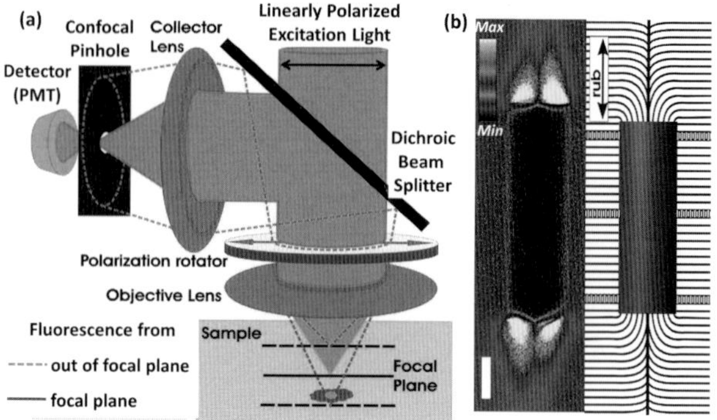

Fig. 6. Fluorescence confocal polarizing microscopy. (a) A basic schematic diagram of the FCPM setup with a polarization rotator; the confocal pinhole assures that only the fluorescence emission light from the focal plane is collected by the photomultiplier tube detector; (b) In-plane FCPM texture of the smectic LC director field around a 4.5 μm cylinder (left) and the corresponding reconstructed director and layer structures that have rotational symmetry with respect to the cylinder axis (right). The white scale bar is 1 μm in length. See Ref. 10 for more details.

When the LC colloidal sample is doped with anisometric dye molecules and these fluorescent molecules are excited by light with controlled polarization, one can not only gain information about spatial distributions of fluorescently tagged components, but also information about orientational ordering of the LC. The absorption efficiency of incident linearly polarized excitation light and the intensity of detected fluorescence can be determined by the angle β between the polarization of the excitation light and the long axis of the dye molecules following the LC director, assuming that the transition dipole moments of both excitation and emission are parallel to the molecular long axis. Hence in the case of collinear polarized detection and excitation, the detected fluorescence signal is proportional to $\cos^4 \beta$.[21] When the linear polarization of excitation light is parallel to the transition dipole moments of dye molecules, the fluorescence signal is at maximum; the signal is at minimum when it is perpendicular to the dye transition dipole moments. This angular dependence is used to probe patterns of the 3D LC director fields assuming the anisometric dye molecules align with the molecules of the studied LC colloidal system. Figure 6a shows how this type of orientation-sensitive imaging is implemented using a basic fluorescence confocal polarizing microscopy (FCPM) setup. FCPM controls polarization of light in both excitation and detection channels by an achromatic polarization rotator. This rotator is based on a twisted nematic cell placed in a common part of excitation and epi-detection fluorescence signals. FCPM offers 3D visualization of director structures found in LC colloidal systems. For example, the 3D FCPM texture shown in Fig. 6b visualizes the director structure around a cylindrical colloidal particle in a smectic LC doped with small amount of anisotropic fluorescent dye molecules that follow orientation of the LC molecules.[10] The texture shown in Fig. 6b (left) was obtained using linearly polarized FCPM probing light perpendicular to the rubbing direction and represents a depth-resolved image of the molecular/director field pattern as well as the corresponding layered smectic structure. A schematic representation shown on the right side of Fig. 6b depicts the reconstructed director configuration around a colloidal cylinder. Thus, FCPM imaging can visualize equilibrium structures of long-range molecular alignment in LC colloidal systems.

7. Nonlinear optical microscopy

Nonlinear optical (NLO) imaging techniques are powerful tools for non-invasive labeled or label-free imaging. They nowadays find increasing uses in the field of soft matter and biological systems, including LC colloids. Since NLO signals are intrinsically sensitive to the electronic, vibrational, and structural properties,[36] they are particularly useful in studies of LC colloidal nanostructures. These strong nonlinear responses can provide the basis for rich and complementary information about the studied samples by using multi-photon excitation fluorescence, luminescence, second harmonic generation (SHG),[37] sum frequency generation,[38] third harmonic generation,[39] and coherent Raman scattering, *viz.*, coherent anti-Stokes Raman scattering (CARS)[6–8,40] and stimulated Raman scattering (SRS)[9,41,42] microscopies. Although each imaging mode can be used separately, integrating several different NLO modalities into a unified multimodal imaging platform provides additional benefits in terms of complementary structural and compositional analysis.

The NLO signal is generated from light-matter interactions involving multiple excitation photons, as schematically shown in Figs. 7a and b. This can provide several advantages as compared to conventional linear optical imaging,[33,36,40] such as low out-of-focus photobleaching, low photodamage, ability to excite UV-excitable fluorophores without using specialized optics, inherent depth-resolved optical sectioning, ability to work with thick specimens, high lateral spatial resolution, high image contrast etc. However,

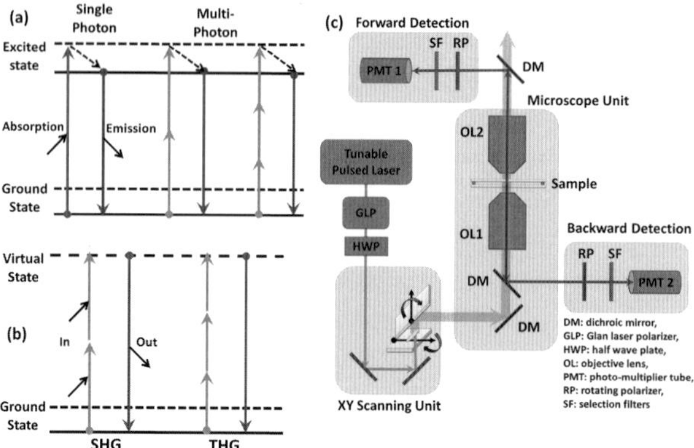

Fig. 7. Nonlinear optical imaging based on multi-photon excitation fluorescence and multi-harmonic generation. (a, b) Energy level diagrams of (a) single and multi-photon absorption processes followed by emission and (b) second and third harmonic generation processes. (c) A simple schematic diagram of a nonlinear optical imaging setup. See Ref. 8 for more details.

NLO microscopy typically requires more expensive pulsed sources (femtosecond or picosecond pulsed lasers) and more complicated microscopy setups that are rarely commercially available. In this section, we will start from introducing the multi-photon excitation fluorescence microscopy and multi-harmonic generation microscopy and then will proceed to the description of coherent Raman scattering imaging.

7.1. *Multi-photon excitation fluorescence and multi-harmonic generation microscopies*

Multi-photon absorption process is based on two or three photons of near-infrared light and is followed by emission of a single photon at a wavelength shorter than the excitation wavelength, as schematically shown in Fig. 7a. Typically, a femtosecond pulsed laser is used as an excitation light source, providing high peak powers needed for an efficient multi-photon absorption within a short period of time (sub-picosecond). The excitation volume is inherently small enough to provide 3D optical sectioning, since the probability of exciting fluorophores in a multi-photon process falls off quickly with the axial distance.[36] Therefore, while providing depth-resolved imaging, the setup of multi-photon excitation fluorescence microscopy does not require a confocal geometry like that in fluorescence confocal microscopy. Figure 7c shows a simple schematic diagram of setup implementation composed of a single tunable pulsed laser, xy-scanning mirrors, a microscope with multiple detection channels, and interference filter sets. Polarizers, wave plates, and polarization rotators are used to control both intensity and polarization of the excitation light. By selecting a proper wavelength of excitation light both the fluorescence and the second or third harmonic signals can be simultaneously collected. For example, the experimental implementation allowing for the fluorescence signal detection in the backward direction (epi-detection) and the SHG signal detection in the forward direction is shown in Fig. 7c.

Polarization sensitive excitation and detection in NLO microscopy is useful for imaging of 3D patterns of long-range molecular orientation in the study of LC colloids. The detected NLO signal scales with the angle β between the linear polarization of excitation light and the LC director $\mathbf{n}(\mathbf{r})$ as $\propto \cos^{2m} \beta$ for detection without a polarizer and as $\propto \cos^{2(m+1)} \beta$ in the case of detection with the polarizer collinear with the polarization of the excitation beam, where m is the order of the nonlinear process ($m = 2$ for two-photon and $m = 3$ for three-photon excitation).[6–9] As an example of practical uses of the nonlinear optical polarizing microscopy, Fig. 8a shows a micrograph of an in-plane slice of a sample obtained using the three-photon excitation fluorescence polarizing microscopy (3PEF-PM). It shows a spherical colloidal particle in a smectic LC imaged using excitation at 870 nm and detection within the 390-450 nm range.[8] In this particular case, LC molecules with biphenyl chemical groups serve as fluorophores themselves. The spatially non-uniform director field configuration arises because of tangential anchoring at the surface of the particle embedded in the LC with a uniform far-field alignment. In the schematic of the inset in Fig. 8a, the double arrow marked with 'rub' shows the direction of substrates rubbing that was utilized to impose the far-field alignment of the layers and director; the thick solid line depicts a defect line and dashed lines enclose the regions of strong layer deformations corresponding to the areas of the strong 3PEF-PM signal.

The multiple harmonic generation, with the energy diagram schematically shown in Fig. 7b, is an instantaneous scattering and energy conserving process. For example, the SHG process does not depend on the excitation wavelength so that SHG signal always appears at exactly half the wavelength (frequency doubled) of the incident light interacting with the material via the second order nonlinear process.[37–39] As an example of the use of SHG polarizing microscopy, Figs. 8b–d show SHG images of a smectic C* LC obtained by using excitation wavelength at 1050 nm and detection

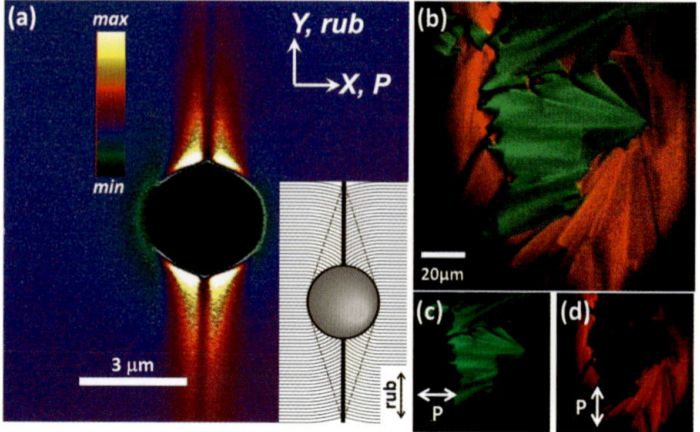

Fig. 8.   Examples of applications of the nonlinear optical polarizing microscopy. (a) A depth-resolved 3PEF-PM micrograph of deformations in smectic LC layers and director field around a spherical particle. The inset shows the reconstructed pattern of smectic layers (thin solid lines) around the inclusion, with the director field being orthogonal to the layers. (b) SHG imaging of a smectic C* LC. In-plane co-localized superimposed texture of two SHG images (c, d) that were obtained separately for two orthogonal polarizations marked by white double arrows. See Ref. 8 for more details.

at 525 nm for two different orthogonal polarizations of excitation light. A strong SHG signal reveals the polar ordering of the smectic C* with focal conic domains.[8] This imaging technique does not require labeling the specimen with a dye and is free from the artifacts related to photobleaching and photodamage. Multiple harmonic generation can also provide insights into the molecular alignment symmetry of the studied LC colloidal systems, since SHG is only allowed in media with non-inversion symmetry while the third harmonic generation is present in all media.

7.2. *Coherent Raman scattering microscopy*

Although the spontaneous Raman scattering process is well known and utilized in Raman spectroscopy and microscopy, it usually requires high laser power and rather long acquisition times. This is because LC colloidal samples can have small Raman scattering cross-sections (e.g. 10^{-28} cm^2 for biologically derived LCs) and the Raman scattering is often hard to separate from much stronger fluorescence signals. To circumvent these shortcomings of spontaneous Raman microscopy, coherent Raman scattering techniques, including CARS and SRS, utilize nonlinear optical processes targeting molecular vibrations using at least two different pulsed laser sources within the near infrared range. The detected signals can be in the forms of either blue-shifted anti-Stokes signal for CARS mode or the gain/loss signal of excitation beams for SRS mode.[6–9] The CARS technique is based on a third order nonlinear four-wave mixing process, in which the so-called pump, Stokes, and probe photons interact with molecular vibration energy levels as shown in Fig. 9a. The coherently driven molecular oscillators are achieved when the difference between a pump/probe ($\omega_p = \omega_{\text{pump}} = \omega_{\text{probe}}$) and Stokes ($\omega_s = \omega_{\text{stokes}} < \omega_p$) optical frequencies matches the frequency of a certain molecular vibration mode ($\omega_{\text{vib}} = \omega_p - \omega_s$). The resultant anti-Stokes Raman signal at $\omega_{\text{as}} = 2\omega_p - \omega_s$ is the basis for the CARS microscopy, which is detected in a blue-shifted wavelength region, as shown in Fig. 9b. The CARS intensity is strongly dependent on the intensities of the excitation beams,

$$I_{\text{CARS}}(2\omega_p - \omega_s) \propto (\chi^{(3)}_{\text{CARS}})^2 I_p^2(\omega_p) I_s(\omega_s) \tag{5}$$

where $\chi^{(3)}_{\text{CARS}}$ is the third order susceptibility, I_p and I_s are the intensities of the pump/probe and Stokes beams, respectively.

In the SRS mode, a pump photon at ω_p and a Stokes photon ($\omega_s < \omega_p$) interact with molecules and the stimulated excitation of the vibrational transition occurs when their frequency difference matches ω_{vib}. Because of this stimulated amplification, the intensity of the light at the pump wavelength decreases due to a stimulated Raman loss, while the intensity of

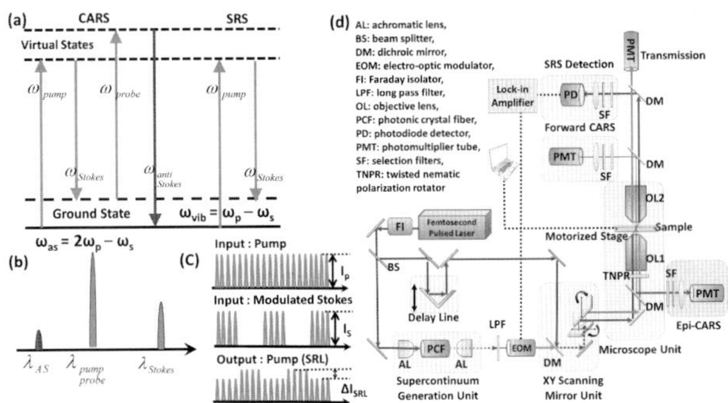

Fig. 9. Principles and setup of coherent Raman scattering microscopy: (a) Energy level diagram of CARS and SRS with modulated Stokes; (b) CARS signal generated at a wavelength shorter than the pump and Stokes wavelengths. (c) Principles of SRS. (d) A schematic diagram of CARS and SRS-polarizing microscopy setup utilizing the synchronized pump and Stokes pulses, xy-scanning galvano-mirrors, and an inverted microscope with both forward and epi-detection channels for CARS and a forward detection channel for SRS. See Refs. 8 and 9 for more details.

the light at the Stokes wavelength increases due to a stimulated Raman gain. For example, the pump beam loses its intensity only in presence of the Stokes beam, as shown in Fig. 9c. Hence these changes in signal intensities are the basis of imaging contrast in SRS microscopy. Due to the small intensity differences, phase-sensitive detection schemes are generally employed to extract the signal via high-frequency modulation (more than 1 MHz) of one of the excitation beams (e.g., modulated Stokes, as shown in Fig. 9c) and by heterodyne detection with a photodiode and a lock-in amplifier.[9,41,42] Figure 9d shows a simple schematic diagram of combined CARS and SRS polarizing microscopy setup based on synchronized pump/probe and Stokes beams, xy-scanning mirrors, and an inverted microscope with forward and epi-detection channels.[8,9] A single tunable femtosecond pulsed laser, in combination with a synchronously-generated super-continuum from a highly nonlinear photonic crystal fiber, allows one to produce a pump beam and a broadband or filter-selected Stokes beam.

The strong dependence of the CARS signal on the angle β between the polarization of excitation light and the director, which is $\propto \cos^6 \beta$ without a detection polarizer and $\propto \cos^8 \beta$ with a detection polarizer collinear to excitation polarization,[6–8] allows for imaging of director structures. As an example of the use of CARS and SRS polarizing microscopy techniques, Figs. 10a and b show superimposed coherent Raman images simultaneously collected by CARS-PM and SRS-PM modes at two orthogonal collinear polarizations of the pump and Stokes beams, i.e., horizontal (red) and vertical (green) polarizations. These images depict the in-plane director field of a focal conic domain in a smectic LC (4-cyano-4'-octylbiphenyl). Since the CN stretching vibration is parallel to the molecular long axis, the Raman signal from it provides information about the spatial pattern of the LC director.[6–8] When the director is parallel to the polarization of excitation light, the intensities of the CARS and SRS signals targeting CN vibration are maximized, whereas the CARS and SRS intensities are minimized when the director is perpendicular to the polarization of incident light. The 3D reconstructed structure of smectic layers in the focal conic domain containing ellipse and hyperbola defect lines is shown in Fig. 10c.[8,9] Another example of coherent Raman imaging of LC colloids in Figs. 10d–f show surface-enhanced SRS-PM and CARS-PM images of homeotropically aligned nematic LC (4-cyano-4'-pentylbiphenyl) with large Raman signal enhancement around a gold nanoparticle with irregular sharp edges.[15] The bright regions around the gold nanoparticle represent the enhanced nonlinear Raman scattering signals from the CN stretching vibration of LC

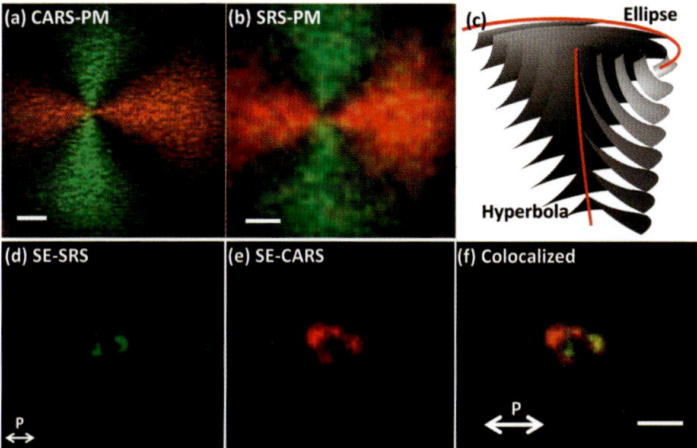

Fig. 10.   Examples of applications of coherent Raman scattering microscopy: (a,b) Superimposed images in the plane of ellipse of a focal conic domain in a smectic LC collected with (a) CARS-PM and (b) SRS-PM using coherent Raman signals collected at horizontal (Red) and vertical (Green) orientations of polarization of excitation beams. (c) Reconstructed 3D structure of smectic layers of the focal conic domain. (d–f) Surface enhanced (SE) images of nematic LC director around a gold nanoparticle: (d) CARS-PM and (e) SRS-PM mode. (f) Colocalized image of (d) and (e). The double white arrows represent polarization direction of excitation beams. White scale bars are 1 μm in length. See Refs. 8, 9 and 15 for more details.

molecules due to strong electromagnetic field enhancement near the edges of the gold nanoparticle, in addition to CARS and SRS signal enhancement enabled by their coherent nature.

8. Non-invasive 3D imaging combined with non-contact optical manipulation of colloids

The optical trapping is nowadays widely used in a variety of different science fields, including LC colloids, and is reviewed in more details elsewhere in this book.   Here we briefly show that the integration of optical manipulation with 3D imaging opens up various opportunities of the design and characterization of LC colloids, revealing the nature of interactions, assemblies and the role of topology.[23–25]   For example, holographic optical trapping (HOT) allows simultaneous multiple optical traps in the focal plane as well as along the axial directions.[24,25]   The HOT shown in Fig. 11a employs a 2D LC-based spatial light modulator (SLM), in which the phase modulation is controlled in real time by displaying holograms corresponding to the specified trap pattern at the video rate.   The HOT system also

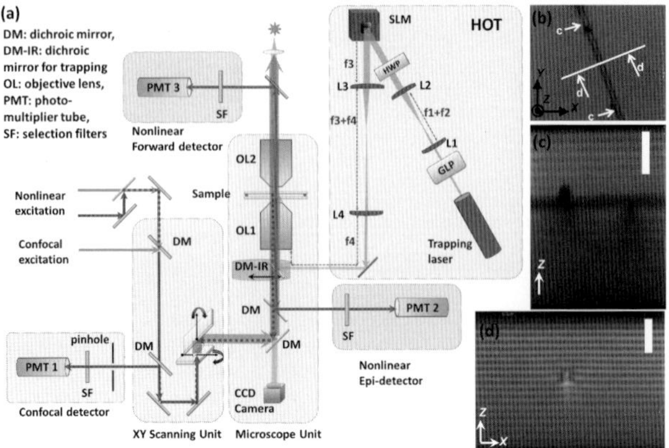

Fig. 11. An integrated 3D optical imaging and manipulation system and its applications: (a) A schematic diagram of the combined HOT, FCPM and NLO. (b) In-plane FCPM image of two particles used to manipulate a Lehman cluster in the vertical direction. (c) Vertical FCPM cross section image along the length of a cluster between end-points marked by the arrows labeled 'c' in (b). (d) Vertical FCPM cross-sectional image of a Lehman cluster along the plane marked 'd' in (b). White scale bars are 10 μm. See Refs. 24 and 25 for more details.

allows generation of Laguerre-Gaussian beams, which can manipulate LC director patterns.[23] As an example, Figs. 11b–d show the simultaneous 3D optical manipulation and imaging capabilities of the integrated system as applied to colloidal particles and defects in a cholesteric LC. The cholesteric layer deformations caused by the presence of elementary oily streak (also called a 'Lehmann cluster') can be clearly seen in the cross-sectional images. The two particles are used to manipulate the cluster of disclinations and the cholesteric configurations are simultaneously imaged in planar and vertical cross-sections, both along the length of the cluster and across the cluster.[24,25]

9. Transient absorption microscopy

Transient absorption microscopy (TAM) is also known as pump-probe microscopy. In TAM, an ultrafast, pulsed laser is used to excite molecules from electronic ground states to excited states and the sample is subsequently probed by a broad-spectral-range light to obtain absorption spectra at various time intervals following the excitation. This time-resolved pump-probe signal reflects population dynamics in different excited states of the system.

The transient absorption technique has been extensively applied to study excited-state dynamics of colloidal and other nanostructures, contributing to the understanding of energy relaxation processes in these systems.[13,43,44] Figure 12a shows a simple energy level diagram of the pump-induced processes. The transient absorption signal originates directly from the studied object. The ground state bleach and stimulated emission processes increase the transmission of the probe light whereas the excited state absorption process decreases it. These spatially-varying changes of transmission of the probe signal generate a TAM image at a certain time delay and wavelength, which can be recorded based on characterization of the sample using a photodiode and a lock-in amplifier and by modulating the pump beam at high frequency (> 1 MHz), as shown in Fig. 12b.

TAM is a highly sensitive technique based on absorption measurement. As an example, Fig. 12c shows a TAM image of a thin graphene flake grown on a glass substrate, which was obtained using a femtosecond pump beam at 780 nm modulated at 4 MHz. The nanostructure was subsequently probed by the light in the form of a super-continuum femtosecond beam generated using a photonic crystal fiber and the same pump pulse at time zero, i.e., pump and probe beams are overlapped in time at the sample. The nonlinear

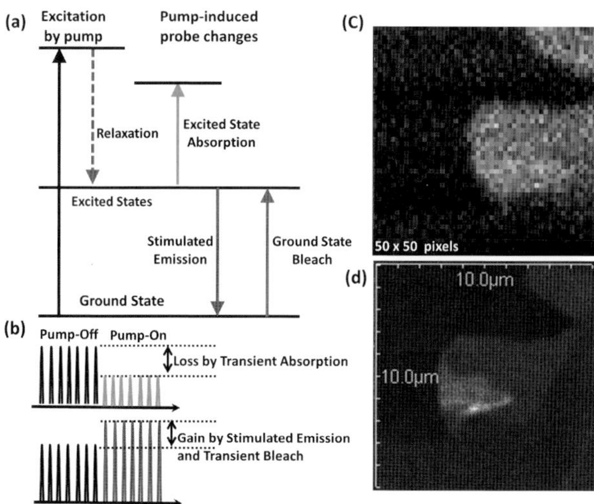

Fig. 12. Principles and applications of TAM. (a) Energy level diagram of pump-induced processes. (b) A schematic detection diagram of pump-induced probe intensity. (c) A TAM image of graphene atomic layers on a glass substrate. (d) A corresponding nonlinear optical photo-luminescence image. See Refs. 5 and 13 for more details.

optical photo-luminescence image corresponding to the area of the TAM image by the same pump beam is shown in Fig. 12d for comparison. For more detailed accounts, in literature, the LC behavior of colloidal graphene and graphene oxide flakes were studied in Refs. 45 and 46 and the carrier dynamics of the graphene flakes has been studied by ultrafast TAM in Ref. 5. The study of excited-state dynamics in LC colloidal systems is of both fundamental and practical interest, e.g. from the standpoint of view of applications of colloidal nanoparticles such as quantum dots, plasmonic metal nanoparticles, carbon nanostructures etc.

10. Super-resolution optical microscopy (nanoscopy)

One of the most important and challenging tasks in the field of optical microscopy is that of achieving sub-diffraction-limited nanoscale resolution. Recently introduced approaches show a promise of providing significant breakthroughs in overcoming resolution limits[2,3,47,48] and, potentially, may also be applied to the orientation-sensitive imaging of long-range molecular alignment patterns in LC colloids. The techniques enabling sub-diffraction-limited super-resolution optical imaging include: (1) single-molecule localization-based techniques, such as photo-activated localization microscopy (PALM),[47–49] stochastic optical reconstruction microscopy (STORM),[50–52] and ground-state depletion followed by individual molecule return (GSDIM/direct-STORM);[53,54] (2) techniques based on the point spread function (PSF) engineering at predetermined positions, such as the structured illumination microscopy[55–58] and stimulated emission depletion (STED) microscopy.[2,3] Super-resolution microscopies rely on the same principle for breaking the diffraction limit, i.e., the unwanted fluorescence signals are switched off during the image acquisition process.

The PALM and STORM techniques apply low levels of activation light so that single molecules are stochastically activated and localized. An activated molecule produces a signal emerging from a diffraction-limited spot, which is fit with a Gaussian function to localize the molecule's position with nanometer precision. After hundreds to thousands of molecules have been localized, their positions are superimposed to create a super-resolution image. The demonstrated lateral and axial resolutions of single-molecule localization techniques are 20 - 30 nm and 50 - 60 nm, respectively.[51] However, it takes long data acquisition time on the order of hours and requires a computational reconstruction process to achieve this resolution improvement. Therefore, many of the fluorescence super-resolution techniques are based on PSF engineering methods. The fluorophores in the outer range of the focal spot are prevented from spontaneous fluorescence by local saturation or depletion of a molecular transition, which can be accomplished by either ground state depletion or STED, while the fluorophores at the center spot remain unaffected. The key advantage of these PSF engineering methods is that the probed voxel is reduced in volume, so that the sub-diffraction-limited image can be obtained directly by fine scanning the sample, like in confocal microscopy, without the need of computational post-processing. Figures 13a and b show the basic scheme of the super-resolution STED microscopy, in which the donut-shaped beam deactivates the spatially selective fluorophores, preventing their participation in the image formation. A simplified energy level diagram of the molecular states involved in STED is shown in Fig. 13a. After initial excitation and vibrational relaxation, the fluorophores can emit fluorescence photons or can be silenced by the red-shifted stimulated emission from electronic excited state to a higher vibrational sub-state of the electronic ground state. The reduction of real lateral PSF size (red) using a donut-shaped STED pattern (orange) and the diffraction-limited excitation (green) are depicted in Fig. 13b. The higher STED beam power results in a smaller effective PSF (red), which can be shrunk 10 times or so (down to 30 - 80 nm) as compared to the PSF in conventional optical imaging (200 - 300 nm).[4,16] Figure 13c shows a simple schematic diagram of the 3D STED microscopy setup. Two separate phase plates, a vortex phase plate for lateral confinement and a ring-like phase plate for axial confinement, yield a laterally and axially restricted PSF. The STED beam is divided into two paths and recombined at the polarizing beam splitters (PBS). The resulting PSF provides a small

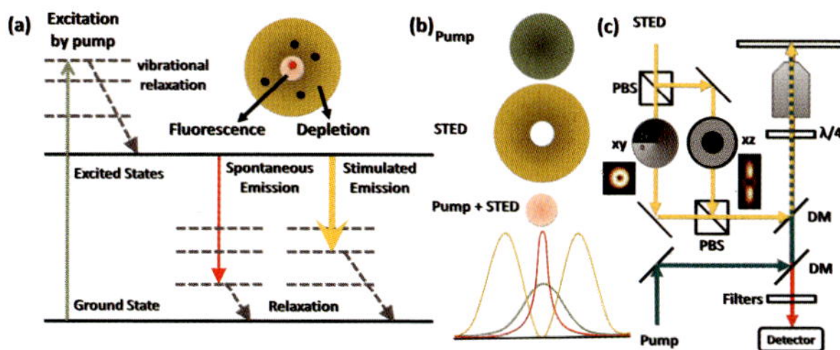

Fig. 13. Principles of STED microscopy. (a) A simplified energy level diagram of the states involved in STED imaging and (b) improvement of lateral resolution (red) using a donut-shaped depletion pattern (orange) by a vortex phase plate and the diffraction-limited excitation pattern (green). (c) Simple schematic diagram of the 3D STED microscopy setup. See Refs. 2–4 and 16 for more details.

3D-probed volume below that associated with the diffraction-limited resolution. The study of soft matter systems, such as colloidal nanoparticle dispersions, will benefit tremendously from the further development and use of these nanoscopy techniques.

The diffraction-limited resolution barrier could also be circumvented by using an illumination aperture of dimensions much smaller than the wavelength of light.[43] This is done in the near-field scanning optical microscopy (NSOM). Improved resolution is achieved by placing the optical probe very close to the studied sample's surface, as shown in Fig. 14a. Probing light passes through a sub-wavelength-sized aperture and illuminates a sample that is placed at a distance smaller than the wavelength of the probing light. The resolution in NSOM is limited by the size of the probe aperture but not by the wavelength of the illumination light. In particular, lateral resolution of 20 nm and vertical resolution of 5 nm or less have been demonstrated.[58] However, NSOM is difficult to operate non-invasively and at large depths, although these problems can be mitigated in some systems. For example, NSOM probes can be immersed into soft matter or biological systems and effectively probe their 3D structure.

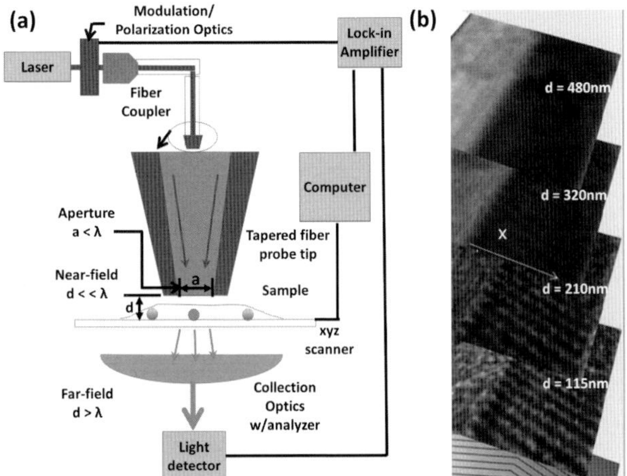

Fig. 14. Near-field scanning optical microscopy. (a) A schematic diagram of NSOM working in the transmission mode. (b) NSOM polarizing images of a nematic LC: from top to bottom, the aperture height is $d = 480, 320, 210$, and 115 nm above the confining surface. The bottom image shows the AFM-scribing pattern. See Ref. 17 for more details. (The image in (b) is reprinted from Ref. 17 with permission).

As an example of applying this technique to imaging of orientational patterns, Fig. 14b shows a series of images of a nematic LC (4-cyano-4'-pentylbiphenyl) thin film are collected in polarized NSOM mode at different heights away from a polyimide substrate with patterned boundary conditions for the director alignment. The probe tip was immersed into the LC and lowered until it reached the polyimide surface and then withdrawn to various different heights up to 480 nm. The periodic patterns on the images laterally coincide with the topographical variation of the surface that is setting the boundary conditions via surface scribing.[17] This example illustrates how the nanopatterned alignment at the confining surface is modified to meet the far-field alignment as one moves away from the confining surface, information that could not be obtained with conventional diffraction-limited imaging approaches. The NSOM and techniques based on it, can potentially provide 3D field configurations around different nanoparticles and nonastructures in LC colloids system, which was so far difficult to achieve with the conventional optical microscopy techniques.

11. Conclusions and outlook

The advent of pulsed lasers and the advances in digital imaging technology led to imaging techniques that allow one to reveal director field configurations and 3D composition patterns of material components in LC colloids with high spatial resolution. In particular, multimodal nonlinear optical microscopy techniques allow to probe these composite soft-matter systems by imaging different constituents in different nonlinear modalities, selectively and simultaneously, avoiding the need of finding appropriate dyes. The sub-diffraction limited optical imaging techniques, such as STED microscopy and NSOM, are promising to extend our abilities of probing 3D structural information of LC-nanocomposites to the nanometer length scales. Further developments in the field of optical microscopy and its applications to the LC colloids are critically important for expanding the body of knowledge in the study of these soft-matter systems such as LC colloids.

References

1. S. Bradbury and B. Bracegirdle, *Introduction to light microscopy. RMS Microscopy Handbooks, 42.* Oxford, UK.: Bios Scientific publishers (1998).
2. S. W. Hell and J. Wichmann, Breaking the diffraction resolution limit by stimulated emission: stimulated-emission-depletion fluorescence microscopy, *Opt. Lett.* **19**(11), 780–782 (1994).

3. T. A. Klar, S. Jakobs, M. Dyba, A. Egner, and S. W. Hell, Fluorescence microscopy with diffraction resolution barrier broken by stimulated emission, *Proceedings of the National Academy of Sciences.* **97**(15), 8206–8210 (2000).
4. C. Coltharp and J. Xiao, Superresolution microscopy for microbiology, *Cellular microbiology.* **14**(12), 1808–1818 (2012).
5. L. Huang, G. V. Hartland, L.-Q. Chu, R. M. Feenstra, C. Lian, K. Tahy, and H. Xing, Ultrafast transient absorption microscopy studies of carrier dynamics in epitaxial graphene, *Nano. Lett.* **10**(4), 1308–1313 (2010).
6. A. V. Kachynski, A. N. Kuzmin, P. N. Prasad, and I. I. Smalyukh, Realignment-enhanced coherent anti-stokes raman scattering and three-dimensional imaging in anisotropic fluids, *Opt. Express.* **16**(14), 10617–10632 (2008).
7. A. Kachynski, A. Kuzmin, P. Prasad, and I. Smalyukh, Coherent anti-stokes raman scattering polarized microscopy of three-dimensional director structures in liquid crystals, *Appl. Phys. Lett.* **91**(15), 151905 (2007).
8. T. Lee, R. P. Trivedi, and I. I. Smalyukh, Multimodal nonlinear optical polarizing microscopy of long-range molecular order in liquid crystals, *Opt. Lett.* **35**(20), 3447–3449 (2010).
9. T. Lee, H. Mundoor, D. G. Gann, T. J. Callahan, and I. I. Smalyukh, Imaging of director fields in liquid crystals using stimulated raman scattering microscopy, *Opt. Express.* **21**(10), 12129–12134 (2013).
10. G. Liao, I. I. Smalyukh, J. Kelly, O. D. Lavrentovich, and A. Jakli, Electro-rotation of colloidal particles in liquid crystals, *Phys. Rev. E.* **72**(3), 031704 (2005).
11. Q. Liu, Y. Cui, D. Gardner, X. Li, S. He, and I. I. Smalyukh, Self-alignment of plasmonic gold nanorods in reconfigurable anisotropic fluids for tunable bulk metamaterial applications, *Nano. Lett.* **10**(4), 1347–1353 (2010).
12. Q. Liu, B. Senyuk, J. Tang, T. Lee, J. Qian, S. He, and I. I. Smalyukh, Plasmonic complex fluids of nematiclike and helicoidal self-assemblies of gold nanorods with a negative order parameter, *Phys. Rev. Lett.* **109**(8), 088301 (2012).
13. S. S. Lo, M. S. Devadas, T. A. Major, and G. V. Hartland, Optical detection of single nano-objects by transient absorption microscopy, *Analyst.* **138**(1), 25–31 (2013).
14. A. Martinez, M. Ravnik, B. Lucero, R. Visvanathan, S. Zumer, and I. I. Smalyukh, Mutually tangled colloidal knots and induced defect loops in nematic fields, *Nat. Mater.* **13**(3), 258–263 (2014).
15. H. Mundoor, T. Lee, D. G. Gann, P. J. Ackerman, B. Senyuk, J. van de Lagemaat, and I. I. Smalyukh, Optically and elastically assembled plasmonic nanoantennae for spatially resolved characterization of chemical composition in soft matter systems using surface enhanced spontaneous and stimulated raman scattering, *J. Appl. Phys.* **116**(6), 063511 (2014).
16. T. Müller, C. Schumann, and A. Kraegeloh, STED microscopy and its applications: new insights into cellular processes on the nanoscale, *ChemPhysChem.* **13**(8), 1986–2000 (2012).
17. C. Rosenblatt, Optical imaging of liquid crystals at the nanoscale,

ChemPhysChem. **15**(7), 1261–1269 (2014).

18. B. Senyuk and I. I. Smalyukh, Elastic interactions between colloidal microspheres and elongated convex and concave nanoprisms in nematic liquid crystals, *Soft Matter.* **8**(33), 8729–8734 (2012).

19. B. Senyuk, J. S. Evans, P. J. Ackerman, T. Lee, P. Manna, L. Vigderman, E. R. Zubarev, J. v. d. Lagemaat, and I. I. Smalyukh, Shape-dependent oriented trapping and scaffolding of plasmonic nanoparticles by topological defects for self-assembly of colloidal dimers in liquid crystals, *Nano. Lett.* **12** (2), 955–963 (2012).

20. B. Senyuk, Q. Liu, S. He, R. D. Kamien, R. B. Kusner, T. C. Lubensky, and I. I. Smalyukh, Topological colloids, *Nature.* **493**(7431), 200–205 (2013).

21. I. I. Smalyukh, S. Shiyanovskii, and O. Lavrentovich, Three-dimensional imaging of orientational order by fluorescence confocal polarizing microscopy, *Chem. Phys. Lett.* **336**(1), 88–96 (2001).

22. I. I. Smalyukh, J. Butler, J. D. Shrout, M. R. Parsek, and G. C. Wong, Elasticity-mediated nematiclike bacterial organization in model extracellular DNA matrix, *Phys. Rev. E.* **78**(3), 030701 (2008).

23. I. I. Smalyukh, Y. Lansac, N. A. Clark, and R. P. Trivedi, Three-dimensional structure and multistable optical switching of triple-twisted particle-like excitations in anisotropic fluids, *Nat. Mater.* **9**(2), 139–145 (2010).

24. R. P. Trivedi, T. Lee, K. A. Bertness, and I. I. Smalyukh, Three dimensional optical manipulation and structural imaging of soft materials by use of laser tweezers and multimodal nonlinear microscopy, *Opt. Express.* **18**(26), 27658–27669 (2010).

25. R. Trivedi, D. Engström, and I. Smalyukh, Optical manipulation of colloids and defect structures in anisotropic liquid crystal fluids, *Journal of Optics.* **13**(4), 044001 (2011).

26. F. D. Bloss, *Introduction to the Methods of Optical Crystallography.* Harcourt School (1961).

27. T. Jue, *Fundamental Concepts in Biophysics: Volume 1 (Handbook of Modern Biophysics).* Humana Press (2009).

28. U. Kubitscheck, *Fluorescence Microscopy: From Principles to Biological Applications.* Wiley-Blackwell (2013).

29. J. Mertz, *Introduction to optical microscopy.* Roberts (2010).

30. M. Muller, *Introduction to confocal fluorescence microscopy.* vol. 69, SPIE press (2006).

31. D. B. Murphy and M. W. Davidson, *Fundamentals of Light Microscopy and Electronic Imaging.* Wiley-Blackwell (2012).

32. W. Nesse, *Introduction to Optical Mineralogy.* Oxford University Press (2012).

33. J. Pawley, *Handbook of Biological Confocal Microscopy.* Springer (2006).

34. L. Spangler, S. Levine, and L. Johnstone, The ultimate guide to your microscope (2009).

35. P. G. de Gennes and J. Prost, *The Physics of Liquid Crystals (International Series of Monographs on Physics).* Clarendon Press (1995).

36. R. W. Boyd, *Nonlinear Optics, Third Edition.* Academic Press (2008).

37. K. Yoshiki, M. Hashimoto, and T. Araki, Second-harmonic-generation microscopy using excitation beam with controlled polarization pattern to determine three-dimensional molecular orientation, *Jap. J. Appl. Phys.* **44**(8L), L1066 (2005).

38. Y. Fu, H. Wang, R. Shi, and J.-X. Cheng, Second harmonic and sum frequency generation imaging of fibrous astroglial filaments in ex vivo spinal tissues, *Biophys. J.* **92**(9), 3251–3259 (2007).

39. R. S. Pillai, M. Oh-e, H. Yokoyama, G. Brakenhoff, and M. Müller, Imaging colloidal particle induced topological defects in a nematic liquid crystal using third harmonic generation microscopy, *Opt. Express.* **14**(26), 12976–12983 (2006).

40. E. Potma and X. Xie, Coherent anti-stokes raman scattering (CARS) microscopy: Instrumentation and applications, *Handbook of biomedical nonlinear optical microscopy.* p. 412 (2008).

41. C. W. Freudiger, W. Min, B. G. Saar, S. Lu, G. R. Holtom, C. He, J. C. Tsai, J. X. Kang, and X. S. Xie, Label-free biomedical imaging with high sensitivity by stimulated raman scattering microscopy, *Science.* **322**(5909), 1857–1861 (2008).

42. W. Min, C. W. Freudiger, S. Lu, and X. S. Xie, Coherent nonlinear optical imaging: beyond fluorescence microscopy, *Annu. Rev. Phys. Chem.* **62**, 507 (2011).

43. G. Fleming, Chemical applications of ultrafast spectroscopy, *Int. J. Quantum Chem.* **31**(6), 989 (1987).

44. J. Shah, *Ultrafast spectroscopy of semiconductors and semiconductor nanostructures.* vol. 115, Springer Science & Business Media (1999).

45. N. Behabtu, J. R. Lomeda, M. J. Green, A. L. Higginbotham, A. Sinitskii, D. V. Kosynkin, D. Tsentalovich, A. N. G. Parra-Vasquez, J. Schmidt, and E. Kesselman, Spontaneous high-concentration dispersions and liquid crystals of graphene, *Nat. Nanotechnol.* **5**(6), 406–411 (2010).

46. B. Dan, N. Behabtu, A. Martinez, J. S. Evans, D. V. Kosynkin, J. M. Tour, M. Pasquali, and I. I. Smalyukh, Liquid crystals of aqueous, giant graphene oxide flakes, *Soft Matter.* **7**(23), 11154–11159 (2011).

47. E. Betzig, G. H. Patterson, R. Sougrat, O. W. Lindwasser, S. Olenych, J. S. Bonifacino, M. W. Davidson, J. Lippincott-Schwartz, and H. F. Hess, Imaging intracellular fluorescent proteins at nanometer resolution, *Science.* **313** (5793), 1642–1645 (2006).

48. R. M. Dickson, A. B. Cubitt, R. Y. Tsien, and W. Moerner, On/off blinking and switching behaviour of single molecules of green fluorescent protein, *Nature.* **388**(6640), 355–358 (1997).

49. S. T. Hess, T. P. Girirajan, and M. D. Mason, Ultra-high resolution imaging by fluorescence photoactivation localization microscopy, *Biophys. J.* **91**(11), 4258–4272 (2006).

50. M. Bates, B. Huang, G. T. Dempsey, and X. Zhuang, Multicolor super-resolution imaging with photo-switchable fluorescent probes, *Science.* **317** (5845), 1749–1753 (2007).

51. B. Huang, W. Wang, M. Bates, and X. Zhuang, Three-dimensional super-

resolution imaging by stochastic optical reconstruction microscopy, *Science.* **319**(5864), 810–813 (2008).

52. M. J. Rust, M. Bates, and X. Zhuang, Sub-diffraction-limit imaging by stochastic optical reconstruction microscopy (STORM), *Nature methods.* **3**(10), 793–796 (2006).

53. A. Egner, C. Geisler, C. Von Middendorff, H. Bock, D. Wenzel, R. Medda, M. Andresen, A. C. Stiel, S. Jakobs, and C. Eggeling, Fluorescence nanoscopy in whole cells by asynchronous localization of photoswitching emitters, *Biophys. J.* **93**(9), 3285–3290 (2007).

54. M. Heilemann, S. van de Linde, M. Schüttpelz, R. Kasper, B. Seefeldt, A. Mukherjee, P. Tinnefeld, and M. Sauer, Subdiffraction resolution fluorescence imaging with conventional fluorescent probes, *Angew. Chem. (Int. Ed.).* **47**(33), 6172–6176 (2008).

55. M. G. Gustafsson, Surpassing the lateral resolution limit by a factor of two using structured illumination microscopy, *Journal of microscopy.* **198**(2), 82–87 (2000).

56. M. G. Gustafsson, L. Shao, P. M. Carlton, C. R. Wang, I. N. Golubovskaya, W. Z. Cande, D. A. Agard, and J. W. Sedat, Three-dimensional resolution doubling in wide-field fluorescence microscopy by structured illumination, *Biophys. J.* **94**(12), 4957–4970 (2008).

57. R. Heintzmann and P. A. Benedetti, High-resolution image reconstruction in fluorescence microscopy with patterned excitation, *Appl. Opt.* **45**(20), 5037–5045 (2006).

58. Y. Oshikane, T. Kataoka, M. Okuda, S. Hara, H. Inoue, and M. Nakano, Observation of nanostructure by scanning near-field optical microscope with small sphere probe, *Sci. Technol. Adv. Mat.* **8**(3), 181–185 (2007).

Chapter 6

X-ray scattering

Goran Ungar,* Zhi Hong Chen and Xiangbing Zeng

University of Sheffield,
Department of Materials Science and Engineering,
Mappin Street, Sheffield S1 3JD, UK
Wuhan University of Technology,
School of Science, Wuhan 430070, China
**Zhejiang Sci-Tech University, Hangzhou 310018, China*
**g.ungar@sheffield.ac.uk*

This chapter will give the reader the necessary background to appreciate what information X-ray diffraction can provide on systems of nano- and microparticles in liquid crystals. We give a brief introduction to scattering of X-rays on an isolated object (Sec. 1), on an isotropic liquid or glass (Sec. 2) and on the nematic liquid crystal (Sec. 3). This is followed by a description of small-angle scattering (SAXS) on particles of spherical shape (Sec. 4) and on anisometric particles (platelets, rods and ellipsoids). Selected examples of SAXS studies of such particles in thermotropic and lyotropic liquid crystals are given in Sec. 6. Diffraction on periodic particle arrays (2-d and 3-d) is introduced in Sec. 7, while in Sec. 8 we deal with grazing incidence X-ray diffraction and X-ray reflectivity. Finally selected examples of X-ray studies of periodic nanoparticle arrays in liquid crystals are described in Sec. 9. Although not specifically stated, most of the material covered by this chapter also applies to neutron scattering.

Contents

1. Brief introduction to X-ray scattering

X-rays are high energy electromagnetic waves, spanning the spectrum between UV and γ-rays. Typical X-rays used for structural characterization have photon energies of several to several tens of keV, with corresponding wavelengths similar to those of inter-atomic distances (Ångströms). Such high energy X-rays have the ability to penetrate bulk samples, in particular those consisting of light elements, without much energy exchange, hence causing little damage to the sample. Elastic X-ray scattering/diffraction is one of the most important and most versatile tools for investigation of structures, from subatomic (Å) to colloidal scale (μm), and of inorganic, organic, biological and organic/inorganic hybrid materials.[1]

X-rays are generated conventionally using an X-ray tube, where a metal target (typically copper) is bombarded by high energy electrons (several tens of keV). The energy of the electron is high enough that on collision with an atom in the target, a core electron is ejected leaving a "hole" in the inner orbital. Subsequent quantum transition of a high-orbital electron to the inner orbital produces an X-ray photon of specific wavelength characteristic of the target material, which is then used for X-ray scattering/diffraction.

One can also generate X-rays in a synchrotron. X-rays are produced when the trajectory of high energy electrons, typically of several GeV, travelling at nearly the speed of light, is deflected by a strong magnetic field. Synchrotron radiation has high brilliance (several orders of magnitude higher than radiation from laboratory sources); it has high directivity and polarization, and with the help of a suitable monochromator can be made highly monochromatic. Such properties make synchrotron radiation suitable for carrying out e.g. time-resolved and high resolution studies of small or weakly scattering samples, or samples under diverse environmental conditions.

X-rays are scattered by electrons in matter. The classical interpretation is that an electron as a charged particle oscillates under the effect of the oscillating electric field of an incident X-ray beam, and hence emits an electromagnetic wave of the same frequency/wavelength. The intensity I_e

of the beam scattered by an electron is given by the Thomson equation:

$$I_e(r) = \frac{I_0}{r^2} \left(\frac{e^2}{mc^2}\right)^2 \frac{1 + \cos^2 2\theta}{2} \tag{1}$$

Here I_0 is the intensity of the incident beam, r the distance from the scattering electron, e the charge and m the mass of the electron, c the speed of light, and 2θ the scattering angle (angle between scattered and incident beam).

When the incident X-ray is scattered by two electrons separated by a vector $\mathbf{r}$ in space, in calculation of the combined scattered intensity the path length difference between the two scattered beams needs to be considered. According to Fig. 1, the path difference between the waves scattered on the two electrons is:

$$(O'AP' - OBP) = \mathbf{r} \cdot (\mathbf{s} - \mathbf{s}_0) \tag{2}$$

where $\mathbf{s}_0$ and $\mathbf{s}$ are the unit vectors of the incident and scattered X-rays. Hence the phase difference is:

$$\mathbf{r} \cdot (\mathbf{s} - \mathbf{s}_0) \cdot 2\pi/\lambda = \mathbf{r} \cdot \mathbf{q} \tag{3}$$

Here $\mathbf{q} = (\mathbf{s} - \mathbf{s}_0) \cdot 2\pi/\lambda$ is the wave vector of scattered light and $|\mathbf{q}| = 4\pi/\lambda \cdot \sin\theta$. Consequently the combined scattered intensity $I(\mathbf{q})$ is:

$$I(\mathbf{q}) = I_e|1 + e^{i\mathbf{r} \cdot \mathbf{q}}|^2 \tag{4}$$

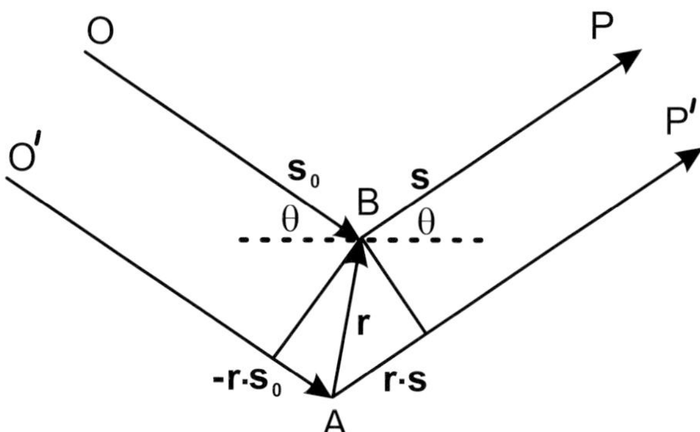

Fig. 1. The path difference between scattered X-rays by two electrons is related to the direction of incident and scattered X-rays (represented by unit vectors s and s₀), and the vector distance (**r**) between them.

For an object (an atom, a molecule, a nanoparticle or a collection of these) that contains N electrons, the nth of which is at position $\mathbf{r}_n (1 \leq n \leq N)$, Eq. (4) can be generalized to:

$$I(\mathbf{q}) = I_e \left| \sum_n e^{i \cdot \mathbf{r}_n \cdot \mathbf{q}} \right|^2 = I_e |F(\mathbf{q})|^2 \tag{5}$$

Here $|F(\mathbf{q})|^2 = F(\mathbf{q})F^*(\mathbf{q})$ is normally called the *form factor* of the object. The summation can also be rewritten as an integration, so the scattering amplitude becomes:

$$F(\mathbf{q}) = \int \rho(\mathbf{r})e^{i\mathbf{r} \cdot \mathbf{q}} d\mathbf{r} \tag{6}$$

with $\rho(\mathbf{r})$ being electron density in the object. $F(\mathbf{q})$ and $\rho(\mathbf{r})$ are Fourier pairs so that:

$$\rho(\mathbf{r}) = \frac{1}{(2\pi)^3} \int F(\mathbf{q})e^{-i\mathbf{r} \cdot \mathbf{q}} d\mathbf{q} \tag{7}$$

While vector $\mathbf{r}$ exists in the physical space, which is normally called the *real space*, $\mathbf{q}$ exists in its Fourier dual space called *reciprocal space*.

In most cases the scattering intensity $I(\mathbf{q})$ is corrected by that of a single electron I_e, and for simplicity in this chapter we will use $I(\mathbf{q})$ to stand for the corrected scattering intensity.

For a system containing many objects (identical or non-identical), scattering intensity is:

$$I(\mathbf{q}) = \sum_j F_j(\mathbf{q})e^{i\mathbf{r}_j \cdot \mathbf{q}} \sum_k F_k^*(\mathbf{q})e^{-i\mathbf{r}_k \cdot \mathbf{q}} \tag{8}$$

This can be rewritten as:

$$I(\mathbf{q}) = \sum_j |F_j(\mathbf{q})|^2 + \sum_j \sum_{k \neq j} F_j(\mathbf{q})F_k^*(\mathbf{q})e^{i(\mathbf{r}_j - \mathbf{r}_k) \cdot \mathbf{q}} \tag{9}$$

While the first component of Eq. (9) is simply the summation of the form factors of all the objects in the system, the second component is related to the more complex interference scattering between objects, and is highly dependent on the positional and orientational order in the system under study.

Typical cases will be examined in the following sections: isotropic liquid, liquid crystals with orientational but no translational order, disordered nanoparticles with narrow size distribution of various shapes, and ordered arrays of nanoparticles in liquid crystals.

2. X-ray scattering on an isotropic liquid

In an isotropic liquid, for each object/molecule $\rho(\mathbf{r})$ and hence $F(\mathbf{q})$ are spherically averaged. Consequently Eq. (6) becomes:[2]

$$F(q) = \int 4\pi r^2 \rho(r) \frac{\sin(qr)}{qr} \, \mathrm{d}r \tag{10}$$

The interference scattering between objects/molecules is spherically averaged too, and the total scattering intensity from all molecules is:

$$I(q) = \sum_j F_j^2(q) + \sum_j \sum_{k \neq j} F_j(q) F_k(q) \frac{\sin(qr_{jk})}{qr_{jk}} \tag{11}$$

Here $r_{jk} = |\mathbf{r}_j - \mathbf{r}_k|$.

For a liquid with N identical objects/molecules:

$$I(q) = NF^2(q) \left[1 + \frac{1}{N} \sum_j \sum_{k \neq j} \frac{\sin(qr_{jk})}{qr_{jk}} \right] = NF^2(q)S(q) \tag{12}$$

Here $S(q)$ is the *interference function* and:

$$S(q) = 1 + \frac{1}{N} \sum_j \sum_{k \neq j} \frac{\sin(qr_{jk})}{qr_{jk}} \tag{13}$$

Note that $S(q)^{1/2}$ is referred to as the "structure factor"; see below. The radial distribution function (or the pair correlation function) $g(r)$ gives the probability of finding the distance between two molecules $r_{jk} = r$, consequently:

$$S(q) = 1 + \frac{N-1}{V} \int 4\pi r^2 g(r) \frac{\sin(qr)}{qr} \, \mathrm{d}r \tag{14}$$

Here $g(r)$ is normalized so that the total volume is:

$$V = \int 4\pi r^2 g(r) \mathrm{d}r \tag{15}$$

At long distances r correlation between objects/molecules is lost in a liquid, and $g(r)$ adopts its average value, hence:

$$\lim_{r \to \infty} g(r) = 1 \tag{16}$$

From Eq. (14) it can be seen that the radial distribution function $g(r)$ and the interference function $S(q)$ (or more precisely $S(q) - 1$) are related by Fourier transformation.

3. X-ray scattering on nematic liquid crystals

In the case of nematic liquid crystals (see Chap. 2 for basic concept definitions) $\rho(\mathbf{r})$ and $F(\mathbf{q})$ are cylindrically averaged for each molecule with the cylinder axis along the director $\mathbf{n}$; hence they become $\rho(x,z)$ and $F(\xi,\zeta)$ in cylindrical coordinates. Assuming $\rho(x,z)$ is centrosymmetric, $F(\xi,\zeta)$ is always real and:[2]

$$F(\xi,\zeta) = \int_0^\infty \int_0^\infty 4\pi x \rho(x,z) J_0(\xi x) \cos(\zeta z) \mathrm{d}x \mathrm{d}z \qquad (17)$$

Here J_0 is the Bessel function of 0th order. In a nematic phase of N identical molecules, the intensity is given by:

$$I(\xi,\zeta) = N F^2(\xi,\zeta) + \sum_j \sum_{k \neq j} F^2(\xi,\zeta) J_0(\xi x_{jk}) \cos(\zeta z_{jk}) \qquad (18)$$

A cylindrical interference function $S(\xi,\zeta)$ can be defined, so that:

$$I(\xi,\zeta) = N F^2(\xi,\zeta) S(\xi,\zeta) \qquad (19)$$

$S(\xi,\zeta)$ is linked to the cylindrical distribution function $w(x,z)$ by Fourier transformation, i.e.

$$S(\xi,\zeta) = 1 + \frac{N-1}{V} \int x w(x,z) J_0(\xi x) \cos(\zeta z) \mathrm{d}x \mathrm{d}z \qquad (20)$$

Here $w(x,z)$ is normalized so that

$$S(\xi,\zeta) = \int 4\pi x w(x,z) \mathrm{d}x \mathrm{d}z = V \qquad (21)$$

and

$$\lim_{x,z \to \infty} w(x,z) = 1 \qquad (22)$$

Instead of treating the nematic system as a collection of molecules as above, we can describe the whole structure using one single electron density function $\rho(\mathbf{r}) = \rho(x,z)$, then we have in cylindrical coordinates:

$$I(\xi,\zeta) = F^2(\xi,\zeta) \qquad (23)$$

and in this case the cylindrical distribution function can be defined as the direct inverse Fourier transform of $I(\xi,\zeta)$, so that

$$w(x,z) = \frac{1}{2\pi^2} \int \xi I(\xi,\zeta) J_0(\xi x) \cos(\zeta z) \mathrm{d}\xi \mathrm{d}\zeta \qquad (24)$$

In fact, $w(x,z)$ is the self-convolution of the electron density $\rho(x,z) \otimes \rho(x,z)$.

Converting to spherical coordinates, we get $w(r, \alpha) = w(x, z)$ where $x = r \sin \alpha$ and $z = r \cos \alpha$, and in the reciprocal space $I(q, \alpha) = I(\xi, \zeta)$ where $\xi = q \sin \alpha$ and $\zeta = q \cos \alpha$. Here the polar angle α (see Fig. 2) is zero when the vector is parallel to the director. $I(q, \alpha)$ can be expanded in a series of Legendre polynomials of even order (P_{2n}):

$$I(q, \alpha) = \sum_{n=0}^{\infty} I_{2n}(q) P_{2n}(\cos \alpha) \tag{25}$$

Where

$$I_{2n}(q) = (4n + 1) \int_0^{\pi/2} I(q, \alpha) P_{2n}(\cos \alpha) \sin \alpha \, d\alpha \tag{26}$$

Similarly

$$w(r, \alpha) = \sum_{n=0}^{\infty} w_{2n}(r) P_{2n}(\cos \alpha) \tag{27}$$

It was found by Deas[3] that:

$$w_{2n}(r) = \frac{(-1)^n}{2\pi^2} \int_0^{\infty} q^2 I_{2n}(q) j_{2n}(qr) \, dq \tag{28}$$

Here j_{2n} is the spherical Bessel function of the $2n^{th}$ order. In equations derived above the distribution of the molecular axes along the nematic director $\mathbf{n}$ is averaged for each and every molecule before their correlation is considered. However, for nematic systems a more realistic representation is to treat the correlations, $S_c(\mathbf{q})$, within a "cluster" of interfering molecular first. Consequently in each cluster the diffraction intensity is cylindrically averaged about the local director $\mathbf{n}'$, so that:

$$I_c(q', \alpha') = N_c F^2(q', \alpha') S_c(q', \alpha') \tag{29}$$

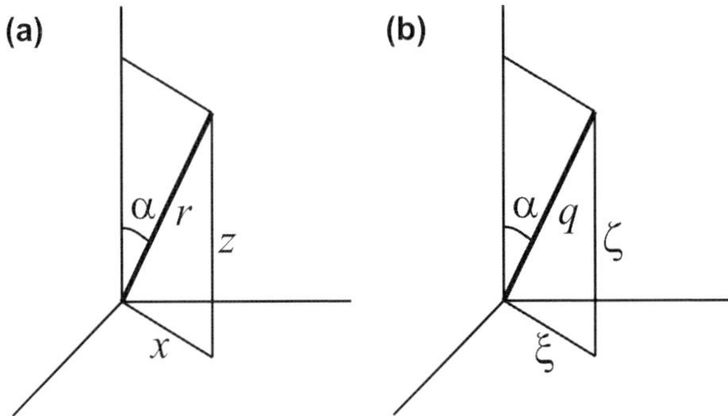

Fig. 2.   Cylindrical and spherical coordinates in (a) real and (b) reciprocal space.

where q' and α' are defined in local cylindrical coordinates with the cylindrical axis along $\mathbf{n}'$. The orientational distribution function, $D(\alpha)$, describes how $\mathbf{n}$'s are distributed cylindrically around $\mathbf{n}$. It has been derived by Deas[3] that the orientation parameters $\langle P_{2n} \rangle$ of $I(q,\alpha)$, $I_c(q,\alpha)$ and $D(\alpha)$ are related by:

$$\langle P_{2n} \rangle_I = \langle P_{2n} \rangle_D \langle P_{2n} \rangle_c \tag{30}$$

Here the orientation parameters $\langle P_{2n} \rangle_I$ of $I(q,\alpha)$, and similarly $\langle P_{2n} \rangle_c$ of $I_c(q,\alpha)$ and $\langle P_{2n} \rangle_D$ of $D(\alpha)$, are defined by equations (31) below.

$$\langle P_{2n} \rangle_I = \frac{\int_0^{\pi/2} I(q,\alpha) P_{2n}(\cos(\alpha)) \sin \alpha d\alpha}{\int_0^{\pi/2} I(q,\alpha) \sin \alpha d\alpha}$$

$$\langle P_{2n} \rangle_c = \frac{\int_0^{\pi/2} I_c(q,\alpha) P_{2n}(\cos(\alpha)) \sin \alpha d\alpha}{\int_0^{\pi/2} I_c(q,\alpha) \sin \alpha d\alpha}$$

$$\langle P_{2n} \rangle_D = \frac{\int_0^{\pi/2} D(\alpha) P_{2n}(\cos(\alpha)) \sin \alpha d\alpha}{\int_0^{\pi/2} D(\alpha) \sin \alpha d\alpha} \tag{31}$$

For an infinitely narrow meridional scattering arc from a cluster $\langle P_{2n} \rangle_c = P_{2n}(\cos 0°) = 1$. For this case of perfect molecular orientation within each cluster, we thus have:

$$\langle P_{2n} \rangle_D = \langle P_{2n} \rangle_I \tag{32}$$

and $D(\alpha)$ can be directly obtained from an azimuthal intensity distribution around the scattering halo. Due regard has to be given in this case to the geometry of the scattering experiment. I.e. in order to cover all polar angles down to $\alpha = 0$ and observe properly the meridional scattering arc whose scattering angle is 2θ, the sample has to be tilted so that the global director subtends an angle $\pi/2 - \theta$ with the X-ray beam (see Figs. 1 and 4, and also Fig. 13).

In practice, a more common situation is where the orientational distribution or the order parameter are determined from the strong scattering arc at the equator. Then, however, $\langle P_{2n} \rangle_c = P_{2n}(0) = (-1)^n [(2n)!/2^{2n}(n!)^2]$ and:

$$\langle P_{2n} \rangle_D = \frac{(-1)^n 2^{2n}(n!)^2}{(2n)!} \langle P_{2n} \rangle_I \tag{33}$$

In this case each of the orientational parameters needs to be obtained according to Eq. (33) to derive the orientation distribution function $D(\alpha)$

experimentally. If only the P_{2n} nematic order parameter is required, it is given by

$$\langle P_{2n}\rangle_D = -2\langle P_{2n}\rangle_I \tag{34}$$

The use of equations (33) and (34) is limited by the fact that an azimuthally narrow distribution is required for the molecular cluster. Ideally it requires knowledge of the orientation parameters of the cluster $\langle P_{2n}\rangle_c$, in order to retrieve $D(\alpha)$ from the recorded X-ray scattering pattern.

Mitchell and Lovell have used the above equations to sharpen the scattering patterns of oriented amorphous polymers and from these they derived the cylindrical distribution function for atactic PMMA and polystyrene; for more details on the experimental procedure see Refs. 4 and 5.

For simple rod-like molecules, Leadbetter *et al.*[6] used the wide angle diffuse ring, corresponding to the lateral mean distance between first neighbour molecules (Fig. 3). They derived the following expression for the angular intensity profile $I(\beta)$ along the equatorial arc:

$$I(\beta) = \int_\beta^{\pi/2} \frac{D(\alpha)\sin\alpha}{\cos^2\beta\sqrt{\tan^2\alpha - \tan^2\beta}}\,\mathrm{d}\alpha \tag{35}$$

The inverse of Eq. (35), to obtain $D(\alpha)$ from $I(\beta)$, can be solved either analytically[7] or numerically.[6] The simplest approach to the problem is by assuming that $D(\alpha)$ takes the Maier-Saupe form:[8]

$$D(\alpha) = \frac{1}{z}e^{m\cos^2\alpha} \tag{36}$$

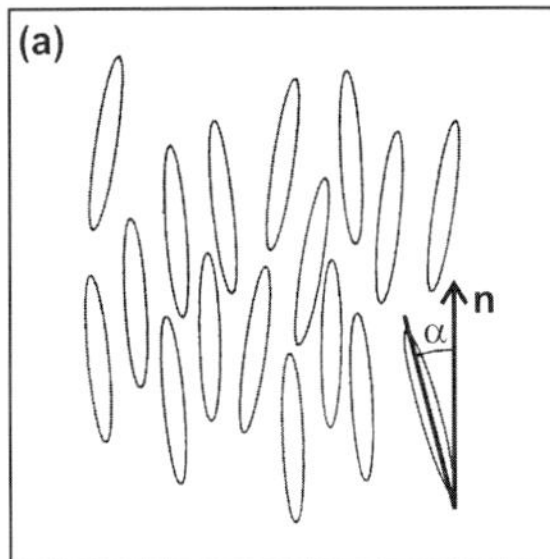

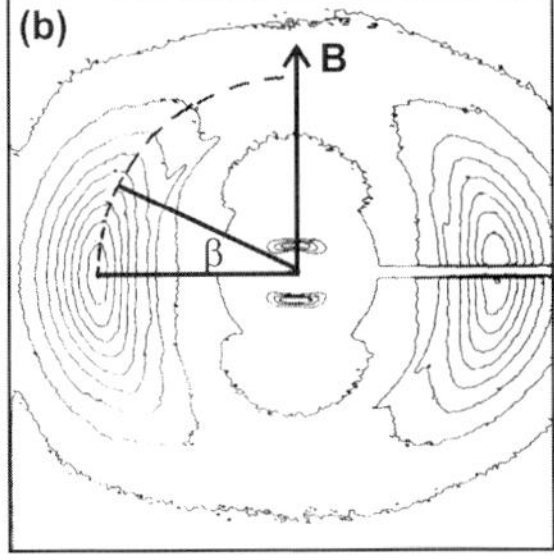

Fig. 3. (a) Definition of the angle α between a rod-like molecule and the nematic director **n**. (b) Definition of the azimuthal angle β describing the scattering in the wide angle diffuse ring (from Ref. 6 with permission from Taylor and Francis Ltd., http://www.tandfonline.com.)

Here Z is a normalization constant and m is the Maier-Saupe nematic interaction parameter (see last section of Chap. 2). Combining equations (35) and (36) one obtains:[9]

$$I(\beta) = \frac{e^{m\cos^2\beta\sqrt{\pi}}}{\sqrt{m}Z\cos\beta}\frac{\sqrt{\pi}}{2}\mathrm{erf}(\sqrt{m}\cos\beta) \tag{37}$$

where $\mathrm{erf}(x) = \frac{2}{\sqrt{\pi}}\int_0^x e^{-y^2}\,dy$ is the error function. Equation (37) can be easily used to fit the experimental $I(\beta)$ curve, and to retrieve the nematic order parameter $S = \langle P_{2n}\rangle_D$. The equation was found experimentally to be reliable within the interval $0.3 < S < 0.8$,[10,11] (Fig. 4). The relationship between the order parameter S and the Maier-Saupe nematic interaction parameter m is given by Eq. (38) below.

$$S = \frac{3}{4m}\left(\frac{e^m}{s(m)} - 1\right) - \frac{1}{2} \tag{38}$$

Here $s(m)$ is an integral given by $s(m) = \frac{1}{\sqrt{m}}\int_0^{\sqrt{m}} e^{x^2}\,dx = \sum_{n=0}^{\infty}\frac{m^n}{n!(2n+1)}$.

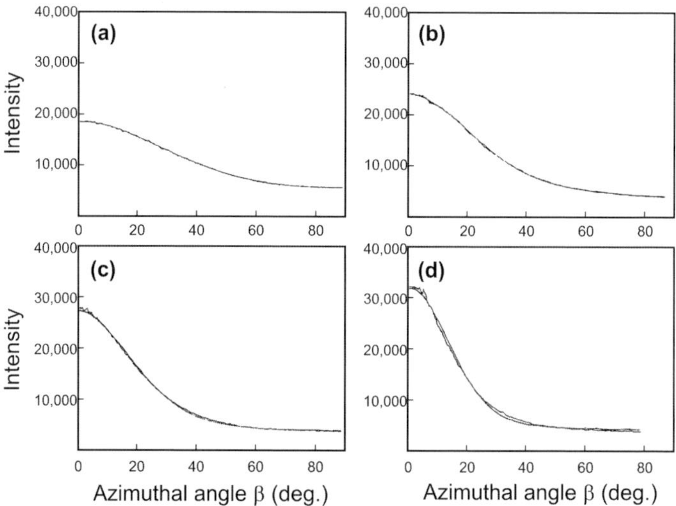

Fig. 4. Scattering intensity I versus azimuthal angle about the wide angle diffuse ring for a side-chain LC polymer in the nematic phase. (a) $T = 108°C$, $S = 0.35$. (b) $T = 86°C$, $S = 0.55$. (c) $T = 63°C$, $S = 0.70$. (d) $T = 25°C$, $S = 0.80$. Reprinted from Ref. 11, Copyright (1995), with permission from Elsevier.

Regarding X-ray diffraction on other LC phases that have long-range positional order and show sharp Bragg diffraction peaks (smectic, columnar, cubic) the theory is essentially the same as that described in Sec. 7 of this chapter for ordered periodic nanoparticle (NP) arrays, so these phases will not be discussed here. A detailed review, particularly dealing with smectic LCs, was published a while ago by Pershan.[12]

4. Principles of small-angle X-ray scattering (SAXS) on disordered particles: Solid, core-shell and hollow spheres

Small angle X-ray scattering (SAXS) is a powerful method to probe the structure of both disordered and ordered systems with electron density fluctuation on the length scale of 1 to 100 nm. As shown by equations (6) and (7), $F(\mathbf{q})$ and $\rho(\mathbf{r})$ are Fourier pairs, which means that larger scale features in real space of $\mathbf{r}$ correspond to smaller q-values in reciprocal space, hence to smaller diffraction angles 2θ since $q = 4\pi/\lambda \cdot \sin\theta$. Typically SAXS covers the region of $q \leq 1$ nm^{-1}. This normally requires special design of X-ray optics in order to separate the scattered X-rays from the undiffracted beam, and best results are obtained from instruments using synchrotron radiation.

As shown in Sec. 2, for isotropic liquids or disordered solids where an individual object/particle is spherically averaged, the scattering amplitude is:

$$F(q) = \int 4\pi r^2 \rho(r) \frac{\sin(qr)}{qr} \, \mathrm{d}r \tag{10}$$

For solid, core-shell and hollow spherical nanoparticles, as shown in Fig. 5a, the above integral can be derived analytically and we obtain, for each type of sphere:

$$F(q)_{\text{solid}} = \rho_1 \frac{4\pi}{q^3} (\sin qR_1 - qR_1 \cos qR_1)$$

$$F(q)_{\text{core-shell}} = \rho_1 \frac{4\pi}{q^3} (\sin qR_1 - qR_1 \cos qR_1)$$

$$+\rho_2 \frac{4\pi}{q^3} [(\sin qR_2 - qR_2 \cos qR_2) - (\sin qR_1 - qR_1 \cos qR_1)]$$

$$F(q)_{\text{hollow}} = \rho_2 \frac{4\pi}{q^3} [(\sin qR_2 - qR_2 \cos qR_2) - (\sin qR_1 - qR_1 \cos qR_1)]$$

$$\tag{39}$$

For a monodisperse particle system, the form factor can be simply calculated using the scattering amplitude expression shown above. However, for a system with particles of different sizes, the calculation of the form

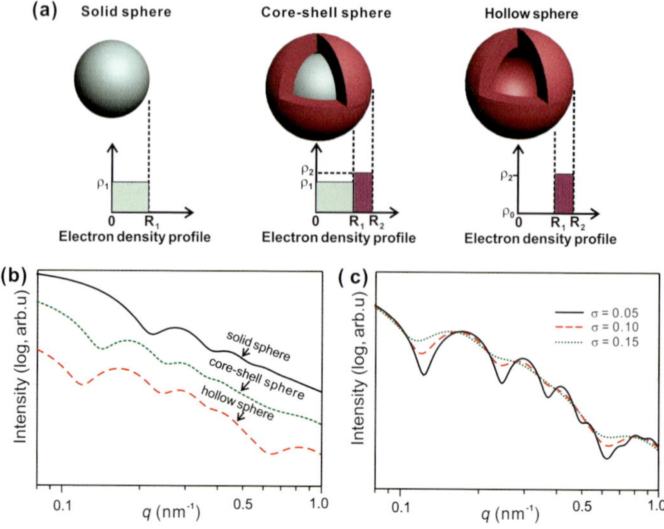

Fig. 5. Illustration of (a) the electron density profiles of solid, core-shell and hollow model spheres, (b) their corresponding form factor curves, and (c) the effect of size distribution on form factor curves of hollow spheres. Parameters used in (b) are: solid sphere $R_1 = 20$ nm, $\rho_1 = 672$ nm^{-3}; core-shell sphere $R_1 = 20$ nm, $R_2 = 30$ nm, $\rho_1 = 672$ nm^{-3}, $\rho_2 = 883$ nm^{-3}; hollow sphere $R_1 = 20$ nm, $R_2 = 30$ nm, $\rho_0 = 0$ nm^{-3}, $\rho_2 = 883$ nm^{-3}. For all three kinds of structures in (b), the size distribution standard deviation σ is 0.1. Parameters used in (c) are: $R_1 = 20$ nm, $R_2 = 30$ nm, $\rho_0 = 0$ nm^{-3}, $\rho_2 = 883$ nm^{-3}, σ as indicated. Schulz distribution function[13] was used in the calculation. (c) is reproduced from Ref. 98.

factor is complicated by the inclusion of the size distribution. The size distribution function is usually a documented probability function. Gaussian, Schulz[13] and log-normal distribution functions are commonly used. While Gaussian distribution is symmetric, Schulz distribution is skewed to larger sizes, and the log-normal to smaller sizes.[14,15] Schulz distribution function is widely used because the skewing feature of it enables its application in biomolecular, microemulsion or other systems that tend to aggregate.[16–19] The Schulz distribution function can be written as:

$$h(R) = \frac{(Rc/\overline{R})^c}{R\Gamma(c)} e^{-Rc/\overline{R}} \tag{40}$$

Here c is an integer related to the normalized standard deviation $\sigma = \left(\frac{\overline{R^2}}{\overline{R}^2} - 1\right)^{1/2}$ by $\sigma = (1/c)^{1/2}$ and $\boldsymbol{\Gamma}$ is the gamma function.

Figure 5b shows form factor curves of solid, core-shell and hollow spheres. The peak positions and shapes are clearly different for different kinds of particles. Figure 5c illustrates the effect of size distribution (Schulz distribution) on the form factor. It can be seen that with the increase in the width of the size distribution, the peaks and troughs tend to iron out. The calculated scattering functions in Fig. 5c can be used to estimate the polydispersity of a system of spherical particles. The above routine for calculating form factors can also be applied to more complex spherical particle types, e.g. core-multishell nanoparticles,[18,20–23] as well as core-shell particles where electron density varies smoothly following a parabolic[22,24,25] or an exponentially defined function.[26]

As shown in Sec. 2 (Eq. (12)), the scattering function is not determined only by the form factor of the particles, but also by the spatial correlation among them. If the particles are polydisperse, the correlation between them may be difficult to model. However, the problem can be greatly simplified by assuming that the spatial arrangement of nanoparticles is not correlated with the particle size. The decoupling approximation $(DA)^{27}$ is usually used, especially for nanoparticle systems with relatively narrow size distribution, since the effect of particle size on their spatial arrangement can be ignored. Within the DA, the correlation between all nanoparticles and their scattering amplitude can be determined separately, and Eq. (12) becomes:

$$I(q) = N[\langle |F(q)|^2 \rangle + |\langle F(q) \rangle|^2 (S(q) - 1)] \tag{41a}$$

$$\langle |F(q)|^2 \rangle = \int |F(q, R)|^2 h(R) \mathrm{d}R \tag{41b}$$

$$|\langle F(q) \rangle|^2 = |\int F(q, R) h(R) \mathrm{d}R|^2 \tag{41c}$$

Here the triangular brackets $\langle \ldots \rangle$ denote the average weighted over the size distribution, $h(R)$ is the size distribution function, and $S(q)$ the interference function related to the pair distribution function $g(r)$ through Eq. (14).

In a dilute system, where the distance between two particles is much larger than their size, the correlation among the particles is negligible and therefore the interference function $S(q)$ is equal to 1. In this case the scattered intensity is simply the addition of the form factors (Eq. (41b)) of all nanoparticles in the system. However, for a concentrated system the interference function $S(q)$ has to be taken into account.

Equation (14) indicates that $S(q)$ can be calculated when the pair correlation function $g(r)$ is known. In a disordered system with weak or no interaction among the particles, the Percus-Yevick (PY) approximation, derived by solving the Ornstein-Zernike integral equation,[28] has been proven to be a successful approximation for calculating the interference function.[29–33] The PY approximation has been used in many systems such as spherical blocks in polymers,[34,35] gas bubbles in liquid-like structures,[36] colloidal hard spheres in aqueous solution,[37] and inorganic nanoparticles in a polymer matrix.[38] The advantage of the PY approximation is that it is valid for very high packing densities of nanoparticles. Additionally, the analytical expression of the structure factor for particle packing in 3D has been derived and is easy to calculate. The interference function in the PY approximation for particle packing in 3D is given by:[30]

$$S(q) = \frac{4\pi R^3}{4\pi R^3 - 3\eta C(q)} \tag{42}$$

where R is the outer radius of the particle, η the particle volume fraction, and $C(q)$ the direct structure factor, i.e. the Fourier transform of the direct pair correlation function $C(r)$. For an isotropic system, $C(q)$ can be expressed as:

$$C(q) = \int_0^{2R} 4\pi r^2 C(r) \frac{\sin(qr)}{qr} \mathrm{d}r \tag{43}$$

$C(r)$ is given by:

$$C(r) = \begin{cases} \alpha + \beta \frac{r}{2R} + \delta \left(\frac{r}{2R}\right)^3, & r < 2R \\ 0, & r \geq 2R \end{cases} \tag{44}$$

where $\alpha = -(1 + 2\eta)^2/(1 - \eta)^4$, $\beta = 6\eta(1 + 0.5\eta)^2/(1 - \eta)^4$, and $\delta = -0.5\eta(1 + 2\eta)^2/(1 - \eta)^4$. Figure 6 shows the calculated form factor, interference function and total scattering intensity of hollow nanoparticles with different volume fractions. One can see how the increasing interparticle correlation with increasing volume fraction affects the shape of the first intensity peak around $q = 0.15$ nm^{-1}. Specifically, two shoulders gradually appear on each side of the first maximum, which is attributed to the smearing of the form factor by the interference function. It can also be seen how sensitive the low-q ($q < 0.1$ nm^{-1}) region is to the increasing volume fraction and inter-particle correlation.

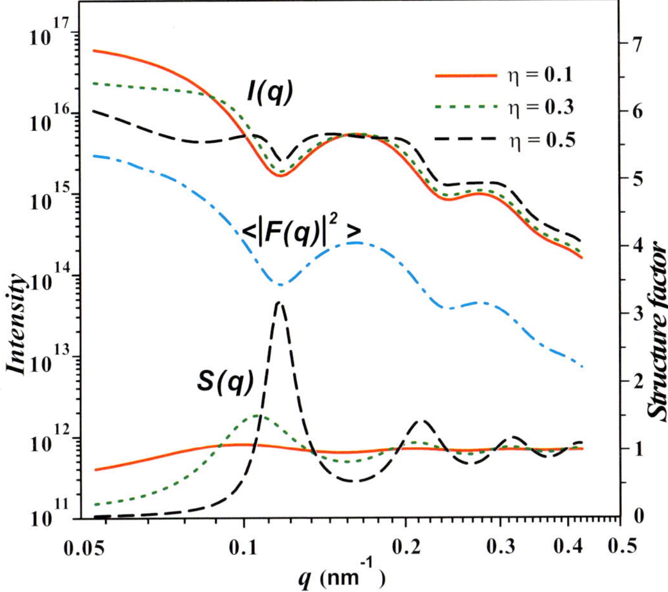

Fig. 6.   Calculated form factor $\langle |F(q)|^2 \rangle$, interference functions $S(q)$ and intensity curves $I(q)$ for nanoparticles with different volume fractions η by taking hollow nanoparticles as the model system. $S(q)$ and $I(q)$ curves are shown for $\eta = 0.1$, 0.3 and 0.5, as indicated. Fixed parameters are $R_2 = 30$ nm, $R_1 = 21$ nm and $\sigma = 0.11$. The curves have been scaled to equal height of the first maximum ($q \sim 0.15$ nm^{-1}). The Schulz distribution function is used to account for polydispersity, and only the size distribution of the outer radius is considered by assuming that the inner-to-outer radii ratio is constant.[38]

5. Principles of SAXS on anisometric particles

Anisotropic metallic, semiconductor and mineral-based nanoparticles are of interest in the context of this book since they are able to display nematic or smectic-like ordering in solution at high concentrations.[39] Some examples include CdSe nanorods forming both nematic and smectic lyotropic LCs,[40,41] CuS nanodisks forming columnar structures,[42] α-Fe$_2$O$_3$ ellipsoid-like nanoparticles forming nematic-like phase[43,44] etc. Equally, anisometric colloidal and nanoparticles have been added to thermotropic LCs in a number of studies; see examples in Sections 6 and 8 of this chapter.

Here we show how SAXS can be applied to obtain morphological and orientational information on disordered anisotropic nanoparticles. In this section we limit our discussion only to dilute systems where the correlation between particles can be ignored and hence no liquid crystalline phase is formed; thus only the particle form factor is considered. Some examples where the structure factor is also considered are given in the next section. Flat particles, rods and ellipsoids are discussed as examples, even though particles of more complex anisotropic geometries have also been described in the literature.[45]

The basic way to obtain the form factors of platelets, rods and ellipsoids is to calculate the Fourier transform of their electron density distribution. Unlike the spherical particle case, the orientation of anisometric particles must be included in the calculation of their scattering amplitude $F(\mathbf{q})$ and intensity $I(\mathbf{q})$. The calculation of the scattering function of non-spherical particles is usually carried out using numerical methods.

SAXS intensity from *flat particles* with diameter much larger than the thickness and having uniform electron density can be written as:[45]

$$I(q) = \frac{2\pi}{tq^2} |F_t(q)|^2 \tag{45}$$

Here $F_t(q) = \Delta\rho \cdot t \frac{\sin(tq/2)}{tq/2}$, where $\Delta\rho$ is the difference in electron density between the particle and the surrounding medium and t is the thickness of the flat particle. The scattering geometry of a circular flat particle is shown in Fig. 7a.

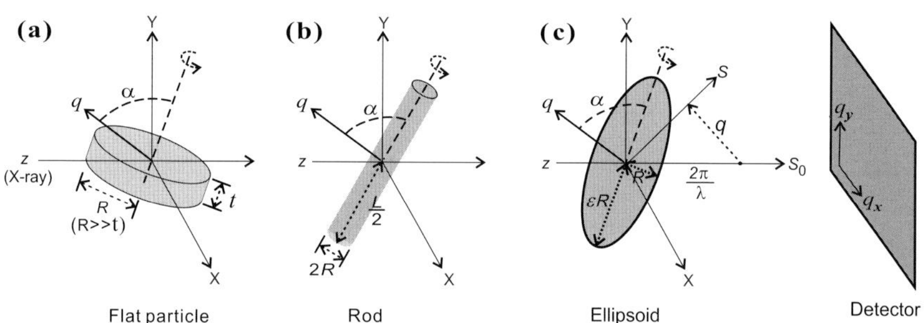

Fig. 7.   Definition of parameters of morphology and scattering geometry for flat particles (a), rods (b) and ellipsoids (c).

The scattering amplitude for *cylindrical rods* can be written as:

$$F(q) = 2\Delta\rho \cdot \pi R^2 L \frac{\sin(qL\cos\alpha/2)}{qL\cos\alpha/2} \frac{J_1(qR\cos\alpha)}{qR\cos\alpha} \tag{46}$$

where L is the length of the rod, R the radius, α the angle between $\mathbf{q}$ and the symmetry axis of the rod, and J_1 the first order Bessel function. The scattering geometry of a cylindrical rod is show in Fig. 7b. As is indicated by the expression for the scattering amplitude, scattering pattern of cylindrical rods vary with their orientation. It should be mentioned that equations (44)–(47) are defined in cylindrical coordinates with cylindrical axis along the symmetry axis of the particle. However, the orientation of anisometric particles is defined in the Cartesian coordinates for calculation of diffraction patterns, hence conversion between the two coordinates are necessary. (Fig. 7) Details for the alignment geometry can be found in model illustration of some scientific softwares such as Scatter and SASview for small angle scattering.

For an *ellipsoid* with uniaxial (C_∞) symmetry and uniform electron density, with the C_∞ axis inclined to the **q**-vector at angle α, (see Fig. 7c) the scattering amplitude can be expressed by:[46–49]

$$F(q) = \frac{\Delta\rho \cdot 4\pi\epsilon}{(qy)^3}[\sin(qRy) - qRy\cos(qRy)] \tag{47}$$

with $y = (\sin^2\alpha + \epsilon^2\cos^2\alpha)^{1/2}$, where R is the radius of the circular cross-section, and ϵ the axial ratio. In a disordered system with randomly oriented particles, integration has to be performed over all orientation angles,[49] giving:

$$\langle F^2(q)\rangle_{\text{angle}} = \int_0^{\pi/2} F^2(q)\sin\alpha d\alpha \tag{48}$$

where $F^2(q)$ is the form factor, and the triangular brackets mean the average over all orientation angles. When the polydispersity of the anisometric particles is further considered, the expression for the form factor can be written as:[38]

$$P(q) = \int_0^\infty h(R)\langle F^2(q)\rangle_{\text{angle}}dR \tag{49}$$

where $P(q)$ represents the form factor of polydisperse randomly oriented particles and $h(R)$ is the size distribution function.

In order to illustrate the effects of polydispersity and orientation on scattering patterns of anisometric particles, example 2D scattering functions for ellipsoids are showed in Fig. 8. From these we can draw several conclusions. (*i*) When the symmetry axis of the ellipsoids is parallel to the X-ray beam, the scattering pattern is the same as that for spherical particles with the same cross section, meaning that only the cross sections contribute to the scattering-see Figs. 8a and b. (*ii*) When polydispersity is involved—see Fig. 8b—the scattering troughs become shallower and the overall fluctuations in the pattern are smeared out. (*iii*) There is an inverse relationship between the anisometry of the particles and that of the

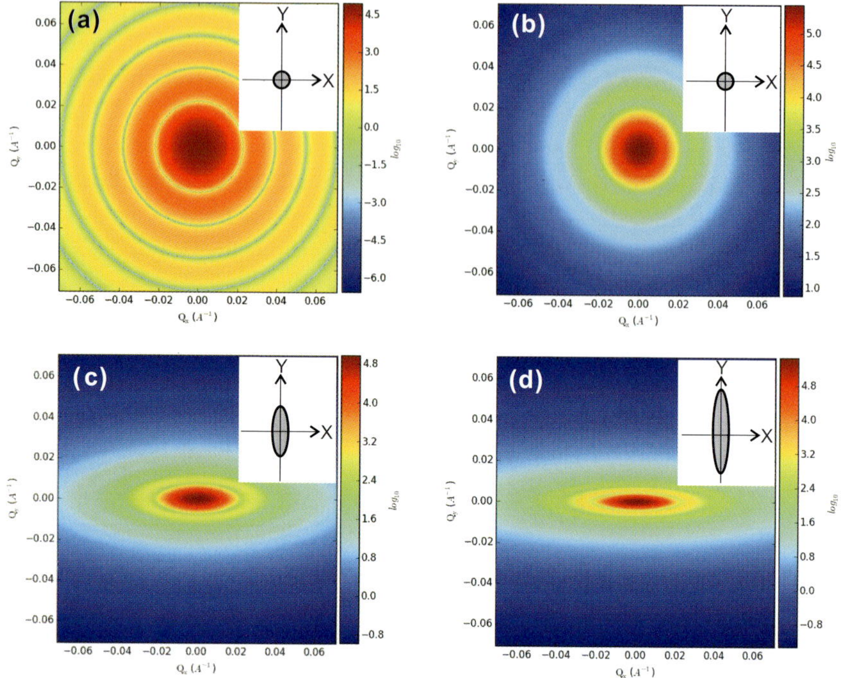

Fig. 8.   2D form factor patterns of ellipsoids with different polydispersities, orientations and axial ratios as examples of scattering from anisometric particles. (a) Monodisperse ellipsoids with their symmetry axis parallel to the X-ray beam (i.e. the z axis), $R = 20$ nm,$\epsilon = 3$, $\sigma = 0$; (b) polydisperse ellipsoids with their symmetry axis aligned along z , $R = 20$ nm,$\epsilon = 3$, $\sigma = 0.1$; (c) as (b) but with the symmetry axis along y; (d) as (c) but with $\epsilon = 5$. The coordinates used here are the same as those in Fig. 7. The patterns are calculated using SASview.

2D scattering function—Figs. 8c, d and the insets. Thus, within limits, the aspect ratio of the particles could be qualitatively determined from the aspect ratio of the scattering pattern provided the orientational order parameter is known or, alternatively, the order parameter could be obtained provided the aspect ratio is known.

6. Examples of diffraction studies of liquid crystals doped with colloidal or nanoparticles

Colloidal or nanoparticles dispersed in LCs are most often positionally disordered, unless the positional order of the mesophase (e.g. smectic layers) is imposed on the particles. In contrast, in concentrated systems of smaller nanoparticles chemically grafted with mesogens, the chances are that structures with long-range positional order in 1, 2 or 3 dimensions will develop by itself. XRD studies of the latter are described in Sections 7–9 of this chapter.

Richardson *et al.*[50] studied silica particles with 50 and 100 nm in diameter dispersed in the nematic phase of 5CB. The particles were surface-treated to induce homeotropic anchoring. Chains of nanoparticles had formed. As the particles were < 1 μm in size, they were surrounded by quadrupolar defects which tend to align the chains perpendicular rather than parallel to the director. SAXS experiments were carried out with the LC aligned under an applied electric field. Figure 9a shows the SAXS pattern, where the direction of the electric field and the nematic director were horizontal. The elliptical scattering blob is elongated horizontally, meaning that the particle chains are oriented vertically (Fig. 9c). The paracrystal theory of Hosemann *et al.*[51] has been applied to simulate the scattering pattern shown in Fig. 9b, with the fitting parameters given in the figure caption. The paracrystal theory deals primarily with the structure factor $S(\mathbf{q})$, and Fig. 9d illustrates clearly the effects of the finite domain size (size of the particle chains) and the extent of distortion of the periodicity within the domains (chains) on the shape of the scattering curve along the vertical (y) direction.

As an example of how SAXS can be used for probing interparticle interactions we take the work by Pansu *et al.*[52] Gold nanoparticles with hydrophobic alkylthiol coating have been inserted in the lamellar phase of a swollen ionic surfactant. Insertion was effective only above a critical hydrophobic thickness that depended on the particle size. Above this critical thickness it was possible to insert large amounts of nanoparticles, forming a 2D fluid in each lamella. The interaction between the nanoparticles has been investigated both in the isotropic solution and in well-oriented doped lamellar samples. First the form factor of the nanoparticles was determined from SAXS on dilute solutions. Then the structure factor $S(q)$ was determined for different nanoparticle concentrations. This was carried out by dividing the experimental SAXS curve by the form factor. The resulting $S(q)$ was then compared to the calculated structure factors based on different interaction potentials.

Figure 10 shows the measured structure factor for the 20 wt% dispersions. The interaction between the particles has an attractive part that can be seen at low q ($q < 0.05$ Å^{-1}), attributed to van der Waals interaction

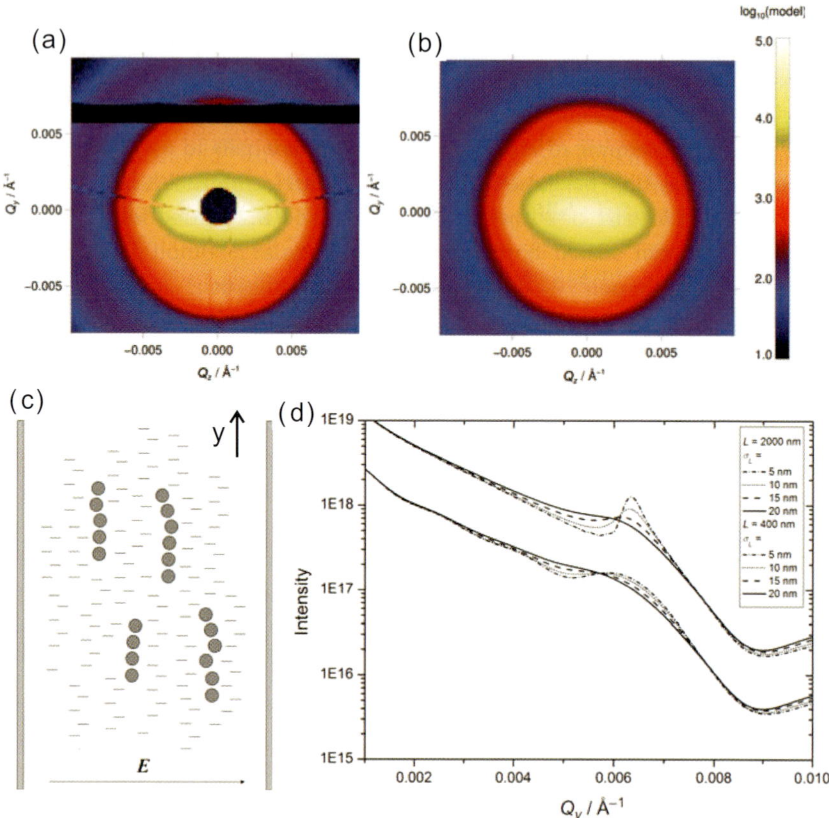

Fig. 9.   Chain-like aggregates of silica nanoparticles dispersed in nematic 5CB aligned in an electric field. (a) Experimental SAXS patterns with electric field horizontal. (b) Simulated SAXS pattern from particle chains with length distributed evenly between 200 and 1000 nm with periodicity 100 nm, longitudinal and transverse distortions both 20 nm, particle diameter 100 nm and chain axis order parameters -0.5. (c) Schematic arrangement of nanoparticle chains; director is horizontal. (d) Simulated vertical (Q_y) scattering curves for 100 nm diameter nanoparticle assemblies of order parameter 1, periodicity 100 nm, length 2000 nm and 400 nm, transverse distortion 20 nm and longitudinal distortion varying between 5 nm and 20 nm. (Ref. 50 with permission from Taylor and Francis Ltd. http://www.tandfonline.com)

between the gold cores, and a repulsive part at $0.07 < q < 0.25$ Å^{-1} attributed to steric repulsion including the interaction between the alkyl thiol capping chains.

A simple theoretical approach has been used to model $S(q)$ and esti-

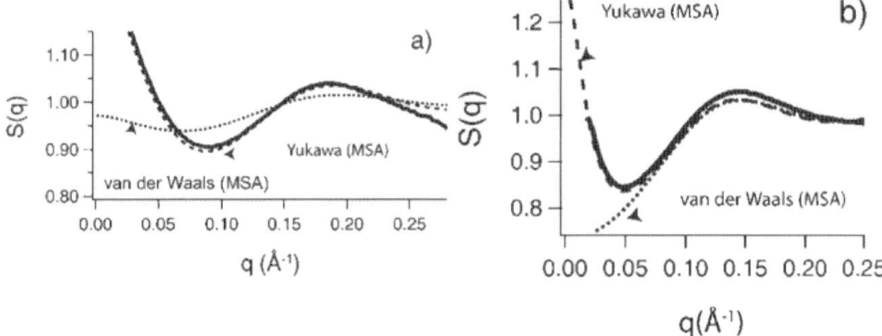

Fig. 10. Structure factor $S(q)$ of the 20 wt% isotropic solutions of gold nanoparticles capped with (a) hexylthiol (Au-C6) and (b) dodecylthiol ligands (Au-C12). Bold line: experimental $S(q)$, dashed lines: theoretical $S(q)$ including hard repulsion between thiol capping and either van der Waals attraction between the gold (dotted line) or the best fit effective Yukawa attraction potential (dashed line). Reprinted with permission from Ref. 52. Copyright (2011) American Chemical Society.

mate the apparent diameter D_{HS} of the nanoparticles (gold + thiol) approximated as hard spheres. A Percus-Yevick approximation, described in Sec. 4, was used. The attractive potential has been described either by the van der Waals potential between the gold cores or by an effective Yukawa potential. Clearly the latter gives a better fit to the experiment (Fig. 10), although it does not have a direct physical interpretation. Since all parameters except D_{HS} involved in the Yukawa potential could be determined independently, the fit had D_{HS} as the only adjustable parameter. The best fits gave D_{HS} as 3.2 nm for Au-C6 and 4.0 nm for Au-C12. By comparison, the gold nanoparticle diameter itself, as determined from the form factor of dilute solutions, was only 2 nm.

The above work also included the study of interaction between the gold nanoparticles when they were confined to the hydrophobic layers of the lamellar phase. There the particles behaved as in a 2-D liquid. The same group also used SAXS to study gold nanoparticles synthesized in situ within the layers of the lamellar phase, as well as gold nanorods.[53]

As an example of both a wide-angle (WAXS) and small-angle (SAXS) X-ray scattering study of nanoparticles dispersed in LC we take the work by Kitzerov *et al.*[54] who dispersed ferroelectric $BaTiO_3$ particles in a nematic LC with negative dielectric anisotropy. The doped LC was loaded in a cell with ITO-coated glass windows with an alignment layer that was also lecithin-treated to induce homeotropic anchoring. A synchrotron X-ray beam at normal incidence was powerful enough to penetrate the cell and give both 2D SAXS and WAXS patterns of acceptable signal-to-noise ratio. The Fredericks transition could be monitored. The P_2 order parameter was measured from the WAXS pattern according to the method described in Ref. 11 This work demonstrates that it is possible, using a synchrotron beam, to obtain decent scattering patterns from a LC film of 30 μm thickness sandwiched between two glass cover-slips of 200 μm overall thickness. The ability of modern synchrotron beamlines to easily change the wavelength is useful here, since a short wavelength high-energy beam increases the beam penetration through the substrate. Ordering of gold nanorods partially capped with nematogens was also studied by SAXS during slow evaporation of solvent while exposed to a magnetic field. Smectic and nematic-like self-assembly was observed.[55]

Suspensions of platelet-like nano- and colloidal particles have been studied both experimentally and by simulation, as exemplified by the studies on gibbsite[56] and other inorganic flat particles. At a certain concentration microscopic droplets (tactoids) were found to form, with a nematic or sometimes columnar internal structure. More recently water suspensions of organic platelet-like nanoparticles such as surface-stabilized fat (triglyceride) have been shown to exhibit similar behavior.[57,58] In Ref. 58 a laboratory SAXS instrument was used based on a microfocus X-ray source with 3D-shaped multilayer mirror that focused the X-ray beam sufficiently to enable mapping of the orientational distribution of the nematic director over a circular sample cell of 20 mm diameter in steps of 1.85 mm, see Fig. 11a. The director of this discotic nematic corresponds was parallel to the line connecting the scattering maxima on each side of the beam centre. Its distribution within the circular cell is plotted in Fig. 11b, showing the typical bipolar radial[59] orientation pattern. It should be mentioned that these days a number of synchrotron beamlines are in operation with a microbeam facility, where the beam is focused down to a μm^2 or even less, so that x, y scanning could be performed at a considerably smaller scale than that in Fig. 11.

The study on tripalmitin platelet dispersion has shown a hierarchical organization at higher concentrations, with the platelets assembling in stacks, as revealed by the SAXS traces in Fig. 12. The 4 nm (001) reflection due to the molecular layers within the flat particles, is present at all concentrations covered in the figure. Since the flat particle thickness contains only a few unit cells along the crystallographic [001] direction, the (001)

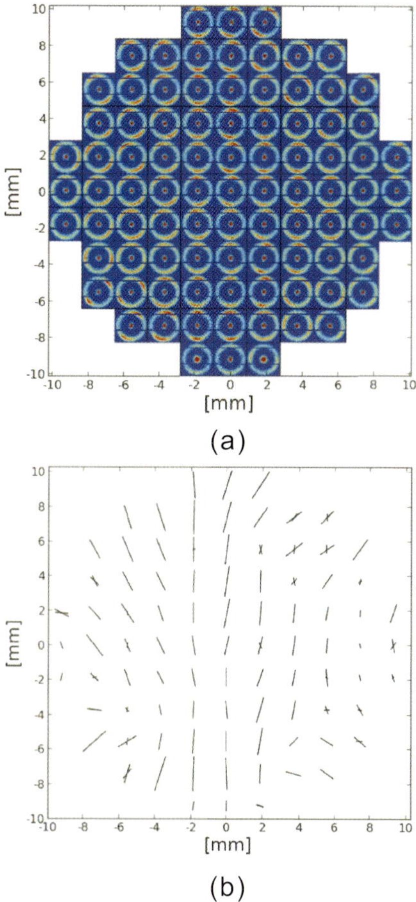

Fig. 11. (a) SAXS patterns of a stabilized native tripalmitin suspension recorded at different positions inside the circular sample holder 20 mm in diameter. The sample was scanned in steps, both horizontal vertical, of 1.85 mm. (b) 2D distribution of the preferential orientations of the flat particles as extracted from the SAXS patterns in (a). The orientation of the lines represent the orientation of the nematic director (platelet normal) and the lengths of the lines correspond to the magnitude of the anisotropy. Reprinted with permission from Ref. 58. Copyright [2014], AIP Publishing LLC.

Bragg reflection is highly broadened. Interestingly, above a critical tripalmitin concentration further interference maxima appear corresponding to lamellar periodicity in the range between 30 and 60 nm, depending on concentration. Thus the individual flat particles self-assemble into lamellae

in which the large (001) base planes of the nanoparticles are aligned parallel
to the planes of the large lamellae. Fits to the SAXS patterns in Fig. 12
were performed using the powder pattern simulation method described in
Ref. 60.

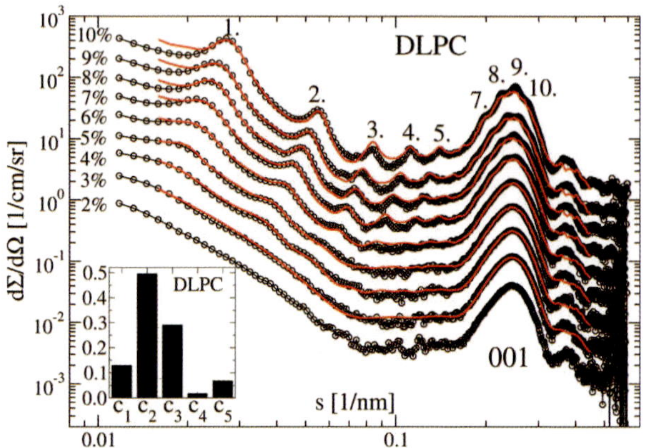

Fig. 12.   SAXS patterns from suspensions of lecithin-stabilized tripalmitin nanoflat particles at different dilution levels (2%-10% tripalmitin). The red lines represent the best fits obtained by the X-ray and neutron powder pattern simulation analysis (XNPPSA) method described in Ref. 60. The inset shows the volume-weighted distribution of the platelet thickness obtained from the fits to the dilute suspensions with 3% tripalmitin. Reprinted with permission from Ref. 58. Copyright [2014], AIP Publishing LLC.

In situ SAXS studies have also been performed while the LC was
sheared. We quote here the example of a lyotropic lamellar LC containing
metallic nanoparticles that was subjected to shear flow in a Couette-type
rheometer. The latter consisted of two concentric polycarbonate cylinders,
fairly transparent to X-rays, the inner one being rotated.[61] Such geometry is convenient because it allows the beam either to skirt the rheometer
tangentially, i.e. in the shear plane, or else radially, i.e. normal to the
shear plane, by passing through the centre of the cylinders. The LC was
sheared between the two cylinders during the synchrotron X-ray experiment. Nanoparticles containing electron-rich tungsten were dispersed in
the lamellar phase of a mixture of water and a nonionic surfactant. It was
found from SAXS patterns that upon increasing the shear rate a transition occurred from the lamellar phase to a multilayer onion-type vesicular
phase. It had been shown previously, from the intensity ratio of the first
and second order layer reflections, that the nanoparticles preferentially set-

tle in the polar layers of the surfactant.[62] The formation of the vesicles was indicated by (a) a compression of the layers (shift of the Bragg reflections to higher q), and (b) broadening of the azimuthally averaged reflections toward the high-q side. The former (a) may be attributed to some compression of the layers in the vesicles. The latter (b) can be understood if one considers that bending a stack of layers would produce broadening or streaking of the diffraction peak normal to the meridian, i.e. parallel to the layers. Where such a streaky reflection then rotationally averaged, as in a vesicle and in a powder pattern, the diffraction peak would broaden at the high-q side.

7. Diffraction on ordered arrays of particles

When nanoparticles form ordered arrays with a periodic structure, Eq. (8) can be rewritten as:

$$I(\mathbf{q}) = I_{NP}(\mathbf{q}) \sum_{i,j} e^{i(\mathbf{r_i} - \mathbf{r_j}) \cdot \mathbf{q}} \tag{50}$$

Here, $I_{NP}(\mathbf{q})$ is the scattering intensity from a single nanoparticle, and $I_{NP}(\mathbf{q}) = |F_{NP}(\mathbf{q})|^2$ can be obtained for different nanoparticles e.g. as given in Eq. (38). The periodic arrangement of nanoparticles means that the positions of ith and j^{th} nanoparticles $\mathbf{r}_i$, $\mathbf{r}_j$ obey the rule:

$$\mathbf{r_i} - \mathbf{r_j} = l\mathbf{a} + m\mathbf{b} + n\mathbf{c} \tag{51}$$

where $\mathbf{a}$, $\mathbf{b}$ and $\mathbf{c}$ are the three basic vectors of the periodic lattice formed by the nanoparticles, the "real lattice". Here l, m and n are integers. Considering such an array of nanoparticles, in which the unit cell is repeated N_a times along $\mathbf{a}$, N_b times along $\mathbf{b}$ and N_c times along $\mathbf{c}$, it can be derived that:

$$I(\mathbf{q}) = I_{NP}(\mathbf{q}) \frac{\sin^2 (N_a \mathbf{q} \cdot \mathbf{a}/2)}{\sin^2 (\mathbf{q} \cdot \mathbf{a}/2)} \cdot \frac{\sin^2 (N_b \mathbf{q} \cdot \mathbf{b}/2)}{\sin^2 (\mathbf{q} \cdot \mathbf{b}/2)} \cdot \frac{\sin^2 (N_c \mathbf{q} \cdot \mathbf{c}/2)}{\sin^2 (\mathbf{q} \cdot \mathbf{c}/2)} \tag{52}$$

When $N_a, N_b, N_c \gg 1$, the function has sharp maxima (in fact becomes a delta function when N_a, N_b and N_c are infinite) when $\mathbf{q}$ satisfies the Laue diffraction conditions:

$$\mathbf{q} \cdot \mathbf{a} = 2\pi h, \ \mathbf{q} \cdot \mathbf{b} = 2\pi k, \ \mathbf{q} \cdot \mathbf{c} = 2\pi l \tag{53}$$

In this case discrete X-ray diffraction peaks, the so-called Bragg peaks, will be observed instead of the continuous scattering. Of course the size of a real crystal is always finite, and the width of the diffraction peak

Δq is inversely proportional to the size of the crystal or of the ordered nanoparticle domain:

$$D = \frac{2\pi}{\Delta q} \tag{54}$$

We now introduce another set of basic vectors $\mathbf{a}^*$, $\mathbf{b}^*$ and $\mathbf{c}^*$, where

$$\mathbf{a}^* = \mathbf{b} \times \mathbf{c}/[\mathbf{a} \cdot (\mathbf{b} \times \mathbf{c})] \tag{55a}$$

$$\mathbf{b}^* = \mathbf{c} \times \mathbf{a}/[\mathbf{a} \cdot (\mathbf{b} \times \mathbf{c})] \tag{55b}$$

$$\mathbf{c}^* = \mathbf{a} \times \mathbf{b}/[\mathbf{a} \cdot (\mathbf{b} \times \mathbf{c})] \tag{55c}$$

These "reciprocal vectors" define the "reciprocal lattice". They satisfy the following conditions:

$$\mathbf{a}^* \cdot \mathbf{a} = 1,\ \mathbf{a}^* \cdot \mathbf{b} = 0,\ \mathbf{a}^* \cdot \mathbf{c} = 0 \tag{56a}$$

$$\mathbf{b}^* \cdot \mathbf{a} = 0,\ \mathbf{b}^* \cdot \mathbf{b} = 1,\ \mathbf{b}^* \cdot \mathbf{c} = 0 \tag{56b}$$

$$\mathbf{c}^* \cdot \mathbf{a} = 0,\ \mathbf{c}^* \cdot \mathbf{b} = 0,\ \mathbf{c}^* \cdot \mathbf{c} = 1 \tag{56c}$$

Consequently the diffraction condition as given in Eq. (53) becomes (the Laue conditions):

$$\mathbf{q} = 2\pi(h\mathbf{a}^* + k\mathbf{b}^* + l\mathbf{c}^*) \tag{57}$$

and the wave-vector of each diffraction peak simply corresponds to a point on the reciprocal lattice with basic vectors $\mathbf{a}^*$, $\mathbf{b}^*$ and $\mathbf{c}^*$.

The length of the vector $h\mathbf{a}^* + k\mathbf{b}^* + l\mathbf{c}^*$ is in fact the reciprocal of the d-spacing, d_{hkl}, i.e. the distance between neighbouring lattice planes with Miller indices (hkl). As $|\mathbf{q}| = 4\pi/\lambda \sin\theta$, the diffraction condition can be expressed by the familiar Bragg equation:

$$\lambda = 2d_{hkl} \sin\theta \tag{58}$$

A useful geometrical tool for representing the diffraction condition as given in Eqs. (57) and (58) above is the Ewald sphere. The Ewald sphere, as shown in Fig. 13 has a radius of $1/\lambda$. A diffracted beam (with diffraction angle 2θ) can be represented by the vector $\mathbf{k}$, hence a point P on the Ewald sphere. If the diffraction condition given by Eq. (56a) is satisfied, it can be easily proven that vector $\mathbf{O'P}$ should be the reciprocal lattice vector $h\mathbf{a}^* + k\mathbf{b}^* + l\mathbf{c}^*$. Consequently under the Ewald construction, as shown in Fig. 13 the diffraction condition requires that the particular reciprocal lattice point lies on the Ewald sphere surface.

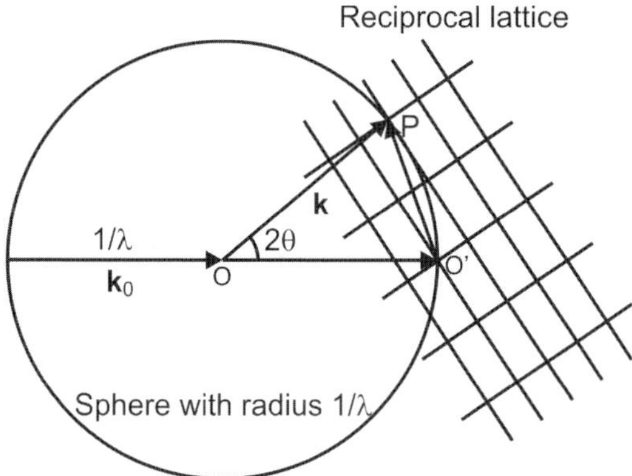

Fig. 13.   Ewald sphere as a tool for constructing the diffraction condition.

For a discrete diffraction peak, what is experimentally measured is in fact its integrated intensity around $\mathbf{q} = \mathbf{q}_{hkl}$, and it is simply:

$$I(\mathbf{q}_{hkl}) = N_a N_b N_c I_{NP}(\mathbf{q}_{hkl}) = N I_{NP}(\mathbf{q}_{hkl}) \tag{59}$$

In the derivation of Eq. (59) it is assumed that there is only one nanoparticle in each unit cell. This can be easily expanded to more complex structures where there are more particles in a unit cell, which may or may not be related by symmetry operations. Denoting the fractional coordinates of nanoparticles in a unit cell as (u_i, v_i, w_i), Eq. (59) becomes:

$$I(\mathbf{q}_{hkl}) = N I_{NP}(\mathbf{q}_{hkl}) | \sum_i e^{i2\pi(hu_i + kv_i + lw_i)}|^2 \tag{60}$$

I_{NP} is now the form factor of the single particle, N is the number of unit cells, and the last factor is a summation over all the nanoparticles in the unit cell. The latter is in fact the square of the interference function (cf. Eq. (12)), which modulates the diffraction intensity of the single particle due to interference between nanoparticles in the unit cell. This interference effect may results in additional "extinction rules" canceling diffraction for certain hkl combinations due to the destructive interference between nanoparticles in the unit cell. One of the simplest examples is that of a body centered cubic (BCC) lattice, where only (hkl) reflections with $h + k + l = 2n$ are observed.

The "systematic extinctions" are used to determine lattice symmetry. In the case of 3-dimensional order, it means determining which of the 230 space groups the system belongs to. Space groups are the possible combinations of symmetry elements of a point group (rotation axis, mirror planes, center of inversion) and x, y, z translations. The resulting complex symmetry elements (screw axes, glide planes) are responsible for the systematic extinctions. In 2-D ordered systems, i.e. columnar phases, periodically modulated smectics the equivalent 2-D space groups or "plane groups" apply, of which there are 17. The most common plane groups found in columnar LCs are hexagonal $p6mm$, rectangular $c2mm$, and oblique $p2$. When calculating the electron density distribution, the space/plane group must be known.

Another correction to Eq. (59) is to consider the distribution, normally assumed to be Gaussian, of the probability of finding a nanoparticle around its equilibrium position. With the average displacement of nanoparticles defined as $\sqrt{\langle u^2 \rangle}$, a Debye-Waller factor can be introduced so that:

$$I(\mathbf{q}_{hkl}) = N I_{NP}(\mathbf{q}_{hkl}) e^{-q^2 \langle u^2 \rangle / 3} \tag{61}$$

Incidentally, $\sqrt{\langle u^2 \rangle}$ can be taken as the order parameter of the nanoparticle array.[63] Note that the Debye-Waller factor describes the equilibrium "thermal disorder", that leaves the diffraction peaks sharp, but reduces their intensity, particularly at higher q-values. Refs. 64 and 65 give examples of $\sqrt{\langle u^2 \rangle}$ being determined experimentally for arrays of LC-coated gold nanoparticles. In contrast, the defects that cause broadening of Bragg reflections, are non-equilibrium lattice distortion and small domain size. The effect of small domain size has already been mentioned above. The former, i.e. lattice distortion, can be treated in a number of ways. One comprehensive theoretical treatment of diffraction on distorted crystals as well as on systems with a relatively high degree of short-range order is that of the paracrystal,[51] already mentioned in Sec. 6. In fact the paracrystal theory, when applied to materials showing several orders of Bragg diffraction, can be used to separate the effects of crystal size and lattice distortion on broadening of the reflections.

The value $|F(\mathbf{q}_{hkl})|$ of the scattering amplitude can be determined by taking the square root of the integrated intensity of the diffraction peak $I(\mathbf{q}_{hkl})$. The Fourier transform relationship between the electron density distribution of the ordered nanoparticle array $\rho(\mathbf{r})$ and its scattering amplitude $F(\mathbf{q})$ becomes a Fourier series. Using Eqs. (59)–(61) we get:

$$\rho(x, y, z) = \sum_{hkl} |F(q_{hkl})| e^{i2\pi(hx+ky+lz)} e^{i\phi_{hkl}} \tag{62}$$

Here, x, y, z are the fractional coordinates of a point in the unit cell so that $\mathbf{r} = x\mathbf{a} + y\mathbf{b} + z\mathbf{c}$.

While Eqs. (59)–(61) are used to simulate the diffraction pattern, Eq. (62) can be used to directly reconstruct the electron density map of the unit cell. The main obstacle is our inability to experimentally measure the phase ϕ_{hkl}; that is the well-known "phase problem" in X-ray crystallography. However, for centrosymmetric structures, true for most ordered nanoparticle arrays studied so far, the scattering amplitude F_{hkl} is always a real value, hence each ϕ_{hkl} has only two possible values, 0 or π. In addition, in most such systems only a limited number of diffraction peaks are observed due to the large $\langle u^2 \rangle$ in liquid crystals. This scenario allows a trial-and-error approach; electron density maps are calculated for different phase combinations and the choice of the "correct" combination can be made on the merit of the maps. The choice is made in combination with any other information on the system, its chemical constitution and physical properties, such as the size and volume fraction of nanoparticles etc. The phase problem for centrosymmetric systems can be compared to solving a quadratic equation, where we have to decide which of the two solutions is correct, based on additional information available. Different methods have also been used to help with phasing. One of them is "isomorphous replacement", where low density atoms (such as hydrogen) are replaced chemically by higher electron density ones (e.g. fluorine) in known positions.[66] The isomorphous replacement technique has been developed originally by protein crystallographers.[67] Another alternative helpful phasing method is to perform neutron diffraction experiments in addition to X-ray experiments on the same system,[68] or to perform neutron experiments on selectively deuterated samples. The method relies on the fact that neutrons are scatters on atomic nuclei, not on electrons, and thus have completely different atomic scattering factors from X-ray ones. Using these phasing aids can be compared to solving an underdeterminate system of equations with multiple unknowns by adding extra equations.

For inorganic nanoparticles, when their concentration is high, as in the cases where they form ordered arrays, the electron density distribution is heavily dominated by the nanoparticles; the weak fluctuations of ρ in the organic matrix are almost negligible in comparison. This is, at once, a blessing and a curse. On the positive side, this makes the choice of the correct phase combination relatively easy. On the negative side, it hampers the determination of the position and orientation of the mesogens, spacers and other moieties containing only light elements. Here again complementary neutron diffraction might prove useful, as it is not necessarily dominated by heavy atoms.[60]

8. X-ray reflectivity and grazing incidence diffraction

While structural studies by XRD are carried out mostly on bulk samples, there are increasing needs to characterize thin film samples, in particular for device fabrication and for studying effects such as surface-induced phase changes and anisotropy, epitaxial growth of crystals at surfaces and interfaces etc. Transmission XRD can be used in principle to study such thin films, but in practice, because of the very small scattering volume, even a strong X-ray source such as synchrotron radiation, is often inadequate. The signal-to-noise ratio is also reduced by the additional background scattering from the substrate. The transmission XRD method is further limited for thin films by the fact that it is impossible to obtain information on structural features in the direction along the film normal. Such limitations are overcome by grazing incidence X-ray diffraction/scattering and X-ray reflectivity methods, where the incident X-ray beam is nearly parallel to the surface of the thin film. A brief introduction to the two methods will be presented below, and more details and examples can be found in Ref. 69

In specular X-ray reflectivity experiments one simply measures the intensity of the reflected beam as a function of incident angle θ_{in}. The reflected beam is in the same plane as the incident beam and has its scattering angle θ_{sc} equals to the incident angle θ_{in} in at all times. While the refractive index n of X-ray in vacuum is 1, in a medium it is *smaller* than 1 and is often written as:

$$n = 1 - \delta \tag{63}$$

Here δ is extremely small ($\sim 10^{-5}$) and proportional to the electron density of the medium. Consequently there exist a critical angle θ_c, which satisfies the condition:

$$\cos\theta_c = n = 1 - \delta \tag{64}$$

Below the critical angle, i.e. for $\theta_{in} < \theta_c$ *external* total reflection will happen (Fig. 14a). The critical angle is very small and is normally less than $0.5°$. In reflectivity experiments, $q = 4\pi \sin\theta/\lambda$ is normally used instead of θ, and the critical q_c:[69]

$$q_c = 3.75 \cdot 10^{-2} \sqrt{\rho_e} \tag{65}$$

Here ρ_e is the electron density of the medium in units $e^-/\text{Å}^{-3}$. Measurement of critical angle (or wave vector q) thus provides a means to directly measure the electron density of the sample. For X-rays reflected by a vacuum/medium interface above the critical angle (Fig. 14b), reflectivity is given by:

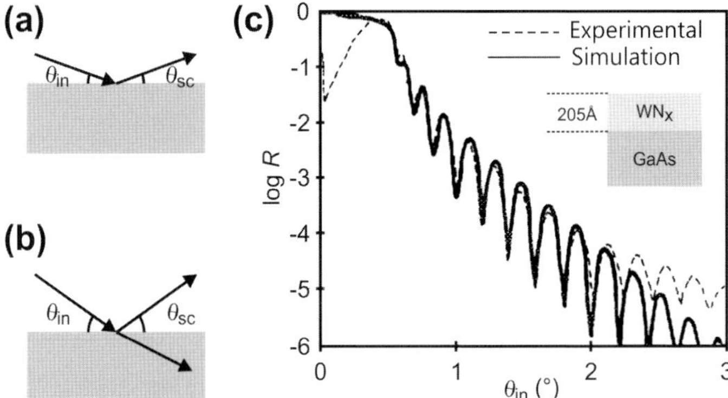

Fig. 14. X-ray reflectivity setup. (a) External total reflection occurs when the incident angle θ_{in} is smaller than the critical angle θ_c; (b) The X-ray is partially reflected when the incident angle θ_{in} is larger than the critical angle θ_c; (c) Reflectivity curve from a single layer film with uniform electron density.

$$R(q) = \frac{I(q)}{I_0} = \left| \frac{q - \sqrt{q^2 - q_c^2}}{q + \sqrt{q^2 - q_c^2}} \right|^2 \tag{66}$$

A thin flat film deposited on a substrate has two interfaces, one with vacuum/air on top and the other with substrate at the bottom. Consequently reflection happens at both interfaces, and interference between the two reflected waves results in tightly spaced maxima and minima in the reflectivity curve, if the film thickness is uniform (Fig. 14c). The thickness of the film can be easily determined from the oscillation frequency in the reflectivity curve. Similar effects exist for multi-layer films of different thicknesses and electron densities. The reflectivity curve of a thin film, single or multiple layer, can be fitted to model density distributions to reveal the depth profile of electron density.

In the above model of X-ray reflectivity, each layer of the thin film is considered to be homogeneous, assuming that there are no lateral fluctuations in refractive index. This assumption is not valid for systems that contain lateral inhomogeneities with either long or short range order, such as nanoparticles dispersed in the LC matrix. In such cases simulation of the reflectivity curve becomes much more complex, requiring that the model take into account the reflection at the matrix/nanoparticle interfaces as well as of parameters, such as shape, size and distribution of nanoparticles, their packing ratio and positional order etc.

An example of the use of X-ray reflectivity in the study of lyotropic systems with gold nanoparticles is shown in Fig. 15. The sample was a monolayer film of gold nanoparticles grafted with ligands containing LC-forming bolaamphiphiles.[70]

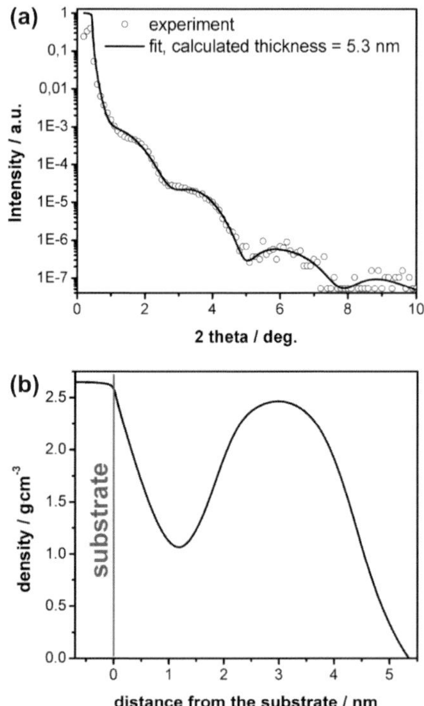

Fig. 15. (a) X-ray reflectivity trace and fitted simulated curve for a self-assembled film of gold nanoparticles functionalized with a LC bolaamphiphile. The calculated thickness of the film is 5.3 nm; (b) electron density profile used in the fit. Reprinted with permission from Ref. 70. Copyright (2013) American Chemical Society.

Beside specular reflectivity, off-specular reflectivity experiments are also sometimes carried out, where the incident angle is usually kept constant while the reflected radiation is scanned. Off-specular X-ray reflectivity can give information about surface roughness.[69]

More information on systems with in-plane electron density fluctuations, either periodic or non-periodic, could be provided by grazing incidence X-ray diffraction/scattering (GIXRD, GISAXS or GIWAXS depending on the angular range covered). While the beam and sample setup can remain the same as that for reflectivity measurement, an area detector is used nowadays most often to record the diffraction/scattering intensities not only in the meridional plane (plane normal to the film containing the incident and the specularly reflected beam), but also off-meridian (Fig. 16). The position of each spot on the detector can be expressed by two angles (θ_{sc}, ψ), as shown in Fig. 16. This can be mapped onto the reciprocal space. For example, in most cases the reciprocal lattices from different ordered domains are cylindrically averaged since usually all domains share the same axis along the film normal. Thus, similar to the case of fibre diffraction, each spot on the reciprocal lattice becomes a circle about the film normal, with Bragg spots appearing where these circles cross the Ewald sphere. Intensities $I(\xi, \zeta)$, where ξ, ζ are the cylindrical coordinates in the reciprocal space, can be obtained by 2-d integration and suitable weighting correction – in the described case, this means multiplying the integral intensity by ξ. From grazing incidence diffraction, important information on the in-plane as well as out-of-plane periodicity of the structure can be obtained. Examples will be given in the next section.

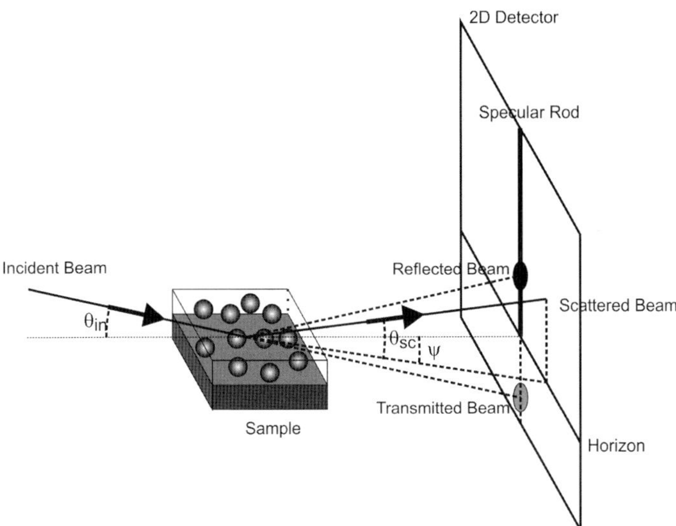

Fig. 16.   Geometry of the GIXRD setup. Information on nanoparticles at the top surface of the sample: size, shape and their distribution, lateral orientational and positional order etc. can be derived from off-specular and off-meridional scattering.

The basic features of diffraction/scattering from thin film samples are in general the same as describes in previous sections. However, in GIXRD geometry, some other factors have to be taken into account. E.g. absorption of the scattered beam: the different scattered beams can have very different path lengths through the sample and the substrate, depending on their direction angles (θ_{sc}, ψ), hence absorption can affect their intensities very differently. Furthermore, scattering can happen from both the incident and the reflected beam, in particular when total reflection occurs at the sample-substrate interface; interference between these beams can produce multiple scattering if strong Bragg peaks are involved. Software packages to fit and simulate GISAXS patterns include IsGISAXS[71] and BornAgain.[72]

X-ray reflectivity and GIXRD methods have the advantages that they can provide information about buried nanoparticles and interfaces, statistically averaged over all the sample. With the use of high intensity synchrotron radiation, experiments can be carried out with a small amount of sample, under environmental conditions (under vacuum or gas atmospheres, with temperature control etc.). Growth or phase transition kinetics of such systems can also be studied in real time.[69] In recent studies of complex self-assembly of liquid crystal and liquid crystal-nanoparticle hybrid systems, GISAXS was found to be extremely useful in indexing of Bragg reflections, determining the unit cell and lattice symmetry.[73] Nonetheless, for accurate determination of diffracted intensities, powder diffraction on bulk samples is still preferred, as the geometrical correction for powder geometry (the Lorentz correction) is more reliable and straightforward. Usually a combination of GISAXS and SAXS works best.

9. Selected examples of SAXS studies of ordered nanoparticles in liquid crystals

In this section we will show on examples how the small-angle diffraction method can help elucidate structure of hybrid LC-nanoparticle systems with long range positional order. The order can be achieved by dispersing nanoparticles in ordered soft matter, such as lyotropic[43,74–78] and thermotropic[79] liquid crystals and block copolymers.[80,81] It can also be achieved by direct self-assembly of nanoparticles coated with soft organic molecules such as DNA.[82,83] In particular we choose examples of self-assembly of dense systems of nanoparticles surface-grafted with mesogens, which are most likely to form ordered arrays. Mesogenic ligands provide nanoparticles both with the driving force and the mobility necessary for them to form ordered arrays. There have been a number of reports in recent years demonstrating various types of ordered arrays of nanoparticles; these are often referred to as superlattices, to distinguish them from the atomic lattices within the particles themselves. These include lamellar phases in rod-like[55] and spherical nanoparticles,[84–89] modulated layers,[84] columnar (hexagonal and rectangular[64,90 92]) and 3-d cubic (simple cubic,[65] BCC,[91,93] FCC[90]) and non-cubic phases (rhombohedral,[64] tetragonal,[94] 3-d hexagonal,[90,95] base-centered orthorhombic[96]). More on the topic of self-assembly in LC-grafted nanoparticles can be found in Ref. 97 and references therein, and in Chap. 16 of this book, written by Lewandowski and Gorecka. Small angle X-ray scattering plays a major role in structural characterization of most of these phases.

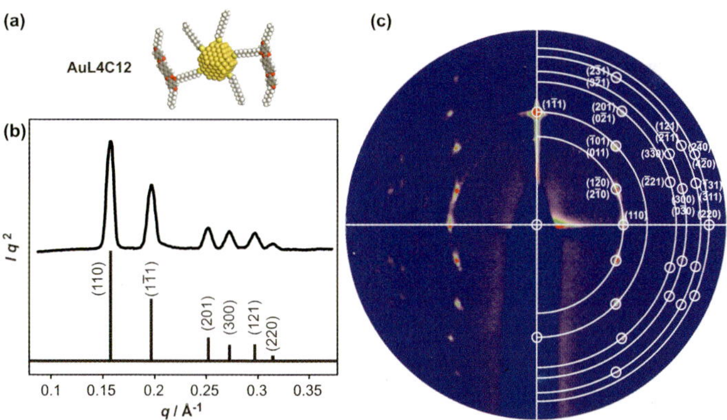

Fig. 17. (a) Schematic picture of the mesogen-covered gold nanoparticle compound **AuL4C12**. (b) Experimental (top) and simulated (bottom) powder diffraction patterns of the material in the rhombohedral phase. (c) GISAXS pattern on a well oriented thin film sample provided vital information for indexing of the diffraction peaks and determination of the space group; note that the $[1\bar{1}1]$ axis, not the $[001]$ axis, is normal to the substrate. Copyright (2009) Wiley. Used with permission from Ref. 64.

In the structural characterization by X-ray diffraction of ordered nanoparticle systems, the normal steps are:

(1) Record the diffraction pattern, determine the q-values (or d-spacings $d = 2\pi/q$) of the diffraction peaks.
(2) On the basis of the measured q values, find the Miller indices (hkl) for each diffraction peak, and thus obtain the basic vectors of the lattice **a**, **b** and **c** (Eq. (56a)). This is often helped by examining the ratio

between the measured q values. For example, for a 1-d structure a ratio series of 1:2:3:4... should be observed; for a 2-d hexagonal structure the ratios should be $1 : \sqrt{3} : 2 : \sqrt{7} : 3\ldots$; for a simple cubic and the BCC structure $1 : \sqrt{2} : \sqrt{3} : 2 : \sqrt{5}\ldots$; for face centered cubic $\sqrt{3} : 2 : 2\sqrt{2} : \sqrt{11}\ldots$ etc.

For more complex lattices the indexing of the diffraction peaks may not be straightforward from a powder diffraction pattern, but indexing can often be helped by the use of aligned samples, by surface alignment, thermal or vapour annealing, mechanical shearing, or the use of an external magnetic or electric field. An example of the use of both small-angle powder diffraction and GISAXS on thin surface-oriented films, is given in Fig. 17.[64] The q-values of the six powder diffraction peaks do not stand in a simple ratio such as those mentioned above. Their indexing would be an almost impossible task without the GISAXS pattern from a well oriented sample, a thermally annealed thin film on silicon substrate. As in such a film domains tend to share one common crystallographic direction $[hkl]$ which is in all domains perpendicular to the substrate, a continuous diffraction ring found normally in a powder sample condenses into two discrete spots, one each side of the meridian (Fig. 17c). Their ξ, ζ cylindrical coordinates can be measured directly from the diffraction pattern, after applying the necessary Bernal correction. This extra information facilitates indexing of the Bragg spots. In the particular case in Fig. 17 it was thus possible to assign the diffraction peaks to a trigonal lattice. As shown in Fig. 17c, a nearly perfect fit to the diffraction peak positions of the GISAXS diffraction pattern has been achieved; compare the positions of the observed diffraction spots and the calculated positions (small white circles).

(3) Determine, or narrow down the choice of the plane or space group symmetry of the lattice, on the basis of the extinction rules observed. In the example given in Fig. 17, the indices (hkl) of observed diffraction peaks always obey the rule $h - k + l = 3n$, where n is an integer, indicating that the space group is rhombohedral $R\bar{3}m$. Sometimes, the determination of the space group is also linked to the way the diffraction peaks are indexed. For example, a cubic phase is observed in a dendrimer-covered gold nanoparticle system.[65] Six diffraction peaks were observed by powder SAXS with q ratios $1 : \sqrt{2} : \sqrt{3} : 2 : \sqrt{5} : \sqrt{6}$, suggesting a cubic lattice (Fig. 18a). However, for both primitive and BCC lattices, the first six diffraction peaks have exactly the same q

ratio. While for a primitive cubic lattice the six peaks would be indexed as (100), (110), (111), (200), (210) and (211), they can be assigned as (110), (200), (211), (220), (310), (222) peaks of a BCC lattice. This ambiguity is solved again by using an oriented thin film sample, the GISAXS pattern of which clearly fits that of a primitive cubic phase with its [001] axis oriented along the film normal (Fig. 18b).

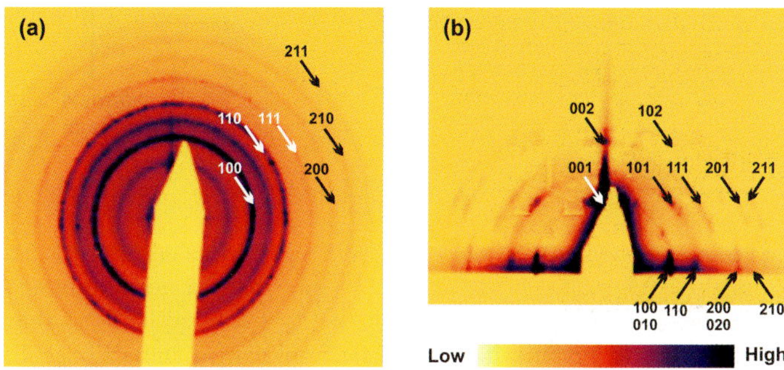

Fig. 18. The powder diffraction pattern (left) of a dendron-coated gold nanoparticle system can be indexed and identified as corresponding to a primitive cubic phase with the help of a GISAXS pattern of an oriented thin film sample (right). Reprinted with permission from Ref. 65. Copyright (2012) American Chemical Society.

(4) Having determined the shape and size of the unit cell, and its symmetry, a model structure can be constructed and its diffraction pattern simulated. In this case, not only the positions, but also the intensities of the diffraction peaks will be quantitatively measured and compared to those simulated. Normally the model can be built fairly straightforwardly, as with few exceptions nanoparticles tend to occupy the highest symmetry positions in the unit cell. Formulae for calculating the form factors of nanoparticles (Sections 4 and 5), and for taking into account the interference between nanoparticles in the unit cell, Eqs. (59) and (60) (Sec. 7), should be used. A simulated powder diffraction pattern is shown in Fig. 15b together with the experimental one. By fitting the experimental data, quantitative information can be retrieved such as the size of the nanoparticles and their average displacement $\sqrt{\langle u^2 \rangle}$, as fitting parameters of the model.

(5) Using Eq. (61), it is also possible to reconstruct the electron density map of the phase directly. Specific formulae for different space group symmetries can be found in Ref. 1. The reconstructed electron den-

sity map of the $R\bar{3}m$ phase formed by **AuL4C12** mentioned above (Fig. 17), is shown in Fig. 19. In the map the number of nanoparticles in the unit cell, and their positions, can be directly determined. This step often comes before step 4, allowing a model to be constructed after inspecting all possible electron density maps.

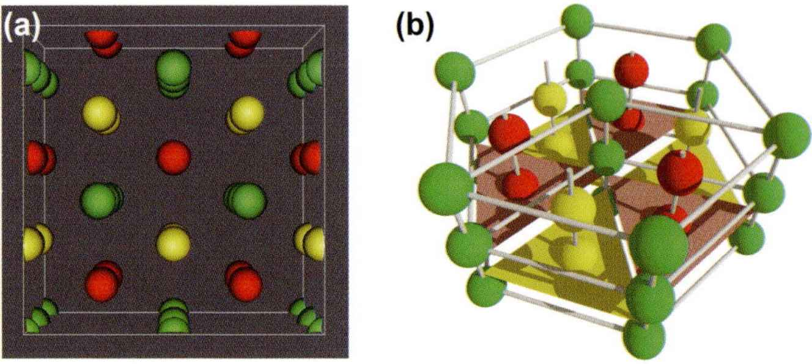

Fig. 19. (a) Reconstructed electron density map of the $R\bar{3}m$ phase formed by nematogen-covered gold nanoparticles **AuL4C12**, viewed along the [001] axis. The isoelectron surfaces envelop the high density regions of gold nanoparticles. The nanoparticles form columns along the c-axis; here they are coloured according to their relative height in the unit cell. (b) Oblique perspective of the above, with yellow and red staircase platforms added at heights $c/3$ and $2c/3$, respectively. Copyright (2009) Wiley. Used with permission from Ref. 64.

10. Conclusions

X-ray scattering/diffraction is a powerful and versatile method for the study of nano- and microparticles in soft media. One of the major advantages of the method over, e.g. electron microsopy, is its ability to probe bulk structures and large areas of thin films, and provide instant averaging over the whole sample without serious damage. As always, however, the method works best when complemented with other tools, such as TEM, SEM and AFM. We hope that the principles and experimental techniques described in this chapter will be useful to the readers studying nano- and colloidal particles in liquid crystal systems. We believe that there is plenty of scope for more elaborate and quantitative applications of X-ray and neutron scattering in this area.

References

1. IUC, *International Tables for Crystallography (The most comprehensive reference on X-ray diffraction techniques)*. vol. A-G, John Wiley and Sons for International Union of Crystallography (1999).

2. D. W. Hukins, *X-ray diffraction by disordered and ordered systems*. Pergamon Press, Oxford (1981).

3. H. Deas, The diffraction of x-rays by a random assemblage of molecules having partial alignment, *Acta Crystallographica*. **5** (4), 542–546 (1952).

4. G. R. Mitchell and R. Lovell, Application of cylindrical distribution functions to wide-angle x-ray scattering from oriented polymers, *Acta Crystallographica Section A*. **37** (2), 189–196 (1981).

5. R. Lovell and G. R. Mitchell, Molecular orientation distribution derived from an arbitrary reflection, *Acta Crystallographica Section A*. **37** (1), 135–137 (1981).

6. A. J. Leadbetter and E. K. Norris, Distribution functions in three liquid crystals from x-ray diffraction measurements, *Mol. Phys.* **38** (3), 669–686 (1979).

7. M. Deutsch, Orientational order determination in liquid crystals by x-ray diffraction, *Phys. Rev. A*. **44** (12), 8264–8270 (1991).

8. W. Maier and A. Saupe, Eine einfache molekular-statistische theorie der nematischen kristallinflüssigen phase. teil II, *Z. Naturf.* **15a**, 287–292 (1960).

9. A. S. Paranjpe and V. K. Kelkar, Chain ordering in the nematic phase of 40ba, *Mol. Cryst. Liq. Cryst.* **102** (10), 289–294 (1984).

10. P. Davidson, X-ray diffraction by liquid crystalline side-chain polymers, *Progress in Polymer Science*. **21** (5), 893–950 (1996).

11. P. Davidson, D. Petermann, and M. Levelut, A., The measurement of the nematic order parameter by x-ray scattering reconsidered, *J. Phys. II France*. **5** (1), 113–131 (1995).

12. P. S. Pershan, *Structure of Liquid Crystal Phases*. World Scientific, Singapore (1988).

13. G. V. Schulz, The kinetics of chain polymerisation v. the influence of various types of reactions on the poly-molecularity, *Z. Phys. Chem. B-Chem. Elem. Aufbau. Mater.* **43** (1), 25–46 (1939).

14. D. S. Thompson, Inelastic light scattering from log-normal distributions of spherical particles in liquid suspension, *J. Phys. Chem.* **75** (6), 789–791 (1971).

15. D. S. Thompson, Inelastic light scattering from distributions of sperical particles in liquid suspendion, *J. Chem. Phys.* **54** (3), 1411–1412 (1971).

16. J. Wagner, Small-angle scattering from spherical core-shell particles: An analytical scattering function for particles with Schulz-Flory size distribution, *J. Appl. Cryst.* **37**, 750–756 (2004).

17. D. O. Tinker, Light scattering by phospholipid dispersions: Theory of light scattering by hollow spherical particles, *Chem. Phys. Lipids*. **8** (3), 230–257 (1972).

18. M. Nayeri, M. Zackrisson, and J. Bergenholtz, Scattering functions of core-

shell-structured hard spheres with Schulz-distributed radii, *J. Phys. Chem. B.* **113** (24), 8296–8302 (2009).

19. S. R. Aragón and R. Pecora, Theory of dynamic light scattering from polydisperse systems, *J. Chem. Phys.* **64** (6), 2395–2404 (1976).

20. J. S. Pedersen, Analysis of small-angle scattering data from colloids and polymer solutions: modeling and least-squares fitting, *Adv. Colloid Interface Sci.* **70**, 171–210 (1997).

21. C. B. He, A. M. Donald, M. F. Butler, and O. Diat, Small angle x-ray scattering analysis of crazing in rubber toughened polymers: Influence of particle deformation, *Polymer.* **39** (3), 659–667 (1998).

22. S. Förster and C. Burger, Scattering functions of polymeric core-shell structures and excluded volume chains, *Macromolecules.* **31** (3), 879–891 (1998).

23. V. Degiorgio and M. Corti, *In physics of amphiphiles: micelles, vesicles and microemulsions.* North Holland Physics Publishing Company, Amsterdam (1985).

24. J. S. Pedersen and M. C. Gerstenberg, Scattering form factor of block copolymer micelles, *Macromolecules.* **29** (4), 1363–1365 (1996).

25. I. Berndt, J. S. Pedersen, and W. Richtering, Temperature-sensitive core-shell microgel particles with dense shell, *Angew. Chem. Int. Edit.* **45** (11), 1737–1741 (2006).

26. A. Halperin, Polymer micelles - a star model, *Macromolecules.* **20** (11), 2943–2946 (1987).

27. M. Kotlarchyk and S. H. Chen, Analysis of small angle neutron scattering spectra from polydisperse interacting colloids, *J. Chem. Phys.* **79** (5), 2461–2469 (1983).

28. L. S. Ornstein and F. Zernike, Acculental deviations of density and opalescence at the critical point of a simple substance, *Proc. K. Akad. Wetensch. Amsterdam.* **17**, 793–806 (1914).

29. A. Vrij, Mixtures of hard spheres in the Percus-Yevick approximation light scattering at finite angles, *J. Chem. Phys.* **71** (8), 3267–3270 (1979).

30. J. K. Percus and G. J. Yevick, Analysis of classical statistical mechanics by means of collective coordinates, *Phys. Rev.* **110** (1), 1–13 (1958).

31. D. J. Kinning and E. L. Thomas, Hard-sphere interactions between spherical domains in diblock copolymers, *Macromolecules.* **17** (9), 1712–1718 (1984).

32. S. Hansen, The structure factor in small-angle scattering and the effect of deviation from spherical symmetry, *J. Appl. Cryst.* **44**, 265–271 (2011).

33. R. J. Baxter, Ornstein–Zernike relation and Percus–Yevick approximation for fluid mixtures, *J. Chem. Phys.* **52** (9), 4559–4562 (1970).

34. E. R. Soule and G. E. Elicabe, Determination of size distributions of concentrated polymer particles embedded in a solid polymer matrix, *Part. Part. Sys. Char.* **25** (1), 84–91 (2008).

35. P. Bartlett and R. H. Ottewill, A neutron scattering study of the structure of a bimodal colloidal crystal, *J. Chem. Phys.* **96** (4), 3306–3318 (1992).

36. A. Y. Terekhov, B. J. Heuser, M. A. Okuniewski, R. S. Averback, S. Seifert, and P. R. Jemian, Small-angle x-ray scattering measurements of helium-bubble formation in borosilicate glass, *J. Appl. Cryst.* **39**, 647–651 (2006).

37. J. Jansson, K. Schillen, M. Nilsson, O. Soderman, G. Fritz, A. Bergmann, and O. Glatter, Small-angle x-ray scattering, light scattering, and NMR study of PEO-PPO-PEO triblock copolymer/cationic surfactant complexes in aqueous solution, *J. Phys. Chem. B.* **109** (15), 7073–7083 (2005).

38. Z. H. Chen, S. H. Hwang, X.-b. Zeng, J. Roh, J. Jang, and G. Ungar, SAXS characterization of polymer-embedded hollow nanoparticles and of their shell porosity, *J. Appl. Cryst.* **46**, 1654–1664 (2013).

39. T. Hegmann, H. Qi, and V. M. Marx, Nanoparticles in liquid crystals: Synthesis, self-assembly, defect formation and potential applications, *J. Inorg. Organomet. Polym. Mater.* **17** (3), 483–508 (2007).

40. L. S. Li, M. Marjanska, G. H. J. Park, A. Pines, and A. P. Alivisatos, Isotropic-liquid crystalline phase diagram of a CdSe nanorod solution, *J. Chem. Phys.* **120** (3), 1149–1152 (2004).

41. L. S. Li, J. Walda, L. Manna, and A. P. Alivisatos, Semiconductor nanorod liquid crystals, *Nano. Lett.* **2** (6), 557–560 (2002).

42. A. E. Saunders, A. Ghezelbash, D.-M. Smilgies, J. Sigman, Michael B., and B. A. Korgel, Columnar self-assembly of colloidal nanodisks, *Nano. Lett.* **6** (12), 2959–2963 (2006).

43. B. J. Lemaire, P. Davidson, P. Panine, and J. P. Jolivet, Magnetic-field-induced nematic-columnar phase transition in aqueous suspensions of goethite (alpha-FeO(OH)) nanorods, *Phys. Rev. Lett.* **93** (26) 267801 (2004).

44. K. Kanie and A. Muramatsu, Organic-inorganic hybrid liquid crystals: Thermotropic mesophases formed by hybridization of liquid-crystalline phosphates and monodispersed alpha-Fe_2O_3 particles, *J. Am. Chem. Soc.* **127** (33), 11578–11579 (2005).

45. O. Glatter and O. Kratky, *Small Angle X-Ray Scattering.* Academic Press, London (1982).

46. S. R. Kline, Reduction and analysis of SANS and USANS data using IGOR pro, *J. Appl. Cryst.* **39**, 895–900 (2006).

47. F. M. Hamzeh and R. H. Bragg, Small-angle scattering of x rays from groups of nonrandomly oriented ellipsoids of revolution of low concentration, *J. Appl. Phys.* **45** (7), 3189–3195 (1974).

48. G. R. Deen, C. L. P. Oliveira, and J. S. Pedersen, Phase behavior and kinetics of phase separation of a nonionic microemulsion of c12E5/water/1-chlorotetradecane upon a temperature quench, *J. Phys. Chem. B.* **113** (20), 7138–7146 (2009).

49. L. Arleth and J. S. Pedersen, Droplet polydispersity and shape fluctuations in AOT bis(2-ethylhexyl)sulfosuccinate sodium salt microemulsions studied by contrast variation small-angle neutron scattering, *Phys. Rev. E.* **63** (6) 061406 (2001).

50. J. E. Hallett, D. W. Hayward, P. Bartlett, and R. M. Richardson, A small-angle x-ray scattering study of nanoparticle assembly in an aligned nematic liquid crystal, *Liq. Cryst.* **41** (12), 1791–1802 (2014).

51. R. Hosemann and S. Bagchi, *Direct analysis of diffraction by matter.* North-Holland Pub. Co. (1962).

52. B. Pansu, A. Lecchi, D. Constantin, M. Imperor-Clerc, M. Veber, and I. Do-

zov, Insertion of gold nanoparticles in fluid mesophases: Size filtering and control of interactions, *J. Phys. Chem. C.* **115** (36), 17682–17687 (2011).

53. W. Abidi, B. Pansu, R. Krishnaswamy, P. Beaunier, H. Remita, and M. Imperor-Clerc, Gold nanoparticles confined in lamellar mesophases, *Rsc Adv.* **1** (3), 434–439 (2011).

54. A. Lorenz, N. Zimmermann, S. Kumar, D. R. Evans, G. Cook, M. F. Martinez, and H.-S. Kitzerow, X-ray scattering of nematic liquid crystal nanodispersion with negative dielectric anisotropy, *Appl. Opt.* **52** (22), E1–E5 (2013).

55. S. Umadevi, X. Feng, and T. Hegmann, Large area self-assembly of nematic liquid-crystal-functionalized gold nanorods, *Adv. Funct. Mater.* **23** (11), 1393–1403 (2013).

56. F. M. van der Kooij, K. Kassapidou, and H. N. W. Lekkerkerker, Liquid crystal phase transitions in suspensions of polydisperse plate-like particles, *Nature.* **406** (6798), 868–871 (2000).

57. S. Gehrer, M. Schmiele, M. Westermann, F. Steiniger, and T. Unruh, Liquid crystalline phase formation in suspensions of solid trimyristin nanoparticles, *J. Phys. Chem. B.* **118** (38), 11387–11396 (2014).

58. M. Schmiele, S. Gehrer, M. Westermann, F. Steiniger, and T. Unruh, Formation of liquid crystalline phases in aqueous suspensions of platelet-like tripalmitin nanoparticles, *J. Chem. Phys.* **140** (21), 214905 (2014).

59. G. P. Crawford, D. W. Allender, and J. W. Doane, Surface elastic and molecular-anchoring properties of nematic liquid crystals confined to cylindrical cavities, *Phys. Rev. A.* **45** (12), 8693–8708 (1992).

60. M. Schmiele, T. Schindler, T. Unruh, S. Busch, H. Morhenn, M. Westermann, F. Steiniger, A. Radulescu, P. Lindner, R. Schweins, and P. Boesecke, Structural characterization of the phospholipid stabilizer layer at the solid-liquid interface of dispersed triglyceride nanocrystals with small-angle x-ray and neutron scattering, *Phys. Rev. E.* **87** (6), 062316 (2013).

61. J. P. de Silva, A. S. Poulos, B. Pansu, P. Davidson, B. Kasmi, D. Petermann, S. Asnacios, F. Meneau, and M. Imperor, Rheological behaviour of polyoxometalate-doped lyotropic lamellar phases, *Eur. Phys. J. E.* **34** (1) 1–9 (2011).

62. A. S. Poulos, D. Constantin, P. Davidson, M. Imperor, B. Pansu, P. Panine, L. Nicole, and C. Sanchez, Photochromic hybrid organic-inorganic liquid-crystalline materials built from nonionic surfactants and polyoxometalates: Elaboration and structural study, *Langmuir.* **24** (12), 6285–6291 (2008).

63. W. L. McMillan, Measurement of smectic-A phase order-parameter fluctuations in the nematic phase of pín-octyloxybenzylidene-p-toluidine, *Phys. Rev. A.* **7** (5), 1673–1678 (1973).

64. X. Zeng, F. Liu, A. G. Fowler, G. Ungar, L. Cseh, G. H. Mehl, and J. E. Macdonald, 3D ordered gold strings by coating nanoparticles with mesogens, *Adv. Mater.* **21** (17), 1746–1750 (2009).

65. K. Kanie, M. Matsubara, X. Zeng, F. Liu, G. Ungar, H. Nakamura, and A. Muramatsu, Simple cubic packing of gold nanoparticles through rational design of their dendrimeric corona, *J. Am. Chem. Soc.* **134** (2), 808–811

(2012).

66. D. R. Dukeson, G. Ungar, V. S. K. Balagurusamy, V. Percec, G. A. Johansson, and M. Glodde, Application of isomorphous replacement in the structure determination of a cubic liquid crystal phase and location of counterions, *J. Am. Chem. Soc.* **125** (51), 15974–15980 (2003).

67. D. E. McRee, *Practical Protein Crystallography.* Academic Press, San Diego (1993).

68. X. Zeng, R. Kieffer, B. Glettner, C. Nuernberger, F. Liu, K. Pelz, M. Prehm, U. Baumeister, H. Hahn, H. Lang, G. A. Gehring, C. H. M. Weber, J. K. Hobbs, C. Tschierske, and G. Ungar, Complex multicolor tilings and critical phenomena in tetraphilic liquid crystals, *Science.* **331** (6022), 1302–1306 (2011).

69. J. Daillant and A. Gibaud, *X-ray and neutron reflectivity : principle and applications.* Springer, Heidelberg (1999).

70. J. Paczesny, M. Wojcik, K. Sozanski, K. Nikiforov, C. Tschierske, A. Lehmann, E. Gorecka, J. Mieczkowski, and R. Holyst, Self-assembly of gold nanoparticles into 2D arrays induced by bolaamphiphilic ligands, *J. Phys. Chem. C.* **117** (45), 24056–24062 (2013).

71. IsGISAXS, http://www.insp.jussieu.fr/oxydes/isGISAXS/isgisaxs.htm.

72. bornagainproject, http://www.bornagainproject.org/.

73. G. Ungar, F. Liu, X. B. Zeng, B. Glettner, M. Prehm, R. Kieffer, and C. Tschierske. GISAXS in the study of supramolecular and hybrid liquid crystals. In ed. G. Ungar and R. Heenan, *J. Phys. Conf. Ser.*, 247, 012032 (2010).

74. P. S. Kumar, S. K. Pal, S. Kumar, and V. Lakshminarayanan, Dispersion of thiol stabilized gold nanoparticles in lyotropic liquid crystalline systems, *Langmuir.* **23** (6), 3445–3449 (2007).

75. Q. Liu, Y. Cui, D. Gardner, X. Li, S. He, and I. I. Smalyukh, Self-alignment of plasmonic gold nanorods in reconfigurable anisotropic fluids for tunable bulk metamaterial applications, *Nano. Lett.* **10** (4), 1347–1353 (2010).

76. K. P. Sharma, G. Kumaraswamy, I. Ly, and O. Mondain-Monval, Self-assembly of silica particles in a nonionic surfactant hexagonal mesophase, *J. Phys. Chem. B.* **113** (11), 3423–3430 (2009).

77. G. J. Vroege, D. M. E. Thies-Weesie, A. V. Petukhov, B. J. Lemaire, and P. Davidson, Smectic liquid-crystalline order in suspensions of highly polydisperse goethite nanorods, *Adv. Mater.* **18** (19), 2565–2568 (2006).

78. Y. Yang, S. Matsubara, M. Nogami, J. L. Shi, and W. M. Huang, One-dimensional self-assembly of gold nanoparticles for tunable surface plasmon resonance properties, *Nanotechnology.* **17** (11), 2821–2827 (2006).

79. S. Kumar, S. K. Pal, P. S. Kumar, and V. Lakshminarayanan, Novel conducting nanocomposites: synthesis of triphenylene-covered gold nanoparticles and their insertion into a columnar matrix, *Soft Matter.* **3** (7), 896–900 (2007).

80. A. Ethirajan, U. Wiedwald, H.-G. Boyen, B. Kern, L. Han, A. Klimmer, F. Weigl, G. Kaestle, P. Ziemann, K. Fauth, J. Cai, R. J. Behm, A. Romanyuk, P. Oelhafen, P. Walther, J. Biskupek, and U. Kaiser, A micellar approach to magnetic ultrahigh-density data-storage media: Extending the

limits of current colloidal methods, *Adv. Mater.* **19** (3), 406–410 (2007).

81. Y. Lin, V. K. Daga, E. R. Anderson, S. P. Gido, and J. J. Watkins, Nanoparticle-driven assembly of block copolymers: A simple route to ordered hybrid materials, *J. Am. Chem. Soc.* **133** (17), 6513–6516 (2011).

82. D. Nykypanchuk, M. M. Maye, D. van der Lelie, and O. Gang, DNA-guided crystallization of colloidal nanoparticles, *Nature.* **451** (7178), 549–552 (2008).

83. S. Y. Park, A. K. R. Lytton-Jean, B. Lee, S. Weigand, G. C. Schatz, and C. A. Mirkin, DNA-programmable nanoparticle crystallization, *Nature.* **451** (7178), 553–556 (2008).

84. M. Draper, I. M. Saez, S. J. Cowling, P. Gai, B. Heinrich, B. Donnio, D. Guillon, and J. W. Goodby, Self-assembly and shape morphology of liquid-crystalline gold metamaterials, *Adv. Funct. Mater.* **21** (7), 1260–1278 (2011).

85. S. Frein, J. Boudon, M. Vonlanthen, T. Scharf, J. Barbera, G. Suess-Fink, T. Buergi, and R. Deschenaux, Liquid-crystalline thiol- and disulfide-based dendrimers for the functionalization of gold nanoparticles, *Helv. Chim. Acta.* **91** (12), 2321–2337 (2008).

86. C. Gautier and T. Buergi, Chiral gold nanoparticles, *ChemPhysChem.* **10** (3), 483–492 (2009).

87. M. Wojcik, W. Lewandowski, J. Matraszek, J. Mieczkowski, J. Borysiuk, D. Pociecha, and E. Gorecka, Liquid-crystalline phases made of gold nanoparticles, *Angew. Chem. (Int. Ed.).* **48** (28), 5167–5169 (2009).

88. W. Lewandowski, D. Constantin, K. Walicka, D. Pociecha, J. Mieczkowski, and E. Gorecka, Smectic mesophases of functionalized silver and gold nanoparticles with anisotropic plasmonic properties, *Chem. Commun.* **49** (71), 7845–7847 (2013).

89. J. M. Wolska, D. Pociecha, J. Mieczkowski, and E. Gorecka, Gold nanoparticles with flexible mesogenic grafting layers, *Soft Matter.* **9** (11), 3005–3008 (2013).

90. X. Mang, X. Zeng, B. Tang, F. Liu, G. Ungar, R. Zhang, L. Cseh, and G. H. Mehl, Control of anisotropic self-assembly of gold nanoparticles coated with mesogens, *J. Mater. Chem.* **22** (22), 11101–11106 (2012).

91. S. Saliba, P. Davidson, M. Imperor-Clerc, C. Mingotaud, M. L. Kahn, and J.-D. Marty, Facile direct synthesis of ZnO nanoparticles within lyotropic liquid crystals: towards organized hybrid materials, *J. Mater. Chem.* **21** (45), 18191–18194 (2011).

92. M. M. Wojcik, M. Gora, J. Mieczkowski, J. Romiszewski, E. Gorecka, and D. Pociecha, Temperature-controlled liquid crystalline polymorphism of gold nanoparticles, *Soft Matter.* **7** (22), 10561–10564 (2011).

93. B. Donnio, P. Garcia-Vazquez, J.-L. Gallani, D. Guillon, and E. Terazzi, Dendronized ferromagnetic gold nanoparticles self-organized in a thermotropic cubic phase, *Adv. Mater.* **19** (21), 3534–3539 (2007).

94. C.-Z. Li, Y. Matsuo, and E. Nakamura, Octupole-like supramolecular aggregates of conical iron fullerene complexes into a three-dimensional liquid crystalline lattice, *J. Am. Chem. Soc.* **132** (44), 15514–15515 (2010).

95. J. Dintinger, B.-J. Tang, X. Zeng, F. Liu, T. Kienzler, G. H. Mehl, G. Ungar, C. Rockstuhl, and T. Scharf, A self-organized anisotropic liquid-crystal

plasmonic metamaterial, *Adv. Mater.* **25** (14), 1999–2004 (2013).

96. W. Lewandowski, K. Jatczak, D. Pociecha, and J. Mieczkowski, Control of gold nanoparticle superlattice properties via mesogenic ligand architecture, *Langmuir.* **29** (10), 3404–3410 (2013).

97. W. Lewandowski, M. Wojcik, and E. Gorecka, Metal nanoparticles with liquid-crystalline ligands: Controlling nanoparticle superlattice structure and properties, *ChemPhysChem.* **15** (7), 1283–1295 (2014).

98. Z. H. Chen, C. Kim, X. B. Zeng, S. H. Hwang, J. Jang, and G. Ungar, Characterizing size and porosity of hollow nanoparticles: SAXS, SANS, TEM, DLS, and adsorption isotherms compared, Langmuir. **28**(43), 15350–15361 (2012).

99. P. Houdy, P. Schiller, and C. Boher, Grazing X-ray reflection analysis of nanometric scale structures, *Journal of Applied Physics.* **68**(12), 6133–6142 (1990).

Chapter 7

Raman spectroscopy

Helen F. Gleeson

Cavendish Professor of Physics,
School of Physics and Astronomy, University of Leeds,
Leeds LS2 9JT
h.f.gleeson@leeds.ac.uk

Raman spectroscopy has been used as a tool to study liquid crystals for several decades. There are several features that make Raman spectroscopy an important characterisation method. It is bond-specific, so can provide information about the interaction of liquid crystals with colloidal systems and can offer an insight into phase transitions. The polarization dependence of the scattering can be used to determine order parameters in liquid crystal systems. Finally, the relatively high spatial resolution of the technique ($\sim$1 μm) can be used to explore spatially-dependent order in soft matter systems. This chapter describes the most important ways in which Raman spectroscopy can be used to reveal information about liquid crystal systems, illustrated by examples. Both the theoretical background and experimental considerations are described, providing a comprehensive introduction to anybody interested in using the technique to understand liquid crystal systems.

Contents

1. Introduction to Raman spectroscopy for the study of liquid crystals

Raman spectroscopy[1,2] detects the very low level of light that is scattered inelastically as a result of interactions with vibrational or rotational modes of molecules – approximately 1 in every 10^7 photons is scattered in this way. In particular, a mode can be observed *via* its Raman spectrum if it causes a modulation of the molecular polarizability; in this sense, Raman spectroscopy is complementary to Infra Red (IR) measurements. Raman spectroscopy is bond-specific for high frequency modes since an individual Raman peak corresponds to a particular vibrational mode within a molecule and hence provides a probe of specific parts of the molecule. Studies of the change in the Raman peak position can provide information about molecular configurations, phase transitions and interactions with the local environment. Consequently, Raman spectroscopy can offer an insight into the interactions of liquid crystals with nano- or colloidal particles through understanding details of the Raman spectra.

Raman scattering can be understood by simple arguments that consider the interaction of electromagnetic radiation with a polarizable medium. The dipole, μ, induced in a molecule by incident electromagnetic radiation can be described in terms of the amplitude E_0 and frequency ν_0 of the field and the molecular polarizability, α, as $\mu = \alpha E_0 \cos{(2\pi\nu_0 t)}$. We can consider the contribution of a vibrational mode of the molecule that distorts the molecular polarizability by assuming the resulting distortion to be small and periodic. Expanding to first order,

$$\alpha = \alpha_0 + \frac{\partial \alpha}{\partial q_k} \cos{(2\pi\nu_{vib}t)} \tag{1}$$

where q_k represents an appropriate displacement co-ordinate and ν_{vib} is the vibrational frequency of the mode (the same arguments apply if the mode is rotational). Clearly, the mode must induce a change in the molecular polarizability (i.e. $\partial\alpha/\partial q_k \neq 0$) for it to be Raman active. The induced dipole can then be written;

$$\mu = E_0 \left(\alpha_0 + \frac{\partial \alpha}{\partial q_k} \cos{(2\pi\nu_{vib}t)} \right) \cos{(2\pi\nu_0 t)} \tag{2}$$

$$= E_0\alpha_0 \cos{(2\pi\nu_0 t)} + E_0 \frac{\partial \alpha}{\partial q_k} \cos{(2\pi\nu_{vib}t)} \cos{(2\pi\nu_0 t)}$$

$$= E_0\alpha_0 \cos{(2\pi\nu_0 t)} + \frac{E_0}{2} \frac{\partial \alpha}{\partial q_k} \cos{(2\pi(\nu_0 \pm \nu_{vib})t)}$$

The first term represents elastically (Rayleigh) scattered light, while the second term shows that light is inelastically scattered at higher and lower frequencies with respect to the Rayleigh peak; this is Raman scattering. These inelastic scattering peaks are known as Stokes ($\nu_0 - \nu_{vib}$) and anti-Stokes ($\nu_0 + \nu_{vib}$) peaks respectively and as the latter require the system to be in an initially excited state, the anti-Stokes peak intensities are always lower than the Stokes by a factor given by Boltzmann statistics. The difference between the wavelengths of the incident and scattered radiation, λ_0 and λ_s, defines the Raman shift $\Delta\nu$,

$$\Delta\nu = \frac{1}{\lambda_0} - \frac{1}{\lambda_s} \tag{3}$$

The spectral range of the Raman shift typically lies between 200 cm^{-1} and 3000 cm^{-1}, with many of the peaks in organic structures concentrated around 1600 cm^{-1}. Table 1 presents a selection of common Raman active modes in liquid crystalline systems, together with an indication of the strength of the mode and the typical Raman shift.

The intensity of light re-radiated from a sample depends on the square of the induced dipole and it follows that the intensity of a Raman peak is proportional to the square of the polarizability derivative,

$$I \propto \left(\frac{\partial \alpha}{\partial q_k} \right)^2 \tag{4}$$

A strongly Raman-active mode is thus one in which there is a large gradient of the polarizability around equilibrium. The anisotropic nature of the vibrational bands means that order can be determined in liquid crystalline systems. The differential polarizability tensor can be expressed as:

$$\left(\frac{\partial \alpha}{\partial q_k} \right) \equiv \alpha'_{ij} = \begin{pmatrix} \alpha'_{xx} & 0 & 0 \\ 0 & \alpha'_{yy} & 0 \\ 0 & 0 & \alpha'_{zz} \end{pmatrix} \tag{5}$$

Table 1.   A selection of Raman-active modes common in liquid crystals. The shifts are typical, but exact values will depend on the system, as described in the text.

Vibrational mode	$\Delta\nu$ (cm^{-1})	Relative strength
Aromatic C-H in-plane deformation	1021	Weak
C-O stretch	1259	Strong
C-C stretch of the biphenyl link	1289	Strong
Phenyl breathing (stretch) mode	1606	Very Strong
C=O stretch	1738	Strong
Cyano stretching mode	2225	Strong

where α'_{xx}, α'_{yy} and α'_{zz} represent the differential polarizability along the principal axes of a molecule. Later in this chapter, this anisotropy, together with that of the liquid crystal phase, will be used to indicate how Polarized Raman Spectroscopy (PRS) can determine order parameters in liquid crystals.

Figure 1 shows the Raman spectrum of the common nematic liquid crystal 4-4'-pentylcyanobiphenyl (5CB), together with the peak assignments. Such a spectrum is typical of many liquid crystals and the figure also demonstrates the dependence of the peak intensities in Raman spectra when measured for different orientations of the nematic system; spectra are also shown for data polarized along and perpendicular to the average preferred direction of the molecules (defined by the director, $\mathbf{n}$). The intensity of the Raman scattered light can be defined as $I_\parallel$ and $I_\perp$ respectively, and Fig. 2 illustrates the geometry associated with polarized Raman scattering of liquid crystals.

This chapter is arranged as follows. Section 2 describes the apparatus that can be used in Raman scattering. Experiments showing how Raman spectroscopy can be employed to glean spatial information in liquid crystal

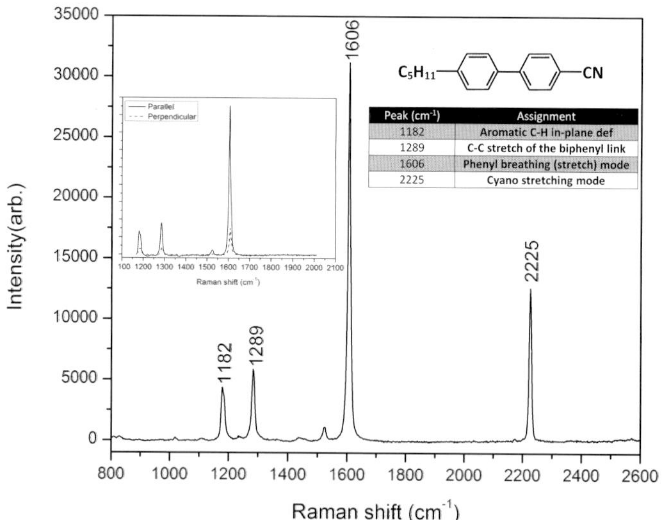

Fig. 1. The Raman spectrum of 5CB, showing the assignments of the peaks for this liquid crystal molecule. The inset shows the spectra measured with the incident laser light polarization aligned parallel (solid line) and perpendicular (dashed line) to the director. (credit: Zhaopeng Zhang, University of Manchester).

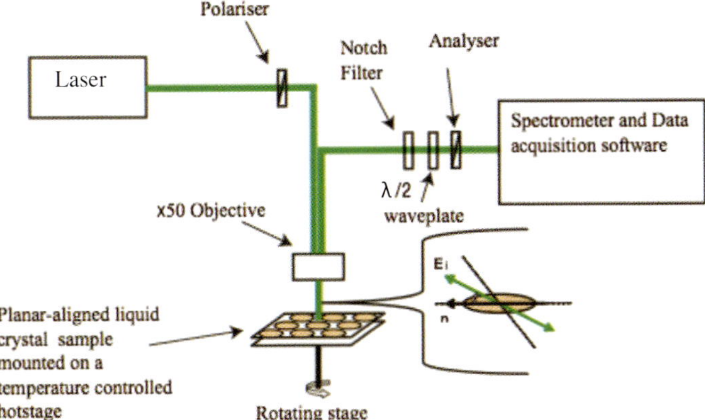

Fig. 2. A schematic demonstrating the geometry in polarized Raman scattering studies of liquid crystals. The incident electric field vector E_i is defined with respect to the director, **n**, and the $\lambda/2$ wave plate allows the scattered light to be detected with either the same polarization as the incident light or perpendicular to it.

systems. Section 3 considers how Raman spectra can offer insight into phase transitions in soft matter systems, while Sec. 4 examines the information that can be obtained from a study of the Raman spectra in colloidal systems. Finally, Sec. 5 describes the use of Raman spectroscopy to determine order parameters in liquid crystal systems.

2. Raman spectroscopic methods; spatial investigations in liquid crystals

The apparatus required to carry out Raman spectroscopy measurements in liquid crystals must satisfy several requirements:

- A narrow line-width (monochromatic) light source such as a stable laser for illumination. Although Raman scattering will occur irrespective of the wavelength of the source, it is important to avoid any fluorescence as this will readily mask the low intensity Raman peaks. It is also worth noting that for non-resonant Raman scattering, the intensity will vary as $1/\lambda^4$, so the signal is more intense at lower wavelengths.
- The ability to detect the very low light intensities typical of Raman scattering peaks. Holographic notch or 'edge' filters are often used to reject the Rayleigh-scattered light so that sensitive detectors such as Charge Coupled Detector (CCD) arrays can be used.

- The possibility of using well-defined liquid crystal samples, often encapsulated in sample cells comprising two glass substrates coated on the inner surfaces with transparent electrodes and/or alignment agents to obtain the required director geometry;
- Polarization optics to allow selection of the polarization state of the incident and Raman scattered light with respect to the liquid crystal director.

A particularly convenient apparatus that is commonly used is a system in which the Raman spectrometer is included in a polarizing microscope arrangement, commonly known as a **Raman Microscope** or micro-Raman spectrometer. The use of polarizing microscopy to characterise liquid crystal samples is well-known[3] and combination of the two techniques is a powerful analytic tool. Typical systems are designed to guide the laser beam into the polarizing microscope and to focus it onto the prepared sample. A significant advantage of this arrangement is that the liquid crystal sample can be held in a conventional microscope hot stage, allowing temperature-dependent measurements to be made. Further, the texture of the liquid crystal sample can be viewed, ensuring that measurements are taken only in the desired (usually well-aligned) areas. The size of the incident laser beam depends on the optics of the system, but is often of the order of microns as long working distance 50x objectives are commonly used. The scattered laser light passes through a series of notch filters which remove the Rayleigh scattered light before reaching the analyzer where it is spectrally resolved before falls onto the detector which measures the Raman scattering intensity.

The dependence of Raman spectra on the polarization direction with respect to the liquid crystal director was demonstrated in Fig. 1. This basic effect can be used to determine information regarding the orientation of a liquid crystalline system in a variety of systems. In order to carry out such experiments, the apparatus must be designed to minimise the effect of instrumental parameters on the polarization state of the incident and scattered light since such factors can contribute as much as 8% to the measured Raman intensities.[4] However, it has been demonstrated that in-situ polarized Raman microscopy can reveal information about liquid crystal orientation in a periodic liquid crystalline composite structure formed with alternate slices of liquid crystal and a polymer.[5] The chemical selectivity of Raman scattering allowed the orientation of the liquid crystal to be determined, finding it to be perpendicular to the polymer layers. Another study has examined the orientation of thin films of a liquid crystal tetra-substituted phthalocyanine, demonstrating that the type of alignment induced (homeotropic or planar) depends on the electrode material.[6] Such data are important in understanding and controlling the electrical conductivity of liquid crystalline films through their alignment.

A particular advantage of a Raman Microscope system is that it is possible to design such an apparatus to detect the Raman scattered light in a **confocal** geometry. This involves including pinholes in confocal planes within the instrument, rejecting out-of-focus scattered light and ensuring that the volume under study is diffraction-limited. In practice, this means that the scattered light is detected with spatial resolution of around a micron or better, which is of particular value in imaging, especially when combined with the chemical selectivity that Raman scattering offers. However, a disadvantage of the Raman microscope is that the power density can be rather high at the focus and care must be taken to ensure that nonlinear phenomena are not induced in liquid crystalline samples. Confocal Raman scattering has been used to determine the molecular orientation in stripe patterns formed in poly(3-hexylthiopene) during a deposition method based on controlled evaporative self-assembly.[7]

There are several other modifications of Raman spectroscopy that are increasingly important in the study of soft matter, especially biological systems. A growing number have been applied to liquid crystalline materials, including examples with dispersed colloidal particles or carbon nanotubes. **Surface Enhanced Raman Spectroscopy (SERS)** requires a system that includes gold or silver; the plasmons associated with the metal are excited by the laser, enhancing the electric field and hence increasing the Raman signal - by factors of up to 10^{11}. In **Stimulated Raman Scattering (SRS)**, two spatially coincident light pulses of frequencies with an energy difference corresponding to an allowed Raman transition are employed, thus exciting the system from the ground state to a vibrational or rotational state. SRS has been used to achieve background-free 3-D imaging of director fields in liquid crystals and composite systems. This is a powerful tool proposed for mapping distributions of molecular orientation that makes use of both the chemical selectivity and polarization dependence of the technique.[8]

Coherent Anti-Stokes Raman Scattering (CARS) uses multiple photons that interact with the sample to generate a coherent beam at the anti-Stokes frequency, which is resonantly enhanced when the frequency difference between the two laser beams employed hits a Raman resonance.

The value of the technique is that the resonance effectively ensures that the signal is several orders of magnitude greater than a Raman scattering signal, while remaining bond selective. Thus CARS can be used for imaging with lower incident power densities than are used in conventional Raman scattering experiments. The use of CARS for 3-D imaging in liquid crystalline systems has been described in some detail by Lavrentovich.[9] Smalyukh and co-workers have combined CARS with **optical trapping** and other spectroscopic techniques, allowing them to visualize and control orientation in soft matter systems, some of which include colloidal material.[10–12]

Raman imaging can also be combined with **Atomic Force Microscopy (AFM)**, see Chap. 9, for example to investigate structures in phthalocyanine thin films,[13] and approaches such as **Tip Enhanced Raman Spectroscopy (TERS)** combines a metal coated AFM or STM tip to enhance the Raman activity of the material in its vicinity. TERS offers a spatial resolution that is approximately the size of the tip apex, i.e. 20-30 nm and could be an invaluable tool in understanding the properties of nanoparticle-dispersed liquid crystals.

3. Raman spectroscopy as a tool to investigate phase transitions

Molecular vibrations and rotations are sensitive to the local environment, a fact reflected in the position and intensity of the Raman peaks of a sample. There are two general phenomena that can be observed in the Raman spectra of a liquid crystalline material as a function of temperature. Firstly, changes can occur that are related to a modification in the packing and rotational freedom of the molecules in different phases.[14] Such changes are generally manifest as small shifts in the Raman peak position, relatively small changes in the peak intensity or the emergence or disappearance of peaks associated with specific molecular vibrations or rotations. The second type of change that can be observed in Raman spectra as a function of temperature is more closely related to orientational phenomena such as those demonstrated in Fig. 1. For example, the transition from a SmA to SmC* phase could result in a reduction in the peak intensity which is entirely attributable to the tilt and helical structure in the lower temperature phase.[15] Consequently, subtle changes in Raman spectra observed as a function of temperature can be used to investigate phase transitions and packing in liquid crystalline systems. This sub-section describes a few examples of such an approach.

The use of Raman spectra to deduce information about molecular packing in different phases of a liquid crystalline system is exemplified by a study of material denoted AS618 that exhibits considerable smectic paramorphism, including ferroelectric, intermediate and antiferroelectric phases.[15] A planar aligned sample of the material was studied using polarized Raman Microscopy over a broad temperature range that encompassed its crystalline, liquid crystalline and isotropic phases. Figure 3 shows the Raman spectrum of the material, together with the chemical structure and peak assignments.

All of the peaks shifted with temperature, with the biggest changes at the isotropic to liquid crystal and liquid crystal to crystal transitions. In the crystal phase, molecules are closely packed with a larger volume density and many parts of the molecule are likely to be co-planar. The changes in the liquid crystal phase were rather more subtle, detailed analysis confirming that there is more freedom for vibrational and rotational modes. Interestingly, anomalous behaviour was observed for the C-C phenyl stretch in the SmC^*_α phase, suggesting that there is a specific interaction between the molecular cores that stabilizes the phase. Some rather weak features also change as a function of temperature, for example a peak appears at $1194\mathrm{cm}^{-1}$ in the crystalline phase. This was assigned to a phenyl mode that is only Raman active in a co-planar configuration, supporting the

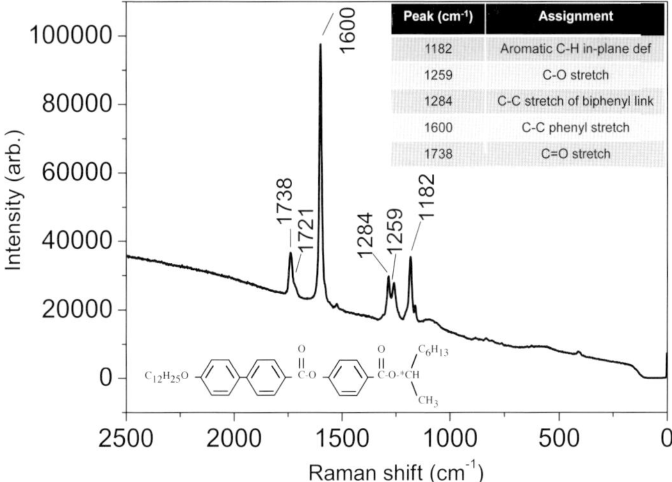

Fig. 3. The Raman spectrum of AS618 in the SmA phase, together with its chemical structure and peak assignments.[15]

interpretation of the peak shifts. The study also shows clear changes in the intensity of the Raman peaks as a function of temperature, again with the largest (discontinuous) changes occurring at the isotropic to liquid crystal and liquid crystal to crystal phase transitions. Within the liquid crystal phases, changes in intensity are discussed in terms of increased order as the temperature is reduced, together with structural implications of forming helical, tilted phases and overall alignment within the phase (for example, a SmA bookshelf structure will deform to a chevron structure in the SmC* phase).

Temperature-dependent Raman scattering has also been used to study the phase transitions in ethyl-[4-(4-decyloxy)benzoyloxy]-benzoate, paying particular attention to Raman peaks corresponding to C-H in-plane bending and C=O stretching vibrations.[16] The data show that the molecules undergo a trans- to cis- conformational change at the crystal to SmA phase transition as a result of intra-molecular rotation.

Another interesting example of the use of Raman spectroscopy to understand phase transitions was reported by Jin *et al.* who studied silk fibroin aqueous solutions from different regions of the silk glands in silk worms.[17] Their work showed that the liquid crystalline structure exhibited by the silk fibronin solutions was initially formed in the anterior part of the middle division of the silk gland.

Polarizing Raman microscopy has also been used to explore electric field-induced transformations in liquid crystals. For example, field-induced changes in the dark conglomerate (DC) phase in a bent-core oxadiazole-based liquid crystalline material[18] have been examined using a number of techniques including Raman spectroscopy.[19] Interestingly, in the system described large changes in chirality and refractive index are reported at field strengths around 18 Vμm^{-1} where a new Raman peak was seen to emerge. The peak occurs at around 1590 cm^{-1} and was assigned to the C-C stretch in the phenyl rings adjacent to the oxadiazole core; the appearance of the peak is important evidence that a reorganization of the DC phase occurs under the influence of the field.

4. Raman spectroscopy as a tool to investigate interactions with colloidal materials

Section 3 described how the sensitivity of Raman spectra to the local environment allows information about packing in liquid crystals to be deduced. The Raman effect is also sufficiently sensitive to allow details of the interaction of liquid crystals with surfaces, nanoparticles and nanotubes to be investigated. Systems in which liquid crystals and nanoparticles are combined have been of significant interest for some time: carbon nanotubes (CNTs) can be aligned through their interaction with lyotropic and thermotropic liquid crystals;[20] the inclusion of functionalized nanoparticles is reported to enhance the properties of liquid crystalline materials;[21] and larger colloidal particles interact through defects allowing photonic crystalline structures to be built up.[22] It is the first of these phenomena that are of particular interest in this section, which seeks to describe some of the insight that Raman spectroscopy has offered to such hybrid systems.

Carbon nanotubes have generated immense scientific and technological interest and although describing them in detail is beyond the scope of this chapter, an excellent summary of the subject can be found in Ref. 20 and Chapters 17 and 18 of this book focus specifically on liquid crystalline dispersions of these nanoparticles. Different types of CNTs exist, including single walled and multi walled nanotubes (SWCNTs and MWCNTs respectively) and the structure of the CNTs (the way in which they are 'formed' from a single sheet of graphene) determines physical properties including the chirality and metallic or semiconductor nature of the particles. Raman spectroscopy can provide information on both graphene and CNTs through details of the Raman peaks that depend on the form of the carbon present.[23]

An early challenge was the control of the alignment of CNTs; they are extremely anisotropic systems and many applications require control of this anisotropy. There are two major approaches to controlling CNT alignment, during their growth or subsequent to it. Liquid crystals have proven to be of significant interest in the latter case and offer one of the most successful alignment strategies for CNTs.[24,25] The surface interaction between the CNTs and the liquid crystal is known to be critical to the success of this approach to their alignment and studies have found that in lyotropic systems in particular, the nanotube needs to be treated with an amphiphilic surface alignment agent to encourage the dispersion interaction with the liquid crystal host. However, some thermotropic liquid crystals are surprisingly good solvents for CNTs and the polarization-dependence of Raman scattering has demonstrated the alignment of SWCNTs with a thermotropic nematic liquid crystal host.[26] Scalia and co-workers used Raman scattering to demonstrate an interaction between the biphenyl core of liquid crystals that proved to be particularly good dispersion/alignment agents, showing a distinct shift in the position of the radial breathing mode

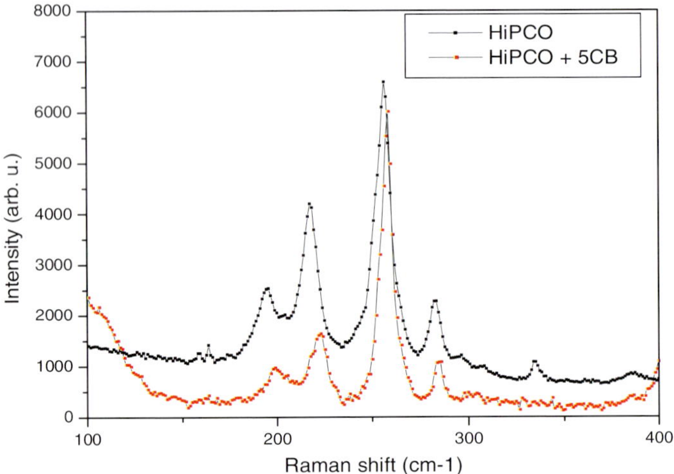

Fig. 4.   Example of the shift observed in Raman spectrum in the vicinity of HiPCO carbon nanotubes (Reproduced with permission from Ref. 27)

associated with the SWCNTs in a mixture 5CB and SWCNTs.[26–28]

CNTs have been dispersed in a number of different liquid crystal phases and Raman spectroscopy is a useful tool to investigate their interaction. Zhao *et al.* investigated the interaction between a ferroelectric liquid crystal and SWCNTs. An emerging Raman peak at 763 cm^{-1} indicates a charge transfer effect between the SWCNTs and the C-Cl groups in the ferroelectric material and it is concluded that the nanotubes are aligned along the smectic layers, rather than in the direction of the molecular long axis.[29] The orientation of SWCNTs in a SmC material was studied via Raman scattering and the nanotubes shown to enhance the alignment close to the glass-ITO interface.[30] Another system in which the orientation of SWCNTs influences the alignment of the liquid crystal is in a phthalocyanine system, where inclusion of the nanotubes led to edge-on orientation of the columnar structure, thereby increasing lateral conductivity.[31]

The use of Raman spectroscopy to study the interaction in nanoparticle systems and at the interface with surfaces is an emerging field. Saha *et al.* report surface-enhanced Raman scattering from nanoparticles in 'hot spots' in graphene oxide liquid crystal[32] and there is clear value in using Raman spectroscopy to understand the interaction of liquid crystals on graphene electrodes that are suggested for use in devices.[33] Finally, it would seem that Raman scattering could be of great value in improving the understanding of the interaction between nanoparticles and liquid crystals in hybrid systems where the nanoparticles are reported to enhance the liquid crystalline properties.

5. Polarized Raman spectroscopy for the study of order parameters

The fact that liquid crystals are fluids defined by their orientational and/or positional order means that the study of order in liquid crystals is central to their understanding. Maier-Saupe (MS) theory[34] (see Chap. 2 for a brief introduction) together with subsequent theoretical extensions[35–37] successfully describes the order in nematic liquid crystals, allowing many of the experimental observations of the phase to be predicted. Central to these theoretical approaches is the orientational distribution function (ODF), $f(\alpha, \beta, \gamma)$, which describes the angular distribution of the director about a defined co-ordinate system. The parameters α, β and γ are Euler angles (as described in Ref. 38); α and β describe the orientation of a molecule with respect to axes perpendicular to and parallel to the director respectively and γ describes rotation about the molecular long axis (coincident with the term α'_{zz}). For a phase such as the nematic phase with uniaxial symmetry, in which (usually) the molecules can be considered to be rod-like, it can be shown that the ODF can be simplified to an expansion of the Legendre polynomials $P_n(\cos \beta)$.

It has long been recognized that measurement of the anisotropy of the Raman scattered light in liquid crystals can lead to the determination of the order parameters of the phase. Jen *et al.*[39] pioneered the approach when they described the measurement of uniaxial order parameters in the nematic material MBBA by analysis of the depolarization ratio of the Raman scattered light, $I_\perp / I_\parallel$, and their approach has been applied widely.[40–44] Polarized Raman Spectroscopy (PRS) is especially valuable since, along with x-ray scattering,[45,46] neutron scattering[47] and ESR spectroscopy,[48] it is one of the very few techniques that enables high rank order parameters in liquid crystals to be deduced. The reason for this possibility in Raman scattering is explained briefly in the following paragraphs; details can be found in several references including Refs. 8 and 49, the former of which offers a review of this approach.

As already mentioned, the intensity of Raman scattered light is proportional to the square of the differential polarizability, $I \propto \left(\frac{\partial \alpha}{\partial q_k}\right)^2$. Since the molecular vibrational bands are anisotropic in a liquid crystalline medium, the scattered intensity can be used to deduce the ordering of the system. It is worth noting that most treatments neglect the birefringence of liquid crystals on the dipole emission, though Jen *et al.*[39] provide a complete analysis. Several references describe the following in detail.[39,49,50] Briefly, the scattering from a molecule can be expressed by transforming the differential polarizability tensor (with derivatives along the primary molecular axes given by α'_{xx}, α'_{yy} and α'_{zz}) into an appropriate reference frame by expressing the scattering as a function of the Euler angles and the incident polarization direction of the light, θ. Since the measured intensity is simply proportional to the square of the electric field contributions for the chosen experimental geometry and these contributions are further governed by the ODF, it can be shown that the observable parameters can be reduced to the generalised Legendre polynomials:

$$P_{200} = \frac{1}{2}(3\cos^2\beta - 1) \tag{6}$$

$$P_{220} = \frac{1}{4}(1 - \cos^2\beta)\cos 2\alpha \tag{7}$$

$$P_{400} = \frac{1}{8}(3 - 30\cos^2\beta + 35\cos^4\beta) \tag{8}$$

$$P_{420} = \frac{1}{24}(-1 + 8\cos^2\beta - 7\cos^4\beta)\cos 2\alpha \tag{9}$$

$$P_{440} = \frac{1}{16}(1 - 2\cos^2\beta - \cos^4\beta)\cos 4\alpha \tag{10}$$

The notation is such that the subscripts L, m and n in $P_{L,m,n}$ represent the conditions on rotations of α, β and γ respectively and there are several important consequences of imposing specific symmetry requirements. Firstly, L, m and n must take even values. Secondly, as Raman bands are generally assumed to have uniaxial symmetry (i.e. $\alpha'_{zz} > \alpha'_{xx} = \alpha'_{yy}$), all of the order parameters associated with a rotation about γ are zero. It is important to note that if such an assumption is not valid, modifications to the treatment must be made as will be discussed further below. The expressions above can be used to express the ODF to 4th order[51] as follows, where the angular brackets indicate a statistical average corresponding to a particular order parameter:

$$f(\alpha, \beta) = \frac{1}{8\pi^2}$$

$$\times \left[\begin{array}{c} 1 + \frac{5}{2}\langle P_{200}\rangle(3\cos^2\beta - 1) + \frac{5}{2}\langle P_{220}\rangle 6(1 - 3\cos^2\beta)\cos 2\alpha \\ \frac{9}{8}\langle P_{400}\rangle(3 - 30\cos^2\beta + 35\cos^4\beta) + \frac{9}{8}\langle P_{420}\rangle 60(-1 + 8\cos^2\beta - 7\cos^4\beta)\cos 2\alpha \\ \frac{9}{8}\langle P_{440}\rangle 70(1 - 2\cos^2\beta - \cos^4\beta)\cos 4\alpha \end{array} \right] \quad (11)$$

The profile of the Raman scattering intensity can be constructed by integrating the ODF over all orientations or, conversely and more useful in practice, order parameters can in principle be deduced from measurements of the Raman scattering intensity. The uniaxial nematic order parameters are $\langle P_{200}\rangle$ and $\langle P_{200}\rangle$, better known as P_2 and P_4, while the other parameters in the equation refer to biaxial order parameters. It is an interesting observation that $\langle P_{440}\rangle$ does not necessarily have to be zero in a uniaxial system, while the other biaxial order parameters must.[18,50]

Many of the early approaches to determining the order parameters defined two orthogonal geometries with co-ordinate axes parallel and perpendicular to the director (planar and homeotropic cell geometries respectively). However, it is now clear that the most robust way of determining order parameters from Raman scattering data is to determine the Raman scattering depolarization ratio for specific bands as a function of angle of the incident polarization vector, $R_\theta = I_\perp(\theta)/I_\parallel(\theta)$, often referred to as the 'full depolarization ratio', and fit to the appropriate equations.[8,11,18,52] The difference between the techniques is especially marked for P_4 which was (erroneously) reported to take very low or even negative values in early work where the full depolarization ratio was not analysed.

Typical data that show the full depolarization ratio determined for 5CB are shown in Fig. 5; these data allow both P_2 and P_4 to be determined, as also shown in the figure, and the values obtained are in good agreement both with theory and with other experimental techniques. As mentioned in the previous section, Raman scattering can be used to probe the orientation in liquid crystal/nanoparticle hybrid materials and PRS can also be employed to make quantitative measurement of the order in such systems. For example, thermotropic liquid crystals containing MWNT functionalised with decyloxy and phenylcyclohexyl (PCH) mesogenic groups at concentrations up to 5 wt% and aligned in a magnetic field were shown by PRS to exhibit rather high order.[53] Puech *et al.* employed PRS to investigate the degree of coupling between carbon nanotubes and nematic suspensions of viruses in aqueous solution.[54] PRS allowed the order of each of these components

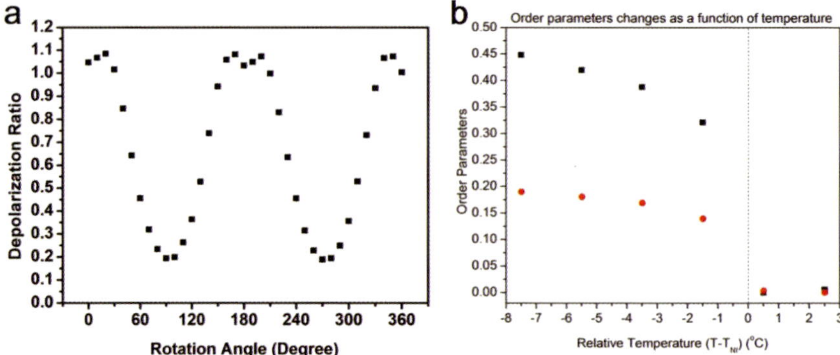

Fig. 5. (a) The depolarization ratio and (b) The P_2 (black squares) and P_4 (red circles) order parameters of 5CB deduced from fits to the depolarization ratio. (Credit: Zhaopeng Zhang, University of Manchester).

to be determined independently demonstrating that the order of the CNTs was systematically lower than that of the virus particles. An investigation of intrinsically conducting nanorods in liquid crystals was made in which the orientational order parameter, deduced from PRS measurements, was correlated with the conductivity anisotropy of the system.[55] The orientational order parameter of SWCNTs at an isotropic-nematic transition reveals much higher order than expected, attributed to the relative shortness of the nanotubes.[56]

It is worth noting that the data presented in Fig. 5, and in many of measurements reported elsewhere, analyse the phenyl stretch mode at 1606 cm^{-1}, though some use the CN stretch at 2225 cm^{-1}. The reason for using the phenyl stretch mode is not just that it is usually the most intense peak, leading to the most accurate data. In fact, it is well-known that order parameters determined using other Raman-active modes can lead to different values,[57] in particular for P_4. The possibility that this discrepancy is due to the formation of dimers, known in the cyanobiphenyls, was ruled out by Gleeson *et al.*[58] However, recent work by Zhang suggests that the source of these discrepancies can be explained by considering the validity of the assumptions that underly the analysis summarised above; that Raman bands are uniaxial, that there is mirror symmetry and that the system is insensitive to a 180° inversion.[59]

An important example of a situation where the usual assumptions that allow PRS to be analysed to deduce order parameters must be modified is in the case of bent-core molecules. The nematic phases formed from bent-core materials have proven to have interesting physical properties[60] and were, in 2004, thought to exhibit biaxial order.[61,62] Southern *et al.* considered the potential for measuring the biaxial order parameters in bent-core nematic liquid crystal materials using PRS, taking advantage of the fitting procedure to deduce the various order parameters.[21] While that work presented evidence that biaxial order parameters could be measured in one particular bent-core system, the large number of fitting parameters involved meant that it was impossible to offer any conclusive evidence of nematic biaxiality. In fact, care must be taken even when determining uniaxial order parameters in nematic phases formed from bent-core phases as erroneous values will be obtained if the molecular bend-angle isn't carefully taken into account.[63] Such a conclusion is unsurprising since the molecular vibrations that contribute to the Raman spectrum typically originate from both of the arms, each at an angle with respect to the director, and anomalously low values are obtained for the order parameters due to this complication if the model used in the analysis fails to take them into account.

Polarized Raman scattering has also been used to deduce the P_2 and P_4 order parameters in dimers that exhibit the twist-bend nematic phase.[64] That paper describes in more detail how a molecular bend angle can be taken into account in the analysis of the Raman data to deduce the order parameters. It shows that there is little change in either the P_2 and P_4 order parameters across the transition from the nematic phase to the twist-bend nematic phase.

The approach described in this section that allows the P_2 and P_4 order parameters in the nematic phase can also be applied to other systems, again taking care that the underlying assumptions apply. Studies have been made of the de-Vries SmC* phase,[42,65] and of the transitions between the Smectic-A phase and low-temperature tilted phases.[66] In the latter case, the differences in the P_4 values that were deduced allowed a clear differentiation between the SmC$_\alpha^*$ phase, in which P_4 should be relatively large, and the de-Vries SmC* phase where it is expected to take rather small values. Polarized Raman Scattering has also been used effectively to deduce changes in biaxiality in an antiferroelectric system,[67] though the biaxiality was inferred from anomalous behaviour of the P_4 order parameter rather than by introducing biaxial terms in the analysis. The power of Raman scattering in understanding order in a variety of systems is clear.

6. Concluding remarks

Raman spectroscopy is a versatile and powerful tool in the study of liquid crystalline systems. Its advantages include the fact that it is non-destructive and can be used with the liquid crystal contained in conventional device geometries. The fact that the peaks reveal information about specific chemical vibrations and their local environment facilitates an understanding of packing in various phases as well as the interaction between nanoparticles and liquid crystalline hosts. The polarization-dependence of Raman spectra offers a powerful tool to investigate liquid crystalline order and to make quantitative measurements of the order parameters. The development of new variants in Raman scattering such as CARS offers a suite of powerful analytic approaches for the study of increasingly complex soft-matter systems.

References

1. J. M. Brown, *Molecular Spectroscopy (Oxford Chemistry Primers)*. Oxford University Press, U.S.A. (1998).
2. J. R. Ferraro and K. Nakamoto, *Introductory Raman Spectroscopy*. Academic Press Inc (1995).
3. S. Cowling. Optical microscopy studies of liquid crystals. In eds. J. W. Goodby, P. J. Collings, T. Kato, C. Tschierske, H. Gleeson, and P. Raynes, *Handbook of Liquid Crystals, Volume 1*. Wiley-VCH, Weinheim (2014).
4. M. Tanaka and R. Young, Polarised Raman spectroscopy for the study of molecular orientation distributions in polymers, *J. Mater. Sci.* **41**(3), 963–991 (2006).
5. M. Castriota, A. Fasanella, E. Cazzanelli, L. De Sio, R. Caputo, and C. Umeton, In situ polarized micro-Raman investigation of periodic structures realized in liquid-crystalline composite materials, *Opt. Express.* **19**(11), 10494–10500 (2011).
6. T. V. Basova, A. Hassan, M. Durmus, A. G. Gurek, and V. Ahsen, Orientation of the liquid crystalline nickel phthalocyanine films confined between electrodes, *Synth. Met.* **161**(17-18), 1996–2000 (2011).
7. G. Xiao, Y. Guo, Y. Lin, X. Ma, Z. Su, and Q. Wang, Controlled evaporative self-assembly of poly(3-hexylthiophene) monitored with confocal polarized Raman spectroscopy, *Phys. Chem. Chem. Phys.* **14**(47), 16286–16293 (2012).
8. T. Lee, H. Mundoor, D. G. Gann, T. J. Callahan, and I. I. Smalyukh, Imaging of director fields in liquid crystals using stimulated Raman scattering microscopy, *Opt. Express.* **21**(10), 12129–12134 (2013).
9. O. D. Lavrentovich, Looking at the world through liquid crystal glasses, *Multi-scale and high-contrast PDE: From modelling, to mathematical analysis, to inversion.* **577**, 25–46 (2011).

10. T. Lee, R. P. Trivedi, and I. I. Smalyukh, Multimodal nonlinear optical polarizing microscopy of long-range molecular order in liquid crystals, *Opt. Lett.* **35**(20), 3447–3449 (2010).

11. R. P. Trivedi, D. Engstrom, and I. I. Smalyukh, Optical manipulation of colloids and defect structures in anisotropic liquid crystal fluids, *J. Optics.* **13**(4), 044001 (2011).

12. R. P. Trivedi, T. Lee, K. A. Bertness, and I. I. Smalyukh, Three dimensional optical manipulation and structural imaging of soft materials by use of laser tweezers and multimodal nonlinear microscopy, *Opt. Express.* **18**(26), 27658–27669 (2010).

13. F. Latteyer, S. Savu, H. Peisert, and T. Chasse, Self-assembly and structure formation in liquid crystalline phthalocyanine thin films studied by Raman spectroscopy and AFM, *J. Raman Spectrosc.* **43**(9), 1227–1236 (2012).

14. P. Etchegoin and J. Seddon, Differing applications of Raman scattering to liquid crystals, *Liq. Cryst.* **28**(6), 811–817 (2001).

15. Y. Wang and H. Gleeson, Phase behaviour of an antiferroelectric liquid crystal studied by Raman spectroscopy, *Ferroelectrics.* **311**, 355–362 (2004).

16. R. Nandi, K. Vikram, S. K. Singh, B. Singh, and R. K. Singh, Synthesis and mesomorphic investigation of calamitic liquid crystalline system ethyl-[4-(4-decyloxy)benzoyloxy]-benzoate (4-EDBB): A temperature dependent micro-Raman study and DFT calculations, *Vib. Spect.* **69**, 40–48 (2013).

17. Y. Jin, Y. Hang, J. Luo, Y. Zhang, H. Shao, and X. Hu, In vitro studies on the structure and properties of silk fibroin aqueous solutions in silkworm, *Int. J. Biol. Macromol.* **62**, 162–166 (2013).

18. V. Görtz, C. Southern, N. W. Roberts, H. F. Gleeson, and J. W. Goodby, Unusual properties of a bent-core liquid-crystalline fluid, *Soft Matter.* **5**(2), 463–471 (2009).

19. M. Nagaraj, K. Usami, Z. Zhang, V. Görtz, J. W. Goodby, and H. F. Gleeson, Unusual electric-field-induced transformations in the dark conglomerate phase of a bent-core liquid crystal, *Liq. Cryst.* **41**(6), 800–811 (2014).

20. J. Lagerwall and G. Scalia. Carbon nanotubes in liquid crystals. In eds. J. W. Goodby, P. J. Collings, T. Kato, C. Tschierske, H. Gleeson, and P. Raynes, *Handbook of Liquid Crystals, Volume 6.* Wiley-VCH, Weinheim (2014).

21. S. Umadevi, V. Ganesh, and T. Hegmann. Nanoparticles: Additives and building blocks for liquid crystal phases. In eds. J. W. Goodby, P. J. Collings, T. Kato, C. Tschierske, H. Gleeson, and P. Raynes, *Handbook of Liquid Crystals, vol. VI*, pp. 27–76. Wiley-VCH, Weinheim, Germany (2014).

22. I. Musevic. Colloidal crystals in nematic liquid crystals in the handbook of liquid crystals. In eds. J. W. Goodby, P. J. Collings, T. Kato, C. Tschierske, H. Gleeson, and P. Raynes, *Handbook of Liquid Crystals, vol. VI.* Wiley-VCH, Weinheim, Germany (2014).

23. M. S. Dresselhaus, A. Jorio, and R. Saito, Characterizing graphene, graphite, and carbon nanotubes by Raman spectroscopy, *Ann. Rev. Cond. Mater. Phys., Vol. 1.* **1**, 89–108 (2010).

24. M. Lynch and D. Patrick, Organizing carbon nanotubes with liquid crystals, *Nano. Lett.* **2**(11), 1197–1201 (2002).

25. G. Scalia, Alignment of carbon nanotubes in thermotropic and lyotropic liquid crystals, *ChemPhysChem.* **11**(2), 333–340 (2010).
26. G. Scalia, M. Haluska, U. Dettlaff-Weglikowska, F. Giesselmann, and S. Roth, Polarized Raman spectroscopy study of SWCNT orientational order in an aligning liquid crystalline matrix, *AIP Conf. Proc.* **786**, 114–117 (2005).
27. G. Scalia, J. P. F. Lagerwall, M. Haluska, U. Dettlaff-Weglikowska, F. Giesselmann, and S. Roth, Effect of phenyl rings in liquid crystal molecules on swcnts studied by Raman spectroscopy, *Phys. Stat. Sol. (b).* **243**(13), 3238–3241 (2006).
28. J. P. F. Lagerwall, R. Dabrowski, and G. Scalia, Antiferroelectric liquid crystals with induced intermediate polar phases and the effects of doping with carbon nanotubes, *J. Non-Cryst. Solids.* **353**(47-51), 4411–4417 (2007).
29. Y. Zhao, Y. Xiao, S. Yang, J. Xu, W. Yang, M. Li, D. Wang, and Y. Zhou, Alignment of single-walled carbon nanotubes with ferroelectric liquid crystal, *J. Phys. Chem. C.* **116**(31), 16694–16699 (2012).
30. M. Petrov, B. Katranchev, M. Rafailov, Peter, H. Naradikian, U. Dettlaff-Weglikowska, and E. Keskinova, Smectic C liquid crystal growth and memory effect through surface orientation by carbon nanotubes, *J. Mol. Liq.* **180**, 215–220 (2013).
31. T. Basova, A. A. Esenpinar, S. Tuncel, M. Durmus, A. G. Gurek, and V. Ahsen, Thin films of liquid crystalline phthalocyanines and their its composites with single-walled carbon nanotubes: properties and alignment, *Mater. Sci. Nanotech. I.* **531-532**, 337–341 (2013).
32. A. Saha, S. Palmal, and N. R. Jana, Highly reproducible and sensitive surface-enhanced Raman scattering from colloidal plasmonic nanoparticle via stabilization of hot spots in graphene oxide liquid crystal, *Nanoscale.* **4**(20), 6649–6657 (2012).
33. P. Blake, P. Brimicombe, R. Nair, T. Booth, D. Jiang, F. Schedin, L. Ponomarenko, S. Morozov, H. Gleeson, E. Hill, A. Geim, and K. Novoselov, Graphene-based liquid crystal device, *Nano. Lett.* **8**(6), 1704–1708 (2008).
34. W. Maier and A. Saupe, Eine einfache molekulare theorie des nematischen kristallinflüssigen zustandes", *Z. Naturf.* **13**(7), 564–566 (1958).
35. S. Chandrasekhar, K. D., and N. V. Madhusudana, Theory of birefringence of nematic liquid crystals, *Mol. Cryst. Liq. Cryst.* **8**, 45–69 (1969).
36. S. Chandrasekhar and N. Madhusudana, Molecular statistical theory of nematic liquid crystals, *Acta Cryst.* **A27**, 303–313 (1971).
37. R. Humphries, P. G. James, and G. R. Luckhurst, Molecular field treatment of nematic liquid crystals, *J Chem Soc. Faraday Trans. 2.* **68**, 1031–1044 (1972).
38. H. F. Gleeson, C. D. Southern, P. D. Brimicombe, J. W. Goodby, and V. Görtz, Optical measurements of orientational order in uniaxial and biaxial nematic liquid crystals, *Liq. Cryst.* **37**(6-7), 949–959 (2010).
39. S. Jen, N. A. Clark, P. S. Pershan, and E. B. Priestley, Polarized Raman-scattering studies of orientational order in uniaxial liquid-crystalline phases, *J. Chem. Phys.* **66**(10), 4635–4661 (1977).
40. D. Bauman, E. Chrzumnicka, E. Mykowska, M. Szybowicz, and N. Grzelczak,

Study of orientational order of some nematogenic compounds by spectroscopy methods using linearly polarized light, *J. Mol. Struct.* **744**, 307–313 (2005).

41. A. Davies, W. Jones, and A. Price, Nonlinear Raman spectroscopy of liquid crystals - polarization measurements and relaxation processes in 4-cyano-4'-heptylbiphenyl (7CB), *J. Raman Spectrosc.* **25**(7-8), 521–529 (1994).

42. N. Hayashi, T. Kato, A. Fukuda, J. Vij, Y. Panarin, J. Naciri, R. Shashidhar, S. Kawada, and S. Kondoh, Evidence for de Vries structure in a Smectic-A liquid crystal observed by polarized Raman scattering, *Phys. Rev. E.* **71**(4), 041705 (2005).

43. W. Jones, D. Thomas, D. Thomas, and G. Williams, Raman scattering studies of homogeneous and twisted-nematic liquid crystal cells and the determination of [p2] and [p4] order parameters, *J. Mol. Struct.* **614**(1-3), 75–85 (2002).

44. W. Jones, D. Thomas, D. Thomas, and G. Williams, On the determination of order parameters for homogeneous and twisted nematic liquid crystals from Raman spectroscopy, *J. Mol. Struct.* **708**(1-3), 145–163 (2004).

45. M. Deutsch, Orientational order determination in liquid crystals by x-ray diffraction, *Phys. Rev. A.* **44**(12), 8264–8270 (1991).

46. A. J. Leadbetter and E. K. Norris, Distribution functions in three liquid crystals from x-ray diffraction measurements, *Mol. Phys.* **38**(3), 669–686 (1979).

47. R. Richardson, J. Allman, and G. McIntyre, Neutron-scattering from mixtures of isotopically labeled molecules a new method for determining the orientational distribution function in liquid-crystals, *Liq. Cryst.* **7**(5), 701–719 (1990).

48. G. Luckhurst and R. Yeates, Orientational order of a spin probe dissolved in nematic liquid-crystals - electron resonance investigation, *J. Chem. Soc.-Faraday Transactions II.* **72**, 996–1009 (1976).

49. C. D. Southern and H. F. Gleeson, Using the full Raman depolarisation in the determination of the order parameters in liquid crystal systems, *Eur. Phys. J. E.* **24**(2), 119–127 (2007).

50. C. D. Southern, P. D. Brimicombe, S. D. Siemianowski, S. Jaradat, N. Roberts, V. Görtz, J. W. Goodby, and H. F. Gleeson, Thermotropic biaxial nematic order parameters and phase transitions deduced by Raman scattering, *EPL.* **82**(5), 56001 (2008).

51. M. Van Gurp, The use of rotation matrices in the mathematical description of molecular orientations in polymers, *Colloid Polym. Sci.* **273**(7), 607–625 (1995).

52. A. Sanchez-Castillo, A. Osipov, Mikhail, and F. Giesselmann, Orientational order parameters in liquid crystals: A comparative study of x-ray diffraction and polarized Raman spectroscopy results, *Phys. Rev. E.* **81**(2), 021707 (2010).

53. H. J. Yoo, S. Y. Lee, N.-H. You, D. S. Lee, H. Yeo, Y. M. Choi, M. Goh, J. Park, K. Akagi, and J. W. Cho, Dispersion and magnetic field-induced alignment of functionalized carbon nanotubes in liquid crystals, *Synth. Met.* **181**, 10–17 (2013).

54. N. Puech, M. Dennison, C. Blanc, P. van, der Schoot, M. Dijkstra, R. van,

Roij, P. Poulin, and E. Grelet, Orientational order of carbon nanotube guests in a nematic host suspension of colloidal viral rods, *Phys. Rev. Lett.* **108**(24), 247801 (2012).

55. C. Zamora-Ledezma, C. Blanc, N. Puech, M. Maugey, C. Zakri, E. Anglaret, and P. Poulin, Conductivity anisotropy of assembled and oriented carbon nanotubes, *Phys. Rev. E.* **84**(6), 062701 (2011).

56. N. Puech, C. Blanc, E. Grelet, C. Zamora-Ledezma, M. Maugey, C. Zakri, E. Anglaret, and P. Poulin, Highly ordered carbon nanotube nematic liquid crystals, *J. Phys. Chem. C.* **115**(8), 3272–3278 (2011).

57. K. Miyano, Raman depolarization ratios and order parameters of a nematic liquid-crystals, *J. Chem. Phys.* **69**(11), 4807–4813 (1978).

58. H. F. Gleeson, P. D. Brimicombe, C. D. Southern, J. Barrett, and A. Hassett, eds., *Measurement of Liquid Crystalline Order Parameters using Polarized Raman Spectroscopy*. Krakow, Poland (2010).

59. Z. Zhang. *Research into order parameters and graphene dispersions in liquid crystal systems using Raman spectroscopy*. PhD thesis (2014).

60. H. F. Gleeson, S. Kaur, V. Görtz, A. Belaissaoui, S. Cowling, and J. W. Goodby, The nematic phases of bent-core liquid crystals, *ChemPhysChem.* **15**(7), 1251–1260 (2014).

61. B. Acharya, A. Primak, and S. Kumar, Biaxial nematic phase in bent-core thermotropic mesogens, *Phys. Rev. Lett.* **92**(14), 145506 (2004).

62. L. Madsen, T. Dingemans, M. Nakata, and E. Samulski, Thermotropic biaxial nematic liquid crystals, *Phys. Rev. Lett.* **92**(14), 145505 (2004).

63. H. F. Gleeson and P. D. Brimicombe, Comment on Raman scattering study of phase biaxiality in a thermotropic bent-core nematic liquid crystal, *Phys. Rev. Lett.* **107**(10), 109801 (2011).

64. Z. Zhang, V. P. Panov, M. Nagaraj, R. J. Mandle, J. W. Goodby, G. R. Luckhurst, J. C. Jones, and H. F. Gleeson, Raman scattering studies of order parameters in liquid crystalline dimers exhibiting the nematic and twist-bend nematic phases, *J. Mater. Chem. C.* **3**(38), 10007–10016 (2015).

65. A. Sanchez-Castillo, M. A. Osipov, S. Jagiella, Z. H. Nguyen, M. Kaspar, V. Hamplova, J. Maclennan, and F. Giesselmann, Orientational order parameters of a de Vries-type ferroelectric liquid crystal obtained by polarized Raman spectroscopy and x-ray diffraction, *Phys. Rev. E.* **85**(6), 061703 (2012).

66. H. S. Chang, S. Jaradat, F. Gleeson, Helen, I. Dierking, and A. Osipov, Mikhail, Stabilization of the smectic-C-alpha* phase in mixtures with chiral dopants, *Phys. Rev. E.* **79**(6), 061706 (2009).

67. N. Hayashi and T. Kato, Investigations of orientational order for an antiferroelectric liquid crystal by polarized Raman scattering measurements, *Phys. Rev. E.* **63**(2), art. no.–021706 (2001).

Chapter 8

Manipulation of inclusions with optical tweezers

Miha Škarabot

Jožef Stefan Institute, Jamova 39, 1000 Ljubljana, Slovenia
miha.skarabot@ijs.si

In this chapter the basic techniques and underlaying concepts of trapping and manipulation of microparticles in liquid crystal (LC) systems are presented. The laser trapping in LCs is extremely efficient and it is based on different principles than laser trapping in isotropic solvents. In addition to conventional laser trapping, the laser light can reorient LC molecules and at high powers also heat the LC in isotropic phase. Due to these optical and thermal effects of laser tweezers on LC different trapping mechanisms are possible at different rate of laser power and all are presented qualitatively and quantitatively by measuring the trapping forces. Besides trapping and manipulation of single inclusions, laser tweezers are also used for assisted self-assembly of variety of periodic 2D and 3D colloidal structures, while most of them can not be assembled without help of laser tweezers. The concepts and different techniques of laser assisted assembly are presented.

Contents

1. Introduction

In last few decades LC colloids, which are dispersions of inclusions in liquid crystalline environment, have attracted a lot of interest. The size of these inclusions are in the range from few nanometers to several micrometers. In order to study properties of inclusions in LCs, especially the properties of single inclusions the controlled manipulation of inclusions is essential. Several manipulation methods have been suggested and it has been shown that laser tweezers are the most powerful tool for manipulation and trapping of all kind of inclusions in LC. Laser tweezers are optical instruments that uses tightly focused laser beam for trapping and manipulation of particles and were developed on the basis of optical trapping experiments performed by Ashkin[1] and first demonstrated by optical trapping of dielectric particles.[2]

In LC systems laser tweezers were first used for manipulation of disclinations and defects in thermotropic LCs[3] and soon after the laser tweezers became extremely useful tool for different kind of measurements in LCs. They were used for manipulation of defects in lyotropic LCs,[4] where authors were measured defect line tension by stretching the line with an optically trapped bead. The same method was used in thermotropic LCs to measure line tension of disclination lines.[5,6] Later the relaxation kinetics of defect lines was studied in thermotropic LCs by simply stretching the defect line directly with laser tweezers.[7] In cholesterics, optical manipulation of nanorods was used for mapping of the patterns of three-dimensional orientational order and defect structures.[8,9] This is possible since in chiral nematics the nanowires follow the local average orientation of rod-shaped LC molecules. In cholesterics laser tweezers were also used for creation of localized chiro-elastic particle-like excitations, called torons.[10] Laser tweezers were also extensively used to manipulate LC droplets. Circularly polarized laser tweezers were used for spinning of nematic droplets and switching their director structure.[11] Here optical angular momentum of circularly polarized light is transferred to nematic LC droplets.[12,13] Even more interesting are chiral LC droplets which are continuously rotated in a linearly polarized laser trap.[14] Recently helicity-dependent 3D optical trapping of chiral droplets was presented,[15] where the interplay of the helicity of light and the chirality of LC droplet determines the trapping force and enables selective trapping of chiral particles.

Another useful application of laser tweezers is studying microrheology associated with micrometre-sized particles suspended in LCs and measuring viscosity coefficients in thermotropic[16] and lyotropic LCs.[17] Next field is laser tweezers trapping of solid particles, which was first demonstrated for high index particles[5,18] and almost at the same time also for low index particles.[19] This unexpected and so-called forbidden trapping was used for trapping of different objects with arbitrary refractive index.[20–22] Once trapping was confirmed, micromanipulation and transport of particles was applied to assembly of 2D and 3D colloidal structures.[23–26] Besides dielectric particles also other kinds of particles were trapped and manipulated by laser tweezers like plasmonic nanoparticles[27] and graphene flakes.[28]

This short overview confirms that laser tweezers are very efficient tool for manipulation and transport of inclusions of different material and different size. There are several other efficient methods for transport of particles in LCs, but they are not suitable for micromanipulation. On macroscopic scale, an external electric field,[29–32] nematic isotropic interfaces[33] and microfluidics[34] were used for this purpose.

In this chapter only trapping of solid particles and manipulation of defects will be presented. Different mechanisms of laser trapping of particles will first be discussed, and then some examples of manipulation of particles with locally induced isotropic phase will be demonstrated.

2. Trapping of particles

Laser trapping is the basic experimental technique for manipulation of single particles in a micrometer range. Laser tweezers have been extensively used for trapping of small colloidal particles since their invention in 1986,[2] when it has been shown that tightly focused laser beam can trap and manipulate micron-sized particles, if their index of refraction is higher than surroundings. This mechanism has been first used in LCs for trapping of solid particles and measuring interparticles forces in nematics by Yada *et al.*[18] and Smaylukh *et al.*[5] At the same time it has been also shown that contrary to expectations, low index silica particles can be trapped in high index nematic LC.[19,20] There are several mechanisms of trapping and manipulation of low index particles in high index LCs:

- trapping by high index nematic "cloud" below the Optical Frederiks Transition (OFT).
- trapping by optically induced "ghost" particle above OFT.
- trapping by thermally induced gradient of the order parameter.

The optically induced Frederiks transition (OFT) is reorientation of LC molecules by light. It occurs above some threshold of light intensity, while below the threshold there is no reorientation.[35,36]

2.1. *Trapping below the optical Frederiks transition*

When the laser power is relatively low, such that it does not induce the reorientation of LC (the system is below OFT), the trapping of low index particles is mediated by the trapping of high index nematic "cloud" which surrounds the particle. This "cloud" is related to the distortion of the LC that the particle causes. It is well known that microparticles in LCs induce reorientation of LC around them. An image of a single silica microparticle with a homeotropic anchoring in a homeotropically aligned nematic LC cell is presented in Fig. 1a.

When such a particle is observed under polarizing microscope, a region around the particle, where molecules are distorted from the vertical orientation, is transmitting the light (Fig. 1b) and the particle looks bigger. On the other hand one can see that the refractive index of distorted LC cloud around the particle is different for certain polarization of the laser

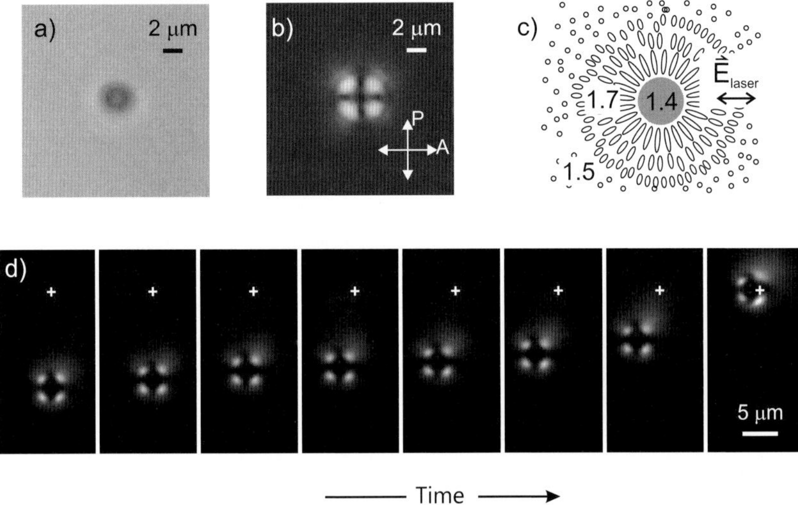

Fig. 1.   Trapping of 2.32 µm silanated micro-sphere with a laser tweezers with the power of 20 mW in a $\sim$ 20 µm thick homeotropic layer of 5CB nematic LC. (a,b) DMOAP-treated micro-sphere induce homeotropic orientation at the surface, which induce transmitted light through crossed polarizers. (c) Schematic diagram of LC orientation around micro-sphere reveals that in the case of horizontal polarization of the laser light the refractive index of molecules at horizontal sides of the colloid is equal to the extraordinary one (1.7) and it is higher than the index of surrounding medium, which is ordinary one (1.5). (d) Sequence of polarizing images of trapping process below the OFT is shown with time separation of 30 seconds between two images.

light (Fig. 1c). In the case of horizontal polarization of the laser light the refractive index of distorted cloud around the particle is close to the extraordinary one ($n_e \approx 1.7$) and it is higher than the refractive index of surrounding medium, which is ordinary one ($n_o \approx 1.5$). So actually we are trapping the cloud, not the particle and the particle is just trapped together with the cloud. The trapping process at low laser power is presented as a sequence of polarizing micrograph images in Fig. 1d. The particle is positioned at the distance of around $13\,\mu$m and it is trapped by the laser tweezers in approximately three minutes. At this low power laser tweezers does not induce any visible reorientation of LC and the particle is trapped via high index nematic cloud around the particle. The stable position of the particle in the optical trap is therefore not in the center of the trap but next to it and it can be calculated by numerical simulation.[20]

This phenomenon is even more evident when several trapping trajectories from different starting positions are presented in the same graph (Fig. 2a). It is clear that there are two stable positions of the particle at the left and at the right side next to the position of the trap, where all eight trajectories from different starting points are ended. That means that the high index nematic cloud is in the center of the trap. On the other hand, all trapping trajectories are approximately equivalent, reflecting the relatively isotropic trapping potential. In order to measure the trapping potential one can measure the time dependence of particle position during the trapping process and the velocity v of the particle can be determined. The trapping force is balanced with the viscous force $F = 6\pi d_{eff}\eta v$, where d_{eff} is an

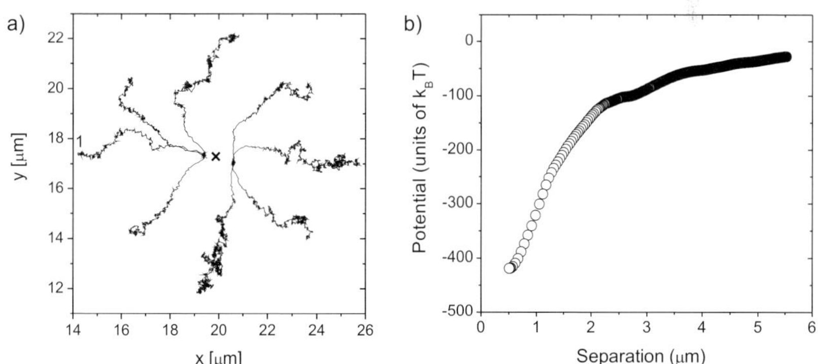

Fig. 2. (a) Set of trapping trajectories of low-index silica particle in a high-index nematic LC with the low laser power $20\,$mW below the OFT. The particle is released from eight different positions and all trajectories end in two symmetrically positioned minima. (b) The laser trapping potential obtained from the bottom trajectory.

effective diameter of the colloid and η is the liquid crystal viscosity.[37] The product of the effective diameter and viscosity $d_{eff}\eta$ can be determined in a separate experiment by observing the thermal motion of a single colloid.[38] The measured trapping force is close to the trap $\approx 1\,\mathrm{pN}$ and by numerical integration of trapping force over the distance the trapping potential can be determined (Fig. 2b). The trapping potential is in the order of several hundreds of $k_B T$ units, meaning that the trapping is very efficient even at low laser power of $20\,\mathrm{mW}$.

2.2. *Trapping above the optical Frederiks transition*

When the laser power of optical tweezers is relatively high, LC molecules can be reoriented by light and the system is above OFT. This reorientation can be easily observed under polarizing microscope (Fig. 3a).

Such reorientation is similar to the reorientation caused by colloidal particle, therefore it can be named "ghost" colloid.[19] Figure 3a shows a sequence of images during the laser trapping process of solid micro-particle with such optically induced ghost colloid. Elastic energy of a solid micro-particle is lower in the optically distorted region, causing additional attract-ing force on the particle comparing to the previous case below OFT. It is interesting that in this case the trapping potential is strongly asymmet-ric. This asymmetry can be analyzed by measuring trapping trajectories from different starting positions (Fig. 3b). For the certain direction of ap-proach (position 1 from the left), there is a strong attraction, while from the opposite side (position 2 from the right) the particle is repelled from the trap and sometimes takes a detour trajectory around the trap. This asymmetrical trapping depends on the direction of the polarization of laser light and on the geometry of the sample and it is due to the breaking of the uniaxial symmetry of an undistorted nematic by light (Fig. 3c). In the homeotropic cell molecules are perpendicular to the glass substrate, while the spherical particle with strong homeotropic anchoring is accompanied with a point hedgehog defect above or below the particle and it is called dipolar particle. The electric field of the focused laser beam reorients LC molecules with a positive dielectric anisotropy in the direction of the field, but outside of the beam they have to orient in such way to fit the orienta-tion at both substrates. The attraction or repulsion of the dipolar particle depends on the direction of the tilt of the molecules above OFT and on the position of the point defect. In the case which is presented in Fig. 3c there is an attraction from the left side of the trap, where molecules from

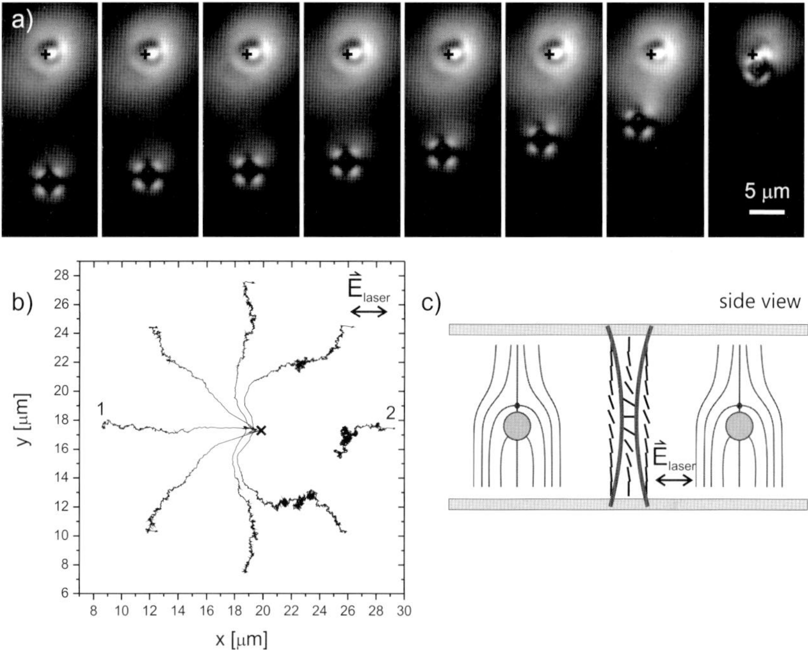

Fig. 3. Trapping of 2.32 μm silanated micro-sphere with a laser tweezers with the power of 70 mW in a $\sim 20\,\mu$m thick homeotropic layer of 5CB nematic LC. (a) Sequence of polarizing images of trapping process below the OFT is shown with time separation of 30 seconds between two images. (b) Trapping trajectories above the OFT are asymmetrical due to the asymmetric trapping potential. (c) Schematic presentation of the interaction of a dipolar colloid with the optically induced "ghost" colloid.

both distortions are parallel to each other and repulsion from the right side where they don't fit.

The trapping force and the trapping potential can be again measured by careful determination of time dependent positions of particle using video monitoring and off-line analysis. In this free release experiment the trapping force is balanced by viscous force and it is presented in log-log scale as a function of separation from the trap in Fig. 4a. Experiments show that the force is in the pN range and it is of Coulomb-like nature $F = F_0/r^2$. This Coulomb like behaviour is valid at all distances, except in the vicinity of the trap $r \leq 1\,\mu$m. By numerical integration of the force over the distance the trapping potential is calculated and it is proportional to the inverse separation $W = -W_0/r$. This Coulomb-like dependence was also calculated numerically[20] and analytically.[39]

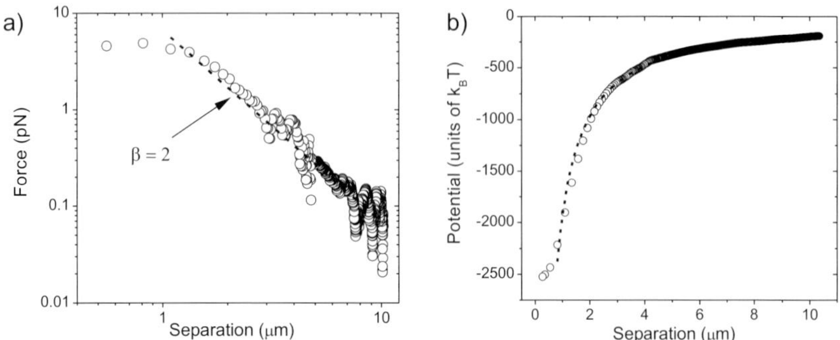

Fig. 4. (a) Trapping force on a $1\,\mu$m silica particle in a homeotropically aligned 5CB nematic LC induced by laser tweezers with the power of $70\,$mW. The line represents best power-law fit in the range $r > 1\,\mu$m. (b) Corresponding trapping potential with the best fit to $W = -W_0/r$.

2.3. *Trapping by thermally induced gradient of the order parameter*

The last presented laser tweezers trapping method is the most robust and the most efficient. It is based on the fact that laser tweezers can locally heat LC by several degrees or even melt into the isotropic phase. Since LC itself does not substantially absorb the light, ITO coated substrates are normally used to increase the absorption. Such heating creates spatially dependent temperature profile around the trap and therefore also spatially dependent profile of the nematic order parameter with its minimum in the center of the trap. The elastic energy of the colloidal particle is proportional to the nematic order parameter S and therefore the particle is driven to the region with lower nematic order. The profile of the nematic order can be determined by measuring the birefringence in the vicinity of the laser trap, which is illuminating the LC layer. Figure 5b presents the measured transmitted spectra along the dashed line in Fig. 5a. At the position of the trap the sample is heated, the birefringence is decreased and the spectra is shifted to lower values. The order parameter S is proportional to the birefringence Δn and is presented in Fig. 5c.

The trapping in such thermally induced gradient of S is presented in Fig. 6. At low laser power the sample is not heated to the isotropic phase and at the position of the trap we only see small decrease of transmitted light due to decreased order parameter (Fig. 6a). On the other hand there is no reorientation of LC and there is no transmitted light through crossed

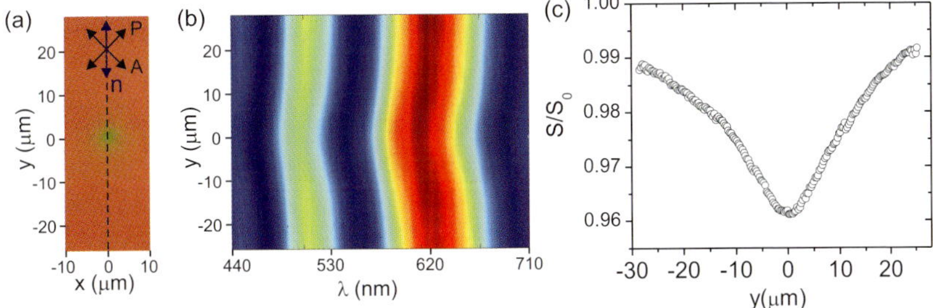

Fig. 5. (a) A thin layer of E12 LC placed between two ITO coated glass substrates is heated by laser tweezers and its colour between crossed polarizers is changed due to the decrease of birefringence. (b) The spectra of transmitted light through this layer are presented along the dashed line ($y = 0$). (c) The relative order parameter along the dashed line is calculated from birefringence with the minimum at the position of the trap.

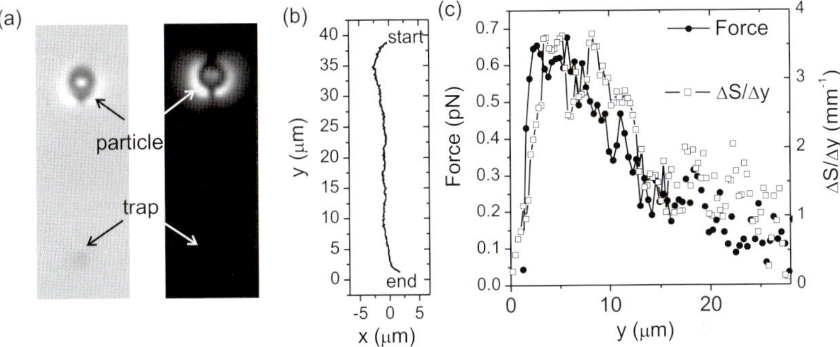

Fig. 6. Trapping of silica particle with laser tweezers of power of $30\,\mathrm{mW}$ in a $5\,\mu\mathrm{m}$ thin layer of E12 nematic LC placed between two ITO coated substrates. (a) The laser tweezers decrease the nematic order and does not induce any reorientation of LC. (b) Trapping trajectories are isotropic and trapping is efficient from large distances. (c) The measured trapping force is proportional to the gradient of the order parameter.

polarizers (Fig. 6b). The particle can be trapped from very large distance ($r > 50\,\mu\mathrm{m}$) and the trapping potential is isotropic. The attractive force on the particle during the trapping process can be determined by measuring the viscous force and it is proportional to the gradient of the order parameter $\Delta S/\Delta y$, expected from the fact that the elastic energy of the particle in LC is proportional to S (Fig. 6d).

The strength of the trapping force depends on several parameters, which can be changed in a controllable way:

- The power of the laser: Higher laser power causes higher absorption and stronger trapping.
- Size of the particle: Bigger particles have larger elastic energy and stronger trapping.
- The LC transition temperature: Gradient of S is higher in the LCs with lower T_c.
- The rate of light absorption can be controlled by choosing different glasses or glass coatings.
- Anchoring at the particles: Stronger surface anchoring causes higher elastic energy and stronger trapping force.

When the laser power is increased or LC with lower transition temperature is used, the LC can be locally heated to isotropic phase and micrometer sized isotropic island is induced (Fig. 7a). Around such isotropic island there is a nematic LC with decreased S and consequently reduced birefringence, which can be observed between crossed polarizers (Fig. 7b). The anchoring at the nematic isotropic interface is planar, which is schematically presented in Fig. 7d and can be observed under crossed polarizers with an additional red wave-plate retarder. The colloidal trapping by isotropic island is very efficient due to the increased gradient of S, but trapping trajectories are not completely isotropic due to the anisotropy of elastic interactions between LC molecules at the nematic isotropic interface and

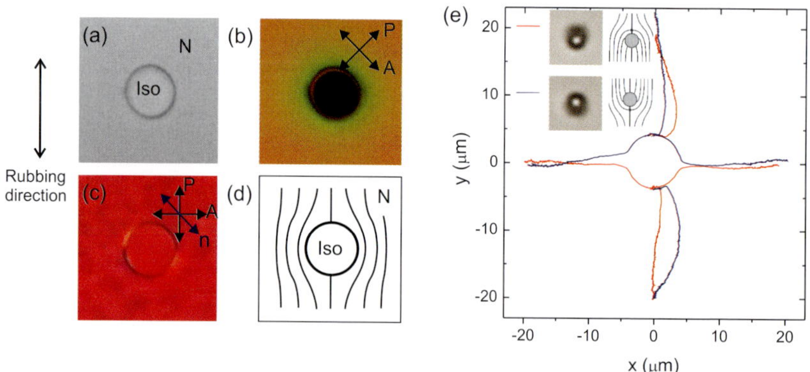

Fig. 7. (a) 5CB LC is locally heated to isotropic phase with laser tweezers with the power 30 mW and the decreased birefringence around the isotropic bubble is observed (b). The weak planar orientation at the nematic-isotropic interface can be observed between crossed polarizers with red wave-plate (c) and schematically presented (d). (e) The trapping trajectories for two orientations of particle with elastic dipole are not completely isotropic and their shape depends on the orientation of dipole.

molecules around the colloid (Fig. 7e). In the case of charged colloids the observed anisotropy was even stronger and was explained by flexoelectric effect.[40]

Laser trapping with optically induced gradient of the order parameter is also very efficient for trapping of nanoparticles[41,42] and molecules.[43] Here results of laser trapping of dye molecules are presented in Fig. 8. Dye doped LC sample was irradiated with laser tweezers and the concentration of fluorescent molecules was monitored with fluorescent microscopy. Figure 8a presents a time sequence of fluorescent images taken during switching on and off the laser trap. The fluorescent signal is increased at the position of the laser trap with the raise time of approximately 2 seconds (Fig. 8b). The same experiment was repeated in the isotropic phase and no increase of the fluorescent signal was observed. Therefore it was assumed that fluorescent molecules locally disturb the degree of orientational ordering of LC molecules and consequently they concentrate at the position of the laser trap, where S has a minimum.

Similar experiment with the gradient of order parameter has been performed with azobenzene-doped nematic LC, where reduced S was achieved by UV illumination.[44]

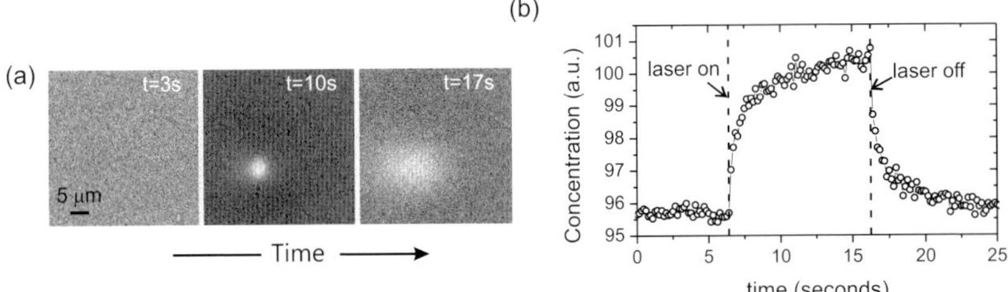

Fig. 8. (a) Time sequence of fluorescent images during the switching on and off the laser trap with the power of 25 mW in a dye doped 5CB LC. Dye molecules are attracted by the heated region with lower nematic order. (b) The dye concentration at the center of the laser spot is increased for around 5% with raise time of 2 seconds.

3. Manipulation of particles with locally induced isotropic phase

The phenomenon of laser induced isotropic bubbles in a nematic LC is very effective for the manipulation of inclusions as well as for trapping.[45,46] The elastic energy of defects in LC is much lower next to or inside the isotropic bubble and therefore it is perfect and stable trapping site for all kind of defects.[6] Besides trapping, optically induced isotropic bubbles were used for different experiments, like defect line tension measurements.[5,7] Here, only few examples of trapping through isotropic islands are presented. Firstly, the manipulation of quadrupolar particle by pulling at the Saturn ring through isotropic bubble is shown. It is well known that particles with homeotropic anchoring can induce dipolar orientation with a point defect or quadrupolar orientation with a Saturn ring defect depends on the size of the particle, surface anchoring energy and the thickness of the nematic layer. Saturn ring defect can be grabbed by the isotropic bubble and stretched from the particle by moving it with laser tweezers. The ring cannot "leave" the particle and therefore the particle is pulled by the ring into the equilibrium position after the ring is pulled away from the particle (Fig. 9a).

The second experiment is the control of different type of defects around the particle and transformations between these types (Fig. 9b). The starting type is dipolar colloid with the point defect on the "upper" side of the colloid. The point defect looks dark due to the light scattering at the non-oriented nematic. With optically induced isotropic bubble it is possible

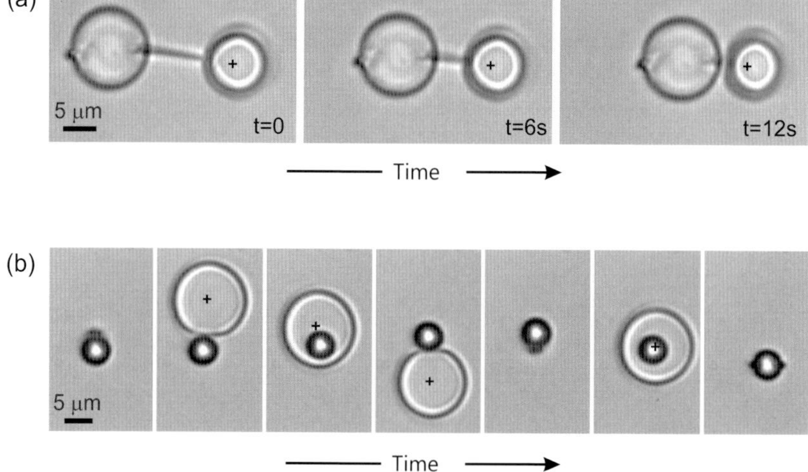

Fig. 9.   (a) The Saturn ring defect loop around a $10\,\mu$m particle in the nematic LC can be grabbed by the isotropic bubble and stretched away from the particle (first panel). The particle is pulled by the Saturn ring into equilibrium position. (b) Switching the point defect around $2.3\,\mu$m particle from "up" to "down" position by moving the isotropic bubble (first five panels) and switching point defect to Saturn ring (last three panels) by switching off the laser when isotropic bubble encircling the whole particle.

to catch this defect and by moving the bubble it is also possible to move the point defect. When the isotropic bubble is moved below the particle, the point defect is apparently inside the bubble (Fig. 9b, fourth panel). When the laser tweezers are switched off the point defect appeared at the "bottom" part of the colloid. This switching the position of dipole defect technique is essential in building up 2D and 3D nematic dipolar colloidal crystals.[23,26] In addition it is also possible to switch the dipole orientation of the nematic around the colloid to quadrupole one with a Saturn ring defect. Here the laser is switched off in the position, when isotropic bubble is encircling the whole particle (Fig. 9b, last two panels).

The creation of isotropic bubble and rapid quenching to the nematic phase by switching off the laser is also very useful technique for the creation of entangled colloidal structures. This technique was first time used for the creation of entangled pairs and wires.[47] Here the laser tweezers are used to heat the large area around two colloids into the isotropic phase which is rapidly quenched by shutting off the light. After quenching the dense tangle of defect lines appear and in a fraction of a second a equilibrium state of entangled colloids with a single defect line can appear (Fig. 10a), which is only one of several possible entanglements. In such way it is possible to entangle several colloids in a colloidal wire, which are all entangled with a single defect line. By using two laser traps it is possible to stretch such colloidal wire (Fig. 10b) and also drive the oscillations of wires and measure their collective motion.[48] Using chiral liquid crystals the entanglement of colloidal structures become very rich ,[24,49] since colloids can be entangled in a controlled way also in 2D. An example of such knotting in 2D is presented in Fig. 10c, where additional colloid is linked to the pair of colloids by melting and rewiring the original connection. Recently the same technique was used for the creation, manipulation and studies of topological charges in the vicinity of long microfibre in a nematic LC.[50]

References

1. A. Ashkin, Acceleration and trapping of particles by radiation pressure, *Phys. Rev. Lett.* **24**, 156–159 (1970).
2. A. Ashkin, J. M. Dziedzic, J. E. Bjorkholm, and S. Chu, Observation of a single-beam gradient force optical trap for dielectric particles, *Opt. Lett.* **11**, 288–290 (1986).
3. J.-i. Hotta, K. Sasaki, and H. Masuhara, Manipulation of liquid crystal textures with a focused near infrared laser beam, *Applied Physics Letters.* **71**, 2085–2087 (1997).

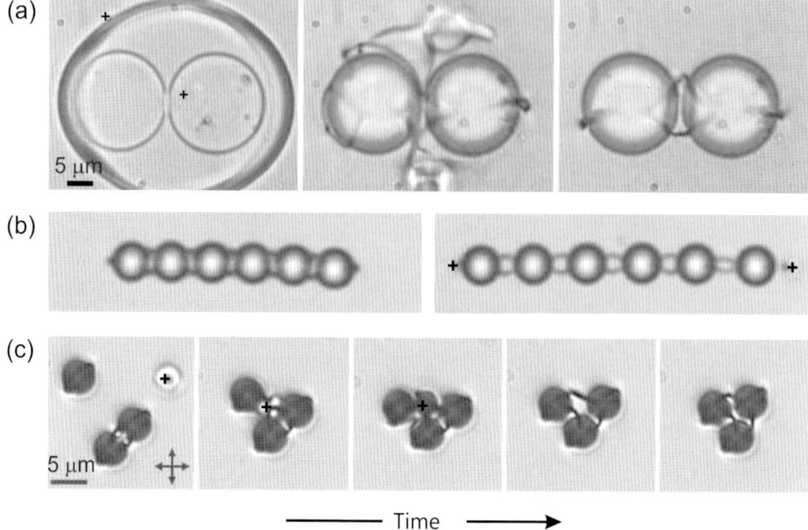

Fig. 10. (a) Assembling entangled colloidal pair by thermal quenching of nematic LC around two 10 µm particles using high power laser tweezers. In a fraction of a second figure of eight entangled state is established. (b) Figure of eight colloidal wire stretched by a pair of laser traps (denoted with cross). (c) Optically induced isotropic bubble is used for connecting and rewiring a third colloid to already assembled colloidal pair in a twist nematic LC cell.

4. Y. Iwashita and H. Tanaka, Optical manipulation of defects in a lyotropic lamellar phase, *Phys. Rev. Lett.* **90**, 045501 (2003).

5. I. I. Smalyukh, A. N. Kuzmin, A. V. Kachynski, P. N. Prasad, and O. D. Lavrentovich, Optical trapping of colloidal particles and measurement of the defect line tension and colloidal forces in a thermotropic nematic liquid crystal, *Applied Physics Letters*. 86:021913 (2005).

6. I. I. Smalyukh, D. S. Kaputa, A. V. Kachynski, A. N. Kuzmin, and P. N. Prasad, Optical trapping of director structures and defects in liquid crystals using laser tweezers, *Opt. Express*. **15**, 4359–4371 (2007).

7. N. Osterman, J. Kotar, E. M. Terentjev, and P. Cicuta, Relaxation kinetics of stretched disclination lines in a nematic liquid crystal, *Phys. Rev. E.* **81**, 061701 (2010).

8. R. P. Trivedi, D. Engstrom, and I. I. Smalyukh, Optical manipulation of colloids and defect structures in anisotropic liquid crystal fluids, *Journal of Optics*. **13**(4), 044001 (2011).

9. D. Engstrom, R. P. Trivedi, M. Persson, M. Goksor, K. A. Bertness, and I. I. Smalyukh, Three-dimensional imaging of liquid crystal structures and defects by means of holographic manipulation of colloidal nanowires with faceted sidewalls, *Soft Matter*. **7**, 6304–6312 (2011).

10. I. I. Smalyukh, Y. Lansac, N. A. Clark, and R. P. Trivedi, Three-dimensional

structure and multistable optical switching of triple-twisted particle-like excitations in anisotropic fluids, *Nat. Mat.* **9**, 139–145 (2010).

11. S. Juodkazis, M. Shikata, T. Takahashi, S. Matsuo, and H. Misawa, Fast optical switching by a laser-manipulated microdroplet of liquid crystal, *Applied Physics Letters.* **74**, 3627–3629 (1999).

12. S. Juodkazis, S. Matsuo, N. Murazawa, I. Hasegawa, and H. Misawa, High-efficiency optical transfer of torque to a nematic liquid crystal droplet, *Applied Physics Letters.* **82**, 4657–4659 (2003).

13. T. A. Wood, H. F. Gleeson, M. R. Dickinson, and A. J. Wright, Mechanisms of optical angular momentum transfer to nematic liquid crystalline droplets, *Applied Physics Letters.* **84**, 4292–4294 (2004).

14. Y. Yang, P. D. Brimicombe, N. W. Roberts, M. R. Dickinson, M. Osipov, and H. F. Gleeson, Continuously rotating chiral liquid crystaldroplets in a linearly polarized laser trap, *Opt. Express.* **16**(10), 6877–6882 (May, 2008).

15. G. Tkachenko and E. Brasselet, Helicity-dependent three-dimensional optical trapping of chiral microparticles, *Nat. Commun.* **5**, 5491 (2014).

16. J. L. Sanders, Y. Yang, M. R. Dickinson, and H. F. Gleeson, Pushing, pulling and twisting liquid crystal systems: exploring new directions with laser manipulation, *Philosophical Transactions of the Royal Society of London A: Mathematical, Physical and Engineering Sciences.* **371**(1988), 20120265 (2013).

17. Q. Liu, T. Asavei, T. Lee, H. Rubinsztein-Dunlop, S. He, and I. I. Smalyukh, Measurement of viscosity of lyotropic liquid crystals by means of rotating laser-trapped microparticles, *Opt. Express.* **19**(25), 25134–25143 (2011).

18. M. Yada, J. Yamamoto, and H. Yokoyama, Direct observation of anisotropic interparticle forces in nematic colloids with optical tweezers, *Phys. Rev. Lett.* **92**, 185501 (2004).

19. I. Muševič, M. Škarabot, D. Babič, N. Osterman, I. Poberaj, V. Nazarenko, and A. Nych, Laser trapping of small colloidal particles in a nematic liquid crystal: Clouds and ghosts, *Phys. Rev. Lett.* **93**, 187801 (2004).

20. M. Škarabot, M. Ravnik, D. Babič, N. Osterman, I. Poberaj, S. Žumer, I. Muševič, A. Nych, U. Ognysta, and V. Nazarenko, Laser trapping of low refractive index colloids in a nematic liquid crystal, *Phys. Rev. E.* **73**, 021705 (2006).

21. I. I. Smalyukh, A. V. Kachynski, A. N. Kuzmin, and P. N. Prasad, Laser trapping in anisotropic fluids and polarization-controlled particle dynamics, *Proceedings of the National Academy of Sciences.* **103**, 18048–18053 (2006).

22. L. Lucchetti, L. Criante, F. Bracalente, F. Aieta, and F. Simoni, Optical trapping induced by reorientational nonlocal effects in nematic liquid crystals, *Phys. Rev. E.* **84**, 021702 (2011).

23. I. Muševič, M. Škarabot, U. Tkalec, M. Ravnik, and S. Žumer, Two-dimensional nematic colloidal crystals self-assembled by topological defects, *Science.* **313**, 954–958 (2006).

24. U. Tkalec, M. Ravnik, S. Čopar, S. Žumer, and I. Muševič, Reconfigurable knots and links in chiral nematic colloids, *Science.* **333**, 62–65 (2011).

25. C. P. Lapointe, T. G. Mason, and I. I. Smalyukh, Shape-controlled colloidal

interactions in nematic liquid crystals, *Science.* **326**, 1083–1086 (2009).

26. A. Nych, U. Ognysta, M. Škarabot, M. Ravnik, S. Žumer, and I. Muševič, Assembly and control of 3d nematic dipolar colloidal crystals, *Nat. Commun.* **4**, 1489 (2013).

27. B. Senyuk, J. S. Evans, P. J. Ackerman, T. Lee, P. Manna, L. Vigderman, E. R. Zubarev, J. van de Lagemaat, and I. I. Smalyukh, Shape-dependent oriented trapping and scaffolding of plasmonic nanoparticles by topological defects for self-assembly of colloidal dimers in liquid crystals, *Nano Letters.* **12**(2), 955–963 (2012).

28. C. W. Twombly, J. S. Evans, and I. I. Smalyukh, Optical manipulation of self-aligned graphene flakes in liquid crystals, *Opt. Express.* **21**(1), 1324–1334 (Jan, 2013).

29. O. P. Pishnyak, S. Tang, J. R. Kelly, S. V. Shiyanovskii, and O. D. Lavrentovich, Levitation, lift, and bidirectional motion of colloidal particles in an electrically driven nematic liquid crystal, *Phys. Rev. Lett.* **99**, 127802 (2007).

30. O. D. Lavrentovich, I. Lazo, and O. P. Pishnyak, Nonlinear electrophoresis of dielectric and metal spheres in a nematic liquid crystal, *Nature.* **467**, 947 (2010).

31. A. V. Ryzhkova, F. V. Podgornov, and W. Haase, Nonlinear electrophoretic motion of dielectric microparticles in nematic liquid crystals, *Applied Physics Letters.* 96:151901 (2010).

32. O. D. Lavrentovich, Transport of particles in liquid crystals, *Soft Matter.* **10**, 1264–1283 (2014).

33. J. L. West, A. Glushchenko, G. Liao, Y. Reznikov, D. Andrienko, and M. P. Allen, Drag on particles in a nematic suspension by a moving nematic-isotropic interface, *Phys. Rev. E.* **66**, 012702 (2002).

34. A. Sengupta, U. Tkalec, and C. Bahr, Nematic textures in microfluidic environment, *Soft Matter.* **7**, 6542–6549 (2011).

35. A. S. Zolotko, V. F. Kitaeva, N. Kroo, N. N. Sobolev, and L. Chillag, The effect of an optical-field on the nematic phase of the liquid-crystal obcp, *JETP Letters.* **32**, 158 (1980).

36. S. D. Durbin, S. M. Arakelian, and Y. R. Shen, Laser-induced diffraction rings from a nematic-liquid-crystal film, *Opt. Lett.* **6**(9), 411–413 (1981).

37. P. Poulin, V. Cabuil, and D. A. Weitz, Direct measurement of colloidal forces in an anisotropic solvent, *Phys. Rev. Lett.* **79**, 4862–4865 (1997).

38. J. C. Loudet, P. Hanusse, and P. Poulin, Stokes drag on a sphere in a nematic liquid crystal, *Science.* **306**, 1525 (2004).

39. B. Lev, A. Nych, U. Ognysta, S. B. Chernyshuk, V. Nazarenko, M. Škarabot, I. Poberaj, D. Babič, N. Osterman, and I. Muševič, Anisotropic laser trapping in nematic colloidal dispersion, *Eur. Phys. J. E.* **20**, 215–219 (2006).

40. S. A. Tatarkova, D. R. Burnham, A. K. Kirby, G. D. Love, and E. M. Terentjev, Colloidal interactions and transport in nematic liquid crystals, *Phys. Rev. Lett.* **98**, 157801 (2007).

41. M. Škarabot and I. Muševič, Direct observation of interaction of nanoparticles in a nematic liquid crystal, *Soft Matter.* **6**, 5476–5481 (2010).

42. A. V. Ryzhkova and I. Muševič, Particle size effects on nanocolloidal inter-

actions in nematic liquid crystals, *Phys. Rev. E.* **87**, 032501 (2013).

43. M. Škarabot, Z. Lokar, and I. Muševič, Transport of particles by a thermally induced gradient of the order parameter in nematic liquid crystals, *Phys. Rev. E.* **87**, 062501 (2013).

44. S. Samitsu, Y. Takanishi, and Y. Yamamoto, Molecular manipulator driven by spatial variation of liquid-crystalline order, *Nat. Mat.* **9**, 816 (2010).

45. M. Škarabot, M. Ravnik, S. Žumer, U. Tkalec, I. Poberaj, D. Babič, N. Osterman, and I. Muševič, Two-dimensional dipolar nematic colloidal crystals, *Phys. Rev. E.* **76**, 051406 (2007).

46. M. Škarabot, M. Ravnik, S. Žumer, U. Tkalec, I. Poberaj, D. Babič, N. Osterman, and I. Muševič, Interactions of quadrupolar nematic colloids, *Phys. Rev. E.* **77**, 031705 (2008).

47. M. Ravnik, M. Škarabot, S. Žumer, U. Tkalec, I. Poberaj, D. Babič, N. Osterman, and I. Muševič, Entangled nematic colloidal dimers and wires, *Phys. Rev. Lett.* **99**, 247801 (2007).

48. M. Gomilšek, D. Seč, M. Škarabot, M. Ravnik, S. Žumer, and I. Muševič, Light-driven oscillations of entangled nematic colloidal chains, *Eur. Phys. J. E.* **33**, 291–296 (2010).

49. V. S. R. Jampani, M. Škarabot, M. Ravnik, S. Čopar, S. Žumer, and I. Muševič, Colloidal entanglement in highly twisted chiral nematic colloids: Twisted loops, hopf links, and trefoil knots, *Phys. Rev. E.* **84**, 031703 (2011).

50. M. Nikkhou, M. Škarabot, S. Čopar, M. Ravnik, S. Žumer, and I. Muševič, Light-controlled topological charge in a nematic liquid crystal, *Nature Physics.* **11**, 183–187 (2015).

Chapter 9

Atomic force microscopy on liquid crystals

Christian Bahr* and Benjamin Schulz

*Max Planck Institute for Dynamics and Self-Organization,
Am Fassberg 17, 37077 Göttingen, Germany*
christian.bahr@ds.mpg.de

This chapter provides an introduction to the atomic force microscopy
(AFM) on thermotropic liquid crystals. We first give a general introduction to the technique of AFM and then describe the special requirements
that have to be met for the imaging of liquid-crystalline surfaces. We
also discuss the relation between the quality or reliability of the imaging
results and various parameters of the scanning conditions. We briefly
review the existing work on AFM on liquid crystals and finally describe
applications beyond the imaging, such as molecular force spectroscopy
or manipulation of surface structures.

Contents

1. Introduction to atomic force microscopy

The imaging of structures that cannot be resolved by optical microscopy
is a standard task in all laboratories working with nanostructured materials or surfaces. For example, the nanogrooves in the alignment layer of a

standard liquid crystal cell cannot be observed with an optical microscope. This problem has been overcome with the advent of scanning probe imaging techniques. Starting with the development of the scanning tunneling microscopy (STM) in 1981,[1] these techniques have become an indispensable tool in physics, chemistry, biology, and material science. In this chapter, the focus will be put on atomic force microscopy (AFM), which was invented in 1986[2] and aimed at reaching a resolution far better than the optical limit also for non-conducting samples which cannot be probed by STM. Since it was shown that the method is also applicable to the surface of low-viscosity liquids,[3] it is also possible to measure the surface structure of liquid crystals. In the following, we give a brief, mainly qualitative introduction to AFM. For further reading, also on other scanning probe microscopy methods, the reader is referred to Refs. 4–6.

The basic idea of scanning microscopy is to probe the surface of a sample using a sharp tip with dimensions in the nanometer range. By moving the tip over the sample while a feedback mechanism maintains a constant distance between tip and surface, the topography of the sample can be reconstructed. For STM, the condition of constant distance is easily achievable as the tunneling probability is strongly and monotonically dependent on the distance. Therefore, keeping the tunneling current constant is a suitable feedback mechanism to image the surface topography. For the case of AFM, the situation is more complex, mainly because of two reasons: First, there is no single physical parameter such as the tunneling current that is a direct and sensitive measure of the distance between tip and surface: the tip is mounted on a cantilever and the feedback mechanism is based on some kind of mechanical distortion or deflection of the cantilever from its equilibrium, caused by the force acting on the tip in the proximity of the surface. Second, a number of different forces enter into the balance of interaction between tip and surface: attractive van der Waals forces and repulsive Pauli interactions are always present and, depending on the properties of the sample, there may be additional electrostatic or magnetic interactions. Furthermore, if the surface is covered by a liquid film, a capillary bridge can be formed, introducing additional forces on the tip.

As the mentioned forces have a different range, it is obvious that the force-distance-dependence between tip and surface is not monotonic: for large distances there is an attractive force between tip and surface while for short distances the force is repulsive. The interaction between tip and surface is often described by standard potentials like the Lennard-Jones or Morse potential. In order to account for the angular dependence of the interaction forces, more advanced potentials like the Stillinger-Weber potential can be applied.[7] Because of their different length scales the forces can be experimentally separated, thereby extracting physical properties of the surface and achieving atomic imaging resolution.[8,9]

Figure 1 shows schematically the basic elements of an AFM setup. The interaction between tip and surface leads to a deflection of the cantilever that in most cases is detected optically by reflecting a laser beam off the cantilever onto a position-sensitive photodiode. The signal of the photodiode is coupled via a feedback loop to a piezoelectric element that adjusts the vertical position (z direction) of the sample and maintains a constant interaction between tip and surface. Additional piezoelectric elements move the sample horizontally (x and y directions) so that a certain area of the surface can be scanned. The use of piezoelectric elements enables tip positioning with sub-nanometer resolution but also sets the upper limit for the scan size which is around 200 μm for the x and y directions and around 15 μm for the z direction. The achievable resolution of AFM measurements is also determined by the geometry of the tip: its opening angle is the restricting factor for the resolution of steep structures (it is obvious that the structures such as overhangs cannot be resolved by AFM) and the diameter of the apex of the tip sets a lower limit for the lateral resolution. Typical radii

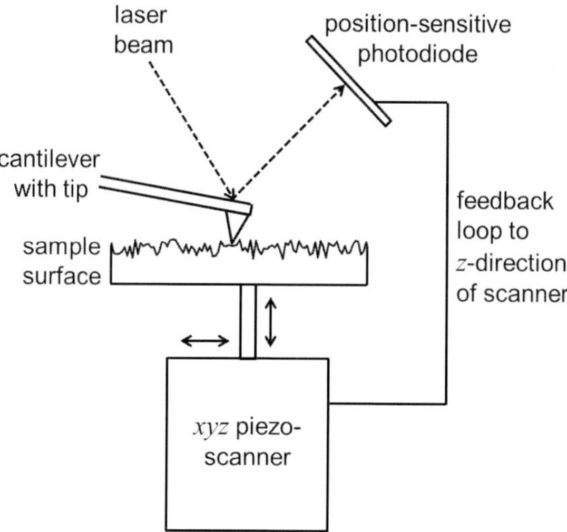

Fig. 1.   Basic elements of an AFM setup.

of commercially available tips are smaller than 10 nm. Sharper probes can also be purchased at the cost of decreased stiffness and increased fragility. Due to the required small distance between tip and surface, it is necessary to decouple the sample from any vibrations in the environment. An effective vibrational isolation and damping of the sample holder is therefore essential.

The cantilever possesses a certain elastic modulus or spring constant k, available over a wide range from < 1 N/m to > 100 N/m. The value of k is important with respect to two points: First, k determines, among other factors, the force which is exerted by the tip to surface. Second, k determines the resonance frequency of the cantilever when it is brought to oscillation in case a dynamic AFM mode (described below) is used. For the study of soft solid surfaces cantilevers with lower k values are used. For liquid surfaces, which are studied in a dynamic AFM mode, usually higher k values are chosen in order to work at higher frequencies, thereby minimizing the time (in each oscillation period) during which the tip is in contact with the surface.

AFM measurements are usually conducted in one of three different modes, designated as contact mode, tapping mode, and non-contact or lift mode (Fig. 2). In the contact mode, the tip is brought in direct mechanical contact with the surface of the sample and the static deflection of the cantilever is used as the feedback signal. As on the molecular level the definition of "contact" is difficult, it is more precise to say that the tip is close enough to feel the Pauli repulsion of the atoms. Therefore, in the contact mode the force between the tip and the sample is always repulsive. As repulsive forces can amount to more than 1 μN,[10] contact mode AFM carries the risk of damaging or changing the surface morphology of the sample significantly. On hard materials, it also quickly wears the tip apex, implying strongly decreased resolution. The contact mode is used for studies of solid surfaces for which an atomic resolution is not required.

Tapping mode and non-contact mode are dynamic AFM modes which have been developed in order to reduce the interaction of the tip with the surface and therefore a possible damage or change of the surface structure. In these modes, the feedback parameter is not the static deflection of the cantilever. Instead, the cantilever with the tip is brought to oscillation and the value of amplitude or frequency serves as the feedback parameter. The tip-surface interactions are significantly smaller since the tip is in contact with the surface only for a small fraction of the oscillation period (tapping mode) or the contact with the surface is completely avoided (non-

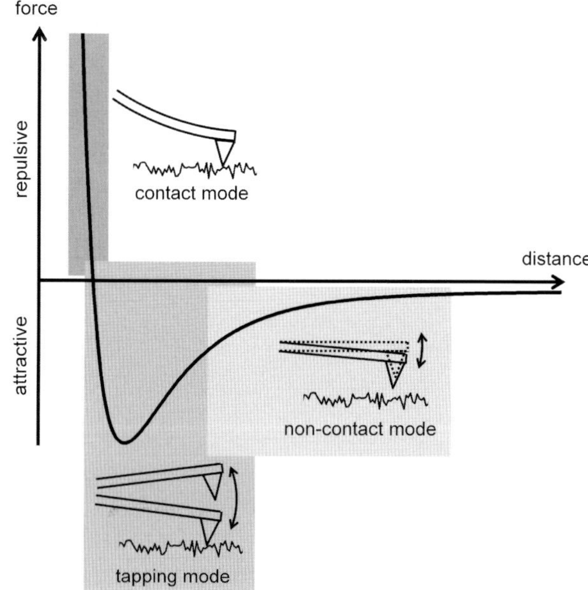

Fig. 2. Three modes of AFM measurements and their approximate working regimes: the non-contact mode works in the region of attractive forces between tip and surface, the contact mode contact in the region of repulsive forces, and the tapping mode in an intermediate region. Approximate distances between tip and surface are 0.5 nm in the contact mode, 0.5 - 2 nm (at the turning point of the oscillation cycle) in the tapping mode, and 1 - 10 nm in the non-contact mode.

contact mode). In the tapping mode the cantilever is oscillating near its resonance frequency (typically a few hundred kHz). When the oscillating tip approaches the surface, the oscillation amplitude becomes smaller and the topography of the surface is imaged by keeping the damping of the oscillation constant (at constant excitation). Besides mapping the z values in the scanned area, resulting in a topographic height image of the surface, also the phase ϕ of the vibrating cantilever is determined. The value of ϕ changes when elastic or other mechanical properties of the surface change. The resulting phase contrast image of the surface often complements the information obtained from the height image. Although the tapping mode still works in the repulsive interaction regime, it is able to image biological samples as well as liquid surfaces, including liquid crystal surfaces.

The non-contact or lift mode is the least interacting mode. Like the tapping mode it is a dynamic mode, but the amplitude of the free oscillation is smaller (only a few nanometers). The intention is to measure completely in the attractive regime of the tip-surface potential and thus to avoid a repulsive contact with the surface. The attractive forces between the tip and the first atomic layer of the surface are of the order of 10^{-11} N.[8] Measuring in the non-contact mode ensures that removing or dragging along of soft surface material is avoided. Therefore, for example, this mode is the preferred mode for probing very thin soft samples. However, for liquid surfaces the non-contact mode bears the risk of formation of a liquid meniscus around the tip since the mean distance to the surface is smaller (because of the smaller oscillation amplitude) than in the tapping mode. For these cases, where soft or liquid materials, such as liquid crystals, are studied and there is a risk of formation of a meniscus, the challenge is to find an intermediate mode between non-contact and tapping: On the one hand the oscillation amplitude should be large enough to avoid meniscus formation and on the other hand it should be small enough to keep the interaction between tip and surface as small as possible. Examples for measurements where different accuracy challenges have to be compromised are presented in the following Section.

2. Imaging conditions for liquid crystal surfaces

The technique of atomic force microscopy was initially developed for solid surfaces. Nevertheless, it was shown that the dynamic modes also offer the possibility to image surfaces of low-viscosity liquids[3,11] and liquid crystals.[12,13]

AFM imaging of liquid surfaces is difficult because of the mobile character of the molecules in a liquid: even very small forces can alter the surface structure significantly and there is always the risk of formation of a permanent liquid meniscus around the tip. In tapping mode AFM, it is assumed that the tip is in contact with the surface only for a short fraction of the oscillation period. When the tip approaches the liquid surface during one oscillation period, one expects either the formation of a transient capillary bridge between tip and surface (which is destroyed when the tip is retracting again) or the complete inhibition of a capillary bridge (because certain effects prevent the formation of a miscroscopic capillary bridge on short time scales[3]). If, however, the amplitude of the tip vibration is too small, a possible capillary bridge may be preserved during the whole oscillation period, resulting in the formation of a permanent meniscus around the tip that prevents any true imaging of the surface. A permanent meniscus can also form if the fraction of the oscillation period, during which the tip is in contact with the liquid, is too large, which is the case when the scan is conducted with a strong damping of the tip oscillation.

Based on capillary forces, a theoretical model for the imaging process in tapping mode AFM has been developed.[14] The model predicts, under certain conditions, reliable imaging for certain values of the surface tension of the liquid, the curvature radius of the tip, and the spreading parameter of the liquid on the tip material (usually silicon) and was successfully applied to polar liquids.[15] However, for organic liquids which are expected to spread on silicon, the model predicts a difficult, if not impossible, imaging by tapping mode AFM. Nevertheless, it is found that tapping mode AFM can be used to image the surface of liquid crystals if two essential parameters are adjusted: the free amplitude A_0 of the oscillating tip and the amplitude setpoint A_s of the feedback loop.

The free amplitude A_0 corresponds to the oscillation amplitude of the tip at zero interaction with the surface (i. e., in a large distance) and the setpoint amplitude A_s is the value of the oscillation amplitude that is maintained by the feedback loop during the scan (Fig. 3). Typically, A_0 can be varied between a few nanometers and some tens of nanometers while A_s can be set to a value between 5% and 95% of A_0. Both values influence the interaction between tip and surface. Choosing a value of A_s close to A_0 ($A_s/A_0 \approx 0.9$) results in a weak interaction between tip and surface, which is favourable with respect to ensure an undistorted surface structure. On the other hand, a certain minimum level of interaction is required to maintain the stability of the feedback loop. The overall interaction with the surface is decreased also by choosing a small value of A_0. Decreasing A_0, however, increases the probability of meniscus formation around the

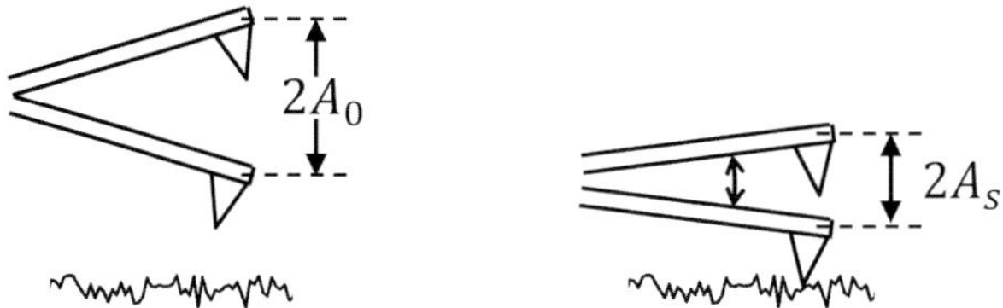

Fig. 3. Tip vibrating amplitudes for tapping mode AFM. Left: When the tip is in a large distance from the surface (before the start of a scan), it vibrates with a free amplitude A_0. Right: During a scan, the tip vibrates with a smaller amplitude A_s because the vibration is damped due to the interaction with the surface. The value of A_s is determined by the choosen setpoint and is held constant during the scan by the feedback loop.

tip. These conflicting requirements have to be balanced, and, since the properties of liquid crystal surfaces can vary considerably between different compounds and phases, it is not possible to give a general recommendation for a perfect set of parameters. In the following, we discuss two examples which illustrate these different needs and demonstrate how AFM measurements can be conducted to produce qualitatively and quantitatively reliable results.

The first example is the measurement of the height of a step formed by a single molecular smectic layer. Bardon *et al.*[13] have presented a systematic tapping mode AFM study of ultra-thin smectic films spreading on a silicon substrate. The compound under investigation was 4-n-octyl-4′-cyanobiphenyl (8CB), which is known to form in the bulk smectic phase interdigitated bilayers with a thickness of 3.16 nm.[16] The films consisted of one such bilayer on top of a tilted monolayer which spreaded first on the silicon substrate. Bardon *et al.* studied the imaging of the film surface in the (A_s, A_0) parameter space and measured the height of the edge of the spreading bilayer which should have the same value as the bulk smectic layer thickness. They found reliable imaging for setpoint settings A_s/A_0 between an upper limit of about 0.9 and a lower limit the value of which was dependent on the value of A_0: the higher the value of A_0, the broader was the A_s/A_0 range in which a goood imaging was obtained. For the step height, values clearly larger than the bulk smectic layer thickness were obtained: The values decreased with increasing setpoint from 6.5 nm at $A_s/A_0 = 0.77$ to 5.0 nm at $A_s/A_0 = 0.88$. Extrapolating the dependence of the apparent step height on the amplitude setpoint to $A_s/A_0 = 1$ yielded a step height comparable to the bulk smectic layer thickness.

Figure 4 shows results we have obtained recently for 8CB films that are similar to those studied by Bardon *et al.* The films were prepared by spin-coating on silicon substrates as described in Ref. 17. They consist of one, two, or three smectic layers (interdigitated bilayers) and enable the study of single layer steps at the boundaries separating domains of different thickness. In addition to the thickness step between zero and one layer (which is the same system as studied by Bardon *et al.*) thickness steps between one and two, and between two and three layers could be studied. The step heights were determined for various setpoint settings, denoted by the amplitude ratio A_s/A_0, for two different values of the free amplitude A_0 of around 8 nm and 25 nm.

The results confirm the observations of Ref. 13. Clearly, the apparent step heights determined by AFM are larger than the true value (3.16 nm),

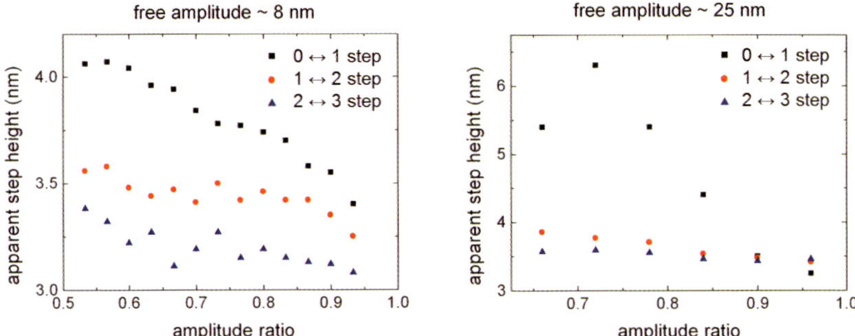

Fig. 4. Apparent step heights of one smectic layer as a function of the amplitude ratio A_s/A_0 measured at domain boundaries between thicknesses of 0 and 1, 1 and 2, and 2 and 3 smectic layers of 8CB on silicon substrates. The free cantilever amplitude A_0 was 8 nm (left) and 25 nm (right). Note the different scales of the ordinate of the diagrams.

but they approach this value if the interaction between tip and surface is reduced, corresponding to a decrease of the free amplitude A_0 and an increase of the setpoint A_s/A_0. It is obvious that the largest deviations occur for the $0 \leftrightarrow 1$ step, indicating that the reason for the erroneous measured step heights is the change of the surface properties when different thickness regions of the film are scanned. An AFM image obtained in tapping mode represents areas of constant damping of the cantilever oscillation. A constant damping is not necessarily identical to a constant distance to the surface since the damping is determined not only by the distance but also by the mechanical properties of the surface. Understandably, the largest change of the surface properties occurs at the $0 \leftrightarrow 1$ step. Accordingly, for this step the overestimation of the height is larger than for the $1 \leftrightarrow 2$ and $2 \leftrightarrow 3$ steps and the determination of the correct height is difficult. However, the extrapolation of the measured step heights to an amplitude ratio $A_s/A_0 = 1$ (corresponding to zero interaction between tip and sample) leads, as in the case of Ref. 13, to good results.

The second example that we consider are smectic films with a thickness of around one micron on solid substrates. Under certain circumstances this type of arrangement is known to form mesoscopic defect structures, designated as focal conic domains (FCDs, more details are given in Sec. 3.2). The presence of FCDs in a smectic film leads to depressions in the film surface that can be imaged by AFM. In contrast to films of molecular thickness, the surface of a micron-thick smectic film can be regarded as the surface of a bulk liquid phase. Thus, care must be taken to avoid the formation of a meniscus around the AFM tip which would prevent any useful imaging of the film surface. The value of the free amplitude A_0 should amount to at least 20 nm in order to ensure a larger mean distance between tip and surface and to avoid the formation of a meniscus.

The influence of the setpoint amplitude ratio A_s/A_0 on the imaging of the surface of such micron-thick smectic films containing FCDs is illustrated in Fig. 5 which shows three AFM images, obtained with different A_s/A_0 values, and corresponding cross sections through the film. For strong damping ($A_s/A_0 = 0.5$), the image is distorted and the FCDs appear asymmetric, indicating that the scan changes the surface topography. A medium damping ($A_s/A_0 = 0.75$) results in a smooth image. For a small damping ($A_s/A_0 = 0.92$) a slightly blurred image is obtained indicative of an unstable contact between tip and sample: the tip is not held at a constant distance to the surface but jumps slightly when moving across. The cross sections in the diagram of Fig. 5 show that only for the amplitude

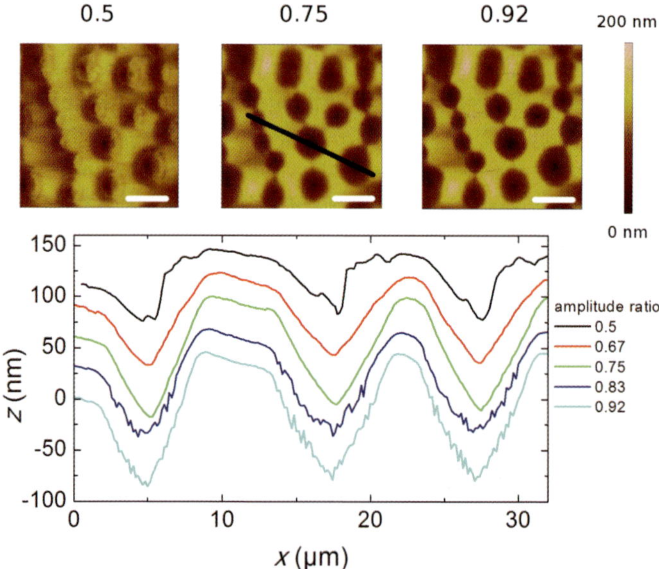

Fig. 5.   Influence of the setpoint amplitude ratio A_s/A_0 on the imaging of micron-thick smectic films containing focal conic domains. The top row shows three height images of the same film area obtained with A_s/A_0 values as indicated on top of the images. The scale bar corresponds to 10 μm. The bottom diagram shows cross sections (along the black line in the middle image) for five different settings of A_s/A_0.

ratios of 0.75 and 0.67 a smooth scan is obtained. However, for the case of $A_s/A_0 = 0.67$ a decrease of the observed height modulation along the FCDs is found. Hence, the interaction is already strong enough to flatten the surface structure which is not yet the case for 0.75. Summarizing, there is an intermediate damping region that leads to a smooth imaging. The reliability of absolute height differences, however, has to be verified using measurements with a low damping for which a strong influence on the surface structure can be ruled out.

Comparing the two examples presented, it should also be underlined that the scanning parameters that led to the best result for the scan of the bulk surface (amplitude A_0 around 25 nm and amplitude ratio $A_s/A_0 = 0.75$) would lead to an overestimation of the step height of a single smectic layer by around a factor of 2. This demonstrates that the scanning parameters always need to be adapted to the particular problem and that quantitative AFM results need to be viewed critically and verified.

3. AFM studies of liquid crystals

Liquid crystals are liquid phases possessing anisotropic physical properties which are due to a certain degree of molecular order that is not present in common isotropic liquids. The simplest liquid crystal phase, the nematic phase formed by small rod-shaped organic molecules, exhibits an orientational order: the molecules tend to align along a common direction. Smectic phases show, in addition to the orientational order, a positional order resulting in a layered structure. The cholesteric phase is the chiral version of the nematic phase: the preferred direction of the orientational order spirals and builds up a helical superstructure.

Because of their internal order, liquid crystals can show a free surface that is not completely smooth as in the case of simple isotropic liquids. For instance, smectic phases, because of their layered structure, can show steps at their surface, resulting in a terraced surface. Another reason for a structured surface consists in a possible competition between the molecular order in the bulk phase and that at the surface which might prefer a different order. Such a competition can give rise to frustration effects resulting in the formation of topological defect structures affecting the shape of the free surface. AFM has been used to elucidate such surface structures of liquid crystals and in the following we give a brief overview on these studies, focussing on thermotropic low-molecular-weight liquid crystals.

  C. Bahr and B. Schulz

3.1. *Cholesteric liquid crystals*

Probably the first AFM study of the free surface of thermotropic liquid crystals was reported in 1992 by Terris *et al.*[12] who studied a number of chiral compounds showing cholesteric, smectic-A, and chiral smectic-C phases. While for the cholesteric and isotropic phases a smooth flat surface was found, the surface of the smectic-A phase showed an undulation pattern of parallel corrugations with a depth of a few tens of nanometers (which will be discussed in the following section). In the following years, the availability of cholesteric liquid crystal oligomer compounds that showed a transition to a glassy state (in which the cholesteric liquid crystal structure is preserved) triggered a few AFM studies of the cholesteric liquid crystal phase. Because of the glassy state, it was not necessary to observe the precautions for the study of liquid surfaces described in Sec. 2.

AFM studies were conducted for microtome cut samples[18,19] as well as for the free surface[19,20] of the cholesteric phase. In both cases, AFM images show striped patterns with a periodicity corresponding to the half of the helical pitch of the cholesteric phase. For the free surface, the stripes form a superstructure consisting of double spirals, as shown in Fig. 6. The structure of the free surface results from the interplay between the sur-

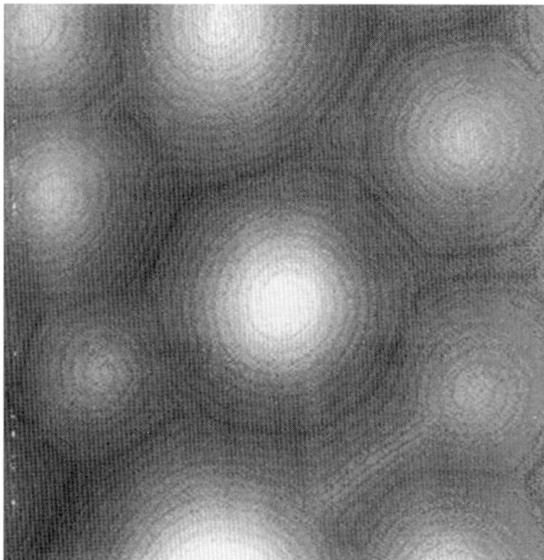

Fig. 6. AFM height image of the free surface of a cholesteric liquid crystal. The double spirals form a conical surface structure, the height difference between the center of a cone and the edge between two cones is of the order of 40 nm. The lateral width of the image amounts to 10 μm. Reproduced from Ref. 19 (http://dx.doi.org/10.1103/PhysRevE.54.3771). Copyright 1996 by The American Physical Society.

face tension and the anchoring and distortion energies of the liquid crystal.[20] For the same (glass forming) cholesteric liquid crystal the effect of adding nanoparticles to the cholesteric matrix was studied.[21] AFM measurements enabled the detection of nanoparticle aggregates and of changes in the striped surface pattern.

Compounds of the glass forming oligomer show above the cholesteric phase also a blue phase (BPI), in which a helical twist of the director field exists along all three spatial dimensions. The blue phase could also be quenched to a glassy state and AFM measurements on microtome cuts were conducted.[22] AFM imaging of free surfaces of glassy blue phases were also performed on a different system based on a discotic compound doped with chiral cellobiose derivatives.[23]

3.2. *Smectic liquid crystals*

Following the pioneering study of Terris *et al.*,[12] a number of AFM studies of smectic liquid crystals were reported focussing mainly on two topics: surface features of molecular scale at the surface of thin smectic films,[13,17,24–27] and mesoscopic surface undulations due to sub-surface defect structures in the arrangement of the smectic layers.[12,28–39] In addition, AFM measurements were used to study the dewetting behavior of smectic films on solid substrates[40] as well as the shape and surface structure of the meniscus of freely suspended smectic films.[41,42]

The surface features of molecular scale consisted in most cases of steps with a height of one or several smectic layers (the thickness of one smectic layer is typically of the order of 2 – 3 nanometers). These structures were studied in Langmuir-Blodgett films,[24] in films or droplets which were spontaneously spreading on solid substrates,[13,27] in initially freely suspended films which were transferred on solid substrates,[25,26] and in films which were generated by spin-coating.[17]

In the studies of the spreading smectic droplets, AFM was used, in conjunction with other techniques, to elucidate the structure of the spreading molecular layers: the first spreading layer which is in direct contact with the substrate, is a monolayer, while the subsequent layers spreading on top of the first layer possess a bilayer structure similar to the layers in the bulk smectic phase of the used material. Apart from the height steps at the edges of the spreading layers, the surface is smooth. In contrast, Langmuir-Blodgett films, transferred freely suspended films, and spin-coated films show a structured surface, characterized by domains of different film thickness leading either to islands or pores on the surface of such films. An example is shown in Fig. 7 showing a spin-coated film of a smectic liquid crystal on a silicon substrate.

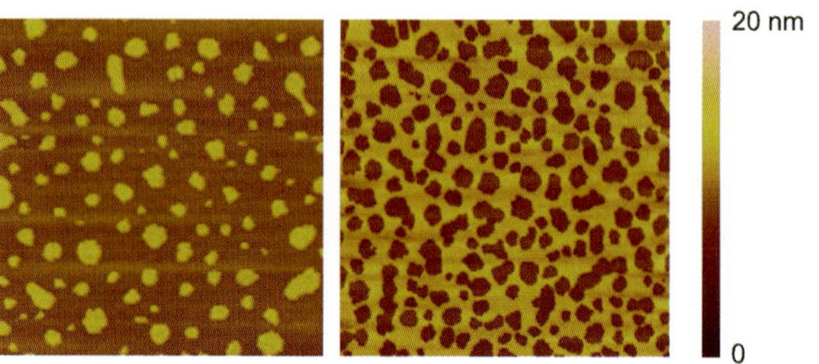

Fig. 7. Height images (area $10 \times 10 \ \mu\mathrm{m}^2$) of the surface of ultra-thin smectic-A films formed by spin-coating from solution on a silicon substrate. The smectic layer on top is formed incompletely, leading either to an island (left) or a pore structure (right), depending on the concentration of the smectic material in the spin-coating solution. The height difference at the domain boundaries amounts to 3.3 nm corresponding to the thickness of one smectic layer. For details see Ref. 17.

While the above described height steps of molecular scale have been studied mainly for films with a thickness of a few smectic layers, smectic films with a thickness in the micrometer range can show mesoscopic surface undulations, i.e., height variations in the range of some hundred nanometers up to a few micrometers. The surface undulations are usually caused by defect structures in the arrangement of the smectic layers, resulting in a bend deformation of the layer planes leading to a curvature of the surface.

The defect structures form in response to competing anchoring conditions on the film surfaces. For instance, consider a smectic film prepared on a substrate with random planar anchoring (the director aligns parallel to the substrate surface, but there is no preferred in-plane orientation). At the second film interface (to air), the director orients perpendicular to the surface. To accomodate the opposite anchoring conditions, the smectic layers form focal conic domains, i.e., defect structures, which are frequently present also in bulk smectic samples. In focal conic domains, the smectic layers are cylindrically bent around a singular line which forms a closed loop with the shape of an ellipse. A second singluar line, with the shape of a hyperbola, runs through the focal point of the ellipse while the planes containing the singular lines are perpendicular to each other. In μm-thick films with antagonistic anchoring conditions as described above, ellipse and hyperbola often degenerate to a circle (on the substrate plane) and a straight line (running from the center of the circle on the subtrate plane to the air interface) and the circular focal conic domains arrange themselves in a hexagonal packing. Figure 8a gives a cross section through the smectic layer structure in two adjacent focal conic domains. The bend deformation of the smectic layers gives rise to circular depressions in the film surface, resembling the dimples in the surface of a golf ball, which can be studied by AFM.[28,30–36,38,39] An example for an AFM height image of the surface of a smectic film with circular focal conic domains is shown in Fig. 8b.

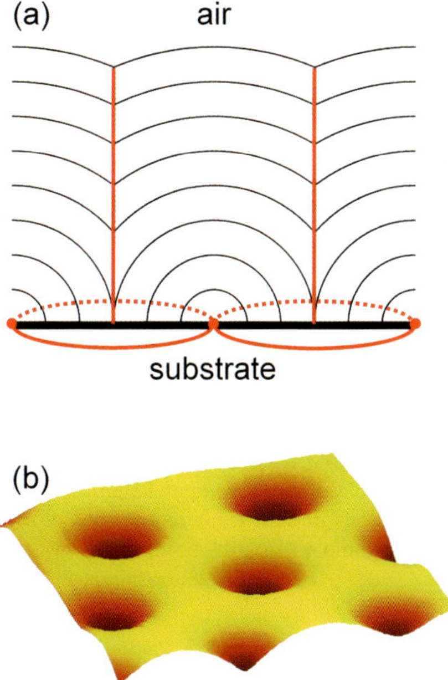

Fig. 8. (a) Schematic cross section the smectic layer structure in two adjacent focal conic domains in a film on a solid substrate. The smectic layers (black lines) are bent around two singular lines (marked in red), a circle on the substrate plane and a straight line between the substrate and the film surface. (b) AFM height image of the surface of a smectic film with circular focal conic domains. Each domain causes a depression in the film surface. The lateral dimension of the shown area is 25 μm. The depth of the depressions is of the order of 250 nm. The distance between two adjacent depressions ($\approx$ 14 μm) corresponds to the diameter of the focal conic domains and the periodicity of the hexagonal packing. Reprinted with permission from Ref. 31. Copyright 2006 American Chemical Society.

While the circular focal conic domains form in films on substrates possessing random planar anchoring conditions, substrates with uniform planar

                    C. Bahr and B. Schulz

anchoring (the director aligns parallel to the substrate surface and along a specific in-plane orientation) enforce the formation of linear defect structures in which the smectic layers are cylindrically bent around straight lines running on the substrate surface in a direction perpendicular to the alignment direction of the director. The free surface of such films, when imaged by AFM, shows a corrugated appearance with linear surface depressions.[29,37] This type of defect structure might also be responsible for the linear undulation pattern observed in the first AFM study[12] of thermotropic liquid crystals, although in that study the observed pattern was proposed to result from a possible chiral layer structure (twist grain boundary phase) in the smectic-A phase. Another type of surface structure of smectic films on solid substrates, that has been studied by AFM, are raised bumplike surface regions which are caused by gold nanoparticles dispersed in the smectic liquid crystal.[35]

Smectic films can also be prepared freely suspended in air by drawing the material in the smectic state over an opening in a thin glass or metal plate. The thickness of freely suspended smectic films can be varied between thousands and only two molecular layers while their area can amount to a few cm^2. These properties render freely suspended smectic films important model systems for the study of surface effects, two-dimensional systems, phase transitions, and structures of smectic phases. The films are connected to their supporting frame through a meniscus, which has a complex structure and plays an important role for some properties of the film, such as the stability and the thinning transitions. AFM has been used to study the shape of the meniscus and certain surface structures that appear at smectic-A to smectic-C transitions.[41,42]

Smectic films or droplets (on solid substrates) have been used as "substrates" for *in situ* AFM studies of Gibbs films of semifluorinated alkane molecules forming at the smectic/air interface. The semifluorinated alkane molecules self-assemble in hexagonal arrays of surface micelles the dimensions of which can be determined by AFM.[43] Figure 9 shows an AFM image of a smectic surface densely covered by surface micelles.

3.3. *Bent-core liquid crystals*

Smectic liquid crystal phases formed by bent-core (or "banana-shaped") molecules possess special properties. Although the constituent molecules are not chiral, these materials can show, as the result of a spontaneous symmetry breaking, polar order and chiral structures. A rich polymorphism

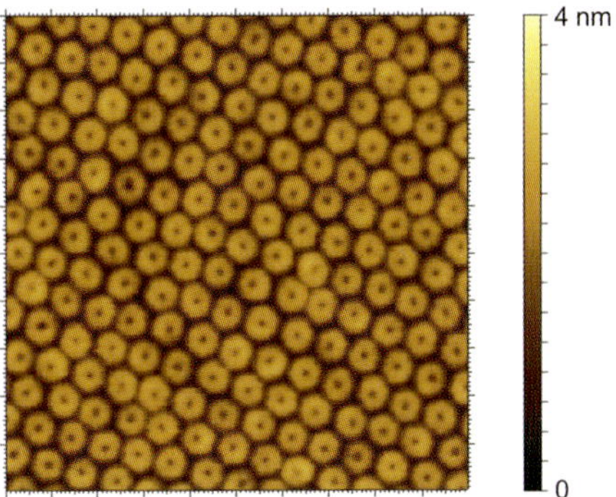

Fig. 9.   AFM height image of the surface of a smectic film formed by spontaneous spreading on a silicon substrate. The smectic liquid crystal is doped with a small amount of a semifluorinated alkane which forms hemimicelles at the free surface of the smectic film. The lateral width of the shown area is 0.5 μm. For more details see Ref. 43.

with several different phases exists. The most common phase, designated as B2 or smectic-CP, is similar to the conventional smectic-C phase, with the difference that the molecules within the layers establish a polar order by aligning the orientation of the bent molecular cores along a common direction. An AFM study[28] of the B2 phase has revealed the existence of focal conic domains which cause depressions in the free surface as described in the previous section and which arrange along defect lines that probably separate domains with different orientation of the polar order.

Other AFM studies have mainly concentrated on the B7 phase type which is characterized by a splay deformation in the vector field describing the orientation of the bent molecular cores, resulting in a periodic modulation in the polarization field. The polarization modulation gives rise to a modulation of the smectic layer structure, and thus a modulation of the free surface of the B7 phase that can be imaged by AFM. Corresponding studies were conducted for films on solid substrates,[28,44] for droplets and filaments,[45,46] and for samples confined to microchannels.[47]

AFM measurements[48,49] were also conducted for the B4 phase the structure of which remained obscure for a longer time. A first AFM study[48] revealed the presence of smectic layers and focal conic domains. More recently, a study[49] combining AFM, freeze fracture electron microscopy, and x-ray diffraction could successfully clarify a complex structure of twisted layers which arrange themselves in helical nanofilaments.

3.4. *Polymer, discotic, and other liquid crystals*

To describe all studies on polymer liquid crystal systems is beyond the scope of this chapter. We just mention here two studies in which polymer materials serve as model systems providing, via AFM, a direct visualization of defect structures in liquid crystals.

The first system is based on diblock copolymer materials. In thin layers, the microphase separation of the two chemically distinct blocks can result in striped patterns, resembling a two-dimensional smectic structure, in which cylinders of one block align parallel in a matrix of the second block. The morphology of the stripe pattern can contain topological defect structures corresponding, for instance, to $+\frac{1}{2}$ and $-\frac{1}{2}$ disclinations in a nematic phase. The coarsening dynamics of the pattern and the annealing dynamics of the defects can be directly visualized and studied by time-lapse AFM measurements.[50,51]

The second system is a liquid crystalline side-chain polymer exhibiting nematic and smectic phases. In thin films an undulation instability at the free surface is observed when the material transforms from the nematic to the smectic state, resulting in a striped surface pattern with the stripes being parallel to the local director. AFM measurements were employed to directly visualize the director field around disclinations and inversion walls.[52] An example is given in Fig. 10 showing AFM height images of areas around $+1$ and -1 disclinations.

Discotic liquid crystals are formed by disk-shaped molecules. Columnar phases, in which the molecules arrange themselves in stacks or columns, are the most common type of discotic liquid crystal phases. Because of their possible applications in molecular electronics, columnar phases have been investigated in a large number of studies the description of which is beyond the scope of this chapter. The study of these materials by AFM can be done in many cases without the precautions necessary for liquid surfaces because columnar phases show a high viscosity and often transform into a glassy state at lower temperatures. AFM was used, often in combination with other methods, to reveal the structure of monolayer[53,54] and multi-layer films[55–57] and the arrangement of the molecular columns in cylindrical pores.[58]

In addition to the common nematic, cholesteric, and smectic phases, liquid crystal materials can form more complex phases, for instance bicontinuous phases of cubic symmetry. Such phases are mainly observed in lyotropic systems but can also be found in thermotropic materials. Monocrystalline

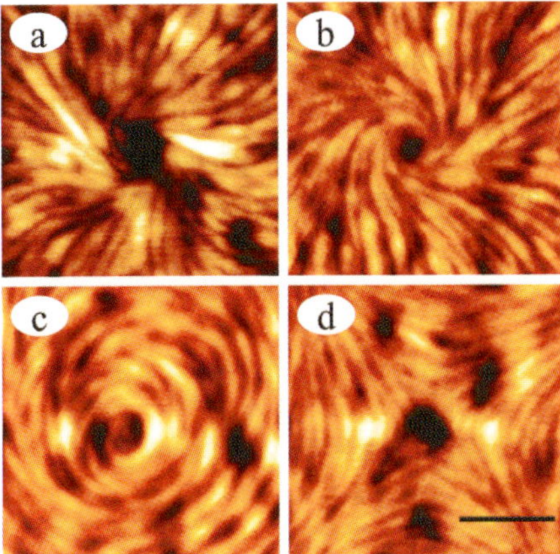

Fig. 10. AFM height images of disclinations in thin films of a liquid crystalline side-chain polymer. (a)-(c) Different types of +1 disclinations, (d) a −1 disclination. Scale bar is 300 nm. Reprinted with permission from Ref. 52. Copyright 2005 American Chemical Society.

droplets of these cubic phases can show an exceptionally rich facetting behavior and AFM measurements were employed to study the surface structure of different facets of such soft crystals.[59]

4. Applications beyond imaging

4.1. *Force spectroscopy*

Besides imaging, a major application of the AFM technique is force spectroscopy. The deflection of the cantilever, as registered by the photodiode, can be translated to the force acting on the tip. The determination of the force as a function of the distance between the tip and the surface sheds light on the interactions between the tip and the surface and allows conclusions about mechanical and structural properties of the surface.

The method has been employed to study the smectic order that exists near the interface between isotropic liquid crystals and solid substrates. A glass sphere of micrometer size was attached to the cantilever and the liquid crystal material was deposited on a glass substrate. The glass substrate and sphere were coated with a silane monolayer inducing homeotropic alignment of the liquid crystal. The glass sphere was immersed into the isotropic liquid crystal and the force F was recorded as the sphere approached the glass substrate. As shown in Fig. 11, at distances $d < 20$ nm undulations were

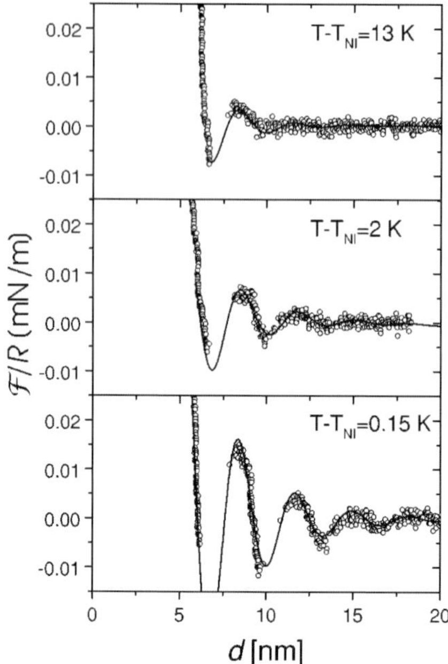

Fig. 11. Normalized force F/R acting on a glass sphere ($R = 8.5\ \mu$m) as function of distance d to a flat glass substrate covered with an isotropic liquid crystal (8CB) at three different temperatures above the nematic - isotropic transition temperature T_{NI}. The undulations reflect the presence of smectic layers at the glass/isotropic interface. Reproduced from Ref. 61 (http://dx.doi.org/10.1103/PhysRevE.65.021703). Copyright 2002 by the American Physical Society.

observed in the $F(d)$ curve that reflect the penetration of smectic layers by the glass sphere.[60,61] By the same technique it was possible to determine the smectic layer thickness and the layer compressibility modulus.[62]

Another topic that was studied by force spectroscopy AFM is the capillary condensation of the nematic phase. Between two surfaces with large homeotropic anchoring strength, the nematic phase can form by capillary condensation at temperatures slightly above the nematic - isotropic transition, resulting in an attractive force between the surfaces which has been proven and quantified by force spectroscopy AFM.[63–65] A more detailed chapter on the application of force spectroscopy AFM on liquid crystals can be found in Ref. 66.

4.2. *Surface manipulation*

An AFM device may be used to manipulate, via the tip-surface interactions, the structure of a surface on the nanoscale in a controlled way. With respect to liquid crystals, AFM was used to design the structure of molecular alignment layers, which are used to orient the director of a nematic phase along a descired direction. Examples of this technique are reported, for instance, in Ref. 67 and the References therein. In this Section, we focus on the surface of the liquid crystal itself and describe briefly how the structure of the surface of a smectic film can be manipulated by an AFM device.

As described in Sec. 2, the suitable way to image a liquid surface by AFM is to use the tapping mode with a small interaction between tip and surface. A small interaction in tapping mode is achieved by choosing a setpoint of the probe vibration amplitude A_s close to the value of the free amplitude A_0 (where the tip is vibrating far from the surface), i.e., $A_s/A_0 \approx 0.9$. Scanning a liquid surface in tapping mode with a stronger interaction, corresponding to a smaller setpoint value ($A_s/A_0 \leq 0.6$) may result in erroneous imaging results, and scanning in contact mode results in the formation of a permanent meniscus around the AFM tip that prevents any useful imaging. Recently, it was found that both scanning modes, which are not suitable for imaging, can be used to modify the surface morphology of smectic liquid crystal films in a controlled way.[68]

Figure 12a shows a height image of a smectic film obtained by spin-coating, exhibiting the typical pattern of domains that differ in thickness by a single smectic layer, similar to what shown in Fig. 7. Scanning the thinner areas in contact mode results in a deposition of an additional smectic layer in the scanned area. Obviously, the additional material stems from the meniscus around the tip. Figures 12b and c show the same film area after scanning in the central region one (b) or ten (c) 10 μm long lines in contact mode. It is also possible to deposit an additional layer on the thicker areas, the detailed behavior depends on the total film thickness and is described in Ref. 68. In contrast to scanning in contact mode, scanning in tapping mode with strong interaction results in the removal of material from the film surface. Figure 12d shows a surface morphology obtained by several deposition and removal scans. The mechanisms of the deposition and removal processes are still under investigation.

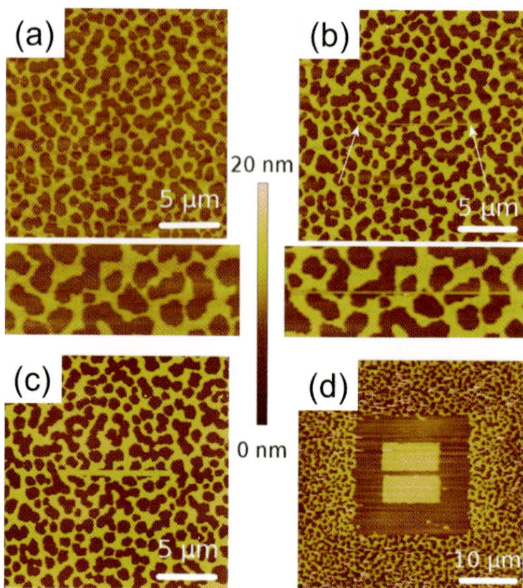

Fig. 12. (a) AFM height image of a smectic film produced by spin-coating, showing a typical domain structure formed by thinner and thicker film regions. (b) The same film after a manipulation by AFM. A single line with 10 μm length is scanned in contact mode. The scanned area appears as a thin line with a constant thickness (endpoints of the line are indicated by arrows). The panels just below (a) and (b) show the corresponding area before and after the creation of the line magnified by a factor of 2. (c) The same film after a scan of ten additional lines in contact mode above the first line. (d) A more complex morphology obtained by several successive scans. The larger region with the smaller film thickness is obtained by scanning with tapping mode with 70% amplitude setpoint. Reprinted with permission from Ref. 68. Copyright 2014, AIP Publishing LLC.

References

1. G. Binning, H. Rohrer, C. Gerber, and E. Weibel, Surface studies by scanning tunneling microscopy, *Phys. Rev. Lett.* **49**, 57–61 (1982).
2. G. Binnig, C. F. Quate, and C. Gerber, Atomic force microscope, *Phys. Rev. Lett.* **56**, 930–933 (1986).
3. S. Herminghaus, A. Fery, and D. Reim, Imaging of droplets of aqueous solutions by tapping-mode scanning force microscopy, *Ultramicroscopy.* **69**, 211–217 (1997).
4. E. Meyer, H. J. Hug, and R. Bennewitz, *Scanning Probe Microscopy: The Lab on a Tip.* Springer, Berlin (2004).
5. V. V. Tsukruk and S. Singamaneni, *Scanning Probe Microscopy of Soft Matter: Fundamentals and Practices.* Wiley-VCH, Weinheim (2012).

6. G. Van Tendeloo, D. Van Dyck, and S. J. Pennycook, eds., *Handbook of Nanoscopy*. Wiley-VCH, Weinheim (2012).

7. F. H. Stillinger and T. A. Weber, Computer simulation of local order in condensed phases of silicon, *Phys. Rev. B.* **31**, 5262–5271 (1985).

8. F. Ohnesorge and G. Binnig, True atomic resolution by atomic force microscopy through repulsive and attractive forces, *Science.* **260**, 1451–1456 (1993).

9. M. Guggisberg, M. Bammerlin, C. Loppacher, O. Pfeiffer, A. Abdurixit, V. Barwich, R. Bennewitz, A. Baratoff, E. Meyer, and H.-J. Güntherodt, Separation of interactions by noncontact force microscopy, *Phys. Rev. B.* **61**, 11151 (2000).

10. J. B. Pethica and W. C. Oliver, Tip surface interactions in STM and AFM, *Phys. Scr.* **T19**, 61–66 (1987).

11. T. Pompe, A. Fery, and S. Herminghaus, Imaging liquid structures on inhomogeneous surfaces by scanning force microscopy, *Langmuir.* **14**, 2585–2588 (1998).

12. B. D. Terris, R. J. Twieg, C. Nguyen, G. Sigaud, and H. T. Nguyen, Force microscopy of chiral liquid-crystal surfaces, *Europhys. Lett.* **19**, 85–90 (1992).

13. S. Bardon, M. P. Valignat, A. M. Cazabat, W. Stocker, and J. P. Rabe, Study of liquid crystal prewetting films by atomic force microscopy in tapping mode, *Langmuir.* **14**, 2916–2924 (1998).

14. A. Fery, T. Pompe, and S. Herminghaus, Nanometer resolution of liquid surface topography by scanning force microscopy, *J. Adhesion Sci. Technol.* **13**, 1071–1083 (1999).

15. S. Herminghaus, T. Pompe, and A. Fery, Scanning force microscopy investigation of liquid structures and its application to fundamental wetting research, *J. Adhesion Sci. Technol.* **14**, 1767–1782 (2000).

16. A. J. Leadbetter, J. C. Frost, J. P. Gaughan, G. W. Gray, and A. Mosley, The structure of smectic A phases of compounds with cyano end groups, *J. Physique.* **40**, 375–380 (1979).

17. B. Schulz and C. Bahr, Surface structure of ultrathin smectic films on silicon substrates: Pores and islands, *Phys. Rev. E.* **83**, 041710 (2011).

18. T. J. Bunning, D. L. Vezie, P. L. Lloyd, P. D. Haaland, E. L. Thomas, and W. W. Adams, Cholesteric liquid crystals: image contrast in the TEM, *Liq. Cryst.* **16**, 769–781 (1994).

19. R. Meister, M.-A. Hallé, H. Dumoulin, and P. Pieranski, Structure of the cholesteric focal conic domains at the free surface, *Phys. Rev. E.* **54**, 3771–3782 (1996).

20. R. Meister, H. Dumoulin, M.-A. Hallé, and P. Pieranski, The anchoring of a cholesteric liquid crystal at the free surface, *J. Phys. II.* **6**, 827–844 (1996).

21. A. Hauser, H. Kresse, A. Glushchenko, and O. Yaroshchuk, AFM investigations of a glassy cholesteric liquid crystal with hydrophobic aerosil particles, *Liq. Cryst.* **26**, 1603–1607 (1999).

22. H. Dumoulin, P. Pieranski, H. Delacroix, I. Erk, J.-M. Gilli, and Y. Lansac, Compared study of a quenched blue phase by direct transmission electron and atomic force microscopy, *Mol. Cryst. Liq. Cryst.* **262**, 221–233 (1995).

23. A. Hauser, M. Thieme, A. Saupe, G. Heppke, and D. Krüerke, Surface-imaging of frozen blue phases in a discotic liquid crystal with atomic force microscopy, *J. Mater. Chem.* **7**, 2223–2229 (1997).

24. J. Fang, C. M. Knobler, and H. Yokoyama, Layer growth in collapsed liquid crystal monolayers studied by scanning force microscopy, *Physica A.* **244**, 91–98 (1997).

25. I. V. Chikina, N. Limodin, A. Langlois, M. Brazovskaia, C. Even, and P. Pieranski, Transfer of smectic films to a solid substrate by the method of maclennan, *Eur. Phys. J. B.* **3**, 189–196 (1998).

26. B.-W. Lee, D. R. Link, and N. A. Clark, Atomic force microscopy of freely suspended liquid crystal films transferred to octadecyltriethoxysilane self-assembled monolayers, *Liq. Cryst.* **27**, 501–507 (2000).

27. L. Xu, M. Salmeron, and S. Bardon, Wetting and molecular orientation of 8CB on silicon substrates, *Phys. Rev. Lett.* **84**, 1519–1522 (2000).

28. A. Hauser, H. Schmalfuss, and H. Kresse, AFM investigations of a sample showing the B2 phase, *Liq. Cryst.* **27**, 629–634 (2000).

29. J.-P. Michel, E. Lacaze, M. Alba, M. de Boissieu, M. Gailhanou, and M. Goldmann, Optical gratings formed in thin smectic films frustrated on a single crystalline substrate, *Phys. Rev. E.* **70**, 011709 (2004).

30. M. C. Choi, T. Pfohl, Z. Wen, Y. Li, M. W. Kim, J. N. Israelachvili, and C. R. Safinya, Ordered patterns of liquid crystal toroidal defects by microchannel confinement, *Proc. Natl. Acad. Sci. U. S. A.* **101**, 17340–17344 (2004).

31. V. Designolle, S. Herminghaus, T. Pfohl, and C. Bahr, AFM study of defect-induced depressions of the smectic-A/air interface, *Langmuir.* **22**, 363–368 (2006).

32. W. Guo, S. Herminghaus, and C. Bahr, Controlling smectic focal conic domains by substrate patterning, *Langmuir.* **24**, 8174–8180 (2008).

33. W. Guo and C. Bahr, Influence of phase sequence on focal conic domains in smectic films, *Phys. Rev. E.* **79**, 061701 (2009).

34. Y. H. Kim, D. K. Yoon, H. S. Jeong, J. H. Kim, E. K. Yoon, and H.-T. Jung, Fabrication of a superhydrophobic surface from a smectic liquid-crystal defect array, *Adv. Func. Mater.* **19**, 3008–3013 (2009).

35. R. Pratibha, W. Park, and I. I. Smalyukh, Colloidal gold nanosphere dispersions in smectic liquid crystals and thin nanoparticle-decorated smectic films, *J. Appl. Phys.* **107**, 063511 (2010).

36. Y. H. Kim, J.-O. Lee, H. S. Jeong, J. H. Kim, E. K. Yoon, D. K. Yoon, J.-B. Yoon, and H.-T. Jung, Optically selective microlens photomasks using self-assembled smectic liquid crystal defect arrays, *Adv. Mater.* **22**, 2416–2420 (2010).

37. B. Zappone, E. Lacaze, H. Hayeb, M. Goldmann, N. Boudet, P. Barois, and M. Alba, Self-ordered arrays of linear defects and virtual singularities in thin smectic-A films, *Soft Matter.* **7**, 1161–1167 (2011).

38. B. Zappone, C. Meyer, L. Bruno, and E. Lacaze, Periodic lattices of frustrated focal conic defect domains in smectic liquid crystal films, *Soft Matter.* **8**, 4318–4326 (2012).

39. D. K. Yoon, Y. H. Kim, D. S. Kim, S. D. Oha, I. I. Smalyukh, N. A. Clark,

and H.-T. Jung, Three-dimensional textures and defects of soft material layering revealed by thermal sublimation, *Proc. Natl. Acad. Sci. U. S. A.* **110**, 19263–19267 (2013).

40. S. Herminghaus, K. Jacobs, K. Mecke, J. Bischof, A. Fery, M. Ibn-Elhaj, and S. Schlagowski, Spinodal dewetting in liquid crystal and liquid metal films, *Science.* **282**, 916–919 (1998).

41. J. C. Loudet, P. V. Dolganov, P. Patrício, H. Saadaoui, and P. Cluzeau, Undulation instabilities in the meniscus of smectic membranes, *Phys. Rev. Lett.* **106**, 117802 (2011).

42. K. Harth, B. Schulz, C. Bahr, and R. Stannarius, Atomic force microscopy of menisci of free-standing smectic films, *Soft Matter.* **7**, 7103–7111 (2011).

43. X. Feng, A. Mourran, M. Möller, and C. Bahr, AFM study of gibbs films of semifluorinated alkanes at liquid crystal/air interfaces, *Chem. Phys. Chem.* **14**, 1801–1805 (2013).

44. H. Schmalfuss, A. Hauser, and H. Kresse, Collective dynamics in some phases consisting of banana-shaped molecules, *Mol. Cryst. Liq. Cryst.* **351**, 221–228 (2000).

45. A. Eremin, L. Naji, A. Nemes, R. Stannarius, M. Schulz, and K. Fodor-Csorba, Microscopic structures of the B_7 phase: AFM and electron microscopy studies, *Liq. Cryst.* **33**, 789–794 (2006).

46. A. Nemes, A. Eremin, R. Stannarius, M. Schulz, H. Nádasi, and W. Weissflog, Structure characterization of free-standing filaments drawn in the liquid crystal state, *Phys. Chem. Chem. Phys.* **8**, 469–476 (2006).

47. D. K. Yoon, R. Deb, D. Chen, E. Körblova, R. Shao, K. Ishikawa, N. V. S. Rao, D. M. Walba, I. I. Smalyukh, and N. A. Clark, Organization of the polarization splay modulated smectic liquid crystal phase by topographic confinement, *Proc. Natl. Acad. Sci. U. S. A.* **107**, 21311–21315 (2010).

48. H. Kresse, J. Salfetnikova, H. Nadasi, W. Weissflog, and A. Hauser, Characterization of the B_4 phase by dielectric and AFM measurements, *Liq. Cryst.* **28**, 1017–1023 (2001).

49. L. E. Hough, H. T. Jung, D. Krüerke, M. S. Heberling, M. Nakata, C. D. Jones, D. Chen, D. R. Link, J. Zasadzinski, G. Heppke, J. P. Rabe, W. Stocker, E. Körblova, D. M. Walba, M. A. Glaser, and N. A. Clark, Helical nanofilament phases, *Science.* **325**, 456–460 (2009).

50. C. Harrison, D. H. Adamson, Z. Cheng, J. M. Sebastian, S. Sethuraman, D. A. Huse, R. A. Register, and P. M. Chaikin, Mechanisms of ordering in striped patterns, *Science.* **290**, 1558–1560 (2000).

51. C. Harrison, Z. Cheng, S. Sethuraman, D. A. Huse, P. M. Chaikin, D. A. Vega, J. M. Sebastian, R. A. Register, and D. H. Adamson, Dynamics of pattern coarsening in a two-dimensional smectic system, *Phys. Rev. E.* **66**, 011706 (2002).

52. S. Zhang, E. M. Terentjev, and A. M. Donald, Atomic force microscopy study for supermolecular microstructures in side-chain liquid crystalline polymer films, *Langmuir.* **21**, 3539–3543 (2005).

53. V. V. Tsukruk, D. H. Reneker, H. Bengs, and H. Ringsdorf, Atomic force microscopy of ordered monolayer films from discotic liquid crystals, *Langmuir.*

9, 2141–2144 (1993).

54. M. L. Bushey, T.-Q. Nguyen, and C. Nuckolls, Synthesis, self-assembly, and switching of one-dimensional nanostructures from new crowded aromatics, *J. Am. Chem. Soc.* **125**, 8264–8269 (2003).

55. N. C. Maliszewskyj, O. Y. Mindyuk, P. A. Heiney, J. Y. Josefowicz, P. Schuhmacher, and H. Ringsdorf, Structural phase transition in ultrathin films of disk-shaped molecules, *Liq. Cryst.* **26**, 31–36 (1999).

56. H. Schönherr, M. Manickam, and S. Kumar, Surface morphology and molecular ordering in thin films of polymerizable triphenylene discotic liquid crystals on hopg revealed by atomic force microscopy, *Langmuir.* **18**, 7082–7085 (2002).

57. P. Morales, J. Lagerwall, P. Vacca, S. Laschat, and G. Scalia, Self-assembled ordered structures in thin films of HAT5 discotic liquid crystal, *Beilstein J. Org. Chem.* **6**, 51 (2010).

58. R. Zhang, X. Zeng, B. Kim, R. J. Bushby, K. Shin, P. J. Baker, V. Percec, P. Leowanawat, and G. Ungar, Columnar liquid crystals in cylindrical nanoconfinement, *ACS Nano.* **9**, 1759–1766 (2015).

59. C. Even, M. Impéror-Clerc, and P. Pieranski, Exploring the facets of "soft crystals" using an atomic force microscope, *Eur. Phys. J. E.* **20**, 89–98 (2006).

60. K. Kočevar, R. Blinc, and I. Muševič, Atomic force microscope evidence for the existence of smecticlike surface layers in the isotropic phase of a nematic liquid crystal, *Phys. Rev. E.* **62**, R3055–R3058 (2000).

61. K. Kočevar and I. Muševič, Surface-induced nematic and smectic order at a liquid-crystal—silanated-glass interface observed by atomic force spectroscopy and brewster angle ellipsometry, *Phys. Rev. E.* **65**, 021703 (2002).

62. G. Carbone, B. Zappone, R. Barberi, R. Bartolino, and I. Muševič, Direct nanomechanical measurement of layer thickness and compressibility of smectic liquid crystals, *Phys. Rev. E.* **83**, 051707 (2011).

63. K. Kočevar, A. Borštnik, I. Muševič, and S. Žumer, Capillary condensation of a nematic liquid crystal observed by force spectroscopy, *Phys. Rev. Lett.* **86**, 5914–5917 (2001).

64. K. Kočevar and I. Muševič, Forces in the isotropic phase of a confined nematic liquid crystal 5CB, *Phys. Rev. E.* **64**, 051711 (2001).

65. A. Borštnik Bračič, K. Kočevar, I. Muševič, and S. Žumer, Capillary forces in a confined isotropic-nematic liquid crystal, *Phys. Rev. E.* **68**, 011708 (2003).

66. T. Rasing and I. Muševič, eds., *Surfaces and Interfaces of Liquid Crystals.* Springer-Verlag, Berlin (2004).

67. J.-H. Kim, M. Yoneya, and H. Yokoyama, Tristable nematic liquid-crystal device using micropatterned surface alignment, *Nature.* **420**, 159–162 (2002).

68. B. Schulz, P. Steffen, and C. Bahr, Nanoscale viscoplastic behavior of smectic liquid crystals and its application in nanolithography, *J. Appl. Phys.* **115**, 074302 (2014).

Micron scale inclusions in liquid crystals

Chapter 10

Solid microparticles in nematic liquid crystals

Igor Muševič

J. Stefan Institute, Jamova 39, 100 Ljubljana, Slovenia
igor.musevic@ijs.si

A brief historic overview of colloidal experiments in the 1990's is given in the introduction. These experiments have later inspired research on nematic colloids, after the technique of laser tweezers manipulation of particles was introduced to this field. Basic topological properties of colloidal inclusions in the nematic liquid crystals are discussed and the nematic- mediated forces between dipolar and quadrupolar colloidal particles in bulk nematic are explained. Structural and topological properties of 2D and 3D colloidal crystals and superstructures made of colloidal particles of different size and symmetry in bulk nematic liquid crystal are described. Laser-tweezer manipulation and rewiring of topological defect loops around colloidal particles is introduced. This results in the colloidal entanglement, as well as knotting and linking of defect loops of the order parameter field. Shape and size- dependent colloidal interactions in the nematic liquid crystals are reviewed. The chapter concludes with the discussion of bulk chiral nematic and blue phase colloids.

Contents

1. Introduction

Dispersions of solid microparticles in a nematic liquid crystal were first considered in the 1970s when topological defects in liquid crystals were studied.[1-3] In these pioneering studies, small colloidal bubbles were dispersed in a liquid crystal and the free surface of the liquid crystal was observed with an optical microscope. Surprisingly, one could observe a spontaneous organisation of microbubbles into a more or less ordered chains, which were following the local orientation of liquid crystal molecules, as shown in Fig. 1. In this way, one could visualise the surface ordering of a nematic director. At that time, similar methods of decoration of material surfaces by small particles were used to visualise the lines of spontaneous electric polarisation in ferroelectric materials and the lines of magnetisation in solid ferromagnets.

This simple experiment of decorating the nematic director field with chains of small particles went unnoticed until the seminal experiments of Poulin *et al.* on nematic emulsions,[4] performed in 1997. They studied the optical appearance of small droplets of a nematic liquid crystal dispersed in water with some surfactant added. Because the liquid crystal does not mix with oil, perfect spherical microdroplets of water were spontaneously formed

Fig. 1. Small colloidal particles arrange themselves into chains, which are following local orientation of the nematic director on a free interface towards the air. The reason for colloidal chaining is a structural force between the particles, which arises because of the elastic distortion of the nematic liquid crystal around each colloidal particle. Image courtesy of V. S. R. Jampani.

in the liquid crystal after mixing. Surprisingly, the researchers could see a spontaneous assembly of water droplets into chains, floating in the nematic liquid crystal, with some unusual defects between each pair of droplets. This experiment clearly demonstrated that there is a force between a pair of water droplets, floating in a liquid crystal. Furthermore, it was also evident that the observed defects prevent spontaneous coalescence of water droplets. These defects therefore act as topological objects that topologically protect the stability of water chains in the nematic liquid crystal.

The force between a pair of water droplets dispersed in a liquid crystal was explained in terms of the elastic distortion of the liquid crystal surrounding the water droplet. The molecules of the nematic liquid crystal are forced to align perpendicular to the water - liquid crystal interface - at all points of the surface of the droplet. This is because of the surfactant, which was added to the mixture. As the surface of the droplet is curved and closed, a topological problem arises: it is not possible by any means to fill the space surrounding the water droplet with liquid crystal molecules without creating topological defects. Due to the fact that nematic liquid crystal molecules tend to be parallel to each other in the far field and they have to follow the orientation on a closed surface, there is clearly a frustration at some points of the space. In these points, liquid crystal molecules have no preferential direction of their orientation, which means there is a defect in the liquid crystal orientation. We therefore have a situation where an object, inserted into a liquid crystal, creates topological defects. These defects are a natural companion of these inserted colloidal particles. They must be created by some physical conservation law and cannot be separated from the particle. The inserted colloidal particle and the topological defect form an inseparable entity, which is in topology called a topological multipole.[5-8] Alternatively, the particle and the accompanying defects are called elastic multipoles. This is because the liquid crystal surrounding the particle is strongly elastically deformed.

The elastic deformation around each particle is the reason why these particles either attract or repel each other, as observed in the experiments. Namely, when one particle is forced to approach the other particle by some external force, the regions of elastic deformation around each particle start to overlap. This overlapping of elastic distortion is either in favor of both particles or not. In case the elastic distortion is energetically favorable for both particles, they will tend to share as much of that region as possible. This means that there will be an attractive force between the two particles and by approaching, the particles will lower their total free energy. In case the elastic distortions do not match and are therefore not favorable in terms of the total free energy of the pair, the particles will repel from each other. Overall, one can see that the elastic distortion of a nematic liquid crystal, created by the insertion of the particle into the liquid crystal, generates forces between particles. In terms of physics, this is a generalized force and has its origin in elastic deformation of the director field. It can be expressed as the total derivative of the free energy $\boldsymbol{F}$ with respect to the separation between the particles d:

$$F = -\frac{\partial \boldsymbol{F}}{\partial d} \tag{1}$$

Alternatively, this structural force has a topological origin. By inserting particles into a continuous nematic ordering field, topological defects are created, which mediate the force between the inserted particles. Topological defects are therefore the generators of forces between colloidal inclusions.

There is a variety of elastic or topological multipoles, which appear when foreign particles are inserted into a liquid crystal. Their complexity depends on the type of the alignment of the liquid crystal on the surface of colloidal insertions, and on the topological complexity of the insertions themselves. Namely, by using modern photolithographic techniques, one can create not only simple objects like microspheres, microfibers, or microplatelets, but also colloidal particles of complex topological form, such as planar handle-bodies.[9] Using a two-photon laser-induced photo-polymerization, topologically complex particles in 3D can be produced, such as polymer knots and links.[10] When such complex particles are inserted into a nematic liquid crystal, novel and fascinating topological phenomena are observed, such as knotting and linking of the nematic director field around inserted knots and links.

The aim of this chapter is to give a clear physical picture of colloidal interactions in a nematic liquid crystal. After introducing simple topological objects and their pair interaction in a nematic crystal, we shall present the assembly of these particles into colloidal crystals in two and three dimensions. In the continuation we shall discuss the phenomenon of the entanglement of nematic colloids. Here defect lines, accompanying each colloidal particle, can be manipulated by the strong light of laser tweezers, which enables one to fuse together two or many defect loops. This results in the entanglement of several colloidal particles by a single or multiple defect loops, which can be themselves knotted and linked. This will lead us to complex topological assemblies in two dimensions, such as the arrays of colloidal particles, which are bound together by a multitude of mutually knotted and linked loops. We shall briefly discuss topological rules, which control the wiring and rewiring of these topologically complex forms.

2. Elastic dipoles and quadrupoles

We shall consider a topologically simple object such as a microsphere or a microfiber, which is inserted into a nematic liquid crystal and has a well-defined anchoring of liquid crystal molecules on its surface. Microspheres, microfibers, and small platelets are topologically equivalent. In terms of topology, they can be smoothly transformed into each other by a continuous deformation of their surfaces. They are characterised by a topological feature called "the genus".[9,11] Objects like spheres are characterised by the genus $g = 0$. The more complex object is a torus, characterised by $g = 1$. In simple terms, the genus equals the numbers of the "holes" perforating the object. Topologically more complex objects are called handlebodies and are characterised by a higher genus.[9] It is evident that in terms of topology the objects with different genera are of different sort and cannot be transformed into each other smoothly.

Depending on the type of surface anchoring of liquid crystal molecules different forms of topological defects are formed, accompanying the inserted particle. In case of a perpendicular surface anchoring of liquid crystal molecules, a point defect, also called a hyperbolic hedgehog, is formed close to the surface of the inserted colloidal particle, as shown in Fig. 2. The

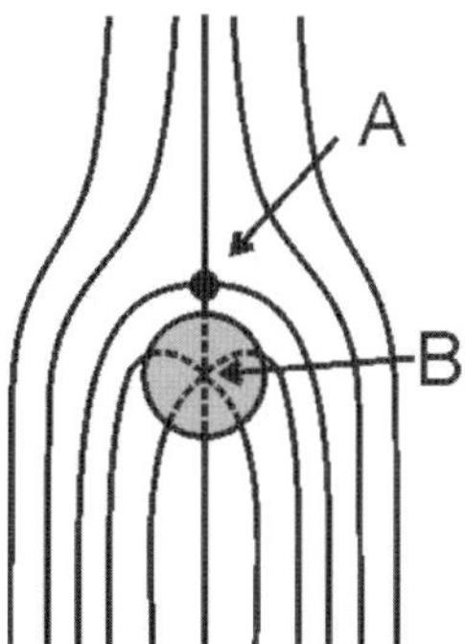

Fig. 2. Schematic drawing of the lines of orientation of a nematic liquid crystal surrounding a microsphere, which imposes perpendicular (homeotropic) surface anchoring of liquid crystal molecules. The hyperbolic hedgehog (A) carries a topological charge of -1, the virtual radial hedgehog (B), residing in the centre of the microsphere, carries by definition the opposite topological charge of +1. Together both charges are perfectly compensated.

particle itself can be considered as carrying another topological defect at its center. This defect is a virtual one; it is called a radial hedgehog and is the counterpart of the hyperbolic hedgehog, residing in the liquid crystal. Together the hyperbolic hedgehog and the virtual radial hedgehog form a topological pair, which is called a topological dipole. This is similar to an electric dipole, which is formed of two opposite electric charges, separated by a distance, d. Note that an electric charge is also a singularity of the electric field. The schematic drawing of the nematic director field around a colloidal particle showing a dipolar symmetry is shown in Fig. 2.

Such elastic dipolar particles were in fact observed in the experiments of Poulin *et al.*[4] Instead of solid microspheres, water droplets were accompanied by the hyperbolic hedgehog defect. Similar to electric dipoles the elastic dipoles also prefer to spontaneously form dipolar chains. In such a chain, each particle is separated from its neighbor by a topological hedgehog defect. It is also clear that these hyperbolic hedgehogs have the role of topological protection. They cannot be annihilated because of the conservation of the total topological charge[6] and they keep the particles separated at all times. This also explains the stability of chains of water droplets, observed in the experiment of Poulin *et al.* They are topologically protected from coalescing and form topologically stable structures.

In fact, the first observation of topological defects, accompanying colloids inserted into a nematic crystal, were reported already in 1990 by Pratibha and Madhusudana,[12] whereas the first theoretical analysis was given by Terentjev in 1995.[13] Pratibha and Madhusudana were studying mixtures of rod-like and disc-like nematic liquid crystals. Due to the immiscibility in a certain range of concentration the two materials became separated and formed droplets of one material in another material. They could observe small ring-like defects, encircling the droplets, as shown in Figs. 3(a, b). The structure of these ring-like defects was later numerically analyzed by Terentjev, who called these rings the Saturn ring in a clear correspondence to the planetary rings encircling Saturn. He showed that the ring is in fact a closed disclination loop of the winding number -1/2, encircling the particle, shown in Fig. 4(a).

When the surface anchoring is planar, favoring parallel orientation of liquid crystal molecules on the surface of particles, two defects are observed on the opposite sides of the particle, as shown schematically in Fig. 4(b). In this case the two defects are called "the boojums" and they each carry one half of the topological charge of a hyperbolic hedgehog defect.

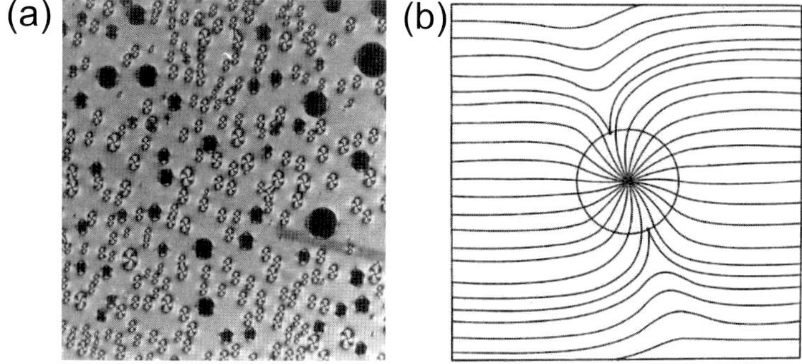

Fig. 3. (a) Microscope image of droplets of a nematic liquid phase of rod-like molecules (N_R), floating in the nematic phase of disc-like molecules (N_D).[12] (b) Schematic drawing of the director field inside and outside the nematic droplet. There is a +1 radial hedgehog in the center of the droplet, whereas there is a -1/2 winding number ring encircling the (N_R) droplet. The winding number is determined by constructing a closed path, encircling the line or a point defect. By moving along this path, the director rotates either clock-wise or counter-clock wise, with the total angle of rotation being equal to the multiples of π. This is the magnitude of the winding nuimber of the defect and the + or - sign describes the sense of director rotation. Image courtesy of R. Pratibha.

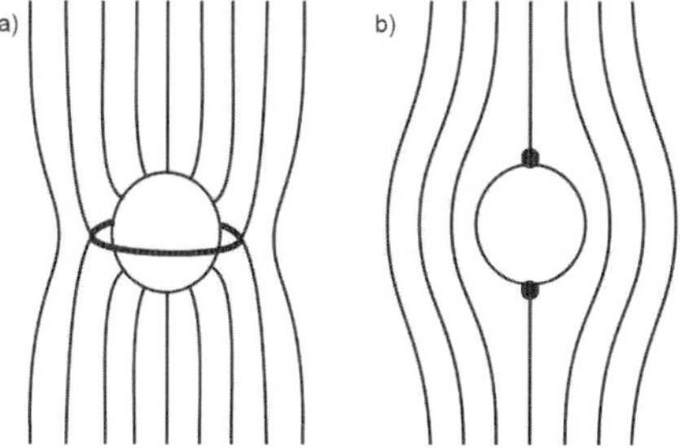

Fig. 4. (a) Schematic drawing of a Saturn ring, encircling a spherical microparticle with homeotropic anchoring of the nematic liquid crystal. (b) Schematic drawing of a pair of boojum defects (dark points), residing on the surface of the particle with a planar surface anchoring of the nematic liquid crystal.

The Saturn ring defects and the boojum defects give rise to a quadrupolar symmetry of the particle and the nematic liquid crystal around it. On the other hand, the hyperbolic hedgehog and the particle shown in Fig. 2 have the dipolar symmetry. This will have a profound effect on the nature of forces between a pair of dipolar or quadrupolar particles.

Topological defects, accompanying colloidal particles in the nematic liquid crystal, can be easily observed under an optical microscope, as shown in Fig. 5 The reason for this clear optical distinction of the defect and the background liquid crystal is in the optical inhomogeneity of the liquid crystal in the vicinity of the defect. By remembering that a nematic liquid crystal is an optically strongly anisotropic and uniaxial material, it is obvious that the defect is optically strongly inhomogeneous because of inhomogeneous molecular orientation. This causes strong scattering of the light, which is used to observe the sample. The defect will therefore appear dark because of the light scattering. Of course the ease of observability depends on the size of the particle. Usually microparticles of several micrometres, up to tens of micrometres, are used in experiments, which makes optical observation of the form of defects quite easy.

Whether a particle with a homeotropic surface anchoring will be a dipole or a quadrupole depends on the strength of the surface anchoring, the particle diameter, the elasticity of the nematic liquid crystal, and the tightness of the confinement, if colloidal particles are observed in thin nematic cells.[6]

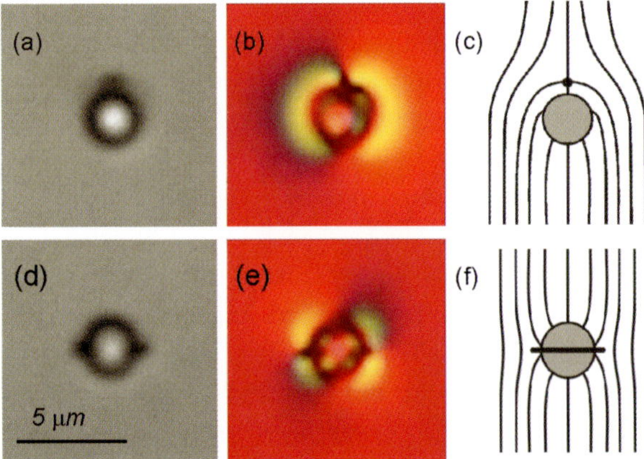

Fig. 5. (a) Non-polarized optical micrograph of a dipolar colloidal particle with perpendicular surface alignment in the nematic liquid crystal. The hyperbolic hedgehog is clearly seen as a dark spot on top of the particle. (b) The same particle is observed between crossed polarizers with a red-plate. (c) Schematic drawing of the director field around dipolar colloidal particle. (d) A microsphere with perpendicular surface alignemt of the nematic liquid crystal. It is encircled with a Saturn ring. The ring appears in a form of two dark spots corresponding to the cross section of the real ring and the plane of the focus of the optical microscope. (d) The same quadrupolar particle imaged with red-plate technique. (f) Schematic drawing of the director field in case of Saturn ring configuration.

For larger particles with a strong surface anchoring, a dipolar form is usually stable in a bulk nematic liquid crystal. If the particle size is decreased, the hedgehog point defect will become unstable and will transform into a small ring. By further decreasing the size of the particle, this ring will approach the equatorial position. Equivalently, the quadrupolar symmetry is also obtained if a dipolar particle is confined between two parallel and flat walls favoring planar alignment. In this case the hedgehog point defect becomes unstable by decreasing the surface separation and transforms into a Saturn ring encircling the particles in closely separated walls.[14]

3. Forces between elastic multipoles in a nematic liquid crystal

When a pair of colloidal particles in a nematic liquid crystal is brought together, the regions of their elastic distortions start to overlap, which results in a force between the two particles. Because the dimension of the elastically distorted region is in the range of several micrometres, the resulting pair interaction force is of long range as well as substantial and comparable to the thermal energies of the particles at a separation of typically ten micrometres.

The exact separation-dependence and also angular dependence of the pair interaction force depend on the symmetry of the distortion of the nematic liquid crystal around each colloidal particle. This means that the pair interaction of two dipolar colloidal particles will be quite different from the pair interaction of a pair of quadrupoles. In addition, one can measure the interaction between a dipole and a quadrupole, which will be different from both mentioned before.

The first theoretical analysis of the force between two spherical microparticles in a nematic liquid crystal was given by Terentjev *et al.*[13,15] which was followed by Kuksenok *et al.*,[16] Ramaswamy *et al.*,[17] Raghunathan *et al.*[18] The theoretical analysis within Landau-de Gennes mean-field theory gives a power-law dependence of the pair interaction force on separation, such as $1/d^5$ attraction force between two elastic *quadrupoles*. Later on, Poulin *et al.* analyzed the mean-field pair interaction energy U_α^β between two elastic *dipolar* colloidal particles, which is given by:

$$U_\alpha^\beta = 4\pi K p_\alpha^z p_\beta^z \frac{1 - 3\cos^2\theta}{d^3} \tag{2}$$

Here, $\vec{p}$ and $\vec{q}$ are the dipoles assigned to each colloidal particle, located at two different positions in space. d is their separation, θ is the angle between the separation vector and the z-axis, and K is the elastic constant of the nematic. This expression is an approximation for the equal elastic constant of the nematic liquid crystal. Note that the dipolar pair interaction force, which is the spatial derivative of the energy (Eq. (2)), depends as $1/d^4$ on particle separation d.

A comprehensive analysis of pair interaction of elastic multipoles and in particular topological dipoles was given by Lubensky *et al.*[19] This work stresses the importance of topology and discusses the role and structure of topological hedgehog defects in dipolar colloidal interaction, which has proven much later to be fundamental in the mechanism of topological entanglement of colloids. Further mean field approaches to nematic colloids include investigations of the stability of colloidal clusters by Lev and Tomchuk[20] and the effects of confining walls on colloidal pair interaction by Fukuda *et al.*[21,22] While these studies concentrated on director approach, thus discarding the effects of spatially varying the degree of order, Fukuda *et al.*[21,22] have used fully tensorial Landau-de Gennes approach to the analysis of colloidal pair interaction in the nematic liquid crystal. Pergamentschik and Uzunova have used a refined approach to the colloidal nematostatics.[23–26] They observed that, in spite of the analogy to the electrostatics, the three-dimensional colloidal nematostatics is substantially different in both its mathematical structure and its physical implications. They formulated a general tensorial structure of the elastic multipoles[23] that allows for a classification of different types of nematic colloids. In this approach, the elastic multipoles have one extra tensorial index, so an elastic dipole is characterized by three coefficients: (i) isotropic strength, (ii) anisotropy and chirality, and (iii) a two-component vector along the unperturbed director.[24] Instead of a single electric dipole, they found several different pure and mixed types of elastic dipoles. A review of this approach can be found in Ref. 25.

The separation dependence of the pair interaction force between two elastic dipoles was first measured by Poulin *et al.*[27] and others.[28–30] These studies found that the interaction force decays as $1/d^4$, which is expected for a dipole-dipole interaction. Figure 6 presents the attractive force between two collinear dipolar nematic colloidal particles, which follows the predicted $1/d^4$ power law. An extensive numerical analysis of the forces between water droplets in a nematic was performed by Stark *et al.*[31] The interaction of two dipolar colloids is very anisotropic and is somewhat similar to the interaction of two electric dipole moments. The force will primarily depend on the direction of each dipole. For two parallel dipoles, the interaction will

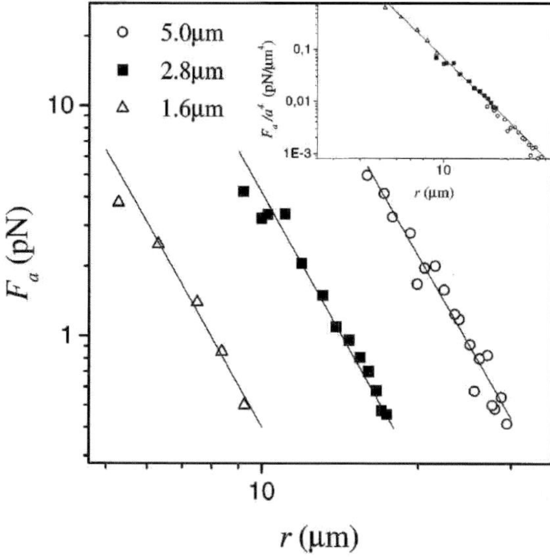

Fig. 6. The attractive force between two dipolar nematic colloidal particles, both pointing into the same direction and along the line connecting both particles. The force is shown for several diameters of the particles, the insert shows that the force is scaling with the particle size. Reprinted with APS permission from Poulin *et al.*, Physical Review Letters 79, 4862 (1997).

be repulsive if they are positioned next to each other. On the contrary, this repulsion will turn into attraction if the two dipoles are positioned along the same line. If we are considering two antiparallel dipoles, the situation will be quite opposite. A pair of antiparallel dipoles will attract if they are positioned next to each other. This will turn into a repulsive force if they are positioned along the same line pointing along the direction of both dipoles.

The force between two colloidal particles is measured using a very simple technique. The particles are brought into a reasonable separation using manipulation with laser tweezers as explained in Chap. 8. Once the particles are at a separation of typically several micrometres, they are released from the laser tweezers focus. Simultaneously, the motion of both particles is video monitored and the frames are stored in the computer. The process of interaction of a colloidal pair may take several seconds to several minutes, depending on the strength of their interaction. In the next step each of the captured video frames (in an experiment tens of thousands of video frames are typically captured) is analyzed by special software, which allows for determining the position of each particle with an accuracy as good as $\pm$ 5nm. This is done by graphically overlapping a small circle to the image of the colloidal particle. When the overlapping is best, the absolute position of the center of that particle is determined in the plane of the sample. This video tracking analysis is surprisingly accurate and allows for the center to be determined with several nanometer accuracy.

From the tracking analysis the trajectories of both particles are exactly determined as a function of time. Having this information, one can numerically calculate the instantaneous velocity of each particle as a function of time. Because the particles are moving through a viscous fluid, their motion is strongly damped and the external force, which drives the particles into motion following Newton's second law, is equal to the viscous drag force of that particle, $F = F_{drag} = 6\pi R_{\text{eff}}\eta\partial r/\partial t$. Using a simple approximation, one can therefore determine the force F on the particle, which is determined by the Stokes equation at each moment of time. This is an approximation, which should hold for well-separated particles, but will break down when the elastically distorted regions around each particle start to overlap. This is due to the coupling between the alignment and flow in liquid crystals. This approximation also takes into account only forces of elastic origin and does not consider other colloidal forces, such as electrostatic force between charged colloidal particles.

The viscosity coefficient, which is unknown in this experiment, can be determined in a second independent experiment, following Brownian motion of the particle. Because of the available thermal energy, a particle in a nematic liquid crystal undergoes easily observable Brownian motion. This motion is very vivid for micrometer-sized particles and is strongly reduced for heavier particles with sizes up to ten micrometres. In the Brownian experiment one is again video recording random motion of a selected particle in a nematic liquid crystal. In an off-line video tracking analysis the position of the particle is determined for each frame. This allows one to construct the noisy trajectory of the particle, which may contain as many as 50,000 of points, as shown in an example in Fig. 7.

One can see from Fig. 7 that there is no difference in the Brownian motion of the particle along the x and y axes, because the cell is homeotropic and there is no physical diference between the x and y directions, which are perpendicular to the nematic director. One can calculate the viscosity coefficient of that particle along the x and y directions, respectively, from both probability distributions. When such a Brownian motion experiment

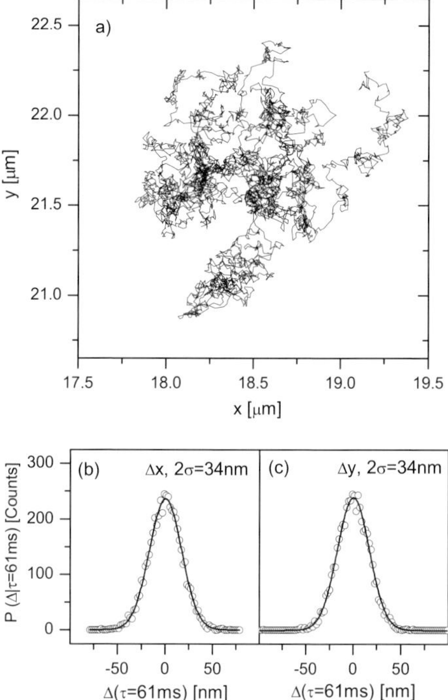

Fig. 7. (a) Recorded trajectory during the Brownian motion of a silanated $0.97\mu m$ silica colloid in a homeotropic cell filled with 5CB. (b) and (c) represent histograms of particle's displacements between two consecutive positions, separated by a time interval of $61ms$, along the two perpendicular directions. The solid lines are Gaussian fits with $2\sigma = 34(1 \pm 0.01)nm$. There is no significant difference between the x and y directions.

is performed in a planar cell, the x and y directions are not equivalent any more. In this case one can observe that the particle diffuses more easily along the molecular ordering (along the director) and its motion is more restricted in the perpendicular direction. This anisotropy is of the order of 10%. It was found that for dipolar particles the anisotrophy of Brownian diffusivity is higher compared to quadrupolar particles.

After having determined both viscosity coefficients, one can actually numerically calculate the force on the particle at each position that was video recorded. Once the force is determined at each point of the trajectory of the particle, one can calculate the pair interaction energy simply by performing an integration of the work along the trajectory of the particle.

Figure 8(c) shows an example of a pair interaction potential of two dipolar particles with antiparallel dipolar moments. The pair interaction

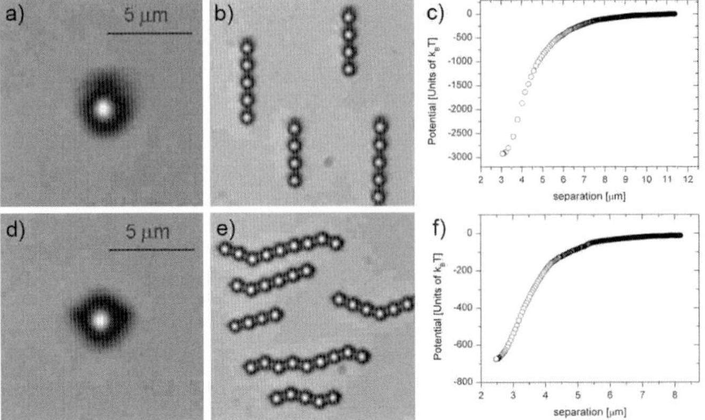

Fig. 8. (a,b) Dipolar colloidal particles spontaneously assemble into straight chains, directed along the nematic director. (c) The strength of the interaction potential for two elastic dipolar colloids exceeds thousands of k_BT and is size-dependent. This potential was measured for $2.3\mu m$ diameter silica colloids with homeotropic surface anchoring in 5CB. (d,e) Quadrupolar colloids self-assemble into kinked colloidal chains in a direction perpendicular to the nematic director. (f) Pair interaction potential for quadrupolar colloids in 5CB is weaker compare to the dipolar, shown in (c).

energies are enormously high and typically reach several thousands of k_BT. One can also notice the long-range nature of the elastic interaction force between the colloidal particles in the nematic. This interaction is substantial over typically tens of micrometers for particle diameters of several micrometers.

Similar experiments were performed for quadrupolar particles and it was found that the colloidal pair interaction is weaker compared to the dipolar interaction, as shown in Fig. 8(f). The separation dependence of the force for quadrupole-quadrupole interaction showed $1/r^5$ power-law dependence, in agreement with the prediction of multipole theory. By using the dipole-dipole or quadrupole-quadrupole interaction it is possible to assemble long and very uniform chains of dipolar particles in a nematic liquid crystal, as shown in Fig. 8(b). If quadrupolar particles are used, the chains are kinked and oriented perpendicular to the nematic director, as shown in Fig. 8(e).

A substantial advancement was achieved by assembling colloidal particles of dipolar or quadrupolar symmetry into two-dimensional colloidal crystals by Muševič *et al.*[14,32,33] The laser tweezers were used to assemble, particle by particle, a perfectly ordered colloidal crystals, consisting of more than hundred particles, as shown in Fig. 9.

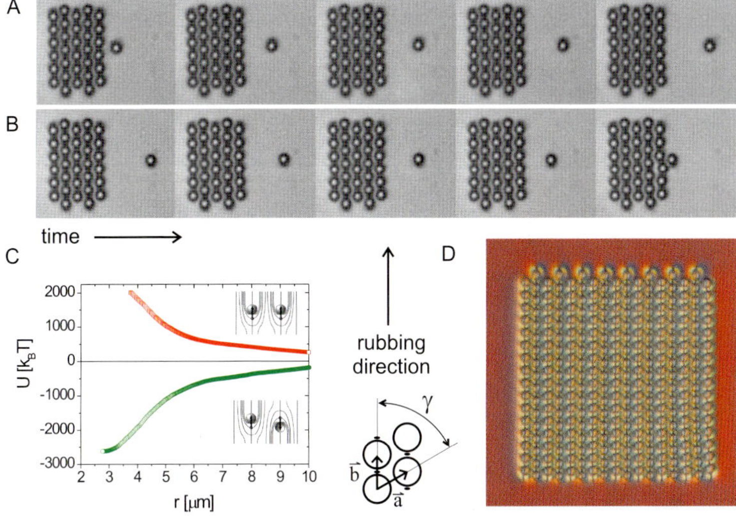

Fig. 9.   Assembly of dipolar colloids into 2D nematic colloidal crystals. (A) Dipolar nematic colloid is repelled from the neighboring "ferroelectric chain" if its dipole is parallel to the dipoles in the chain. Time difference between images is $9s$. (B) It is attracted to the chain, if its dipole is antiparallel to the dipoles in the chain. Time difference between images is $4s$. (C) Measured attractive and repulsive elastic potential for two different orientations of the colloidal dipole. Like-dipoles are repelled from, unlike-dipoles are attracted to the chain. (D) 2D dipolar colloidal crystal is formed by pairs of antiparallel dipolar chains. Different colors represent different orientation of the nematic molecules.

As each particle is bound to the others by a very large potential reaching thousands of $k_B T$, such a crystalline platelet is extremely robust and easily resists external perturbation. Using strong light of laser tweezers, it is possible to move 2D colloidal platelets over large separations, which makes this colloidal material interesting for application in photonics. It was also shown that an external electric field applied perpendicular to the 2D colloidal platelets modifies the lattice constant of these 2D colloidal platelets. The crystal shrinks under the applied electric field for up to 20% along one direction and $\sim 2\%$ along the perpendicular one at an electric field of $\sim 1V/\mu m$.[34]

Further advancement in optical manipulation of colloidal particles in a nematic liquid crystal was needed to assemble 3D nematic colloidal crystals, which presented quite an experimental challenge. This was achieved by Nych *et al.* in 2013.[35] The problem of spatial visualisation of colloidal particles was solved by performing a step-by-step protocol, where, firstly,

     Igor Mušević

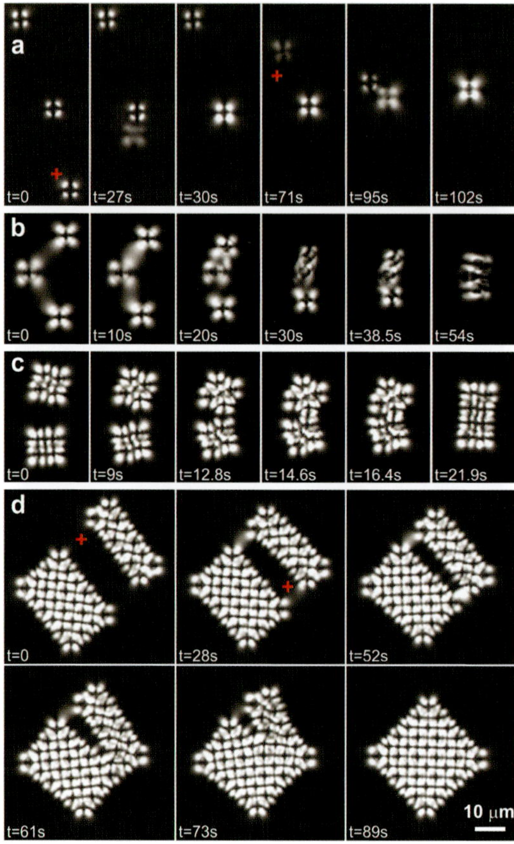

Fig. 10.   Laser-tweezers assembly of a 3D dipolar colloidal crystal observed under crossed polarizers. **a**, Three isolated colloidal particles of $4\mu m$ diameter in the ZLI-2806-filled homeotropic cell of $\sim 25\mu m$ thickness appear as bright objects with a dark cross in the center. Using laser tweezers, one particle is brought close to the other and they spontaneously form a chain of two particles in a direction perpendicular to the plane of the image. The pair appears like a single but larger and brighter particle (3rd image from the left). The third particle is brought to the couple and it spontaneously forms a dipolar colloidal chain of three particles on top of each other. **b**, Three chains, each made of three dipolar particles, are brought close to each other and they start to assemble into a frustrated colloidal trio. Note the tilting of the chains. **c**, Two colloidal blocks of 2 x 2 x 3 particles self-assemble into 2 x 4 x 3 blocks. **d**, Colloidal blocks of 2 x 6 x 3 and 4 x 6 x 3 particles assemble into the final 6 x 6 x 3 dipolar colloidal crystal. The assembly at the initial stage was guided by the laser tweezers until blocks started to attract themselves. In all images, the small red cross is the optical trap, used to navigate the colloidal assembly.

chains of particles were assembled in a homeotropic cell, as shown in Fig. 10. After the chains of particles were assembled, they were brought together by laser tweezers and they spontaneously formed regular 3D blocks of colloidal particles. Finally, as prepared colloidal block were brought together, they spontaneously assembled into a perfectly organized 3D colloidal crystal in the nematic liquid crystal. Figure 10 shows a sequence of microscope images during the 3D colloidal crystal assembling using the laser tweezers.

The force between two elastic quadrupolar colloidal particles with a tangential surface alignment of liquid crystal molecules was studied by Smalyukh *et al.*[36] Similar to quadrupolar particles with homeotropic boundary conditions, this colloids assemble into kinked chains, forming kinetically trapped colloidal network. The separation dependence of the pair interaction force showed significant deviation from theoretical predictions. The discrepancies are not surprising as the model[15,17] assumes that particle separation is much larger than the diameter of the particles and the surface anchoring is weak.

The colloidal forces were studied by different groups in different experimental settings with different experimental conditions and by varying different experimental parameters. Kotar *et al.*[37] used magneto-optical tweezers and determined the force between two superparamagnetic beads with planar surface anchoring in the nematic liquid crystal. Vilfan *et al.*[38] performed a similar experiment and observed screening of the power law potential by the confining walls. Jampani *et al.*[39] studied colloidal pair interaction in chiral nematic liquid crystals and found metastable states and screening of the pair potential by increasing chirality. Ognysta *et al.*[40] were studying the mixed interaction of dipolar and quadrupolar particles in the nematic liquid crystal. They found a variety of different 2D colloidal motifs, where different clusters of either dipolar or quadrupolar particles were assembled in a geometrically regular order. Škarabot *et al.*[41] studied interactions of small and big colloidal particles and found that Saturn rings of larger particles can be filled-in with smaller colloidal particles. These necklace-like structures could be interesting for the application as split-ring resonators in metamaterials.

4. Entanglement of spherical colloidal particles in nematics

As the colloidal interactions in the nematic liquid crystals imply forces, which are generated by localized topological defects, new colloidal interactions were predicted first theoretically and later observed in the experiments

                    Igor Muševič

by various groups.[42–45] Numerical studies of defect structures around a pair of colloidal particles with perpendicular surface anchoring in a nematic liquid crystal predicted several different scenarios. As a trivial solution, two separated Saturn rings are expected to encircle each colloidal particle. However, Landau-de Gennes theory also predicted an unusual defect structure, where one defect ring encircles both colloidal particles, and the second ring or point is situated in between, as shown in Fig. 11.

These numerical studies predicted the existence of "entangled" defect structures, where two Saturn rings are somehow fused together into a single loop. The first experimental realisation of these entangled structures was presented by the Ljubljana group in 2007.[45] It was experimentally shown and theoretically supported that colloidal dimers and 1D structures bound by entangled topological defect loops could be created by locally thermally quenching a thin layer of the nematic liquid crystal around the selected colloidal particles. A strong laser light was used to locally melt the liquid crystal into the isotropic phase. This isotropic island contained two or many freely floating colloidal particles. After switching off the light, the liquid crystal underwent a rapid temperature quench across the isotropic-nematic transition, as illustrated in Fig. 12.

Figure 12(a) presents the time sequence of unpolarized optical micrographs where the formation of a single disclination loop out of a dense tangle of topological defects can be seen. In a fraction of a second the entangled

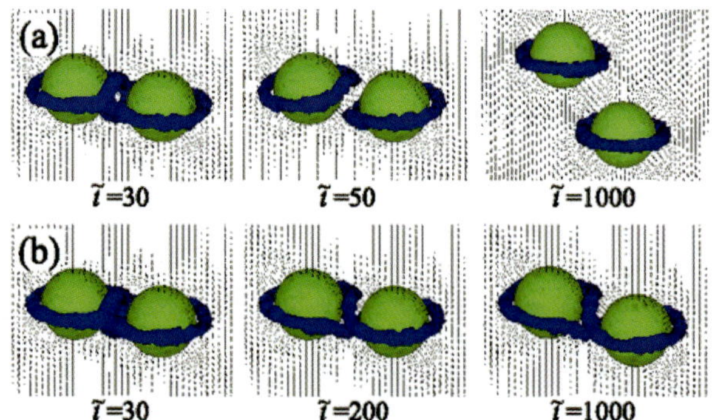

Fig. 11.   Two types of defect formation processes around a pair of particles. A transient defect structure formed in the early stage (t =30) becomes unstable and transforms into either (a) the lowest energy structure stabilized by the quadrupolar interaction or (b) a new type of (quasi-)stable configuration, in which a single disclination loop is shared by two neighboring particles. Reprinted with APS permission from Araki and Tanaka, *Physical Review Letters* **97**, 127801 (2006)

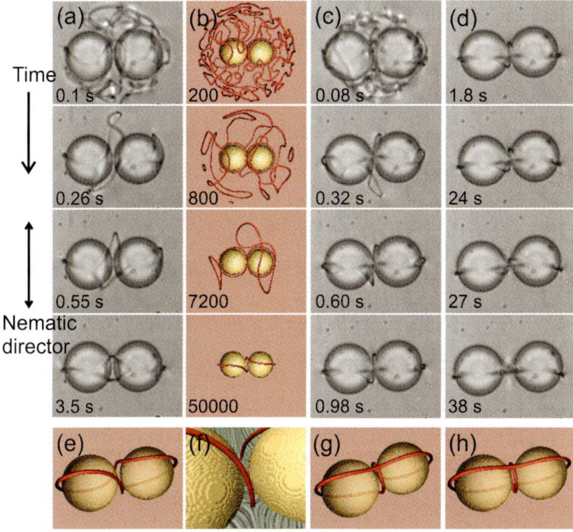

Fig. 12. Assembling entangled colloidal pairs by thermal quench using light. The diameter of the particles is $19\mu m$, the cell thickness is $21\mu m$. (a) "Figure of eight" entangled state. The disclination loops are visible under non-polarizing optical microscope due to the scattering of light. (b) Numerical simulation of the time evolution of entanglement, measured in the number of iteration steps. Defects are represented by drawing the surfaces of constant order parameter S (colored red, corresponding to $S = 0.5$). (c) Evolution of the "figure of omega" entangled state.(d) "Figure of omega" was unstable and transformed into the "entangled hyperbolic defect". (e) The calculated "figure of eight" structure. (f) Close look at the director field in the gap between the microspheres for the "figure of eight". (g) Calculated "figure of omega" structure. (h) Calculated "entangled hyperbolic defect" structure.

topological defect encircles both particles in the form of a loop, which is twisted. The structure was named the "figure of eight". Two other types of binding were observed in the experiments for two colloidal particles. Figure 12(c) presents the formation of a more complicated, asymmetrically entangled single disclination loop which is called the "figure of omega". In contrast to the figure of eight, the figure of omega has a straight defect line at the front side, sinking behind the particles and making an additional loop in between them. It was observed in the experiment that this configuration is metastable and usually slowly transforms into another more stable configuration, shown in Fig. 12(d). In this configuration, the particles are separated by a large gap with a topological point defect residing in between. The structure was called the "entangled hyperbolic defect" structure. In many experiments performed, 52% of the final states were entangled whereas the rest was not entangled. It was found that the figure of eight was thermodynamically the most stable with a 36% probability to be formed. 13% of the observed entangled structures were the figure

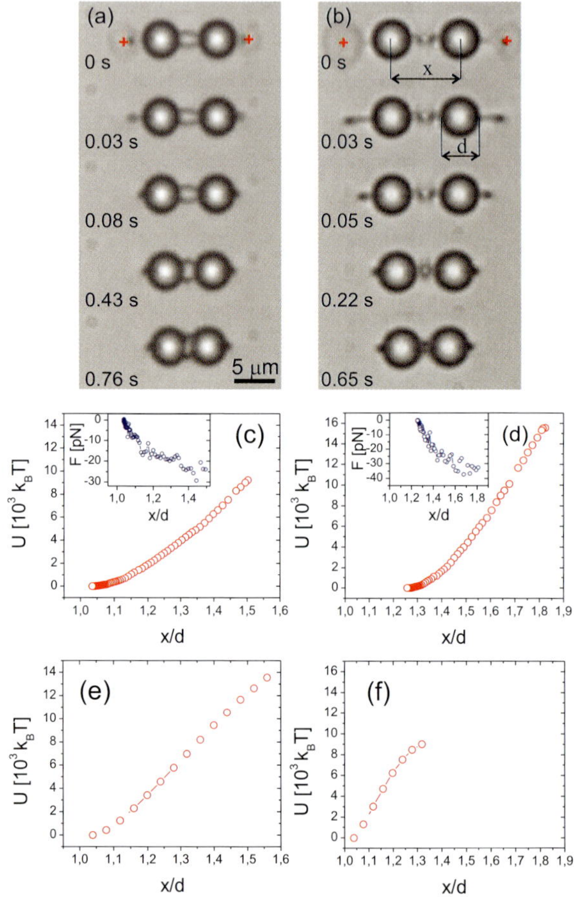

Fig. 13.   Stretching and releasing the topologically bound colloidal pair using light. (a) Using focused light of the laser tweezers (two red crosses on left and right), the "figure of eight" colloidal pair is first stretched and then released by switching-off the light. The diameter of the particles is $4.7\mu m$, the thickness of the cell is $6\mu m$. The force and the binding energy are calculated from the video frames (a), and shown in (c). (b) The same is done for "entangled hyperbolic defects", shown in (d). (e) The pair binding energy, calculated for the "figure of eight", as a function of particle separation x, normalized to the particle diameter d. (f) The pair binding energy, calculated for the "entangled point defect" as a function of separation x, normalized to the particle diameter d.

of omega and only 3% were entangled hyperbolic point defect structures. Figure 12(b) shows the snapshots of the numerical simulations of the entanglement, as calculated within the Landau-de Gennes theory.

The strength of the colloidal pair entanglement can be measured by using two separate light traps, which are grabbing each of the colloidal particles. Using the light force, the entangled pair can be stretched by moving both traps in the opposite direction, and then the traps are switched off. The two particles are driven back together by the force of the entangling defect loop, as shown in the sequence of images in Figs. 13(a)–(b). Using the video tracking technique, one can calculate the force and the potential of the entanglement, as shown in Figs. 13(c)–(f).

The experiments have shown that the entangling defect loops act as (non-elastic) strings because the force needed to elongate the loop is practically independent of the length. Using the same technique of laser tweezers micro quechning it was possible to assemble "colloidal wires", where an arbitrary number of colloidal particles were entangled by defect loops of different topology. Interestingly, all these entangled structures in planar nematic cells could be produced only when they were directed perpendicular to the overall direction of the nematic liquid crystal. All attempts to assemble the entangled colloidal structures in a non-chiral nematic liquid crystal failed.

A significant breakthrough in colloidal topology was achieved in 2011 by Tkalec *et al.*[46] Using a chiral nematic liquid crystal instead of a non-chiral one and assembling colloidal particles in a liquid crystal cell with a 90-degree twist, they were able to demonstrate reconfigurable knotting and linking of topological defect loops on an array of colloidal particles. When spherical particles are introduced into a slightly twisted nematic surrounding, each Saturn ring is slightly twisted, minimizing the elastic energy in a twisting surrounding, as shown in Fig. 14(A). From the viewpoint of topology, this isolated ring is an unknot. Laser tweezers were used to bring together several particles and isolated Saturn rings of these particles, which was followed by either spontaneous or laser-assisted fusion of the rings. This lead to the formation of longer loops that entangled two or more particles, as shown in Fig. 14. In smaller colloidal clusters, presented in Figs. 14(B–E), all the loop conformations were likewise topologically equivalent to the unknot.

The simplest and non-trivial topological configuration that was created by laser tweezers micro quenching was the Hopf link (Fig. 14(F)). In this structure, there are two interlinked loops entangled around four colloidal

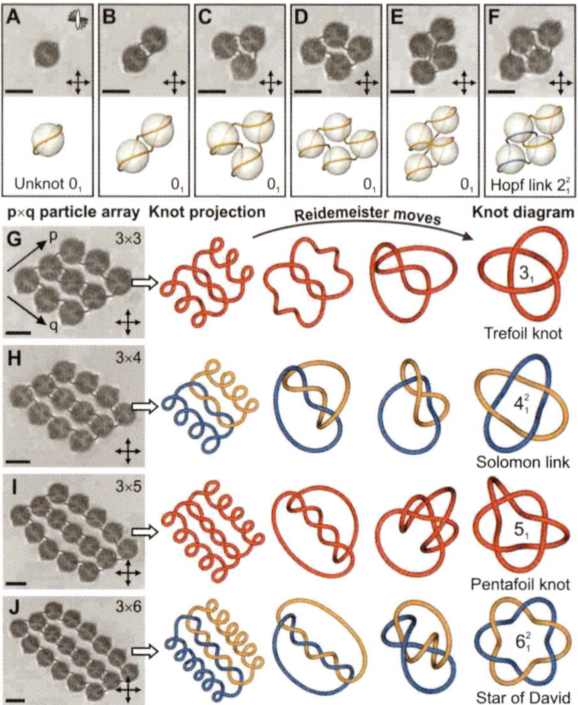

Fig. 14.   Topological defect lines tie torus links and knots in chiral nematic colloids. (A) A twisted defect ring is topologically equivalent to the unknot and appears spontaneously around a single microsphere. The molecular orientation on the top and bottom of the cell coincides with the orientation of the crossed polarizers. (B–E) Defect loops of colloidal dimer, trimer and tetramers are equivalent to the unknot. (F) The Hopf link is the first nontrivial topological object, knitted from two interlinked defect loops. In (A–F) the corresponding loop conformations were calculated numerically using the Landau-de Gennes free-energy model (13). (G–J) A series of alternating torus knots and links on $3 \times q$ particle arrays are knitted by the laser-induced defect fusion. The defect lines are schematically redrawn using a program for representing knots (24) to show the relaxation mapping from the initial planar projection to the final knot diagram, performed by the sequence of Reidemeister moves. The designations of knots follow the standard notation C_i^N, where C indicates the minimal number of crossings, i distinguishes between different knot types, and N counts the number of loops in multi-component links. The scale bars correspond to 5 μm.

particles. Despite this being the simplest topological structure, the true richness of the knots and links was observed by introducing additional particles, which formed arrays of p $\times$ q particles (Figs. 14(G–J)).

Using the laser tweezers, it was possible to knit isolated defect loops at multiple knitting sites so as to connect the neighbouring defect rings.

The result was a series of nematic braids realised on p × q particle arrays, as shown in Figs. 14(G–J). To reveal the topology of these complicated structures one performs a sequence of topology-preserving Reidemeister moves.[47,48] These moves are used to smoothen the loops, and it is not allowed to cut and rejoin any loop. Reidemeister moves therefore virtually

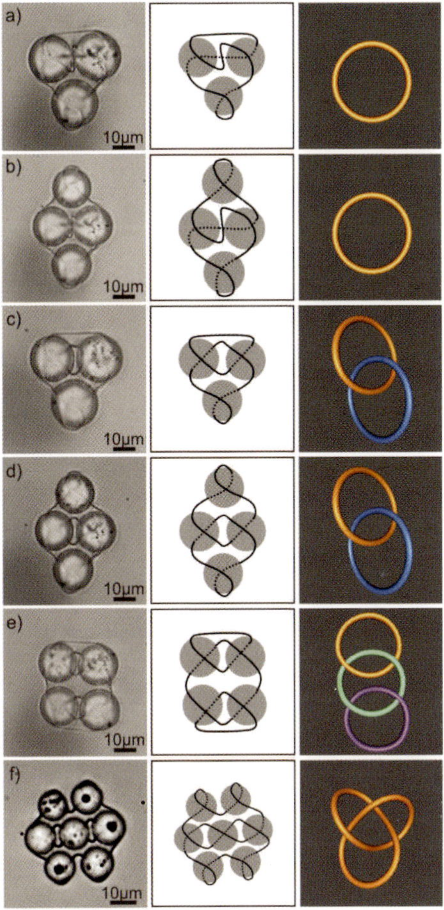

Fig. 15. Entangled colloidal clusters in the right-handed π-twisted CLC cell. The images on the left are taken under crossed polarizers. The panels in the middle column represent drawings of the defect loops, as deduced from images on the left. The right panels show the topologically minimized defect loop structure, after performing Reidemeister moves. These panels were drawn using KnotPlot 1.0000 (http://knotplot.com/). (a–e) Colloidal particles of diameter $d = 20\mu m$ in $h = 22\mu m$ thick cell. (f) Colloidal cluster of $h = 10\mu m$ silica microspheres in a $h = 12\mu m$ thick cell.

transform the real confirmation of the loop into the corresponding planar projection with the minimum number of crossings. The relaxation mappings, illustrated in Figs. 14(G–J), reveal a series of alternating torus knots and links: trefoil knot, the Salomon link, the pentafoil knot, and the Star of David.[47] This generically knotted series of knots and links indicates production of the arbitrary knot and link on an array of colloidal particles in a chiral nematic liquid crystal simply by adding and interweaving additional rows of particles.

It was also demonstrated that knots and links could also be reversibly rewired by using laser tweezers assisted micro quench. It was noticed that the region of a liquid crystal in between the colloidal particles formed a tetrahedron unit with the four corners of the tetrahedron being located on the defect loops.[46] When the local temperature quench is applied, the two loops forming tetrahedron are redirected, and there are several possible outcomes. However, it was shown that all these possible outcomes in fact correspond to the local rotation of this tetrahedron by an angle of 120°. This local rotation of the tetrahedron results in local rewiring of the defect loops, and this, of course, changes the overall topology of the structure. As it is possible to predict all possible configurations for each of the crossing sites, it is therefore possible to predict all possible configurations of topological defect loops for an arbitrary array of colloidal particles. As expected, it was shown that practically any knot and link could be constructed on a sufficiently large number of particles.[49–51]

When the chirality of the supporting nematic liquid crystal structures is increased, and the helical period is decreased, a variety of novel colloidal phenomena were observed in chiral nematic colloids.[39,52] The total twist of the chiral nematic structure in cells with parallel boundary condition is set to $N \times \pi$ and particles with perpendicular surface boundary condition are introduced. It was observed for a single colloidal particle that a single defect loop was winding around the particle, with the winding pattern being more complex in cells with higher total twist. When two such particles are allowed to interact, entangled clusters are observed where the defect loops entangle two or several colloidal particles. The complexity of topological structures in twisted nematics is far richer compared to the lower twist. For example, for colloidal pairs in 180-degree twisted cells, at least 17 different entangled structures were identified, some of them were identified as Hopf links. With a higher number of colloidal particles, they are not only linked but also knotted, as shown in Fig. 15.

The chirality of the nematic liquid crystal not only influences the topological structure of entangled colloidal particles, but also has a strong effect on the dynamics of colloidal pair interaction.[39] When the colloidal pair interaction is measured in a planar cell, hosting a multiple of helical periods of a chiral nematic liquid crystal, one can observe two new phenomena. First, there are metastable states in the chiral nematic colloidal pair interaction, which are observed as a temporarily arrested position of a colloidal pair, as shown in Fig. 16(a). After being released a relatively large separation, the two particles slowly approach each other. After a certain time, the two particles remain at a fixed separation, indicating a state with zero mutual force. However, thermal fluctuations destroy this temporal state after some time, and the particles start to move towards each other until they finally spontaneously entangle at a very close spacing.

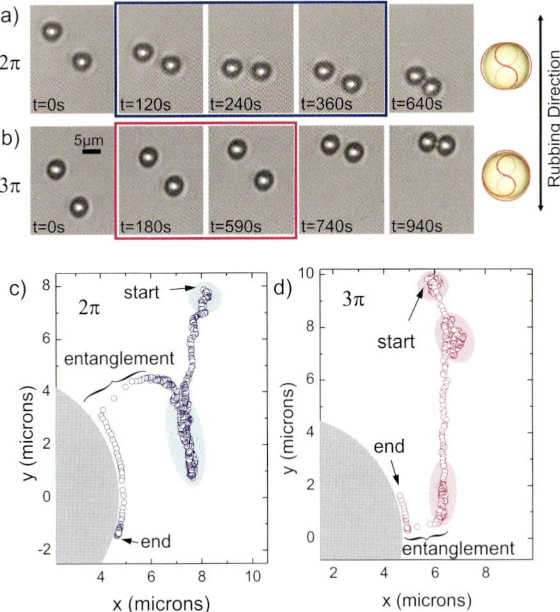

Fig. 16.   Colloidal pair attraction in chiral nematic cells. (a) Snapshots of a colloidal pair in a 2π-cell demonstrate metastable states in the pair interaction. Between $\sim 120s$ and $\sim 360s$ the particles fluctuate at a practically fixed separation. (b) In 3π-cell the two particles are temporarily bound between $\sim 180s$ and $\sim 600s$. (c) Trajectory of a particle approaching the second particle in 2π-cell. The particles' separation is measured from center-to-center. Shaded regions indicate metastable states. (d) Colloidal trajectory in a 3π-cell reveals three metastable regions.

The number of metastable states depends on the number of helical twists of chiral nematic structure in the cell. By increasing the number of turns, the number of metastable states also increases. The second phenomenon, which is observed in the interaction of chiral nematic colloids, is the chirality screening of their interaction. The experiments showed that the colloidal interaction is the strongest when the helical period is equal to the diameter of the colloid. By increasing the chirality, the colloidal pair interaction becomes weaker.

5. Shape-dependent colloidal interactions

Whereas most of the studies of colloidal interactions were focused on spherical microparticles with a diameter in the range of up to 10 micrometers, recently, more complex objects immersed in a nematic liquid crystal were studied. Previously, such studies were not possible because it is not trivial to produce colloidal particles of different shapes, and this has been solved by using two new experimental techniques: i) Two-photon polymerization using intense pulsed lasers, which can create objects of arbitrary shape and complexity, ii) Standard planar photolithography, which can be used to produce planar colloids - platelets of different shapes.

The rod-like particles, such as micrometer diameter glass rods in the nematic crystals were studied experimentally by different groups.[53–55] Topologically, rods are equivalent to spheres in the nematic liquid crystal and this was proved in an experiment by Tkalec *et al.*[55] They used the laser tweezers and optical microscopy to characterize the defect structures around microrods with homeotropic surface anchoring in a thin planar layer of a nematic liquid crystal. Two different symmetries of microrods were observed, as shown in Fig. 17, the dipolar and quadrupolar particles, which is equivalent to the observations of defects around spherical microparticles in the nematic liquid crystal.

Using laser tweezers, it is possible to grab and manipulate the position of the point defect in the dipolar configuration of the micro-rod. This defect can be transformed into a ring, sliding along the microrod. The interaction of two dipolar microrods was found to be similar in the reach and strength of the interaction between the two spherical microparticles. The interaction range for micrometre diameter rods is of the order of ten micrometres and the binding potential can easily reach several thousand of k_BT.

Solid platelets of different shapes and their pair interaction in a planar nematic liquid crystal were first studied in the experiments by Lapointe *et*

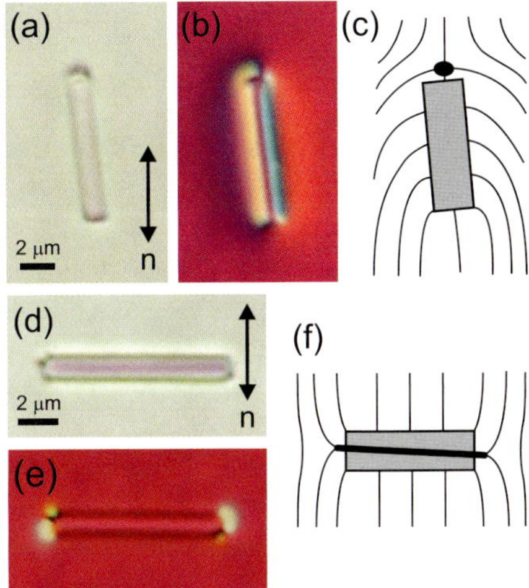

Fig. 17. (a–c) Micro-rods of dipolar symmetry. (a) A dipolar micro-rod with homeotropic surface anchoring in a 3 μm thick planar cell of 5CB, as observed under a non-polarizing optical microscope. (b) When a red-plate (i.e. λ plate for 530 nm) is inserted, the differently colored regions of the birefringent nematic indicate different orientation of the liquid crystal molecules. (c) The director pattern, as reconstructed from the color image (b). (d–f) Quadrupolar micro-rods in a planar cell. (d) Unpolarized micrograph of a micro-rod, which was spontaneously oriented perpendicularly to the rubbing direction. (e) The same micro-rod, as observed using the red-plate. (f) Schematic drawing of the director field, as deduced from (d) and (e).

$al.$[56] They produced polygons with different numbers of sides and observed that polygons with an odd number of sides align with one side parallel to the overall director. The resulting structure for particles with an odd number of sides were elastic dipoles. These dipoles formed chains, as expected for topological dipoles and observed for spherical particles. Particles with an even number of sides, such as squares, oriented with their diagonal parallel to the overall director. When this kind of platelets interacted, they formed kinked chains, similar to spherical microparticles with quadrupolar symmetry. Because platelets have anisotropic dielectric properties, determined by their shape, an external electric field could reorient them when applied to a nematic liquid crystal - platelet dispersion. Platelets of different symmetries and the effect of the electric field were theoretically analysed by Dontabhaktuni et $al.$[57] They found that the platelet interaction depends, in a complex way, on the orientation of the platelet exhibiting the easy and hard reorientation axis and multiple minima.

Topologically more complex platelets and their interaction were studied by Senyuk *et al.*[9] They fabricated topologically distinct platelet-like silica particles in planar geometry and handlebody topology of genus varying from 1 to 5. The director field around these handlebody colloids with homeotropic surface anchoring of a nematic liquid crystal was probed optically by a combination of polarizing microscopy and three-photon excitation fluorescence polarizing microscopy, as illustrated in Fig. 18. Colloidal handlebodies spontaneously aligned with their ring planes either perpendicular or parallel to the overall nematic direction. Optical micrographs obtained by different imaging techniques revealed that those handlebody colloids, which were aligned perpendicular to the overall nematic direction,

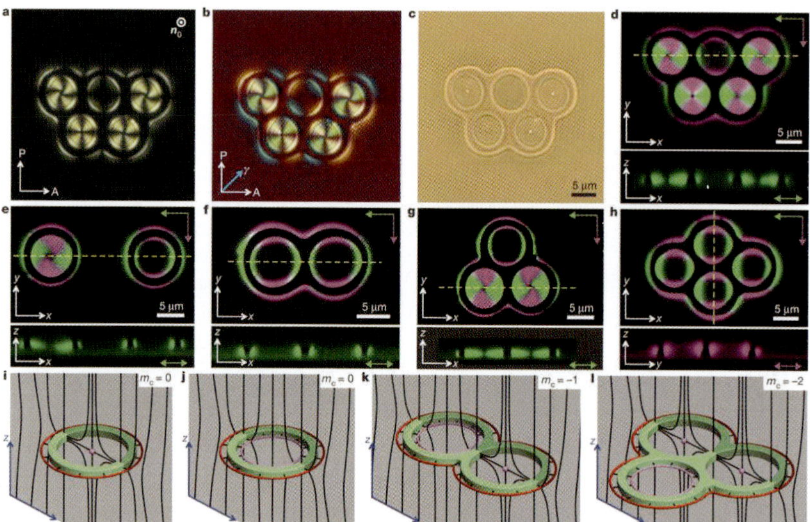

Fig. 18. (añd) Genus $g = 5$ handlebodies and induced n(r) structures imaged by PM without (a) and with (b) a retardation plate, bright-field microscopy (c) and 3PEF-PM (d) techniques. eñh, 3PEF-PM textures of single (e), double (f), triple (g) and quadruple (h) handlebodies. P, A and γ mark the crossed polarizer, analyser and a slow axis of a retardation plate (aligned at 45 ∘ to P and A), respectively. In the images (dñh) obtained by overlaying 3PEF-PM fluorescence intensity patterns for two orthogonal polarizations of excitation light, green and magenta colours correspond to the polarization directions marked by green and magenta arrows, respectively. Cross-sectional xz and yz images were obtained along yellow lines shown on the corresponding in-plane images. iñl, Diagrams of n(r) (black lines) around g handlebodies. Red and magenta lines show outer and inner disclination loops of $m = -1$ and $m = +1$ hedgehog charges, respectively. Magenta spheres show $m = +1$ hyperbolic point defects. Reprinted by permission from Macmillan Publishers Ltd: Nature 493, Issue 7431, 200-205, copyright (2013).

were all surrounded by single half-integer disclination loops with topological point defect charge -1 and had different defects within their interiors. It was found that each genus-*g* particle had g defects in its holes, which were either disclination loops or hyperbolic point defects with topological charge +1. Colloidal handlebodies that oriented with their rings parallel to the overall nematic director tended to induce point defects both within the holes and next to the particles. These points could occasionally open into small disclination loops following the curved edge faces of particles. Even though the handlebodies that oriented perpendicular and parallel to the overall director induce quite different director field, it was nevertheless demonstrated that the sum of hedgehog charges due to points and loops compensates for the colloidal particles hedgehog charge and is uniquely predetermined by particle topology.

Topologically even more complex 3D particles were produced by Martinez *et al.*[10] by using two-photon polymerization in 3D. They produced polymer particles with the surface topology of torus knots. The particles were formed by knotted polymeric tubes that were looped p times through the hole of an imaginary torus, with q revolutions about the torus rotational symmetry axis. Thus obtained knotted colloidal particles exhibited a variable number of crossings of the polymeric tube, which is the so-called crossing number. When dispersed in liquid crystals, these knotted colloidal particles forced the nematic director field to follow curved and knotted surface of particles. The director field was studied by using bright-field and polarizing optical micrographs and three-photon fluorescence excitation microscopy. The images revealed the formation of topological defects that were mutually tangled with colloidal knots.

6. Interactions between nanoparticles in nematics

Whereas particles of complex topology helped us to understand topological phenomena of the nematic ordering field, the interest was also directed towards the interaction and behavior of very small colloidal particles in the nematic liquid crystals. This interest was driven by predictions of various novel phenomena, such as the stabilization of blue phases by the incorporation of nanoparticles into the defects, which formed the blue phase. Further, there is an interest in the synthesis of novel materials, such as metamaterials and plasmonic[58–61] which are based on dispersions of nanoparticles with specific material properties in the nematic liquid crystal. It is therefore important to understand the pair interactions of nanocolloids as well as the interaction of nanocolloids with defect lines.

One of the most interesting questions in nematic colloids is: how small particles still interact in the nematic liquid crystal due to the structural force between them? It is clear that in the limit of very small, nano-sized particles, the director field distortion around such a particle will be negligibly small because of the excess free energy that has to be paid to create the elastic distortion on such a small scale. A typical diameter of the particles still mutually interacting will therefore be determined by their surface extrapolation length. This is a balance between the elastic constant of the liquid crystal (in a one-constant approximation) and the surface anchoring strength (energy). When the surface orientational anchoring is strong, it will still be possible to sustain the elastic deformation at very small diameters (and large curvatures) of the particles. Typically, the surface extrapolation length is in the range of 10-100 nm for very strong surface anchoring, so this was the expected limit of the particles sizes for their interaction in the nematic liquid crystal.

The colloidal pair interaction was measured directly by optical dark field microscopy in a systematic study of a family of chemically identical silica particles with identical surface preparation,[62–64] presented in Fig. 19. The result was rather surprising, as the particles as small as 35 nm still self-

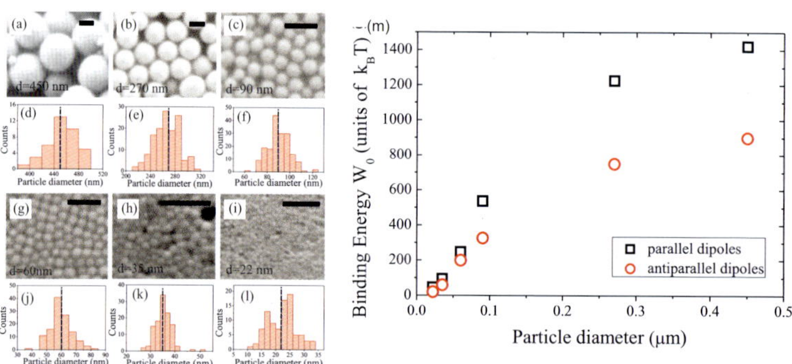

Fig. 19.   SEM images of silica nanocolloids and histograms of colloidal size distribution. (a), (b), (c), (g), (h), (i) 500 nm, 300 nm, 100 nm, 70 nm, 50 nm and 30-nm sized particles functionalized with DMOAP. (d), (e), (f), (j), (k), (l) - histograms of colloidal size distribution, derived from SEM images analysis. The calculated mean values of colloidal diameters are 450 nm, 270 nm, 90 nm, 60 n, 35 nm and 22 nm. The scale bars are 200 nm in all panels. (m) Dependence of dipolar colloidal pair binding energy on particle diameter. (-□-) Pair-binding energy of parallel dipolar particles. (-○-) Pair-binding energy of antiparallel dipolar particles. The measured binding energy of dipolar pair is decreasing by reducing the colloid size.

assembled into clusters, which means thermal cut-off for assembly is around 20 nm diameter.[64] This study also clearly demonstrated the importance of surface-charge of DMOAP-coated silica nanocolloids.

Trapping of plasmonic nanoparticles of different shapes around bigger colloidal particles was discussed by Senyuk *et al.*[65,66] Nanoparticles of different shapes and materials, such as gold microrods, starfruit, nanobursts and nanorods, were surface covered with acrylate or polystyrene. Their position and movement was tracked in the nematic liquid crystal using dark field and two-photon luminiscence. It was found that topological defects in a form of singular points (hedgehogs) and lines (Saturn rings) possess quite strong trapping potential of the order of several $k_B T$ that depends on the shape and size of a trapped nanoparticle. Colloidal inclusions of microscopic sizes therefore create topological defects of different kind, which serve as a scaffold that is trapping the nanoparticles; topological scaffold is therefore decorated by nanoparticles. Hung and Bale studied the defect structures and the potentials of mean force that arise when faceted nanoparticles, namely cubes and triangular prisms, are immersed in a nematic liquid crystal using a mesoscale theory for the tensor order parameter.[67]

Three-dimensional colloidal crystals in liquid crystalline blue phases were first considered theoretically by Ravnik *et al.*[68] Using LdG modeling, they showed that colloidal particles can self-assemble into 3D periodic structures in blue phase LCs. The blue phases provide a 3D template of trapping sites for colloidal particles. The mechanism, which is driving colloidal particles into defects is the reduction of the free-energy. Namely, a singular topological defect with a defect core, where the order parameter is reduced, is energetically costly. This energy is reduced if the particles of foreign material are incorporated in energetically costly regions, therefore decreasing the overall free energy. Similar trapping mechanism is observed between colloids and defect lines and walls in nematics.[69] Face-centered cubic colloidal crystals form in type-I blue phases, whereas body-centered crystals form in type-II blue phases, with the effective binding energy up to for a 100 nm particle. Interestingly, it is found that colloidal particles with weak surface anchoring substantially increase the range of thermal stability of this colloidal-blue phase. The influence of nanoparticles on the temperature range of the blue phase has been addressed in several experiments.[70–72] Colloidal assembly in strongly confined cholesteric structures was studied within the phenomenological modeling in,[73] details of mesoscopic modeling are explained in Ref. 74.

7. Colloidal topology of fibers and microspheres in nematics

The entanglement of spherical microparticles in nematic liquid crystals shows an amazing diversity of topological phenomena, and it was therefore quite unexpected that the entanglement of microspheres and long fibres is even more complex. If we consider a microfibre, it is topologically equivalent to a microsphere, as they both have equal genus $g = 0$. One could therefore expect one-to-one correspondence in the number of topological defects on a fibre and a microsphere.

It was demonstrated as a surprise by Nikkhou *et al.* in 2015[75,76] that by using laser tweezer induced micro quench, it is possible to create several pairs of topological defects on a long fibre, as shown in Figs. 20(a–e). When an isotropic island is created in the nematic liquid crystal by local heating, it is separated from the nematic by a sharp isotropic-nematic interface, see Fig. 20(a). After the light is switched off, a dense tangle of defects

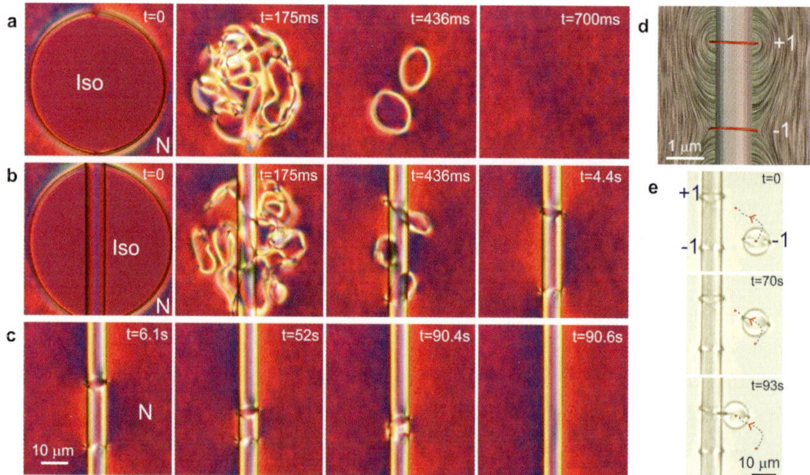

Fig. 20. (a) The NLC is heated into the isotropic phase by the strong light of the laser tweezers, thus creating an isotropic island. At $t = 0$ the light is switched off and the NLC is quenched into the nematic phase. The dense tangle of defects annihilate in less than a second. (b) The NLC is quenched from the isotropic island surrounding a fibre. A pair of defects is created, each carrying the opposite topological charge. (c) If let free, the pair annihilates into the vacuum. Images a-c, f were taken between crossed polarizers and the red-plate, which visualizes average molecular orientation in different colours. (d) LdG simulation of the Saturn ring and the Saturn anti-ring with opposite charges and windings. (e) The sign of the charge is tested using the repulsive force between like topological charges.

is created, which annihilates back to the nematic state after some time, with no defect left. However, if the same experiment is performed with a microfibre inserted, the outcome is quite different.

A pair of topological defects in the form of two rings, encircling the fibre, is created instead of the emptiness, as shown in Fig. 20(b). These two rings are quite stable by themselves; however, if left free, they will approach each other and annihilate into a vacuum (Fig. 20(c)). This indicates that the two rings are somehow opposite in their nature; they are similar to the pair of a particle and an antiparticle, like an electron and a positron. In fact, the two rings are the Saturn ring and the Saturn anti-ring, which can only mutually annihilate into the vacuum. They have opposite winding numbers and also carry the opposite topological charges (Fig. 20(d)). This assures the conservation of the overall topological charge. It was also shown that each of the two rings can be entangled to a colloidal microsphere with a Saturn ring.[76] This results in a peculiar structure of entangling topological rings, where the local winding of the ring is changing its polarity. Furthermore, it was demonstrated that an arbitrary number of topological rings, monopoles, and even zero charge loops could be created on a fibre with a different orientation with respect to the nematic liquid crystal orientation.[76]

8. Conclusions

This chapter aims at presenting rapid development in the field of nematic liquid crystal colloids. These studies were initiated by the emergence of a new experimental technique of laser tweezing, which allowed for the first time contactless control and manipulation of particles in liquids. Using the laser tweezers, it was possible for the first time to grab and move individual silica particles, immersed in liquid crystals and to observe them under an optical microscope. This technique was therefore crucial for the emergence of an entire new area of research, which was first focused on microspheres in liquid crystals but soon evolved into a much broader spectrum of activities. The pair-interaction forces between particles could be studied and measured and the particles could be assembled into regular colloidal crystals. Later on, tweezers were used to entangle colloids particles by applying a localised thermal shock, which eventually led to complex topological structures, such as knotted and linked nematic colloids. At this point, topology became a point of interest and many new studies of the topological properties of nematic and chiral nematic colloids of complex shape appeared. Another technique that had a strong impact on this field was the two photon polymerisation in 3D, which allowed the creation of colloidal particles of complex shape, such as knotted polymer particles, spirals and linked chains of polymer rings.

On the other hand, there was a strong development in the field of photonic properties of dispersions of liquid crystals in immiscible fluids, such as water and different polymers. It was demonstrated that microlasers and optical microfibers could be created in this way.[77–81] Recently, new optical properties of liquid crystals were demonstrated in the fast and ultrafast optical regimes, including nanosecond control of fluorescence[82] in liquid crystals, nanosecond electric Kerr effect[83] and ultrafast optical Kerr effect in nematic liquid crystals.[84] This opened a unique opportunity of merging together three different research directions: dispersions of microparticles in liquid crystals, self-assembled photonic microstructures, and ultrafast all-optical control of light. In future, this could lead to new and unconventional photonic devices, based entirely on soft matter and liquid crystals.[85]

References

1. P. E. Cladis, P. Pieranski. Sur une nouvelle methode de decoration de la phase mesomorphe du MBBA. C. R. Acad. Sc. Paris 273, 275 (1971).
2. J. Rault. Sur une methode nouvelle d'etude de l'orientation moleculaire a la surface d'un cholesterique. C. R. Acad. Sc. Paris 272, 1275 (1971).
3. P. G. de Gennes, J. Prost. The Physics of Liquid Crystals, Oxford Science Publications, Oxford, ed. 2, 1993.
4. P. Poulin, H. Stark, T. C. Lubensky, and D. A. Weitz. Novel colloidal interactions in anisotropic fluids. Science 275, 1770 (1997).
5. N. D. Mermin. The topological theory of defects in ordered media. Rev. Mod. Phys. 51, 591-648 (1979).
6. H. Stark. Physics of colloidal dispersions in nematic liquid crystals. Phys. Rep. 35 281, 389 (2001).
7. M. Kleman, O. D. Lavrentovich. Topological point defects in nematic liquid crystals. Phil. Mag. 86, 4117 (2006).
8. T. C. Lubensky, D. Pettey, N. Currier, H. Stark. Topological defects and interactions in nematic emulsions. Phys. Rev. E 57, 610 (1998).
9. B. Senyuk, Qingkun Liu, Sailing He, R. D. Kamien, R. B. Kusner, T. C. Lubensky, I. I. Smalyukh, Topological colloids. Nature 493, 200-205 (2013).
10. A. Martinez, M. Ravnik, B. Lucero, R. Visvanathan, S. Žumer, I. I. Smalyukh, Nature Materials 13, 259-264 (2014).
11. M. Monastyrsky, Rieman, Topology, and Physics, Birkhauser Boston 1999.
12. R. Pratibha, N. V. Madhusudana, Mol. Cryst. Liq. Cryst. 178, 167 (1990).
13. E. M. Terentjev. Disclination loops, standing alone and around solid particles in nematic liquid crystals. Phys. Rev. E 51, 1330 (1995).
14. M. Škarabot, M. Ravnik, S. Žumer, U. Tkalec, I. Poberaj, D. Babič, N. Os-

terman, I. Muševič, Interactions of quadrupolar nematic colloids. Phys. Rev. E, **77**, 031705 (2008).

15. R. W. Ruhwandl, E. M. Terentjev. Monte Carlo simulation of topological defects in the nematic liquid crystal matrix around a spherical colloid particle. Phys. Rev. E 56, 5561 (1997).

16. O. V. Kuksenok, R. W. Ruhwandl, S. V. Shiyanovskii, E. M. Terentjev. Director structure around a colloid particle suspended in a nematic liquid crystal. Phys. Rev. E 54, 5198 (1996).

17. S. Ramaswamy, R. Nityananda, V. A. Raghunathan, J. Prost. Power law forces between particles in a nematic. Mol. Cryst. Liq. Cryst. 288, 175 (1996).

18. V. A. Raghunthan, P. Richetti, D. Roux, F. Nallet, A. K. Sood. Colloidal dispersions in a liquid crystalline medium. Mol. Cryst. Liq. Cryst. 288, 181 (1996).

19. T. C. Lubensky, D. Pettey, N. Currier, H. Stark. Topological defects and interactions in nematic emulsions. Phys. Rev. E 57, 610 (1998).

20. B. I. Lev, P. M. Tomchuk. Interaction of foreign macrodroplets in a nematic liquid crystal and induced supermolecular structures. Phys. Rev. E 59, 591 (1999).

21. Jun-ichi Fukuda, B. I. Lev, H. Yokoyama. Effect of confining walls on the interaction between particles in a nematic liquid crystal. J. Phys.: Condens. Matter 15, 3841-3854 (2003).

22. Jun-ichi Fukuda, H. Stark, M. Yoneya, H. Yokoyama. Interaction between two spherical particles in a nematic liquid crystal. Phys. Rev. E 69, 041706 (2004).

23. V. M. Pergamenshchik, V. O. Uzunova. Elastic charge density representation of the interaction via the nematic director field. Eur. Phys. J. E 23, 161 (2007).

24. V. M. Pergamenshchik, V. O. Uzunova. Coulomb-like interaction in nematic emulsions induced by external torques exerted on the colloids. Phys. Rev. E 76, 011707 (2007).

25. V. M. Pergamenshchik, V. A. Uzunova. Dipolar colloids in nematostatics: Tensorial structure, symmetry, different types and their interaction. Phys. Rev. E 79, 021704 (2009).

26. V. M. Pergamentschik, V. A. Uzunova. Colloidal nematostatics. Cond. Matt. Phys. 13, 1-29 (2010).

27. P. Poulin, V. Cabuil, D. A. Weitz. Direct measurement of colloidal forces in an anisotropic solvent. Phys. Rev. Lett. 79, 4862 (1997).

28. M. Yada, J. Yamamoto, H. Yokoyama. Direct Observation of Anisotropic Interparticle Forces in Nematic Colloids with Optical Tweezers, Phys. Rev. Lett., 2004, 92, 185501.

29. C. M. Noel, G. Bossis, A.-M. Chaze, F. Giulieri, S. Lacis. Measurement of elastic forces between two colloidal particles in a nematic liquid crystal. Phys. Rev. Lett. 96, 217801 (2006).

30. K. Takahashi, M. Ichikawa, Y. Kimura. Force between colloidal particles in a nematic liquid crystals studied by optical tweezers. Phys. Rev. E, 2008, 77, 020703(R).

31. H. Stark, J. Stelzer, R. Bernhard. Water droplets in a spherically confined nematic solvent: A numerical investigation. Eur. Phys. J. B, 1999, 10, 515-523.

32. I. Muševič, M. Škarabot, U. Tkalec, M. Ravnik, S. Žumer, Science **313**, 954/958 (2006).

33. M. Škarabot, M. Ravnik, S. Žumer, U. Tkalec, I. Poberaj, D. Babič, N. Osterman, I. Muševič, Phys. Rev. E, **76**, 051406 (2007).

34. M. Humar, M. Škarabot, M. Ravnik, S. Žumer, I. Poberaj, D. Babič, I. Muševič, Eur. Phys. J. E, **27**, 73 (2008).

35. A. Nych, U. Ognysta, M. Škarabot, M. Ravnik, S. Žumer, I. Muševič, Nat. Commun., **4**, 1489 (2013).

36. I. I. Smalyukh, O. D. Lavrentovich, A. N. Kuzmin, A. V. Kachynski, and P. N. Prasad. Elasticity-Mediated Self-Organization and Colloidal Interactions of Solid Spheres with Tangential Anchoring in a Nematic Liquid Crystal. Phys. Rev. Lett. 95, 157801 (2005).

37. J. Kotar, M. Vilfan, N. Osterman, D. Babic, M. Copic, M Ravnik, I. Poberaj. Interparticle potential and drag coefficient in nematic colloids. Phys. Rev. Lett., 2006, 96, 207801.

38. M. Vilfan, N. Osterman, M. Copic, M. Ravnik, S. Zéumer, J. Kotar, D. Babic, I. Poberaj. Confinement Effect on Interparticle Potential in Nematic Colloids. Phys. Rev. Lett., 2008, 101, 237801.

39. V. S. R. Jampani, M. Škarabot, S. Čopar, S. Žumer, I. Muševič, Chirality Screening and Metastable States in Chiral Nematic Colloids, Phys. Rev. Lett. 110, 177801 (2013).

40. U. Ognysta, A. Nych, V. Nazarenko, I. Muševič, M. Š karabot, M. Ravnik, S. Ž umer, I. Poberaj, D. Babič, Phys. Rev. Lett., **100**, 17803 (2008).

41. M. Škarabot, M. Ravnik, S. Žumer, U. Tkalec, I. Poberaj, D. Babič, I. Muševič, Phys. Rev. E, **77**, 061706 (2008).

42. O. Guzman, E. B. Kim, S. Grollau, N. L. Abbott, J. J. de Pablo. Defect structure around two colloids in a liquid crystal. Phys. Rev. Lett. 91, 235507 (2003).

43. T. Araki, H. Tanaka, Phys. Rev. Lett., **97**, 127801 (2006).

44. S. Žumer, Plenary Talk at the 21st International Liquid Crystal Conference, Keystone, Colorado, July 2ñ7, 2006.

45. M. Ravnik, M. Škarabot, S. Žumer, U. Tkalec,2 I. Poberaj, D. Babič, N. Osterman, I. Muševič, Phys. Rev. Lett., **99**, 247801 (2007).

46. U. Tkalec, M. Ravnik, S. Čopar, S. Žumer, I. Muševič, Science 333, 62 (2011).

47. C. C. Adams, The Knot Book (American Mathematical Society, Providence, 2004).

48. L. H. Kauffman, Knots and Physics (World Scientific Publishing, Singapore, ed. 3, 2000).

49. U. Tkalec, I. Muševič, Topology of nematic liquid crystal colloids confined to two dimensions, Soft Matter 9, 8140-8150 (2013).

50. S. Čopar, U. Tkalec, I. Muševič, S. Žumer, Knot theory realizations in nematic colloids, Proc. Nat. Acad. Sciences 112, 1675-1680 (2015).

51. S. Čopar, Physics Reports, **538**, 1 (2014).
52. V. S. R. Jampani, M. Škarabot, M. Ravnik, S. Čopar, S. Žumer, I. Muševič, Colloidal entanglement in highly twisted chiral nematic colloids: Twisted loops, Hopf links, and trefoil knots. Phys. Rev. E 84, 031703-1-92011 (2011).
53. C. Lapointe, A. Hultgren, D. M. Silevitch, E. J. Felton, D. H. Reich, and R. L. Leheny, Science **303**, 652 (2004).
54. C. Lapointe, N. Cappallo, D. H. Reich, and R. L. Leheny, J. Appl. Phys. **97**, 10304 (2005).
55. U. Tkalec, M. Škarabot, I. Muševič, Interactions of micro-rods in a thin layer of a nematic liquid crystal, Soft Matter **4**, 2402-2409 (2008).
56. C. P. Lapointe, T. G. Mason, I. I. Smalyukh. Shape-controlled colloidal interactions in nematic liquid crystals. Science 326, 1083-1086 (2009).
57. J. Dontabhaktuni, M. Ravnik and S. Žumer, Shape-tuning the colloidal assemblies in nematic liquid crystals. Soft Matter 8, 1657 (2012).
58. Ch. Blanc, D. Coursaultc, and E. Lacaze, Ordering nano- and microparticles assemblies with liquid crystals, Liquid Crystals Reviews, http://dx.doi.org/10.1080/21680396.2013.818515 (2013).
59. J. S. Pendery, *et al.*, Gold nanoparticle self-assembly moderated by a cholesteric liquid crystal, Soft Matter 9, 9366 (2013).
60. Qingkun Liu, B. Senyuk, J. W. Tang, T. Lee, Jun Qian, Sailing He, I. I. Smalyukh, Plasmonic Complex Fluids of Nematiclike and Helicoidal Self-Assemblies of Gold Nanorods with a Negative Order Parameter, Phys. Rev. Lett. 109, 088301 (2012).
61. Y. Zhang, Qingkun Liu, H. Mundoor, Y. Yuan, I. I. Smalyukh, Metal Nanoparticle Dispersion, Alignment, and Assembly in Nematic Liquid Crystals for Applications in Switchable Plasmonic Color Filters and E-Polarizers, ACS Nano 9, 3097-3108 (2015).
62. M. Škarabot, I. Muševič, Direct observation of interaction of nanoparticles in a nematic liquid crystal, Soft Matter 6, 5476-5481 (2010).
63. A. V. Ryzhkova, I. Muševič, Particle size effects on nanocolloidal interactions in nematic liquid crystals, Phys. Rev. E 87, 032501 (2013).
64. A. V. Ryzhkova, M. Škarabot, I. Muševič, Surface charge and interactions of 20-nm nanocolloids in a nematic liquid crystal, Phys. Rev. E 91, 042505 (2015).
65. B. Senyuk and I. I. Smalyukh, Elastic interactions between colloidal microspheres and elongated convex and concave nanoprisms in nematic liquid crystals. Soft Matter 8, 8729 (2012).
66. B. Senyuk, J. S. Evans, P. J. Ackerman, Taewoo Lee, P. Manna, L. Vigderman, E. R. Zubarev, J. van de Lagemaat, and I. I. Smalyukh, Shape-dependent oriented trapping and scaffolding of plasmonic nanoparticles by topological defects for self-assembly of colloidal dimers in liquid crystals. Nano Lett. 12, 955-963 (2012).
67. F. R. Hung and S. Bale, Faceted nanoparticles in a nematic liquid crystal: defect structures and potentials of mean force. Molecular Simulation 35, 822-834 (2009).

68. M. Ravnik, G. P. Alexander, J. M. Yeomans, and S. éumer. Three-dimensional colloidal crystals in liquid crystalline blue phases. Proc. Natl. Acad. Sci. 108, 5188-5192 (2011).

69. D. Voloschenko, O. P. Pishnyak, S. V. Shiyanovskii, and O. D. Lavrentovich. Effect of director distortions on morphologies of phase separation in liquid crystals. Phys. Rev. E 65, 060701 (2002).

70. E. Karatairi, B. RoûiË, Z. Kutnjak, V. Tzitzios, G. Nounesis, G. Cordoyiannis, J. Thoen, C. Glorieux, S. Kralj. Nanoparticle-induced widening of the temperature range of liquid-crystalline blue phases. Phys. Rev. E 81, 041703 (2010).

71. H. Kikuchi, M. Yokota, Y. Hisakado, H. Yang and T. Kajiyama. Polymer-stabilized liquid crystal blue phase. Nature Materials 1, 64-68 (2002).

72. H.Yoshida, Y.Tanaka, K. Kawamoto, H. Kubo, T. Tsuda, A. Fujii, S. Kuwabata, H. Kikuchi, M. Ozaki. Nanoparticle-Stabilized Cholesteric Blue Phases. Appl. Phys. Express 2, 121501 (2009).

73. M. Ravnik, Jun-ichi Fukuda, J. M. Yeomans and S. Zumer. Confining blue phase colloids to thin layers. Soft Matter 7, 10144 (2011).

74. M. Ravnik, G. P. Alexander, J. M. Yeomans, S. Zumer. Mesoscopic modelling of colloids in chiral nematics. Faraday Discuss. 144, 159-169 (2010).

75. M. Nikkhou, M. Škarabot, S. Čopar, M. Ravnik, S. Žumer, I. Muševič, Nat. Physics, **11**, 183 (2015).

76. M. Nikkhou, M. Škarabot, I. Muševič, Eur. Phys. J. E, **38**, 23 (2015).

77. M. Humar, M. Ravnik, S. Pajk, I. Muševič, Nat. Photonics, **3**, 595 (2009).

78. M. Humar, I. Muševič, Opt. Exp., **18**, 26995 (2010).

79. K. Peddireddy, V. S. R. Jampani, S. Thutupalli, S. Herminghaus, C. Bahr, I. Muševič, Opt. Exp., **23**, 30233 (2013).

80. V. S. R. Jampani, M. Škarabot, H. Takezoe, I. Muševič, S. Dhara, Opt. Exp. **21**, 20506-20516 (2013).

81. M. Humar, I. Muševič, Opt. Exp., **21**, 19836-19844 (2011).

82. M. Vitek,and I. Muševič, Nanosecond control and optical pulse shaping by stimulated emission depletion in a liquid crystal, Opt. Exp. 23(13), 16921-16932 (2015).

83. V. Borshch, S. V. Shiyanovskii, and O. D. Lavrentovich, Nanosecond electro-optic switching of a liquid crystal, Phys. Rev. Lett. 111, 107802 (2013).

84. L. Cattaneo, M. Savoini, I. Muševič, A. Kimel,and Th. Rasing, Ultrafast all-optical response of a nematic liquid crystal, Opt. Exp. 23(11), 14010-14017 (2015).

85. I. Muševič, Integrated and Topological Liquid Crystal PhotonicsLiq. Cryst. **41**, 418 (2013).

Chapter 11

Inclusions in freely suspended smectic films

Ralf Stannarius* and Kirsten Harth

*Institute of Experimental Physics, Otto-von-Guericke-University,
D-39106 Magdeburg*
**ralf.stannarius@ovgu.de*

Smectic liquid crystal phases have a unique property: Like soap solutions, they can form stable freely suspended films. Their aspect ratios can be larger than one million to one. Such films can serve as models for two-dimensional (2D) fluids, with or without in-plane anisotropy. Solid or liquid inclusions trapped in these films by capillary forces can move in the film plane and interact with other inclusions, with film thickness gradients or the film boundaries, and even with the local orientation field. We describe preparation techniques to incorporate particles or droplets in thin smectic films, and optical observation methods. Several aspects make inclusions in freely suspended films interesting research objects: They provide rich information on capillary forces as well as surface and interfacial tensions, they can serve as platforms for hydrodynamic studies in 2D, and they may help to understand coalescence dynamics at the transition from 2D to 3D.

The shapes of liquid inclusions are governed by surface and interface tensions. Micrometer sized inclusions are connected to the film by menisci which can be decorated with characteristic spontaneously formed director patterns. The anchoring of the c-director in tilted phases at the inclusion boundaries leads to distortions of the uniform director field and is related to elastic interactions.

Hydrodynamic phenomena in 2D fluids are often essentially different from their 3D counterparts. The diffusion or drift of inclusions in the smectic film plane can be used to test hydrodynamic models and to provide viscoelastic coefficients. Experiments and their modeling may serve as templates for membrane dynamics. In tilted smectics, there are additional cross-couplings of moving objects with the director field.

Contents

1. Freely suspended smectic films

Freely suspended films (FSF) of smectic liquid crystals are unique fluid objects with considerable aspect ratios. Their thickness can be as small as molecular dimensions, lateral extensions in microscopy experiments are usually in the range of millimeters, but in principle such films can be drawn with areas of hundreds of square centimeters.[1] Owing to their interface tensions, these films form minimal surfaces in equilibrium. Provided that other external forces are absent, the frames in which the films are suspended completely define their shapes. In optical microscopy experiments, one usually uses planar supports to obtain flat films. However, catenoid shaped,[2–4] spherical[5–7] or other minimal surface films[8] have been prepared and investigated as well. FSF are usually studied in the high temperature smectic-A and smectic-C (C*) phases, but a variety of other smectic configurations of bent-core mesogens have been shown to form such films as well. Often the films can even be cooled into lower-temperature liquid crystalline phases.

Owing to their geometrical properties, one can treat these films as models of two-dimensional (2D) fluids or membranes. Interactions of embedded liquid or solid objects with the film are practically restricted to the film plane, therefore assemblies of inclusions in the films resemble 2D colloids. Depending upon the symmetries of the involved mesophases (for example, D_∞ in smectic-A or C_{2h} in smectic-C), the films either behave like isotropic or anisotropic 2D fluids. These symmetry properties have considerable consequences for interactions and dynamic properties of embedded particles or droplets. In this chapter, we describe the structure and interactions of small (micrometer sized) inclusions in such FSF. In this size range, the Eötvös number is sufficiently small and the films are not deformed by the inclusions. The dominating forces acting on the particles are capillary forces and elastic forces related to director distortions.

In smectic-C films and other tilted phases, the c-director (local projection of the n-director onto the film plane) defines a direction in the film plane and a vector field that can mediate interactions with and between inclusions. These interactions can lead to chaining, clustering, or the formation of two-dimensional lattices of embedded particles or droplets in the film plane.

In phases with D_∞ symmetry (e.g. smectic-A), all directions in the film plane are equivalent and therefore interactions by means of elastic director forces are absent in flat films. Nevertheless, the inclusions can interact with film thickness gradients due to wetting of the droplet or particle material by the film. A review of interactions and pattern formation of droplets in freely suspended films can be found in an article by Bohley.[9]

In addition to the static properties like director configurations around particles and spontaneously formed structures, single inclusions in free standing films can serve another important purpose: The study of their dynamics under well defined external forces, e.g. gravitation or optical tweezers, or under stochastic (thermal) forces, may provide important insight into two-dimensional hydrodynamics. Such experiments have been performed[10–12] to verify the justification of different approximations for the motion of disks in 2D fluids (Saffman-Delbrück equations).

Smectic FSF are stabilized by their internal layered structure. This makes them qualitatively different from the otherwise very similar soap films. In equilibrium, thin films have homogeneous thicknesses, the number of molecular layers is uniform in the film plane. In practice, however, one frequently encounters long-term persisting dislocation steps enclosing regions with surplus layers ('islands') or depleted layers ('holes'), or separating terraces. Small islands and holes behave in many respects very similar to liquid or solid inclusions in the films, as will be detailed below.

2. Film preparation and observation techniques

Planar films can be prepared straightforwardly by spreading a small amount of smectic material across a solid frame, using a sharp edge. The film thickness can be controlled to some extent by the spreading velocity. It is possible to thin a film by rapidly expanding the film area. Then, 'holes' can be generated which often have the tendency to grow until a uniform, thinner film is formed.[13] One can also exploit thinning transitions[14–16] when the films are heated to the bulk transition temperature to a non-layered phase. As we will see below, this technique can also be used to create liquid inclusions in the films. Figure 1 depicts typical images of a smectic film with inhomogeneous thickness, demonstrating the optical appearance in reflected light. The film spans a hole of about 1 mm diameter. It is only a few layers thick in the center of Fig. 1a (dark area), while its thickness increases by discrete steps towards the meniscus (outer grey area). Interference colors in the first three orders indicate approximately a dozen (multilayer) steps, at the outer border of the film to the meniscus of this film is approximately 600 nm thick. In unpolarized light, the film reflectivity R of a planar film at normal incidence is given by

$$R(\lambda_0) = \frac{4\rho^2 \sin^2 \psi}{(1 - \rho^2)^2 + 4\rho^2 \sin^2 \psi}, \tag{1}$$

$\psi = 2\pi n_0 d/\lambda_0$ is the phase lag between light reflected at the front and rear surfaces, respectively, $\rho = (n_0 - 1)/(n_0 + 1)$ is related to the refractive index n_0, for simplicity we assume an average index of refraction normal to the layers, λ_0 is the vacuum wavelength of the incident light, and d is the local film thickness. Figure 2a sketches the optical geometry and shows

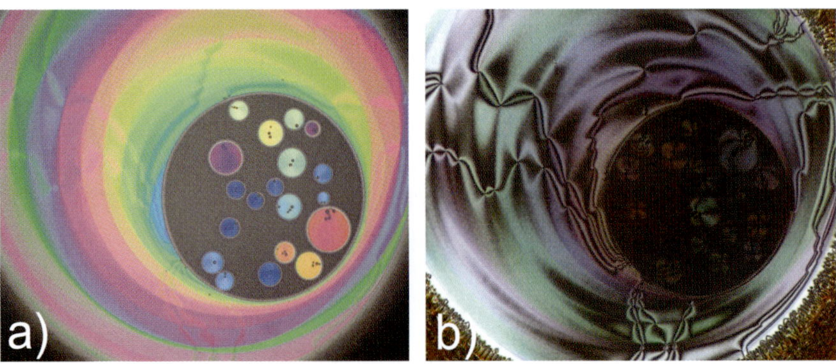

Fig. 1.   Freely suspended planar smectic film, material SF20 (abbreviations, structures and mesomorphisms of materials can be found at the end of the chapter) in the synclinic SmC$_s$ phase at 96°C. Image dimensions 790 μm $\times$660 μm. a) reflected white light with only one polarizer, b) with crossed polarizer and analyzer parallel to the image edges (see text).

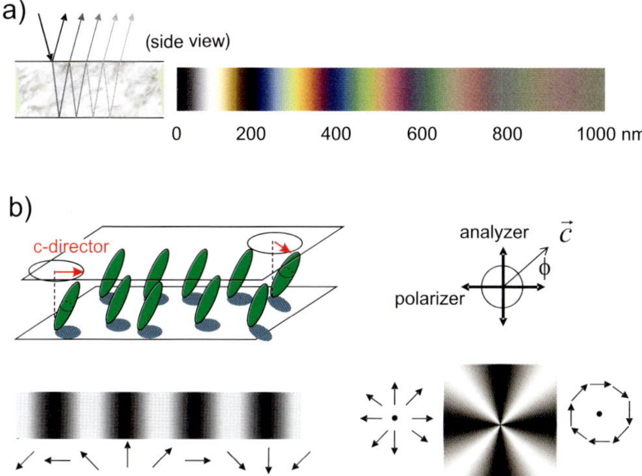

Fig. 2. Optics of thin FSF: (a) reflectivity of a film in unpolarized light, caused by interference of multiply reflected beams at upper and lower film surfaces; (b) In smectic-C films, the c-director, i.e. the projection of the director on the film plane, determines the reflectivity in polarized light. Typical transmission patterns under crossed polarizers are sketched. The two radially symmetric director configurations on the right cannot be distinguished between crossed polarizers.

the typical interference colors of reflected light for films with an effective refractive index of 1.5.

In the center of the film in Fig. 1, islands with uniform thicknesses are embedded in the film (with diameters between 25 μm and 85 μm). Their colors indicate different thicknesses in the range from 300 nm to 500 nm. They perform slow disordered (Brownian) motion in the thin film region. An interesting aspect is the coexistence of small (approx. 5 μm diameter and smaller) droplets of the same material within these islands. Since only one polarizer is present (but no analyzer), some director structures are faintly recognized in the outer film regions. They arise from small reflectivity differences for light polarized in tilt direction and perpendicular to it (see below). These are caused by the different effective refractive indices in the film plane.

The terraces of different film thicknesses do not represent stable equilibrium structures. Depending on the smectic material, thinner regions may shrink or grow by exchanging material with the meniscus, on the time scale of approximately an hour. Their long-term behavior depends on the substance and on the temperature of the film. In the present example, the thin inner region slowly shrinks and finally disappears. Growth or shrink-age of islands (by Ostwald ripening) also take place, but the time scale of these processes is considerably slower. As mentioned, the meniscus plays the role of a reservoir. Not too fast film area changes are compensated by meniscus deformations.[17,18] Exceptions are freely floating films without contact to a support.[7] The observation of inclusions in these structures is much more difficult than in planar films for several reasons. The bent film shape complicates optical microscopy experiments, and special measures (e.g. microgravity) have to be taken to keep the films at the observation spot.

In smectic-C or C* films, the tilt azimuth defines the c-director. Under crossed polarizers, the reflectivity is minimal in all regions where the c-director is parallel to either analyzer or polarizer, the two bright diagonal directions cannot be distinguished from each other. Figure 2b exemplarily sketches textures of a 360° wall and point defects of topological strength +1.

Figure 1b was taken with crossed polarizers. One can identify c-director textures in the thicker regions (contrast is too weak in the thin black film region). In particular, the islands are decorated inside with radial beam or spiral patterns imposed by the anchoring of the c-director at the droplet and island boundaries.[19,20] This will be explained in more detail below. The terraces are crossed by several inversion walls of the c-director.

If one uses elliptically polarized incident light, or if the polarizers are slightly decrossed, one can distinguish the two diagonal orientations, as seen in Fig. 3. This image shows that not only inside islands (Fig. 1b), but

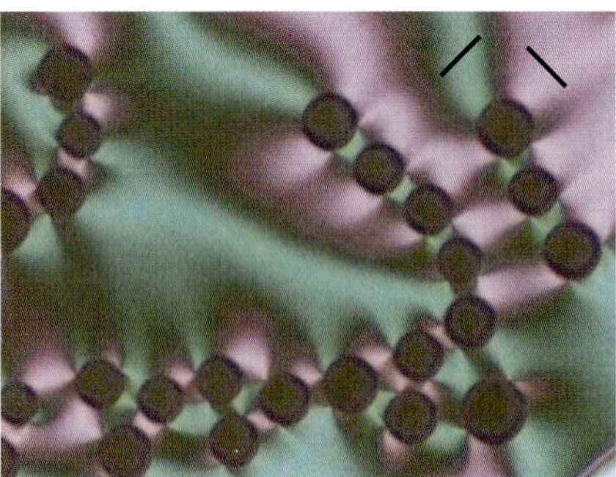

Fig. 3.   Image of an FSF of SF20 in the synclinic SmC$_s$ phase with isotropic liquid inclusions, taken with slightly decrossed polarizers. The dark regions mark regions with the director horizontal or vertical, green and purple correspond to diagonal c-director orientations, as marked in the graph. Image size 160 μm ×120 μm.

also in the surrounding film the director field is substantially influenced by anchoring conditions at the inclusion borders. Inserting a λ phase plate diagonal to crossed polarizers can also be employed to distinguish the two diagonal orientations, the phase lag in the film and in the phase plate is either additive or subtractive (same or opposite signs of optical phase lags), respectively. A method to determine the sign of the c-director is the observation of films in transmission under oblique incidence.[21] It usually requires a tilt of the film in the microscope.

3. Preparation of inclusions

In order to create liquid droplets in freely suspended films, two methods have proven successful. Most studies have been performed with droplets of the same material as the film, in another phase. The film is heated up towards the phase transition into the neighboring non-layered phase.[22] An alternative is shooting microdroplets of an immiscible liquid onto the films by means of a picoliter dispenser,[23] spray deposition of liquids[11,24] or condensation of silicon oil droplets on the films.[12]

Islands on freely suspended films can be created by different procedures. One is a fast shrinkage of the film area (e.g. Refs. 7, 25), whereby excess smectic material forms small circular islands. Another option is to blow air from thin needles across the film surface,[12] thereby larger islands may split into smaller ones and new islands are created.

A few studies have been performed with solid inclusions in smectic FSF, where the particles are dropped onto the equilibrated film.[11,24,26]

3.1. *Liquid droplets*

When smectic FSF are heated to a phase transition into a nematic, cholesteric or isotropic phase, molten droplets of the film material form in the smectic film above the bulk transition temperature.[22,27–40] It has been demonstrated that above the bulk clearing point or bulk smectic-nematic transition, the smectic films can persist as stable structures. The superheated films undergo thinning processes,[14] whereby the molten material of the inner layers can accumulate in droplets. The number and size of droplets can be controlled to a certain extent by means of appropriate heating rates and temperatures. The positions and initial arrangement of the droplets cannot be influenced by the experimenter, but with suitable preparation routines, relatively uniform and monodisperse droplet distributions as shown in Fig. 4 can be achieved. In the figure, the c-director field stabilizes this locally hexagonal arrangement.

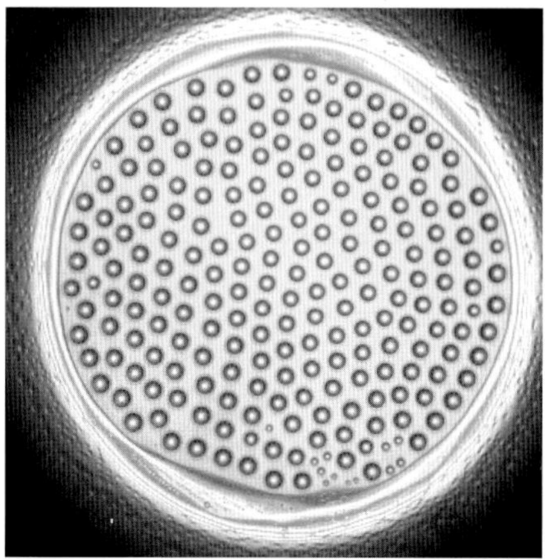

Fig. 4. Image of an 11OAB film in the SmC phase with nearly uniformly distributed isotropic liquid inclusions, photographed in reflected unpolarized white light. Image size 1 mm × 1 mm.

Droplet sizes can be subsequently manipulated by proper heating protocols. Existing droplets can be grown by slow increase of the temperature after their formation, they can be shrunk by slow decrease of temperature. Fast heating creates new droplets, cooling leads to the formation of circular smectic terraces around the inclusions. Another method of controlling droplet formation near the clearing point is the usage of photosensitive mesogens. This method has been successfully employed in Refs. 41, 42. A smectogen containing a central azoxy group was used to prepare freely suspended films. Under illumination with UV light, a certain fraction of the mesogens switches from the *trans* to the *cis* configuration of the central azoxy group. The conformation of the kinked mesogen is incompatible with the smectic phase, and thus the phase transition temperature into the isotropic state is lowered,[43] a phenomenon well known for mesogens containing azo groups. Thus one can control the formation of embedded isotropic droplets by a control of the illumination intensity.[41]

The method described above is suitable to study general properties and interactions of inclusions in a 2D liquid, but it suffers from two limitations. The choice of material combinations is limited to one material in different mesophases, and the temperature interval where the droplets are stable is a very narrow range above the bulk phase transition. An alternative is the use of microdroplet dispensers that can shoot droplets with picoliter volumes (several dozen up to hundred micrometers in diameter) onto the films.[23] This allows a controlled placement of inclusions, sizes can be controlled in discrete steps by shooting multiple droplets onto the same spot, and there is a large selection of possible materials that can be used. Figure 5 shows the impact of droplets with approximately 40 μm diameter on smectic films, seen from the side. One can distinguish three different scenarios. At low impact speeds (in this experiment below 2-3 m/s), the droplets are embedded in the film within less than a millisecond (Fig. 5a). At high impact speeds, they tunnel through the film without destroying it (Fig. 5b). Thereby, the droplet becomes completely wrapped in a thin smectic shell. In an intermediate velocity range (around 4 m/s) the droplets may even rebound after impact. Droplets that are embedded develop a meniscus within few seconds. The shape of these inclusions is discussed in the next section.

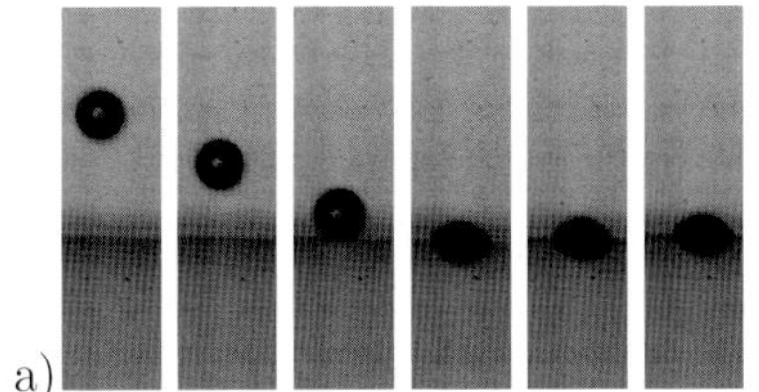 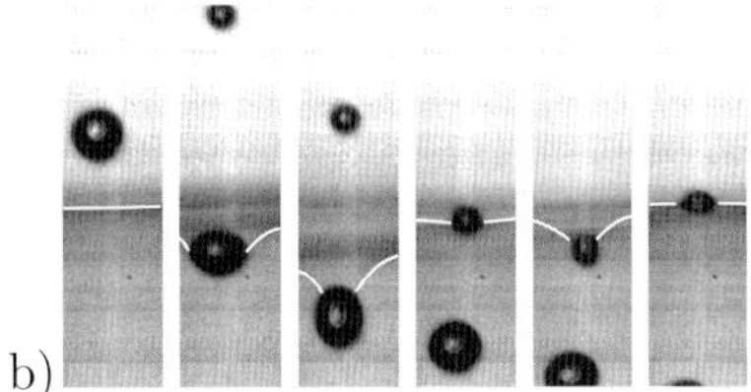

Fig. 5. Impact of droplets (water with 5 % ethylene glycol) on a smectic FSF of the PP mixture: a) droplet embedding, impact velocity 0.8 m/s, frame rate 18 kfps, b) tunneling, impact velocity 5.4 m/s, frame rate 48 kfps. The large droplets have approximately 45 μm diameter. The slow droplet is captured in the film plane and it deforms to a lentil-like shape, symmetrically embedded in the film. The fast droplet penetrates the film and leaves it with a velocity of about 1.7 m/s. The film closes again so that a successive smaller droplet is trapped. Image sizes are 346 μm $\times$93 μm. In b), the deformations of the film are emphasized by bright lines. Images are courtesy of S. Dölle.

Spraying of an aerosol onto the films[11,24] or condensation of oil droplets[12] are other options to prepare microinclusions in FSF. One can achieve rather monodisperse droplet ensembles. In the latter method, a rotary pump is used to reduce the pressure in a closed chamber containing the film down to a few Torr. After some time, vaporized pump oil condenses on the film and forms droplets with diameters of a few micrometers.

3.2. *Solid particles*

Glass or polystyrene spheres are suitable objects to study interactions of the films with solid particles. When micrometer-sized particles are dispersed in the bulk liquid crystal before drawing the film, they are captured by capillary forces in the meniscus. Therefore, one has to prepare a homogeneously thick film first. A colloidal dispersion of a larger ensemble of beads can be prepared when solid microspheres (e.g. polystyrene) are dispersed in water or another liquid with sufficiently low vapor pressure. Such a suspension is sprayed onto the smectic FSF, and after evaporation of the dispersion medium, the dispersant forms a 2D suspension in the film.[26] Alternatively, if one is interested in the dynamics of individual inclusions, one can drop them directly onto the film using a microrod carrier.[11]

4. Shapes of liquid inclusions

For droplets created by melting, the shape is given by capillary forces. Shape and size dynamics are determined by the temperature ramp and the time scale of the melting process. Practically, the capillary forces can always be considered to be in balance. In contrast, droplet inclusions created by shooting immiscible liquids on the film experience complex geometric changes after impact. The droplet impacts shown in Fig. 5 are characterized by Weber numbers (ratio between kinetic and capillary energies) around one and Ohnesorge numbers (viscous force versus inertial and capillary forces) well below one.[23] The droplet in Fig. 5a first is captured at the film surface, after a few microseconds it adopts a shape of two sphere caps that are connected with each other at the contact line with the film (cf. Fig. 6). Both caps initially have different radii of curvature, evidencing that the two surfaces of the droplet are not equivalent (an accurate quantitative estimate would require that the capillary forces are in equilibrium). The upper cap remains bare while the lower one is covered by a smectic film.[23] The droplet gradually sinks into the film plane.

A rapid change occurs after about 300 μs, when the droplet quickly adopts a symmetric shape with similar radii of curvature of both caps (Fig. 6). A reasonable explanation is that a thin smectic layer wets the upper droplet surface, making both droplet surfaces nearly equal. The droplet surface at each cap is composed of a droplet/smectic interface and a smectic/air interface. Thereafter, the droplets slowly adopt a stationary shape and develop a meniscus within a few seconds.[23]

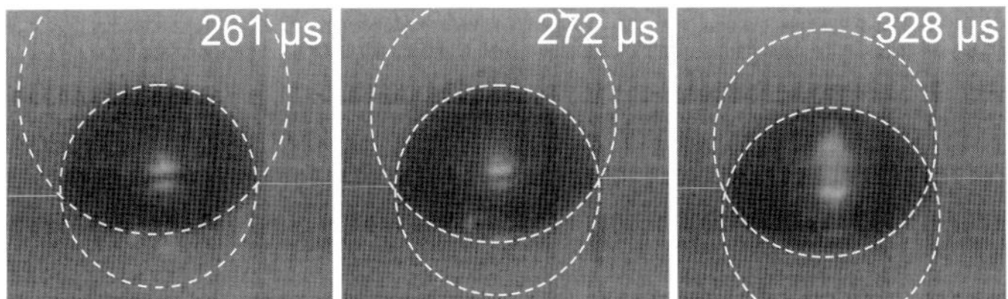

Fig. 6. Shape transformation about 300 μs after impact: the droplet (water with 5 % ethylene glycol), seen from a side view, sinks into a symmetric position respective to the film midplane (indicated by straight white lines). The radii of curvature of upper and lower cap (indicated by dashed circles) equilibrate within a few μs. Image widths 68 μm. Pictures courtesy of S. Dölle.

From the elevations of the asymptotic droplet shapes and their stationary radii (or, alternatively, from the contact angle of droplet slope and film plane), one can obtain accurate information about the involved interface tensions.[31,32] Isotropic droplets of molten material are usually circular flat lenses. In equilibrium, their shape is determined by a minimum of the surface energy. The shape of such droplets is sketched in Fig. 7a. The smectic-isotropic interface is minimal when the droplet circumference is circular, and it is connected with a tension $\sigma_\perp$ (smectic-isotropic interface perpendicular to the layers). The droplet surface is formed by two spherical caps.

The surface tension of the droplet material, σ_i, must be larger than that of the surrounding smectic film, σ_s, otherwise no equilibrium shapes exist,

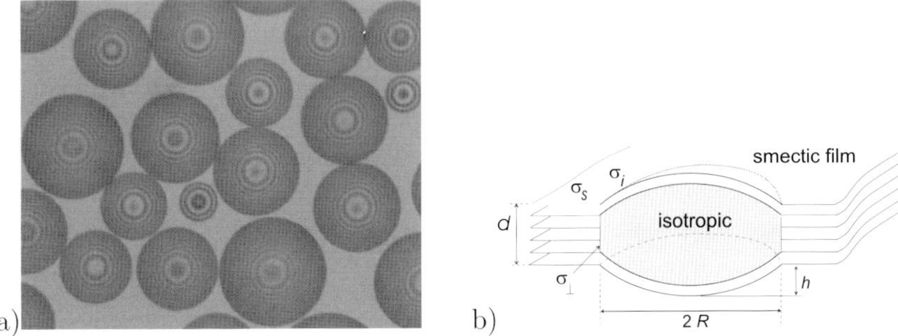

Fig. 7. a) Isotropic droplets of CM11B in a smectic film of the same material at 59.3°C, top view, image size 1 mm $\times$ 0.8 mm, monochromatic illumination with 550 nm green light, and b) schematic model of an isotropic droplet with the definition of the parameters R, h, and d. The droplet surfaces are spherical caps, smectic surface layers on the isotropic droplet are sketched. The vertical scale is exaggerated.

the droplet spreads. This condition is always fulfilled when the droplet and the film consist of the same material, because the isotropic droplet is covered by a smectic surface region, so that the interface tension σ_i has two contributions, a small inner smectic-isotropic interface tension σ_{is}, and the smectic surface tension to air σ_s (Fig. 7b). Schüring $et\ al.$[31] have derived equations relating these interface tensions to the droplet geometry. In equilibrium, droplet height h and radius R of inclusions in thin films are related by

$$h(R) \approx \sqrt{\frac{\sigma_i - \sigma_s}{\sigma_i + \sigma_s}}R, \quad \sigma_i = \sigma_{is} + \sigma_s. \tag{2}$$

The consideration of a finite film thickness d leads to a small correction (small negative offset of about $-d/2$ of the graphs).[9,31] For droplets of molten isotropic film material, heights h are usually one order of magnitude lower than their radii r.

Droplets in a film of smectic CM11B above the bulk clearing transition are shown in Fig. 7a. After heating, the droplets appear randomly distributed in the film plane. There is obviously no long-range interaction between them. Even droplets that touch each other show no tendency to merge, unless they approach each other with a finite relative velocity. When the film temperature is kept constant, the droplet cluster keeps its appearance for hours.

Since the droplets are very flat ($h/R < 0.1$), it is possible to extract the complete droplet shape from interference fringes in reflection microscopy. The measurement of droplet shapes thus provides information on surface and interface tensions of the mesogenic material in the vicinity of the clearing point. Sufficiently far from the clearing point of the film, the ratio of σ_{is} and σ_s is of the order of 0.005 to 0.01 in most of the materials. It gradually drops towards zero on approaching the clearing transiition.[31]

A large number of experiments have been performed not with isotropic, but with nematic (mostly chiral nematic, N*) droplets in smectic films. Obviously, one obtains droplet shapes comparable to isotropic droplets in the cholesteric phase, although no reports of droplet profiles are available so far. A large number of experiments has been performed with this combination of phases by Cluzeau, Dolganov and collaborators (e.g. Refs. 22, 27, 29, 33–35, 39, 44, 45).

In smectic-C films, the c-director field around a liquid droplet breaks the cylindrical symmetry, therefore one may expect that in principle, the outer droplet circumference should deviate from circular shape. The anisotropy of the interface should lead to a deformation of the droplets. For droplets of isotropic material, such deformations are below experimental resolution, whereas for nematic inclusions, such deformations have been described: The director field in the droplets and the external c-director field correspond with each other at the droplet boundary. In particular, the internal director field influences the droplet geometries. The energy related to elastic distortions decreases logarithmically with the droplet radius in 2D, while the surface energy decreases linearly. Thus, elastic terms may overcome the comparably weak nematic-smectic interface tensions for small droplets. Droplets with prolate cross sections in the film plane were first described by Cluzeau *et al.*,[30] Dolganov *et al.*[40] have analyzed elongated cross sections of nematic droplets in an FSF of a smectic-C mixture. The aspect ratio was shown to increase with decreasing droplet sizes, reaching a value of about 2 for the smallest droplets evaluated (length of the order of only 10 μm).

In some materials, e.g. in 8CB, well above the bulk transition into the nematic phase the FSF may still be stable but the interface tension between the non-chiral nematic and the smectic-A phase becomes very small. In that case, the droplets have no well-defined sphere cap shapes but they rather form tactoids (Fig. 8). These structures have no clear boundaries, they merge smoothly with the surrounding film. One consequence is a long-range attractive capillary force mediated by the film thickness gradient around these droplets.[9] When the droplet elevation vs. radius is evaluated using Eq. (2), one can estimate that the interface tension σ_{ns} between the nematic and smectic phases is of the order of only $10^{-5}\sigma_s$.

Droplets of other liquids in smectic FSF have in general larger surface tension differences, so that the droplets are much thicker. In that case, reflection microscopy fails to yield droplet profiles. With special observation techniques[23] it is possible to determine the shape from side views of the droplet. By fitting sphere caps to the upper and lower surfaces of the

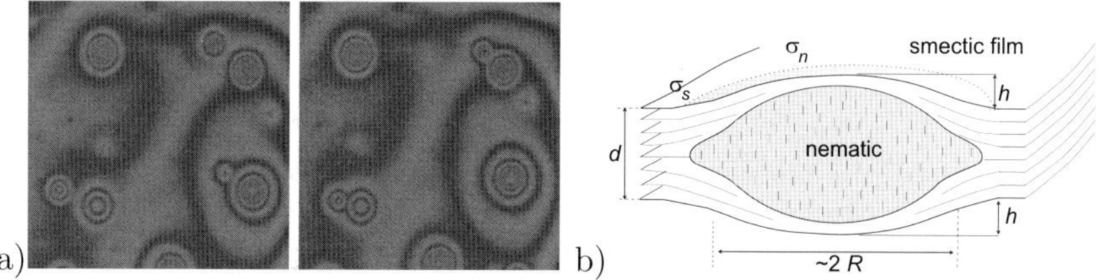

Fig. 8. a) Nematic droplets of 8CB in a smectic FSF far above the SmA-N phase transition (at 40°C), image sizes 1 mm × 1 mm, 2 s time interval between both images, and b) schematic model of a droplet cross section. The vertical scale is exaggerated.

droplets, one obtains surface tension ratios as well. One can even distinguish tensions of both droplet surfaces. Equation (2) can be rewritten in the form

$$\sigma_i = \frac{R^2 + h^2}{R^2 - h^2}\sigma_s.$$

One finds, for example, for the droplet in Fig. 6 right (thickness $2h = 28.5$ μm and diameter $2R = 43.5$ μm, 5% ethylene glycol in water mixture) a surface tension $\sigma_i = 2.50\sigma_s$ as stated above. Surface tensions of isotropic droplets of the same material as the film usually differ from those of the smectic phase by values of the order of a few per mil, sometimes even less.[31]

Thick droplets develop a meniscus around their outer boundary. It can reach heights of several micrometers and extensions of several dozen micrometers already when the droplet radius and height are of the order of 10 μm. Figure 9a shows the reflection microscope view, under crossed polarizers, of such a droplet containing a 5% glycerol solution in water. The meniscus of smectic-C or C* films is often decorated with striking director textures, which will be described in Sec. 5.3. The meniscus slope measured optically and by AFM[24,46] is of the order of 5°.

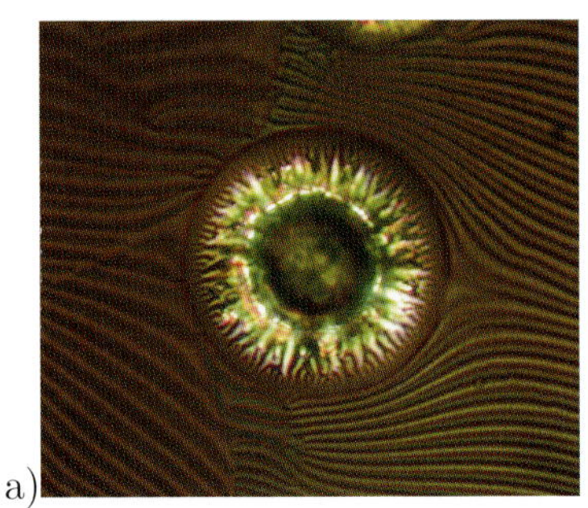
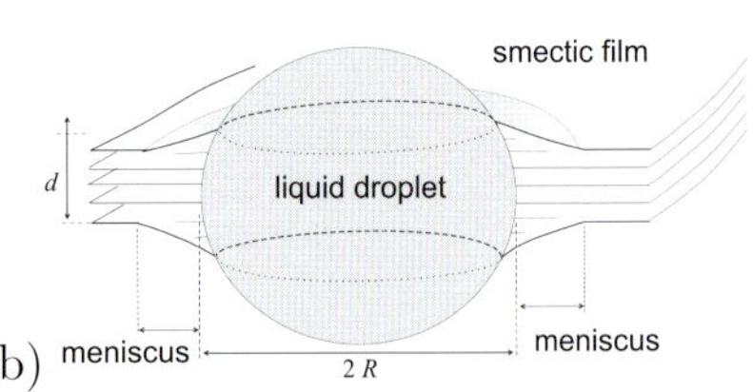

Fig. 9. a) Glycerol/water droplet surrounded by a meniscus, embedded in a stripe textured FELIX 16-100 smectic-C film at room temperature, droplet diameter 31.5 μm, meniscus diameter 69 μm. b) Schematic sketch of droplet and meniscus, a potential wetting layer of smectic material on the isotropic droplet is not shown here, the vertical scale is exaggerated.

After a fast temperature quench into the smectic range, droplets of the film material can partially freeze. The smectic material cannot redistribute sufficiently fast over the film. Then, ring-shaped terraces of surplus layers form on the surrounding film.[47] These terraces (Fig. 10) are not long-term stable structures, they vanish after few hours. In contrast to the menisci around big droplets, the wedge angle of these freezing terraces is not a

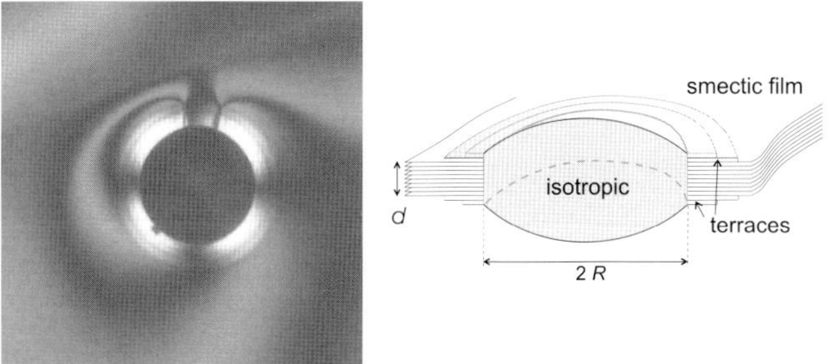

Fig. 10.   Droplet of isotropic, molten material SF20 (33 μm diameter) after temperature quench back into the smectic-C phase. The droplet is surrounded by a disk (47.5 μm diameter) built of terraces of smectic layers. Note that director deformations are squeezed into narrow inversion walls inside the terraced region (see Sec. 5.3). In contrast to menisci such as shown in Fig. 9, these terraces are transient structures, they vanish on the time scale of hours.

material or film property but depends upon the cooling rate. It is approximately one order of magnitude smaller than that of menisci. Physically, these terraces can be treated as part of the inclusions when dynamic properties or elastic interactions are considered (see following sections): They increase the effective radius of the inclusion.

Before we analyze interactions between these inclusions mediated by the director field in tilted smectic phases, we note that all types of inclusions experience capillary interactions in films with inhomogeneous thickness.[31,32] When they get in contact with the meniscus, they are dragged in, leaving a planar film behind. When the films possess layer steps (dislocations), inclusions are lined up at such steps as soon as they get in contact with them. In that situation, the islands or droplets or solid particles move into the thicker film region and remain trapped at the step (Fig. 11). Details of the trapping geometry can be resolved at large film thickness steps such as seen in Fig. 11b. In a rough approximation one can treat the problem for flat droplets as quasi two-dimensional. Then, one may assign interfacial energies to the borders of the droplet in the form of a line tension, and compare them to a line tension related to the thickness step height d_s, $\gamma = \sigma_{s\perp} d_s$. Here, $\sigma_{s\perp}$ is the surface tension of the smectic respective to air for an interface vertical to the layers. The different line tensions between the isotropic droplet and the surrounding film are obviously reflected in the different slopes of the droplet profile at the edges toward the thinner and thicker film regions. The radii of the two boundaries (black and white dashed circles) are $R_1 = 19$ μm and 15 μm, resp., they relate to the line tensions

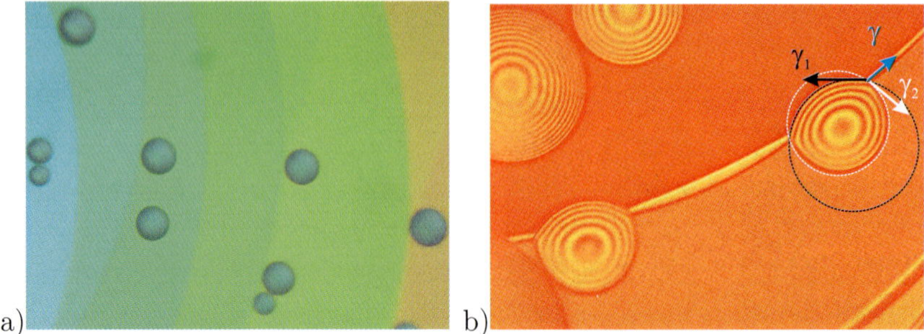

Fig. 11.   a) CM11B droplets in an inhomogeneously thick film in reflected white light, all droplets are pinned at terrace edges, on the upper plateau. The film thickness increases in discrete steps from left to right, from about 450 nm to 500 mn. Image size 333 μm $\times$250 μm. b) Details of the droplet pinning geometry in a PBOT film, with a large thickness step (approx. 250 nm, about 100 molecular layers). The film thickness increases from top left to bottom right in the image. The arrows symbolize the line tensions related to the droplet borders and film thickness step. Monochromatic light of 589 nm wavelength in reflection, image size 128 μm $\times$93 μm.

as $R_1/\gamma_1 = R_2/\gamma_2$. Their ratio of ≈ 1.26 is very close to the elevation of the droplet apex above the film surfaces, 490 nm and 392 nm, respectively. The arrows in Fig. 11b show exemplarily the line tensions at the droplet border, in the intersection point of droplet border and terrace step. All three tensions compensate each other in equilibrium. In most situations, however, terraces are only a few layers high and γ is small compared to the line tensions of the droplet boundary, then the droplet contour is hardly deformed, but the trapping forces are still present. The droplets are almost completely shifted to the upper plateau as in Fig. 11a.

The exact droplet profile can be determined from the interference fringes on the inclusions, which represent lines of equal elevation. In principle, an accurate computation of the 3D droplet profile would therefore also yield information about line tensions of dislocation steps. Moreover, it is evident that the force balance pins the droplet in a position where the droplet center is on the higher plateau. The effect is more pronounced for smaller (shallower) droplets where the ratio of elevations and consequently the radius ratio R_1/R_2 is larger. The ratio approaches one in the limit of large droplets.

A particular clustering mechanism by capillary interactions has been demonstrated with polystyrene beads of 2.8 μm diameter in films of micrometer thickness.[26] These beads were shown to form clusters of two to four particles surrounded by a ray-shaped texture ('corona') in a smectic-A film. This corona was interpreted as an undulation of layers in the meniscus surrounding the inclusions. Meniscus width and stripe distances were both independent of the number of beads trapped in the cluster. Unlike all other publications on inclusions in freely suspended films, this study assumed that the beads remain, unsymmetrically, trapped at one of the film surfaces.

5. Interactions with the director field

5.1. *Director patterns*

In smectic-C and C* films, elastic distortions of the c-director are required to satisfy the specific anchoring conditions of the c-director (which is defined in Fig. 2b). In the discussion of shapes of liquid inclusions, we have neglected forces related to the orientational elasticity of the smectic material. This is justified since these forces are at least 4 orders of magnitude smaller than capillary forces. However, they can exert forces and torques on inclusions in a uniformly thick film area.

The continuum equations for nematics can be adapted to freely suspended smectic films by introducing elastic constants for the c-director. The free energy density in the general case reads

$$f = \frac{1}{2}K_S(\nabla \cdot \vec{c})^2 + \frac{1}{2}K_B(\nabla \times \vec{c})^2 + \beta(\nabla \times \vec{c}) \cdot \vec{k}. \tag{3}$$

Here, $\vec{c} = (\cos\varphi(x,y), \sin\varphi(x,y))$ is a two-dimensional vector in the (x,y) film plane, and $\vec{k}$ is a unit vector along the layer normal. In thin films, the director field can be treated as uniform in the direction normal to the layers, and a 2D description is appropriate. We will consequently use this approximation in the following. The free energy of a homogeneously thick film can be computed by integrating over the film area A and multiplying with the film thickness d,

$$F = d \int_A \left[\frac{1}{2}K_S(\nabla \cdot \vec{c})^2 + \frac{1}{2}K_B(\nabla \times \vec{c})^2 + \beta(\nabla \times \vec{c}) \cdot \vec{k}\right] dA. \tag{4}$$

One can relate the elastic constants to the nematic constants for the director $\vec{n}$, K_{11}, K_{22} and K_{33} by $K_S = K_{11}\sin^2\theta$, $K_B = K_{22}\sin^2\theta\cos^2\theta + K_{33}\sin^4\theta$, with the tilt angle θ. Since K_{22} is in general the smallest of the nematic constants, one has usually $K_B < K_S$ in nonpolar SmC films. A spontaneous splay term with $(\nabla \cdot \vec{c})$ is not allowed in the bulk for symmetry reasons: If the film is turned upside-down, which represents an allowed symmetry operation in SmC and SmC*, this term changes sign. It can only be effective

378   *R. Stannarius and K. Harth*

at surfaces, with opposite contributions on top and bottom film sides that cancel each other. The spontaneous bend term $(\nabla \times \vec{c})$ is allowed in chiral SmC* films (symmetry C_2), but not in SmC (C_{2h}). The volume integral of the latter term can be transformed by Stokes' lemma into a surface integral,

$$F_{\mathrm{sb}} = d \int_A \left[\beta(\nabla \times \vec{c}) \cdot \vec{k} \right] dA = d \int_s \beta\, \vec{c} \cdot d\vec{s}, \tag{5}$$

where the latter is a line integral over the film boundaries. This means that the spontaneous bend term does not contribute to bulk deformations of $\vec{c}$, but it can influence the boundary conditions. For example, it may select preferential clockwise or counterclockwise alignment of the c-director at inclusion boundaries in SmC* films. In ferroelectric SmC* films, one must include electric self-energies related to polarization splay into an effective constant K'_{B}[20] that replaces K_{B} in Eqs. (3, 4), but such an effective bend constant would be film thickness dependent. For sufficiently large polarizations, this may change the above inequality to $K'_{\mathrm{B}} > K_{\mathrm{S}}$.[48]

Introducing $K = (K_{\mathrm{S}} + K_{\mathrm{B}})/2$ and $\kappa = (K_{\mathrm{S}} - K_{\mathrm{B}})/2$ in Eq. (3), this equation is equivalent to

$$f = \frac{1}{2}(K + \kappa)(\nabla \cdot \vec{c})^2 + \frac{1}{2}(K - \kappa)(\nabla \times \vec{c})^2 + \beta(\nabla \times \vec{c})\vec{k}.$$

A special simplification is the one-constant approximation $K_{\mathrm{S}} = K_{\mathrm{B}} = K, \kappa = 0$. It can be used to make qualitative predictions for the director field, the bulk energy term simplifies to

$$F = d \int_A \frac{K}{2}(\varphi_{,x}^2 + \varphi_{,y}^2)\, dA,$$

where the indices denote spatial derivatives (e.g. $\varphi_{,x} = \partial\varphi/\partial x$). The Euler-Lagrange method yields the Laplace equation $\nabla^2\varphi = 0$ as the minimal free energy condition. The beauty of this approximation is that the equilibrium equations for φ become analytically solvable in a number of simple geometries by means of conformal mapping methods.[45,49] The equations for $\varphi(x,y)$ become fully equivalent to the electrostatic equations for the electric potential in vacuum. One can therefore find straightforward analogies between topological defects of the c-director field, which represent topological charges in smectic FSF, and electrostatic problems.[50]

The c-director in smectic-C films usually obeys strong anchoring conditions at the inclusion interfaces, which is evident in Figs. 1b, 3, 9, and 10. This is fully analogous to the director field around water droplets in nematic emulsions,[51] but the 2D geometry of freely suspended films is much simpler than the nematic bulk problem. In non-polar SmC phases, the c-director aligns tangentially at the surface of islands or droplets (see, e.g. Ref. 47). However, in polar smectic-C*, a splay of the spontaneous electric polarization $\vec{P}$ contributes to the free energy, so that configurations with $\vec{\nabla} \cdot \vec{P} \neq 0$ may become energetically unfavorable. Since $\vec{P}$ is perpendicular to the c-director in SmC*, polarization splay is strictly coupled to director bend and vice versa. In the case of sufficiently strong spontaneous polarizations P (large K'_B), radial c-director alignment at the boundary of a circular inclusion may be preferred since it is related to c-director splay and absence of polarization splay. For SmC* films, this type of anchoring was postulated, e.g. by Cluzeau *et al.*[22,27]

In the continuum elastic theory [Eq. (3)], both types of boundary conditions can be treated analogously, when one exchanges tangential by radial anchoring as well as K_S by K_B, and replaces φ by $\varphi + \pi/2$. Also, some viscosity coefficients change their functions then. We will consider in the following almost exclusively the case of tangential (parallel) anchoring. The first type of c-director configuration is an inclusion with the same direction sense (clockwise or counterclockwise) of the c-director everywhere on the circumference. This boundary condition corresponds to the creation of a virtual topological defect of the c-director with strength $S = +1$ inside the inclusion (cf. Fig. 2). Such a structure is the equivalent of a charged particle (line charge) in electrostatics. In a uniformly oriented smectic-C film, the creation of such a droplet alone (e.g. by local melting of smectic film material into an isotropic phase) is impossible, since the topological charge is a conserved quantity. With the insertion of a particle with uniform (tangential or radial) anchoring, compensating topological defects of total strength -1 must be created simultaneously in the smectic film.

In real experiments, such inclusions often have two sections with opposite senses of c-director alignment on their circumference. Then, the c-director field has two half-integer defects of topological strength $S = -1/2$ at the inclusion boundary. Each of them is pinned to the droplet border, since the c-director is a vector field that cannot contain half-integer defects. Together with virtual defects of total effective strength $+1$ inside the inclusion, the total defect strength is zero. These structures of topological net charge zero can spontaneously form out of a uniform film by local melting, or they appear when a droplet or particle is dropped onto the film. Altogether, the two peripheral defects and the oppositely charged virtual inner defects form a topological multipole.[50] Since the two peripheral $-1/2$ defects repel each other (like electric charges), their equilibrium positions are on opposite sides of the inclusion, forming a topological quadrupole in combination with the virtual defects inside the inclusion.[45,52,53] This is seen in the experimental image of Fig. 12g and sketched in Figs. 12h, i.

The described symmetry may be broken in several cases: One possible reason can be chirality of the smectic material,[45,52,54,55] which is connected with a spontaneous bend $\beta \neq 0$ in Eq. (3). Then, the energy term F_{sb} in

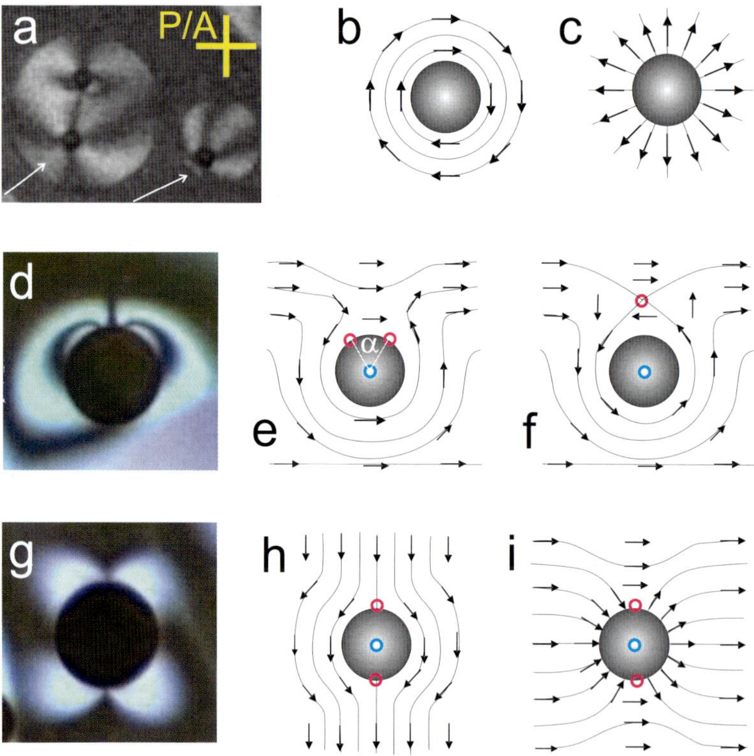

Fig. 12. Topological multipoles around circular inclusions: a) experimental image of monopoles with $S = +1$ inside islands, with tangential anchoring, same film as in Fig. 1, and b) sketch of the corresponding director field (black arrows), c) $S = +1$ defect with radial anchoring, d) topological dipole with two $S = -1/2$ defects of the c-director at the boundaries in experiment, e) sketch of the director field, f) isolated $S = -1$ satellite defect, g) topological quadrupole with two $S = -1/2$ defects of the c-director at the border and tangential anchoring, h,i) sketches of the quadrupolar director field for tangential and radial anchoring, respectively. For simplicity, not all virtual defects are shown (see text), only the central virtual defects inside the droplets are indicated. Crossed polarizers P/A in all experimental images.

Eq. (5) can decrease when the two peripheral defects leave their opposition. The displacement of both peripheral defects to an angle $\alpha \neq 180°$ creates a topological dipole (see Figs. 12d, e). The deviation of α from $180°$ in mixtures of chiral and racemic materials has been shown to increase systematically with increasing chirality.[54] For high chirality (large β) the two defects can merge to one single defect at the droplet boundary. The relative equilibrium positions of the two peripheral defects have even been calculated analytically,[53] $\tan(\alpha/2) = \pi K/(2\beta R)$. A non-symmetric arrangement of the peripheral defects was also found for nonchiral materials[47] where $\beta = 0$. There, it can be related to interactions of the defects with the surrounding c-director field or with layer dislocations. In particular, inclusions embedded in an inversion wall have dipolar defect configurations.

Another situation is the formation of isolated $S = -1$ defects in the surrounding film. If the two half-integer defects combine to one $S = -1$ defect, they can leave the droplet border,[56] forming a real -1 defect, acting as a dipolar structure in combination with the virtual topological charge in the droplet (Fig. 12f). This is the 2D analogy of the hyperbolic hedgehog defects observed for inclusions in nematics.

Analytical solutions for the c-director fields of multipole defect configurations, in one constant approximation, are[45,50,53]

$$\varphi(x,y) = \sum_i S_i \Phi_i + \text{const}$$

where Φ_i are the angles of the vectors $\vec{r}_i = r_i(\cos \Phi_i, \sin \Phi_i)$ between the position $\vec{r} = (x, y)$ and the centers of the defects i with topological strength S_i. The constant selects between radial or tangential anchoring. In the situations sketched in Figs. 12e, h, and i, the defects that have to be considered are two real $-1/2$ defects at the outer droplet boundary, two virtual $-1/2$ defects at the same positions but on the inner side of the droplet boundary, and a central $+2$ defect. In Fig. 12f, one has a real -1 defect and in addition two virtual defects of total strength $+1$ inside the inclusion: One defect of strength $+2$ is located in the inclusion center, in a distance of $r_d > R$ from the real hyperbolic defect, the second one is a virtual -1 defect in a distance of R^2/r_d from the inclusion center, towards the real -1 defect. This arrangement fulfils the anchoring conditions on the border of a disk with radius R around the $+2$ defect. The corresponding topological dipole moment can be defined as $p = (r_d^2 + R^2)/r_d$.[50] A limiting case is $r_d = R$, where the two hyperbolic defects reach the inclusion boundary. The elastic energy of this configuration is minimal, when the detached -1 defect is located in a distance $\sqrt{2}R$ from the inclusion center. Bohley *et*

$al.$[49] have calculated the energy in one-constant approximation for different defect positions, the results are shown in Fig. 13. On the left, the energies correspond to different positions of two half-integer defects on the droplet boundary. The right hand side gives the position of a detached defect of strength -1. The energetically favored configuration is that of opposing half integer defects ($\alpha = \pi$). The -1 defect has its optimal position at $\sqrt{2}R$. However, within this one-constant model the configuration with two opposing $-1/2$ defects corresponds to the absolute energy minimum. The detached defect is separated by a flat energy barrier from the inclusion border.

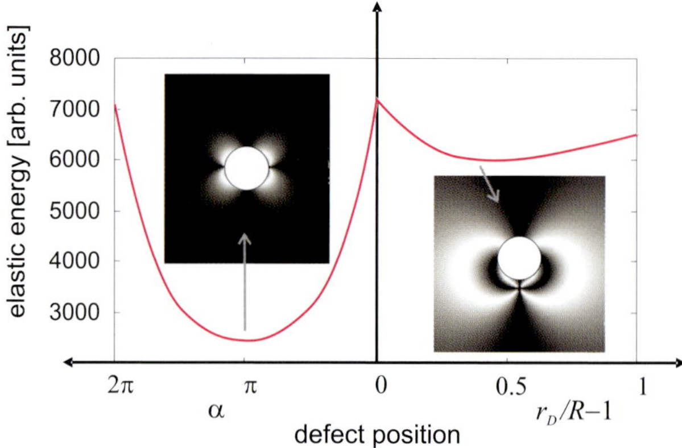

Fig. 13. Calculated free energy of the equilibrium c-director field around a single droplet in dependence on the defect positions, in one-constant approximation. In the left part, the configurations of two half-integer boundary defects in constellations with angle α are evaluated, the right part evaluates configurations with a single detached -1 defect. (Data taken from Ref. 49)

In the case of $K_\mathrm{S} \neq K_\mathrm{B}$, analytical solutions are not available, numerical solutions can be found e.g. by finite elements methods. Likewise, one can calculate solutions for weak anchoring conditions at the inclusion boundary. Weak anchoring can be described by a surface energy term at the inclusion boundary

$$F_0 = \frac{1}{2}W_0(\vec{c}\cdot\vec{e}_n)^2,$$

where $\vec{e}_n$ is a unit vector normal to the droplet boundary. $W_0 = \infty$ for strong tangential anchoring, and $W_0 = -\infty$ for strong radial anchoring. Figure 14 shows simulated optical images for the cases of one constant ap-

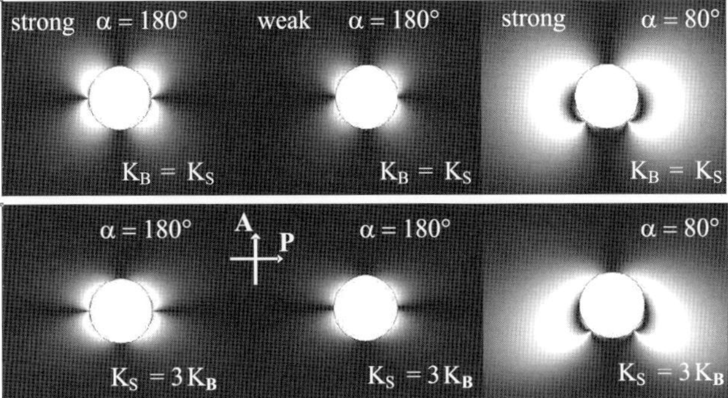

Fig. 14.   Numerically calculated textures around a single droplet in dependence on the defect positions for weak (middle column) and strong (left and right) anchoring, and different elastic constants ratios. (Data taken from Ref. 49)

proximation (top row) and $K_S = 3K_B$ (bottom row), for strong tangential anchoring, $W_0 = \infty$, and weak anchoring, $W_0 = 3(K_S + K_B)/(2R)$.

With fixed defect positions, the solutions for $\varphi(x, y)$ are independent of the spontaneous bend term in Eq. (4). The coefficient β selects only the angle α and thus the boundary conditions for the tangentially anchored c-director. In the situation with a detached hyperbolic defect, $\beta \neq 0$ selects a preferential sense of orientation of the c-director along the droplet boundary. Typically, all droplets in such films will then have the same c-director sense.

Temperature can change the relative contributions of spontaneous bend β and/or of the effective bend K'_B, leading to a reorganization of the director at the boundaries. The first situation has been described by Dolganov et al.[39] for 11BSMHOB. At low temperatures, the configuration has one peripheral -1 defect, thus the rotation sense of $\vec{c}$ at the droplet border is uniform ($\alpha = 0$ for large, say positive, β). At heating, this spontaneous bend contribution decays and the defect splits into two half-integer peripheral defects. They move toward the opposing positions ($\alpha = 180°$, $\beta \approx 0$). Thereafter, with a sign change of β, they approach each other again at the other side of the droplet, and merge to a -1 defect there ($\alpha = 360°$, at large $\beta < 0$). This process is visualized in Fig. 15, left.

The second scenario was also discovered by Dolganov et al.[39] in 9BSMHOB. There, the anchoring changed reversibly from preferentially tangential at high temperatures to preferentially radial at low temperatures. A possible reason could be changes of the spontaneous electric polarization and a correspondingly changed effective bend elastic constant K'_B.

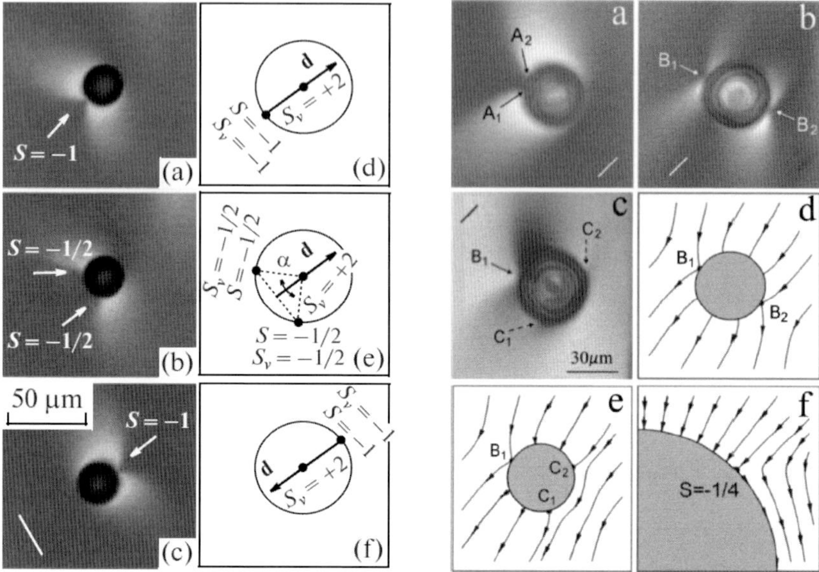

Fig. 15. The left image shows the reversal of the preferential director orientation ($\vec{c} \rightarrow -\vec{c}$) at the droplet circumference for 11BSMHOB when the temperature is increased from a) to c). The image was reproduced from Ref. 55, courtesy of P. Dolganov. The right image shows the transition from tangential to radial anchoring in 9BSMHOB: The low temperature tangential configuration with two half-integer defects A_1 and A_2 at $T = 105.6°$C changes to a quadrupolar configuration with two opposing half-integer defects B_1 and B_2 and radial anchoring at $T = 105.9°$C. The transition at $T = 105.8°$C takes place via a splitting of the A_1, A_2 defects into two $S = -1/4$ defects each, which reunite pairwise to B_1 and B_2. The image was reproduced from Ref. 39, courtesy of P. Dolganov, cobyright by APS.

Naturally, the question arises how the dipolar and quadrupolar droplets orient in an otherwise uniform c-director field. Pettey *et al.*[50] have predicted that in an infinite sample, all orientations are equivalent under the assumption of one-constant approximation. In a finite film, the inclusion multipole interacts with the film boundaries, but the effects of related forces and torques are usually weak compared to thermal motion so that large fluctuations are observed. This is different when other inclusions are in the vicinity, i.e. in a distance of the same order of magnitude as their diameters. Then, attractive interactions mediated by elastic director distortions are a consequence of the c-director anchoring at the inclusion borders. They exert forces and torques on embedded particles, as described in the next section.

Dislocations at film thickness steps can also interact with nearby inclusions via elastic director forces. These forces are in general repelling, but weak compared to the capillary forces that trap droplets at film thickness steps. In addition, a torque is exerted on the defect multipoles. Experimentally, one can observe a weak tendency of dipoles to align parallel to dislocation steps when they are in the immediate vicinity of such steps. Similarly, there is a trend for quadrupoles to align the three defects in line parallel to a layer step. This can be seen as an effect of virtual 'mirror' defects on the opposite side of the layer step. Chaining of inclusions (see next section) never extends across layer steps, the c-director anchoring at the dislocations of the layer step decouples inclusions on opposite sides of the step. Inclusion chains tend to align parallel to film thickness steps when they are very close to them.

So far, we have only considered droplets that deform the surrounding director field and create topological multipoles of the surrounding c-director field. The same interactions can be observed between smectic islands in SmC films (and in principle also between holes and the surrounding film). In that case, one has a c-director field inside and outside the inclusion. The boundary of an island is formed by a circular dislocation or an array of dislocations in the smectic layer structure. The c-director has a preferential alignment at this border similar to the alignment at droplet peripheries. Silvestre *et al.*[57] studied c-director fields around islands in SmC films. The main difference to isotropic droplets seems to be that the c-director around their islands usually has a uniform sense of direction along the boundary. They observe only dipolar structures with the -1 defect detached from the island circumference. The sense of rotation discriminates two chiral island types, R and L for clockwise and counterclockwise c-director configurations. Figure 16 shows examples of optical images and c-director fields around island pairs.

5.2. *Self-organization of inclusions*

The long range elastic interactions mediated by the c-director field in smectic-C and C* films can lead to pairing of embedded particles, to chaining and the formation of lattices. This interaction is comparable to elastic interactions between inclusions in nematic bulk samples (see Chap. 10), but owing to the two-dimensional geometry of the films, the mathematical treatment simplifies considerably, in particular within one-constant approximation. There, the equations are fully analogous to the electric interactions

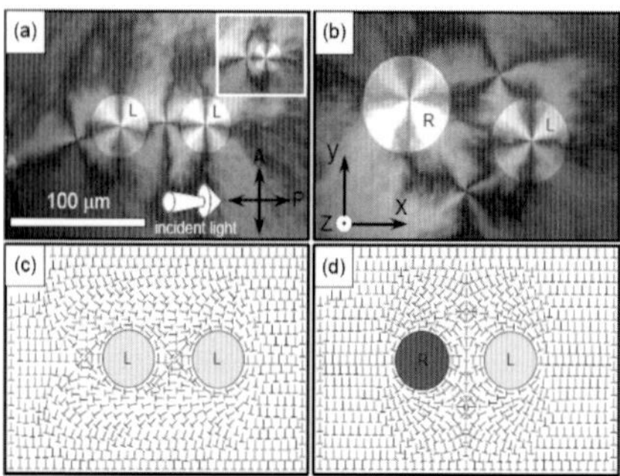

Fig. 16.   Chiral islands in a SmC FSF (MX8068, see Ref. 57). The depolarized reflected light microscope images show two islands containing +1 defects with the same handedness (a) and opposite handedness (b). The internal +1 defects are accompanied each by a −1 defect in the surrounding film, forming dipolar pairs. The inset in (a) shows a single island with accompanying −1 defect. The oblique laser illumination indicated by the arrow allows to differentiate between left- and right-handed islands by comparing the brightness of the brushes in their upper and lower halves. Image taken from Ref. 57, copyright by APS.

between electrical multipoles (e.g. Refs. 9, 45, 50, 53). The analogy can be used to classify interactions between inclusions into two types: those that have a dipolar character and those with a quadrupolar character. Droplet pairs with dipolar interactions are depicted in Fig. 17. Their relative orientations and positions are determined by the locations of the peripheral or the accompanying detached defects. Images 17c, d show situations with antiparallel dipoles. They arrange side by side in dimers and thereby compensate their dipole moments. Parallel droplets arrange themselves in line, thus increasing their dipole moment as shown in Figs. 17a, b. This arrangement can be continued to form chains. Note that for smectic islands in SmC FSF, one finds configurations very similar to images 17a, d.[57] This is intuitively clear because the anchoring conditions of the external c-director at the inclusion borders are identical.

Figure 18 shows examples of self-organized chains of liquid inclusions with quadrupolar and dipolar defect configurations in freely suspended films of SF20. The 'quadrupolar' chain has the same director field on both sides, the chain segments are aligned in an angle of approximately 30° respective to the undistorted c-director.[28,49] The 'dipolar' chain separates two regions of antiparallel c-director orientations, it is aligned with the external c-director far from the chain. The sense of bend deflection in the inversion wall separating these two regions determines the location of the defect pairs

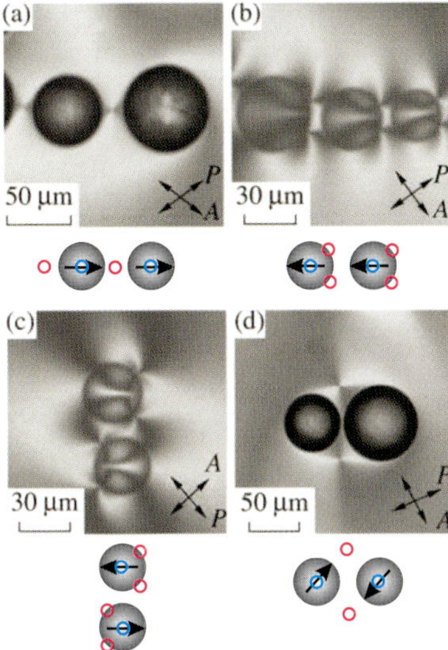

Fig. 17. Dipolar interactions between droplet pairs in ferroelectric 11BMSHOB in SmC*: a) parallel dipoles with separated -1 defects align to form dimers or chains, b) parallel dipoles with peripheral $-1/2$ defects align and form dimers or chains.[28] Antiparallel droplets with c) pairs of $-1/2$ defects and d) isolated -1 defects form dimers but no chains. Image adapted from Ref. 55, courtesy of P. Dolganov.

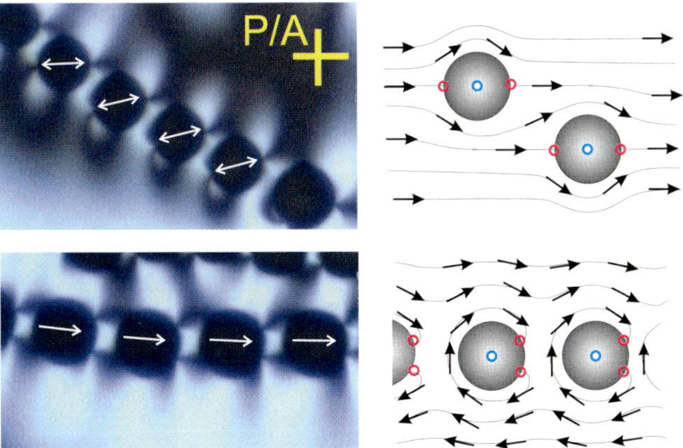

Fig. 18. Chaining of droplets with quadrupolar (top) and dipolar (bottom) defect configurations in smectic-C films of SF20 above the bulk clearing temperature. Crossed polarizers P/A in the experimental images, image widths approximately 60 μm. Directions of the topological multipoles are indicated by white arrows. Black arrows in the right hand images symbolize the c-director orientations.

on dipolar droplets. Chains of droplets with quadrupolar configuration are not necessarily linear, since two possible 'docking' sites are possible to continue a chain ($\pm 30°$). They can form zigzags (central part of Fig. 19), and even branch.

Chains of droplets possess a certain bending elasticity. In absence of external fields, they are in a straight configuration with minimal elastic energy (dipolar and quadrupolar droplets) or they may develop kinks separating straight segments (quadrupolar droplets) as seen in the center of Fig. 19. A deflection of the chains from these optimal configurations costs elastic energy. In certain configurations, a deflection can be induced by external forces. The outer region of Fig. 19 contains concentric inversion walls of the c-director that have been obtained by vortex flow in the film center.[58] In the bend regions of these inversion walls, dipolar droplet chains are embedded.[41,42] The droplet density can be controlled: The material is photosensitive, illumination leads to an increased droplet formation in the film. When these droplets appear in the region near the chain arrays, they are incorporated in these chains, and the latter have to develop a buckling

Fig. 19. Left: SmC film of he photosensitive material 11OAB at $T = 122°C$, with concentric-director inversion wall arrays that are filled with chains of quadrupolar droplets. The closed, ring-shaped chains buckle when additional droplets are incorporated such that the chain length becomes larger than the diameter of the enclosed film area. Image size 420 μm $\times$420 μm, crossed polarizers in reflected light. Right: larger magnification of the wall array with resolved individual droplets in the chains (see arrow). The droplet chains compress the bend deformation into a band with roughly the droplet diameter, increasing the width of the adjacent splayed region and thus relieving elastic deformations. Reflection image with elliptically polarized incident light and linear analyzer.

instability. The spatial periodicity of this buckling pattern can give some hints on the elastic properties of inclusion chains in smectic films.[41,42]

Finally, when the droplet density is sufficiently large, chains can align to form more complex structures and lattices. The simplest lattice is one formed by quadrupolar droplet chains that align with a displacement of half a segment along their axes (Fig. 20). Different lattice types have been found by numerical simulations.[49] Experimentally, the observed lattices are very close to a hexagonal packing of the inclusions, where the sixfold symmetry is broken by the direction of the aligned quadrupoles (positions of the topological $-1/2$ defects), see Fig. 20 and Refs. 9, 49.

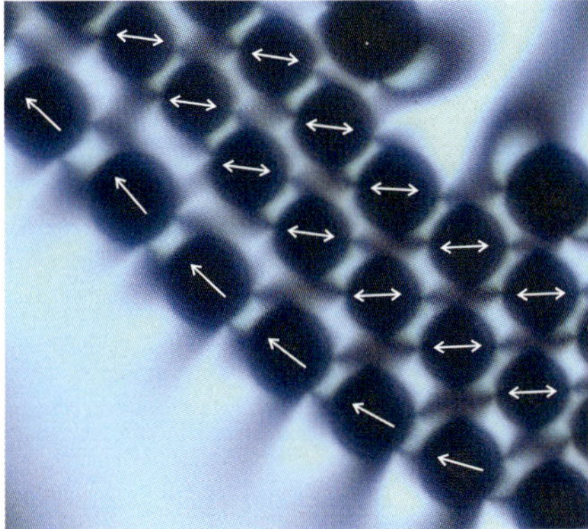

Fig. 20. SmC film of SF20 with isotropic droplets during the lattice formation process: Two chains of quadrupolar droplets have already aligned and begin to form a lattice. The bottom chain consists of dipolar droplets, its characteristics is the inversion of the c-director from one side of the chain to the other. This prevents the transformation into quadrupolar droplets and integration into the lattice. Nevertheless, there is an attractive force towards the lattice. Directions of the topological multipoles are indicated by white arrows. Image width approximately 65 μm.

5.3. *The meniscus around inclusions*

The inclusions treated in the previous two paragraphs, formed by isotropic film material, possess no visible meniscus. They are flat objects with thicknesses not exceeding a few micrometers and height to diameter ratios of the order of 1:10. In contrast, objects like solid beads or droplets of immiscible liquids with substantially different surface tensions disturb the surrounding smectic film structure significantly. After an initial equilibration phase, they will embed into the film, see Sec. 4 for the geometries. In tilted smectic phases, the reorganization of the smectic layers to terrace or meniscus structures has significant consequences for the surrounding c-director field. This affects the interactions between inclusions.

The formation of terraces of film material, e.g. during a rapid temperature quench, has been described above (cf. Fig. 10). These terraces consist of concentric arrays of layer steps. There, the preferential defect configuration of the c-director field around the inclusion body is preserved. The surrounding director field is biased in the terrace region: The c-director possesses a preferentially parallel alignment to layer steps. Thus, any π or 2π wall originating from a defect at the inclusion body, will be distorted such that regions with the director perpendicular to the dislocation contract and those with parallel alignment expand, see Fig. 21. When the distance between the dislocations is sufficiently small, the walls extending from the defects at the inclusion boundary into the surrounding film appear as thin stripes between crossed polarizers (Fig. 10). The width of these walls is related to the wedge angle (dislocation step density), an average elastic constant, the anchoring energy of the c-director at single dislocations and the film thickness.[47]

As a consequence of the wall trapping, the defect structure is transferred practically unchanged to the outer border of the terrace. These inclusions appear as 2D objects with a diameter corresponding to the terraced region when they interact via the director field. As mentioned in Sec. 4, the terraced regions are quite persistent but not long-term stable.

Around inclusions of liquid or solid guest material, a wedge shaped meniscus forms as an equilibrium structure, provided the smectic material wets the inclusion surface. Its extension may exceed the inclusion radius by far. Similar to the menisci at the support frame, the shapes of smectic menisci around inclusions are very distinct from those of unstructured liquids: The border of the meniscus toward the homogeneous film is sharply

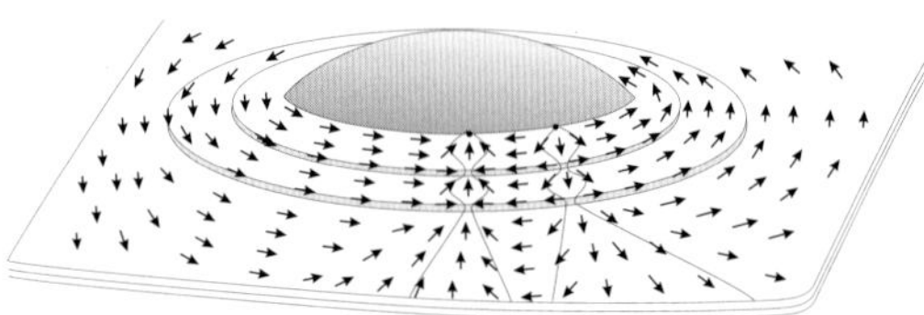

Fig. 21. c-director field around a liquid inclusion with terraces, cf. Fig. 10 in Sec. 4. The inversion walls that start from point defects are compressed due to the alignment of the c-director at layer steps.

defined (within the resolution of optical experiments). The thin region is approximately linear, wedge-like up to a thickness of $\approx 1~\mu m$, the thicker part turns over to a slightly bent profile.[46] In SmC films, this is accompanied by small transverse, at few micrometers thickness also longitudinal, undulations of the meniscus surface.[46,59] They occur as a consequence of layer rearrangement into stripes and focal conics. It is evident that the meniscus significantly influences the interaction of the inclusion with the surrounding film director field, but also the dynamics of the inclusion in the film.

In smectic-C or C* materials, menisci above $\approx 1~\mu m$ thickness are covered with a sequence of characteristic patterns, see e.g. Refs. 13, 24, 46, 59, 60. Figure 22 shows a pair of glass beads enclosed by a meniscus with stripe and grid decorations with crossed polarizers (left), in unpolarized light (middle) and under crossed polarizers with a λ phase plate inserted in diagonal orientation.

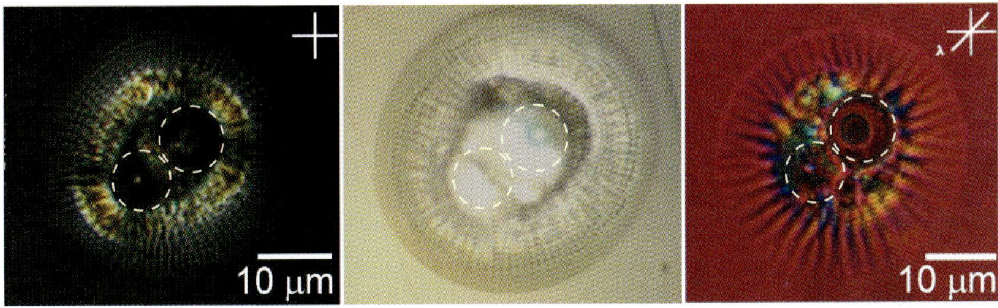

Fig. 22.   Meniscus around a pair of glass beads in a smectic film (OMCBP) with stripe and grid decorations with crossed polarizers (left), in unpolarized light (middle) and under crossed polarizers with a λ phase plate inserted in diagonal orientation. The end of the meniscus toward the homogeneous film is clearly visible. The left and middle images are SmA at 45°C, the right one is SmC* at 27°C. The approximate bead positions are indicated by dashed circles.

The most prominent texture is a regular array of stripes directed along the thickness gradient. The ratio of periodicity and meniscus thickness appears to be rather material-independent.[24] Meyer and Pershan[61] proposed that this pattern originates from the interaction of a spontaneous surface polarization with the c-director field: Stripes represent "splay domains", separated by defect lines on the surfaces, shifted midway between each other on the top and bottom of the meniscus. Recently, an alternative explanation connected to surface wrinkling was proposed.[59] However, the models suggested so far[59,61] have problems in describing the phenomenon, and the director field within the stripes has not yet been elucidated satisfactorily. When menisci decorated with stripe patterns are heated to a smectic-A phase, the patterns reversibly disappear in a finite temperature interval above the phase transition. They become less structured and faint with increasing temperature.[13,24] Stripes vanish first, so that grid patterns may remain visible (left and middle images of Fig. 22). The observation of such corona-like patterns above the SmC to SmA transition suggests an alternative interpretation of the corona patterns observed around polystyrene beads in smectic-A films,[26] i.e. they may have a similar origin as the well-known SmC meniscus stripes. Stripe textures in SmA films have been found so far only when the material also possesses a smectic-C phase.

The striped corona patterns are characteristic for a certain thickness range of the meniscus, typically around one micrometer to a few micrometers. Toward the thicker regions, a crossover to a square texture, presumably parabolic focal conics, then eventually to more irregular layer arrangements is observed. Menisci in thin films (< 1 μm) can develop structures with the characteristics of loops and hooks. They may reflect a continuous rotation of the c-director.[13] The director field around such inclusions with large menisci is not the same as that discussed in the previous section. Rather, the meniscus patterns usually end in a number of defects. The expansion of a sun-ray pattern over the complete film area may be observed: a few dislocations from the outer circumference of the meniscus spread radially outward, dragging attached defects with them. The film area fills with an array of walls, with continuous rotation of the c-director in the area surrounding the inclusions (Fig. 23). For the director field, the inclusion can then be considered as a defect of high topological strength (cf., for example, similar patterns described by Maclennan[62]).

6. Hydrodynamics of inclusions in 2D

Fluid flow in reduced geometries plays an important role in physics, chemistry and biology, for instance in lipid membranes. Smectic freely suspended films can serve as ideal model systems to study flow in isotropic and anisotropic 2D fluids, including the coupling of velocity gradients and orientation and the driving of flow by external mechanical or electromagnetic fields.

In a three-dimensional geometry, flow in smectic materials is in general a comparably complex phenomenon, even when the samples are well aligned. The full dynamic equations for SmC and their derivation can be found e.g.

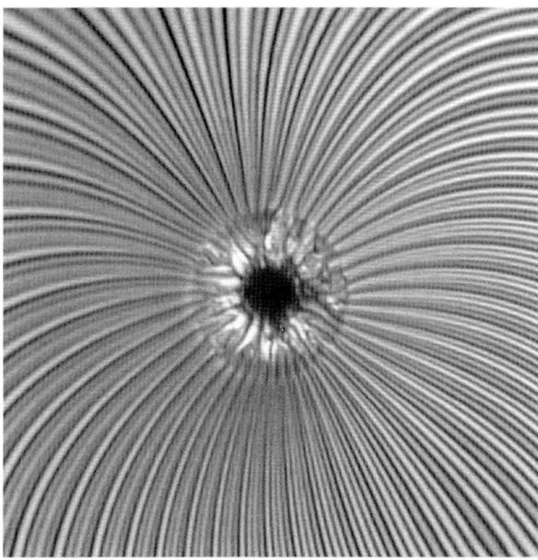

Fig. 23. 'Sun-ray' texture around an inclusion (glycerol/water droplet). The film material is the commercial ferroelectric smectic C* mixture FELIX-16 at room temperature. The inclusion is surrounded by a meniscus with a defect pattern equivalent to topological defects of a total strength of $|S| = 43$, i.e. the director rotates by $86\,\pi$ along a closed path around the included object. The image size is 250 μm $\times 250$ μm, courtesy of Ch. Bohley.

in the textbook by Stewart.[63] The treatment simplifies for films in which the c-director field is uniform along the layer normal. The description of flow processes in sufficiently thin free-standing films reduces to a 2D equivalent of the Ericksen-Leslie equations for nematic phases[58,64] when coupling to air flow can be neglected. In the most general, anisotropic case, a coupled system of a torque balance arising from viscous and elastic torques on the c-director and the incompressible Navier-Stokes equations must be solved in the film plane (for convenience, we label the two in-plane coordinates here with x_1, x_2 to facilitate the notation). Five independent viscosities can enter the problem. This problem reduces in smectic-A films to the much simpler case of an isotropic fluid in 2D, with only one effective viscosity parameter.

Nevertheless, even the description of simple hydrodynamic geometries in 2D can become quite complex, compared to the respective 3D situation. An example is the 2D Stokes' paradox, the fact that one has no steady flow field around an infinitely long cylinder which satisfies Stokes' equations except the trivial state. A workaround for this paradox has been proposed by Oseen.[65] The consequence of Stokes' paradox in 2D is that one has no non-trivial steady-state solution to the Navier-Stokes equations at low

Reynolds number which satisfies the boundary conditions at the surface of a disk and at infinity. The effect of the disk on the velocity profile reaches very far, so that at large distances the Reynolds number becomes comparable to one and the laminar flow condition breaks down. When one deals with the motion of inclusions in thin smectic films, this problem becomes highly relevant.

6.1. *Smectic-A*

We start with the description of the in-plane isotropic situation in smectic-A materials. The equations that need to be solved in SmA films are the Navier-Stokes equation

$$\rho \dot{\vec{v}} = -\nabla p + \nabla \cdot \boldsymbol{\sigma}^{(\mathrm{v})} + \vec{F}, \tag{6}$$

and the continuity equation

$$\nabla \cdot \vec{v} = 0, \tag{7}$$

where in the latter, we assume that the film thickness is uniform and conserved. In Eq. (6),

$$\sigma_{ij}^{(\mathrm{v})} = \frac{1}{2}\alpha_4 (v_{i,j} + v_{j,i})$$

is the viscous stress tensor with the Leslie coefficient α_4, p is the pressure, ρ is the density of the film material, and $\vec{v}(x_1, x_2)$ is the flow field in the film plane. With $v_{i,j}$ we denote the spatial derivative of v_i with respect to x_j.

$\vec{F}$ denotes external forces, e.g. of mechanical, electromagnetic or gravitational origin. In the context of this chapter, it is interesting to discuss the flow around a circular inclusion with radius R in a SmA film (or, equivalently, the motion of an inclusion in such a film relative to the supporting frame). This problem is interesting both from a general point of view for the understanding of flow in restricted geometries, but also for the determination of the viscosity of the smectic material.

Commonly, flow phenomena in membranes are studied by observing Brownian motion of inclusions. Their mobility $b = v/F$ is the most interesting quantity, where v is the velocity of the inclusion relative to the film and F is the drag force. A complication in experimental studies is the difficulty to find 2D fluids whose physical properties can be varied conveniently over wide parameter ranges. Smectic freely suspended films offer unique conditions to study hydrodynamic phenomena in quasi-2D fluids. Particle mobilities are easily determined either from diffusion or drift experiments, and film thicknesses are readily adjustable. The materials used in these studies can be either smectic islands, solid inclusions or liquid droplets.

Motion of a disk in a real 2D fluid experiment can be described successfully if appropriate corrections are introduced in the hydrodynamic equations. Two specific hydrodynamic regimes have been proposed.[66,67] They take into account that membranes in all practical situations have finite extensions and are typically embedded in a surrounding 3D fluid. The full hydrodynamic description of the translational motion of an inclusion in a 2D membrane of finite radius R_0 has to take into account that the flow field has to match the boundary conditions (no flow) at the film borders. On the other hand, one has to consider the viscosity of the embedding 3D fluid which is treated as infinitely extended. A criterion which of the two approximations is relevant is the Saffman length

$$\ell_{\mathrm{S}} = \frac{\eta d}{2\eta'} \,,$$

with the film viscosity η, the film thickness d and the viscosity η' of the surrounding medium. In the geometry $R_0 \gg \ell_{\mathrm{S}}$, the viscous effects of the embedding 3D fluid dominate and the mobility of a circular inclusion with radius R is given by[66,67] (SD)

$$b = \frac{1}{4\pi\eta d} \left(\ln \frac{2\ell_{\mathrm{S}}}{R} - c \right), \tag{8}$$

where $c \approx 0.577$ is Euler's constant. This equation is applicable for $\ell_{\mathrm{S}} \gg R$. An extension for arbitrary ℓ_{S}/R has been proposed by Hughes, Pailthorpe and White[68] (HPW). When $R_0 \ll \ell_{\mathrm{S}}$, then the lateral film boundaries have a dominant influence, and the mobility is determined by[67]

$$b = \frac{1}{4\pi\eta d} \left(\ln \frac{R_0}{R} - \frac{1}{2} \right). \tag{9}$$

For an infinitely long, rectangular membrane of finite width W, we assume that the mobility of an embedded particle may be described in reasonable approximation in a similar way,

$$b = \frac{1}{4\pi\eta d} \left(\ln \frac{W}{2R} - 0.88 \right). \tag{10}$$

The different flow regimes, including the transition from the restricted geometry regime, Eq. (8), to the air drag regime, Eqs. (9, 10), can be accessed by controlling the film thickness d and the inclusion diameter $2R$.[10,11]

The mobility can be determined in conventional horizontal films from measurements of the Brownian motion of inclusions of the film. There, it is necessary to separate the random diffusive motion of the inclusions from any film fluctuations caused e.g. by air flow, and a sufficiently long observation period is needed to separate diffusive from drift motions. Nguyen *et al.*[10] were able to demonstrate the validity of the Saffman-Delbrück theory in 2D fluids experimentally, exploiting island diffusion on SmA LC films.

An alternative is the tilt of the film, creating an inclined plane where inclusions slide down under the action of gravity.[11] In that experiment, it is easy to control the effective gravity $g \sin \delta$ by the film tilt angle δ. Figure 24 shows the microscope view of a droplet with radius $R = 40$ μm sliding down a smectic-A film and the flow field created in the film. Both film and microscope were tilted to the left in the image, so that the viewing plane remains parallel to the film. The local flow was visualized here by spraying glycerol droplets with sizes below 5 μm diameter on the film. Multiple exposures of the film during the motion of the inclusion were overlayed to create the image. One recognizes an extended laminar flow field, the maximum backflow occurs approximately halfway from the particle to the lateral film boundaries.[11]

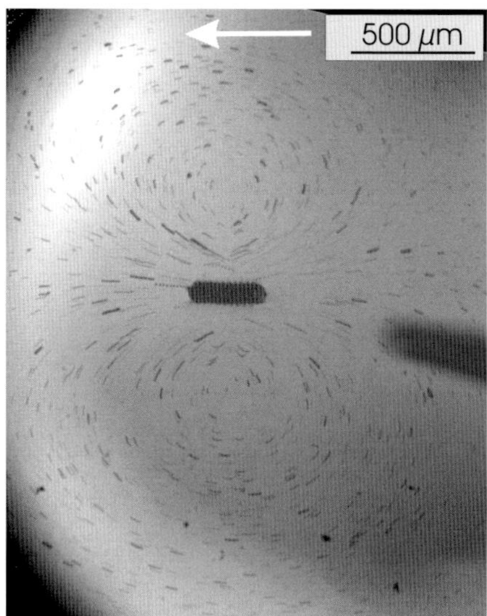

Fig. 24. Flow field around a glass sphere of 80 μm diameter moving in a tilted FSF (leftward in the image), visualized by overlay of a sequence of microscope images. 8CB at room temperature, smectic-A. The tracers are tiny glycerol droplets. The white arrow indicates the downward slope. Image courtesy of A. Eremin.

In 8CB, the mobility of glass beads and of smectic islands has been measured in such a 2D falling ball rheometer and a transition from the boundary influenced to the air drag influenced regimes was found.[11] Figure 25 compares experimental data with the predictions of Eqs. (8, 10). The same type of experiments can also be performed with liquid droplets, but the results are less reliable. The reason is presumably the shape transformation of the inclusions after embedding in the film (see Sec. 4), which changes the effective hydrodynamic radius.

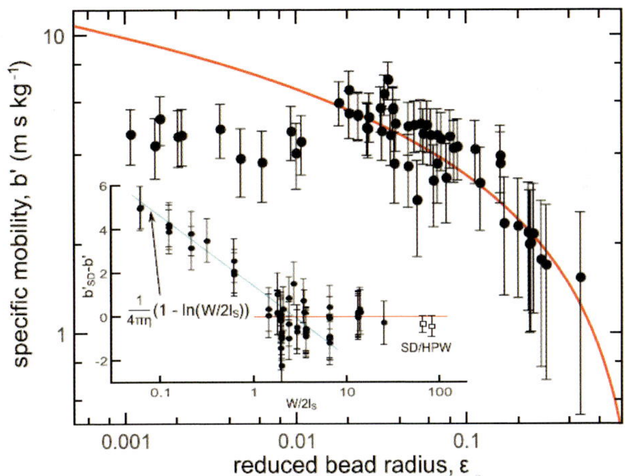

Fig. 25. Specific mobility $b' = bd$ of beads as a function of reduced radius $\varepsilon = R/\ell_S$ in 8CB films with thicknesses between 100 nm to 22 μm and width W = 4 mm, $\delta = 14°$ at room temperature. The red curve indicates the approximation for the air drag regime $\ell_S \ll W$, Eq. (8). For the data in the left part, the confinement regime, Eq. (10), is relevant. The inset shows the difference between the measured bead mobilities and SD/HPW theory as a function of $W/(2\ell_S)$. The blue and red lines show predictions in the confinement and air drag regimes, respectively. The bead mobilities (filled circles) merge smoothly with the data obtained from the drift of smectic islands (open symbols). Image reproduced from Ref. 11 with permission, copyright by APS.

In the measurements discussed so far, smectic-A films were considered, which are isotropic in the film plane. Only one effective viscosity has to be taken into consideration. smectic-C and C* films add two complications. First, there are different viscosities for motions in the direction of $\vec{c}$ and perpendicular to it. Second, the motion of an inclusion has some feedback effect on the c-director field. This is shown in the next section.

6.2. *Smectic-C*

Thin smectic-C films represent quasi 2D anisotropic fluids: flow in the film plane will always be coupled to director reorientations and vice versa. In general, the coupled system of a torque balance arising from viscous and elastic torques on the c-director, Eq. (11), and the incompressible Navier-Stokes equation, Eq. (12) must be solved in the $(x_1\text{-}x_2)$ plane together with the continuity Eq. (7):

$$\left(\frac{\partial f}{\partial C_{i,j}}\right)_{,j} - \frac{\partial f}{\partial C_i} = (\alpha_3 - \alpha_2)N_i + (\alpha_3 + \alpha_2)A_{ip}C_p, \tag{11}$$

$$\rho\dot{\vec{v}} = -\nabla p + \nabla \cdot (\boldsymbol{\sigma}^{(e)} + \boldsymbol{\sigma}^{(v)}), \tag{12}$$

where C_i are the components of $\vec{C}$, the projection of the director $\vec{n}$ onto the film plane. The vector $\vec{C} = (\sin\theta\cos\varphi, \sin\theta\sin\varphi)$ has the same direction as the c-director, its length $\sin\theta$ is determined by the tilt angle θ. The $C_{i,j}$ denote the partial derivatives $\partial C_i/\partial x_j$, and summation over equal indices in product terms applies, f is the free energy density. The $\alpha_1 \ldots \alpha_6$ are the Ericksen-Leslie viscosities (for the n-director) and $\vec{N}$ is the so-called co-rotational time flux, $\vec{N} = \dot{\vec{C}} - \mathbf{W}\vec{C}$. $A_{i,j} = (v_{i,j} + v_{j,i})/2$ and $W_{ij} = (v_{i,j} - v_{j,i})/2$ are elements of the usual shear rate and vorticity tensors. The stress tensor comprises both an elastic ($\boldsymbol{\sigma}^{(e)}$) and a viscous ($\boldsymbol{\sigma}^{(v)}$) contribution

$$\sigma_{ij}^{(e)} = -\frac{\partial f}{\partial C_{k,j}}C_{k,i} \tag{13}$$

$$\sigma_{ij}^{(v)} = \alpha_1 C_i C_j C_k A_{kp} C_p + \alpha_2 N_i C_j \\ + \alpha_3 C_i N_j + \alpha_4 A_{ij} + \alpha_5 C_j A_{ip} C_p + \alpha_6 C_i A_{jp} C_p. \tag{14}$$

In order to account for defects of the c-director field, the concept of the c-director is slightly revised in this treatment: The variable length of the projection of the n-director onto the layer plane, $0 \leq |\vec{C}| \leq 1$, serves as an order parameter. This yields additional Landau terms in the free elastic energy density f

$$f = f_L + f_{el} = L_2|\vec{C}|^2 + L_4|\vec{C}|^4 + f_{el}, \tag{15}$$

where $L_2 < 0$ and $L_4 > 0$. The ratio of the Landau coefficients determines the equilibrium tilt angle in the material, $\theta_0 = \arcsin\sqrt{-L_2/(2L_4)}$. The magnitude of L_2 and L_4 determines the resistance against tilt angle changes. Towards defect positions, $|\vec{C}|$ will decrease to zero, so that the material is smA in the defect core. The size of the defect can be estimated by $r_{\text{core}} \approx \sqrt{-K/4L_2}$. Any anchoring employed at inclusion surfaces will be effectively weakened, as the tilt may be reduced. External forces may be added to the equations, e.g. to model the influence of an in-plane electric field. The equation system usually has to be solved numerically. In smectic-A films, see previous Section, only the contribution with α_4 remains, and all components $\sigma_{ij}^{(e)}$ vanish.

For a qualitative description in defect-free states, this model may be simplified using the tilt azimuth φ of the director, neglecting material flow $(\vec{v} = \vec{0})$ and employing the one-constant approximation $K_S = K_B = K$. Then, a diffusion equation results. The only viscous damping term is preserved for rotations of the local director respective to the surrounding fields. It is introduced using the rotational viscosity $\gamma_1 = \alpha_3 - \alpha_2$,

$$\gamma_1 \dot{\varphi} = K \Delta \varphi. \tag{16}$$

Depending on the film thickness, and the film and inclusion sizes, the effects of confinement and air friction will again influence the dynamics, see previous section. Similar experiments to those in SmA films, i.e. diffusion of inclusions and their driven motion or interaction can in principle yield information not only on the anisotropic viscous properties of a uniformly aligned film, but also on the distortions of the director field by the moving particle. An initial state of a uniform c-director field in a homogeneously thick film can be prepared using electric or magnetic fields, or even by exploiting the anchoring of the c-director at film boundaries and menisci. The anisotropy of the smectic viscosities yields different mobilities for motion in different directions relative to the c-director alignment. Coupling of flow and c-director reorientation can be visualized by polarizing microscopy.

The following experiment has been performed with an inclined smectic-C film, in a setup similar to that used in Ref. 11 and described in the previous section. A glass bead is dragged down the slope under the action of gravity, and the film is observed in a polarizing microscope under crossed polarizers (Fig. 26). The film was aligned by means of an AC electric field in the film plane, normal to the slope of the film. After the field is removed, the c-director field forms a 180° bend from one film edge to the opposite film edge (yellow bars). After deposition, the glass bead slides down the inclined film. The strong material flow around the inclusion induces large, persisting distortions of the c-director field, visible in polarized light microscopy. The left image shows a transient state 2.4 s after the deposition of the bead, while in the right image the c-director near the inclusion has adopted some

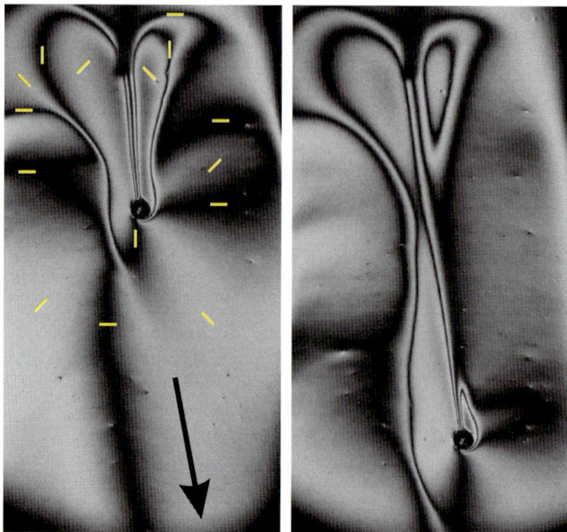

Fig. 26. Motion of a glass sphere in a smectic-C film (PP mixture) under the influence of gravity. The film thickness is 7.6 micrometers, much thinner than the inclusion diameter. The film is tilted by 13.5°, polarizers are horizontal and vertical in the images. The yellow lines indicate the local c-director axes. The left image was taken 2.4 s after bead deposition, the right image 3.4 s later. The image size is 3.25 mm × 1.75 mm, the arrow indicates the downward slope. Images courtesy of S. Dölle.

steady state in the co-moving frame of reference. The bead leaves a "distortion wake" of increasing length behind. The symmetry respective to the axis of bead motion is broken. This is the result of an asymmetric constellation of the bead and its accompanying defect(s). Behind the inclusion, a wall marks the path of motion. Another curved inversion wall precedes and accompanies the moving bead.

The film thickness is $\approx 7.6\ \mu$m and air friction is therefore irrelevant for the mobility. Most remarkably, the bead velocity is not influenced measurably when the bead crosses a c-director inversion wall in the film. This means that the anisotropy of the viscosities is practically irrelevant, at least in the above described experiment with the smectic-C mixture of two phenylpyrimidine derivatives. Very likely, the inhomogeneous director field around the moving inclusion averages out anisotropies of the viscosities to a substantial part.

7. Coalescence of droplets and islands

Inclusions at fluid interfaces may in general interact through capillary forces mediated by the curvature of the interface that is induced by them.[69–71] This leads to attractive drag forces. But even in liquid crystalline FSF of uniform thickness (SmA or SmC/C*), where such forces are absent, inclusions are prone to erratic diffusion in the film plane. Thereby they can collide with neighbors, and subsequently agglomerate or coalesce to form larger objects. Liquid inclusions in FSF can merge after collisions in specific ways.

The coalescence of fluid objects is an interesting field on its own due to its mathematical beauty, with the divergence of physical quantities at the beginning. It has large practical relevance, e.g. in rain drop formation or in sintering processes. There have been several investigations of 3D coalescence and subsequent dynamics during the past decade, see e.g. Refs. 72–75. In smectic films, the different geometries and types of inclusions provide access to the study of coalescence scenarios from 3D spheres and non-spherical (flattened) objects down to the 2D dynamics of coalescing disks: As islands on these films are flat, pancake-like structures (see Sec. 4), their coalescence shall be governed essentially by 2D fluid dynamics (see Sec. 6.1) and the smectic layer structure. Droplets on films are of curved shape but lack an internal layer structure, thus their dynamics are expected to be intermediate between 2D and 3D effects, an example is shown at the end of this section.

Islands of various sizes and thicknesses in smectic films may be prepared by blowing air jets over the film surface. By means of optical tweezers, these islands can be trapped and pulled at their borders. This provides a tool to control the initiation of coalescence and to select specific islands.[74] Various experimental scenarios can be realized: merging of island with similar or different sizes, islands of same or different thicknesses, different background film thicknesses and sizes, or different gas atmospheres. In smectic films, such islands coalesce via an aperiodic relaxation without oscillations, inertial effects are irrelevant. The relaxation of the outer contour can be roughly divided into two stages: a quick initial relaxation phase of few milliseconds towards a convex elongated object, followed by a slow relaxation to a circular shape within few seconds (see Fig. 27).

For a hydrodynamic treatment, the coalescence of two islands (thicknesses of N_1 and N_2 layers, respectively), in a film of N_f layers can be mapped to a 2D flow problem by treating the material in the islands and film

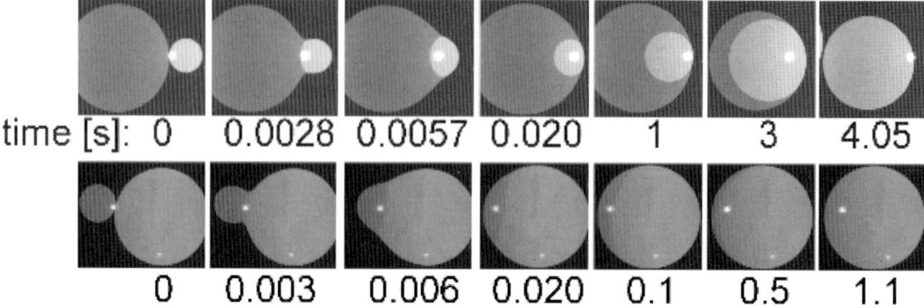

Fig. 27.   Two scenarios encountered in the coalescence of islands in smectic films: The initially thicker island determines the final thickness. Experiments were performed in the SmA phase of 8CB at room temperature. The bright spots are the optical tweezers. Film and island thicknesses are measured from reflectivity. Top row: Coalescence of islands with $N_1 = 12$, $N_2 = 19$, $N_f = 6$, image size 226 μm $\times$ 203 μm. Bottom row: $N_1 = 17$, $N_2 = 20$, $N_f = 6$, image size 259 μm $\times$ 213.5 μm.

as different phases. The respective 2D viscosities are $\eta_{2D,i} = \eta_{3D} N_i d_1$. As a 2D equivalent of the surface tension, line tensions $\gamma = \Gamma_1 \Delta N \approx \sigma \Delta N d_1$ at the phase boundaries are introduced. Here, σ is the surface tension of the smectic material, ΔN is the respective difference in the number of smectic layers and d_1 is the thickness of a single smectic layer. The line tension of a single layer step Γ_1 can be measured, e.g., from the deformed shapes of islands sitting on the meniscus in a vertical film.[74] For two coalescing islands of different thicknesses $N_1 < N_2$, the final state is represented by a circular island of thickness N_2, see Fig. 27. The total film area covered by the merged island is smaller than the sum of the initial island areas. When the thicker island is smaller than the thin one (see Fig. 27 top), the thick island is first entrained into the thinner one. Then it incorporates the material of the thin island within a few seconds. In case the smaller island is thinner, its material will initially spread along one side of the thick island, forming a sickle after a few milliseconds. Then it is slowly absorbed. When the surrounding air is neglected, the first stage of the coalescence process becomes equivalent to the mutual wetting of two infinitely long cylinders of viscous, immiscible fluids in an embedding fluid. The second stage has similarities with permeation through phase boundaries.

A hydrodynamic calculation of the complete 2D flow problem is complex, but numerically solvable. However, many important aspects of smectic dynamics already become evident in the simplest case, the coalescence of two equally sized, equally thick SmA islands: This phenomenon has many formal analogies with the coalescence of two equal, infinitely long viscous cylinders in a non-viscous environment in 3D. This mathematical problem was analytically solved by Hopper.[75,76,a] During the coalescence process, the shapes of the cross-sections normal to the cylinder axes are Booth's lemniscates. They are given in terms of a time-dependent parameter $m \in [0, 1]$, where $m = 0$ corresponds to the end state of a single circular island ($t \to \infty$) and $m = 1$ to two touching circles ($t = 0$). The commonly measured quantity is the time dependence of the width w of the fluid bridge connecting the two cylinders (i.e. the neck between the coalescing islands). The time evolution is given by[75]

$$w(m) = 2R_0 \frac{1 - m}{\sqrt{1 + m^2}}, \tag{17}$$

$$t = \frac{\pi}{4} t_c \int_{m^2}^{1} \frac{1}{\mu \sqrt{1 + \mu} K(\mu)} d\mu. \tag{18}$$

Here, $K(\mu) = \int_0^{\pi/2} (1 - \mu \sin^2 \theta)^{-1/2} d\theta$ is the complete elliptical integral of the first kind, and η the dynamic viscosity of the cylinder material. R_0 is the final radius of the merged object. The characteristic time scale

$$t_c = \frac{\eta_{3D} R_0}{\sigma} \approx \frac{R_0 \eta_{2D}}{N_i \Gamma_1} \tag{19}$$

for the smectic island coalescence is set by the viscosity, the line tension, the size and the thicknesses of the islands. Initially, the growth is expected to be linear with a logarithmic correction, in the late stages exponential.[75] The background film and air viscosities are neglected in this model.

Corresponding experiments were performed with 8CB films in air.[74] The border of the island was detected using an image processing routine (except for manual checking at very small cusp widths), and the cusp width was extracted. Figure 28 shows the evolution of the neck with time. The equilibrium radius R_0 and the characteristic time $t_c \approx 12$ ms in Hopper's model, Eqs. (17)–(19), were calculated from independent experiments ($\Gamma_1 = 10 \pm 1$ pN, $\eta_{3D} = 0.052$ Pa s,[78] $\eta_{air} = 1.827 \cdot 10^{-5}$ Pa s, $d_1 = 3.17$ nm[79]). Obviously, the evolution of the neck width does not follow the model, but proceeds much slower. The retarded initial dynamics can presumably be attributed to the smectic layer dislocation dynamics at the island circumference.

After the first millisecond, the relaxation proceeds approximately linearly as predicted by Hopper, but at a significantly reduced velocity. The deviations both in speed *and* in shape of the neck width relaxation can be

---

[a]An extension to islands of different radii is possible.[77] The time evolution is then obtained by the numerical solution of an ordinary differential equation.

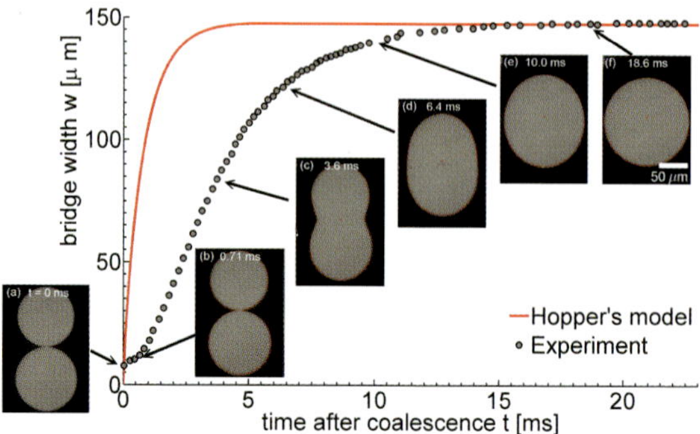

Fig. 28. Coalescence of a pair of approximately equally sized islands of initial radii $R_1 = 50.7$ μm, $R_2 = 54.6$ μm and identical thickness $N_1 = N_2 = 27$ layers in a $N_f = 4$ layer film of 8CB at room temperature, recorded at 21 kfps. The neck width is compared to the model by Hopper,[76] with a characteristic time $t_c = 12$ ms calculated from the material parameters. Data are courtesy of Z. Nguyen.[74]

attributed to viscous flow contributions: As a next approximation in the analytical model, the contribution of air drag above and below the film (cf. Sec. 6.1) can be included. The Saffman length $\ell_S \approx 122$ μm is only slightly smaller than the final island diameter $2R_0 \approx 145$ μm, so that the coalescence dynamics are expected to be influenced by air drag. The time scale t_c can be estimated to increase by about 50%. An even better agreement with $w(t)$ is obtained by numerical solution of the 2D flow problem, including the film material as a surrounding viscous fluid and an effective contribution of air drag in both phases. However, a single, time-independent length scale and thus a single efficient radius for air dissipation is still a strong simplification. The relevant flow region in the film changes its size considerably with the growth of the neck.

The coalescence of fluid droplets in a SmC film offers manifold options to study the coalescence of inclusions at the crossover from comparatively flat objects (e.g. inclusions of the film material in the isotropic phase) to nearly spherical droplets (e.g. glycerol-water droplets). In ordinary low molecular mass calamitic mesogens, the dynamics of this process on a time scale of milliseconds can be followed only by high speed imaging. In smectic polymer films, the coalescence can be substantially slower and it can be resolved with common video technique. Figure 29 shows a snapshot of droplets in a smectic-A side chain polymer during coalescence. The image was taken in monochromatic blue light (488 nm), and lines of constant thickness of the droplet profile appear with similar brightness. Neighboring

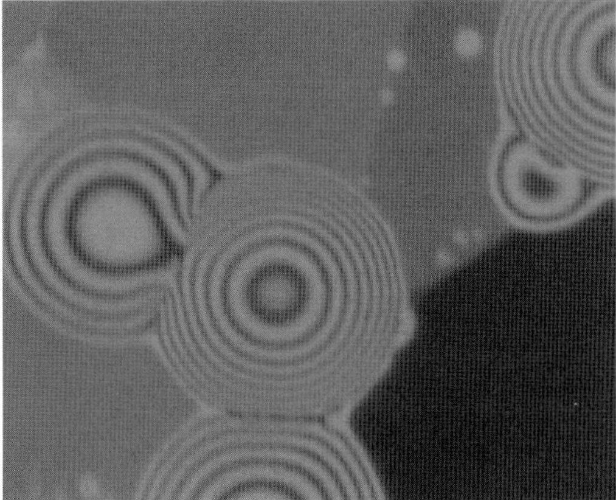

Fig. 29. Isotropic droplets of a smectic-A polymer (molecular structure see Ref. 80) in a free-standing film of the same material during coalescence, 488 nm monochromatic light in transmission. Image size 130 μm $\times$105 μm.

lines of equal brightness correspond to thickness changes of approximately 160 nm.

8. Summary and outlook

Micrometer or nanometer sized inclusions in freely suspended films provide a rich source of information about the behavior of quasi two-dimensional fluids. Thin films, in particular such with thicknesses down to few molecular layers, can often be described with two-dimensional models. When they are uniform along their layer normal, flow processes as well as interactions between embedded particles are basically limited to the film plane. On the one hand, this restricts the variety of observable structures considerably. Defect loops, as observed for example in nematic colloids, are impossible in a 2D geometry. On the other hand, the mathematical description of interactions between inclusions is considerably facilitated with respect to the 3D nematic counterparts. In the one-constant elastic approximation, topological interactions between inclusions of in-plane anisotropic (SmC and SmC*) films are described by the Laplace equation. One can establish direct quantitative analogies to other physical situations, viz. electrostatic interactions of electric line charges and multipoles, or flow fields of incompressible fluids. These analogies do not only help to find equilibrium configurations of assemblies of inclusions by means of analytical approaches, they also provide simple visualizations of corresponding electrostatic or hydrodynamic structures.

The preparation of micrometer or nanometer sized inclusions in the films can be achieved in different ways: One of the simplest techniques to achieve quasi 2D colloids is heating the smectic films into the adjacent higher-temperature isotropic or nematic (cholesteric) phases. A special modification is the exploitation of photosensitive mesogens with azo or azoxy linking groups, where a transition into a nematic or isotropic state can be triggered by UV illumination, and droplet properties can be manipulated to a certain extent.

A more controlled method is the deposition of droplets of immiscible liquids or solid objects on the film by means of dispensers or mechanical tools. A preparation of particle-laden free-standing films from an existing suspension of particles will be successful only if particle sizes are much smaller than the film thickness, otherwise the dispersed particles remain trapped in the meniscus when the film is pulled.

From height profiles of droplets, shapes of the film menisci around inclusions and the interactions of inclusions with layer steps and thickness gradients of the film one gains surface and interface tension data. Shapes of such molten droplets provide a unique access to interface tensions between smectic and isotropic phases as well as surface tensions of isotropic material. In rare cases, droplet shapes reflect competing influences of internal director deflections and capillary forces, then one can derive ratios of capillary forces and orientational elasticity.

Interactions between inclusions can be of capillary and elastic origin. Of particular interest are the topological multipoles that form in consequence of the c-director anchoring at inclusion boundaries. In one-constant approximation, topological dipoles and quadrupoles are perfect analogies of their electrical counterparts. Attractive or repulsive interactions, chain and lattice formation have been described. One can imagine various applications of these self-organized structures. One option is the polymerization of photo-crosslinkable film material containing regular lattices of lens-shaped transparent objects, for optical or chemical purposes. Another option is the transfer of films onto a solid substrate to create regular arrays of droplets or solid particles on a surface.

Apart from these static geometric problems, hydrodynamic processes in 2D can be easily accessed in freely suspended films. If one is interested in the mobility of inclusions in thin fluid membranes, smectic films provide simple biomimetic templates. The motion of objects like islands or droplets in the film plane can be evaluated to test hydrodynamic descriptions, no matter whether one is interested in flat films or closed bubbles. One can adjust film thicknesses and lateral extensions to study quasi-infinitely extended membranes (Saffman length smaller than lateral film dimensions) or membranes with restricted size. For both situations, and even for the crossover region between both limits, experimental data have been reported in smectic-A films. In horizontal films, the diffusion of inclusions was exploited, and in tilted films an effective gravity was adjusted to study drift velocities.

The more complex in-plane anisotropic SmC films still represent an rather unexplored territory. Further interesting future subjects include the study of anisotropic objects (rods, platelets) in SmA and SmC films and the investigation of the complex relations between elastic and hydrodynamic forces on such inclusions in SmC. These studies require very thin films, where the Saffman length is smaller than the largest lateral extensions of the observed solid objects. Substantial progress in the understanding of anisotropic hydrodynamics and the 2D hydrodynamics of anisotropic particles can be expected from those experiments, with substantial impact e.g. on the understanding of lipid membrane dynamics.

For the physics of liquid crystals, there is another practically unexplored field: inclusions in free standing films of the more complex mesophases formed by bent-shaped mesogens, films with intercalated layers exhibiting surface undulations,[81] and films which spontaneously form terraced labyrinths.[82] In such films, more or less ordered film structures may align liquid or solid inclusions by capillary interactions.

Inclusions that have been considered in smectic films so far were essentially of diamagnetic and dielectric nature. In principle, ferromagnetic beads included in freely suspended films are another promising extension of present research lines. These may serve as motors to drive flow in the smectic film plane, and they may also be used to study 2D colloids in which the interactions can be switched from attractive (magnetic field and particle magnetizations in the film plane) to repulsive (magnetic field perpendicular to the film plane). This opens new perspectives in the study of 2D colloidal systems. The same applies to an extension to active colloids. Self-propelled inclusions in films of micrometer thickness may resemble the active propagation of cells or micro-organisms in membranes. As long as the problem of embedding living matter in conventional smectic materials has not been solved, artificial microswimmers may be considered, that are driven by chemical or thermal gradients. Another promising approach could be the study of living inclusions in biocompatible chromonic liquid crystal materials that form smectic of lamellar phases.

9. Structures and mesomorphisms of the materials

<u>11BSMHOB</u>: (S-4'-undecyloxybiphenyl-4yl 4-(methylheptyloxy)benzoate)
phase sequence: Cryst 56.5 °C SmC* 106.4 °C N* 123.9 °C I
<u>11OAB</u>: (4,4'-bis-n-undecyloxy-azoxybenzene)
phase sequence: Cryst 80.8 °C SmC 121.4 °C Iso
<u>8CB</u>: (4-n-octyl-4'-cyanobiphenyl)
phase sequence: Cryst 21.5 °C SmA 33.5 °C N 40.5 °C Iso
<u>9BSMHOB</u>: (S-4'-nonyloxybiphenyl-4yl 4-(methylheptyloxy)benzoate)
phase sequence: Cryst 56.8 °C SmC* 104.6 °C N * 131.4 °C Iso
<u>CM11B</u>: ((2S, 3S)-2-chloro-3-methylpentanoic acid-[4'-(undec-10-enyloxy)-
biphenyl]-ester)
phase sequence: Cryst 50.0 °C Sm A* 57.0 °C Iso
<u>CT86</u>: random block-copolymer with siloxane backbone [80]
phase sequence: SmX 65 °C SmC* 95-96 °C SmA 125 °C Iso
<u>FELIX-16/100</u>: commercial mixture (*Clariant*), composition unknown,
phase sequence: X -20 °C SmC* 72 °C SmA 85 °C N* 94-90 °C Iso
<u>MX8086</u>: commercial mixture (*Displaytech, Inc.*), composition unknown,
phase sequence: X -22 °C SmC/SmC* 60.5 °C SmA 78 °C N 80.5 °C Iso
<u>OMCPB</u>: 4n-octyloxy-4'-(2-methylbutyloxy)-carbonyl-phenylbenzoate
phase sequence: Cryst (34.8 °C SmC*) 30.5 °C SmA 57.6 °C Iso
<u>PBOT</u>:   (3-n-Octyl-5-[4-(4-n-pentyloxybenzoyloxy)benzylidene]-4-
oxothiazolidin-2-thione)
phase sequence: Cryst 106 °C SmA 119 °C Iso
<u>PP mixture</u>: 50%:50% by weight mixture of 2-(4-n-Hexyloxyphenyl)-5-n-
octypyrimidine and 5-n-Decyl-2-(4-n-octyloxyphenyl)pyrimidine
phase sequence: SmC 52 °C SmA 68 °C N 72 °C Iso
<u>SF20</u>:   4-(3-n-nonyloxyphenyliminomethyl)phenyl
4-n-dodecyloxycinnamate
phase sequence: Cryst 85 °C SmC$_a$ 93 °C SmC$_s$ 102 °C Iso

Acknowledgments

Alexey Eremin, Christian Bohley, Sarah Dölle, Zoom Nguyen and Pavel Dolganov are acknowledged for kindly providing data and photos.

References

1. P. Oswald and P. Pieranski, *Smectic and Columnar Liquid Crystals: Concepts and Physical Properties Illustrated by Experiments.* Taylor & Francis, Boca Raton (2005).
2. M. Ben Amar, P. P. da Silva, M. Brazovskaia, C. Even, and P. Pieranski, Vibrations of smectic films, *Philos. Mag. B Phys. Cond. Matt.* **78**, 115–130 (1998).
3. M. Ben Amar, P. P. da Silva, N. Limodin, A. Langlois, M. Brazovskaia, C. Even, I. V. Chikina, and P. Pieranski, Stability and vibrations of catenoid-shaped smectic films, *Eur. Phys. J. B.* **3**, 197–202 (1998).
4. F. Müller and R. Stannarius, Collapse of catenoid-shaped smectic films, *Europhys. Lett.* **76**, 1102 (2006).
5. R. Stannarius and C. Cramer, Surface tension measurements in freely suspended bubbles of thermotropic smectic liquid crystals, *Liq. Cryst.* **23**, 371–375 (1997).
6. R. Stannarius, C. Cramer, and H. Schüring, Self-supporting smectic bubbles, *Mol. Cryst. Liq. Cryst.* **329**, 423–431 (1999).
7. K. May, K. Harth, T. Trittel, and R. Stannarius, Dynamics of freely floating smectic bubbles, *Europhys. Lett.* **100**, 16003 (2012).
8. K. Harth and R. Stannarius, Measurement of the interface tension of smectic membranes in water, *Phys. Chem. Chem. Phys.* **15**, 7204 (2013).
9. C. Bohley and R. Stannarius, Inclusions in free standing smectic liquid crystal films, *Soft Matter.* **4**, 683 (2008).
10. Z. H. Nguyen, M. Atkinson, C. S. Park, J. Maclennan, M. Glaser, and N. Clark, Crossover between 2d and 3d fluid dynamics in the diffusion of islands in ultrathin freely suspended smectic films, *Phys. Rev. Lett.* **105**, 268304 (2010).
11. A. Eremin, S. Baumgarten, K. Harth, R. Stannarius, Z. H. Nguyen, A. Goldfain, C. S. Park, J. E. Maclennan, M. A. Glaser, and N. A. Clark, Two-dimensional microrheology of freely suspended liquid crystal films, *Phys. Rev. Lett.* **107**, 268301 (2011).
12. Z. Qi, Z. H. Nguyen, C. S. Park, M. A. Glaser, J. E. Maclennan, N. A. Clark, T. Kuriabova, and T. R. Powers, Mutual diffusion of inclusions in freely suspended smectic liquid crystal films, *Phys. Rev. Lett.* **113**, 128304 (2014).
13. K. Harth, A. Eremin, and R. Stannarius, A gallery of meniscus patterns of free-standing smectic films, *Ferroelectrics.* **431**, 59 (2012).
14. T. Stoebe, P. Mach, and C. C. Huang, Unusual layer-thinning transition observed near the smectic-a-isotropic transition in free-standing liquid-crystal films, *Phys. Rev. Lett.* **73**, 1384–1387 (1994).
15. E. I. Demikhov, V. K. Dolganov, and K. P. Meletov, Step-by-step thinning of free-standing films above the smectic-a–nematic phase transition, *Phys. Rev. E.* **52**, R1285 (1995).
16. P. Mach, P. M. Johnson, E. D. Wedell, F. Lintgen, and C. C. Huang, Layer compression in free-standing liquid-crystal films, *Europhys. Lett.* **40**, 399–404 (1997).

17. J. C. Geminard, R. Holyst, and P. Oswald, Meniscus and dislocations in free-standing films of smectic-a liquid crystals, *Phys. Rev. Lett.* **78**, 1924–1927 (1997).

18. F. Picano, R. Holyst, and P. Oswald, Coupling between meniscus and smectic-a films: Circular and catenoid profiles, induced stress, and dislocation dynamics, *Phys. Rev. E.* **62**, 3747 (2000).

19. I. Kraus and R. B. Meyer, Polar smectic films, *Phys. Rev. Lett.* **82**, 3815–3818 (1999).

20. J. B. Lee, D. Konovalov, and R. B. Meyer, Textural transformations in islands on free standing smectic-c-* liquid crystal films, *Phys. Rev. Lett.* **73**, 051705 (2006).

21. N. Chattham, M.-G. Tamba, R. Stannarius, E. Westphal, H. Gallardo, M. Prehm, C. Tschierske, H. Takezoe, and A. Eremin, Leaning-type polar smectic-c phase in a freely suspended bent-core liquid crystal film, *Phys. Rev. E.* **91**, 030502(R) (2015).

22. P. Cluzeau, P. Poulin, G. Joly, and H. T. Nguyen, Interactions between colloidal inclusions in two-dimensional smectic-c*∗ films, *Phys. Rev. E.* **63**, 031702 (2001).

23. S. Dölle, K. Harth, T. John, and R. Stannarius, Impact and embedding of picoliter droplets into freely suspended smectic films, *Langmuir.* **30**, 12712 (2014).

24. K. Harth and R. Stannarius, Corona Patterns around Inclusions in Freely Suspended Smectic Films, *Eur. Phys. J. E.* **28**, 265 (2009).

25. F. Caillier and P. Oswald, Collapse dynamics of smectic-a bubbles, *Eur. Phys. J. E.* **20**, 159–172 (2006).

26. M. Conradi, P. Ziherl, A. Šarlah, and I. Muševič, Colloids on free-standing smectic films, *Eur. Phys. J. E.* **20**, 231–236 (2006).

27. P. Cluzeau, V. Dolganov, P. Poulin, G. Joly, and H. T. Nguyen, Droplets nucleation in smectic-c* free-standing films, *Mol. Cryst. Liq. Cryst.* **364**, 381–391 (2001).

28. P. Cluzeau, G. Joly, H. T. Nguyen, and V. K. Dolganov, Two-dimensional ordering of inclusions in smectic-c films, *JETP Letters.* **75(9)**, 482–486 (2002).

29. P. Cluzeau, G. Joly, H. T. Nguyen, C. Gor, and D. V. K., Free-standing smectic films at high temperature, *Liq. Cryst.* **29(4)**, 505–513 (2002).

30. P. Cluzeau, G. Joly, H. T. Nguyen, and V. K. Dolganov, Two-dimensional ordering of inclusions in smectic-c films, *JETP Letters.* **76(6)**, 351–354 (2002).

31. H. Schüring and R. Stannarius, Isotropic droplets in thin free standing smectic films, *Langmuir.* **18**, 9735–9743 (2002).

32. H. Schüring and R. Stannarius, Surface and interface tensions determined from isotropic droplets in freely suspended smectic films, *Mol. Cryst. Liq. Cryst.* **412**, 425 (2004).

33. P. Cluzeau, F. Bougrioua, G. Joly, H. T. Nguyen, and L. Lejček, On the chaining dynamics of inclusions in smc* free standing films, *Czech. J. Phys.* **54(3)**, 365–376 (2004).

34. P. Cluzeau, F. Bougrioua, G. Joly, L. Lejček, and H. T. Nguyen, Mechanism of inclusion chaining in smc* free-standing films, *Liq. Cryst.* **31(5)**, 719–726

(2004).

35. P. Cluzeau, F. Bougrioua, G. Joly, L. Lejček, and H. T. Nguyen, Inclusions in smectic c films as modeled by disclinations, *Czech. J. Phys.* **55(6)**, 719–737 (2005).

36. F. Bougrioua, P. Cluzeau, P. Dolganov, G. Joly, H. T. Nguyen, and V. K. Dolganov, Light-induced layer by layer thickening in photosensitive liquid crystal membranes, *Phys. Rev. Lett.* **95**, 027802 (2005).

37. P. Cluzeau, G. Joly, L. Lejček, and H. T. Nguyen, Inclusions in chiral and non-chiral smectic c free-standing films, *Ferroelectrics.* **344**, 103–109 (2006).

38. P. V. Dolganov, P. Cluzeau, G. Joly, V. K. Dolganov, and H. T. Nguyen, Interaction of surfaces in smectic membranes and their instability near thinning transitions, *Phys. Rev. E.* **72**, 031713 (2005).

39. P. V. Dolganov, H. T. Nguyen, E. I. Kats, V. K. Dolganov, and P. Cluzeau, Rearrangement of topological defects and anchoring on the inclusion boundary in ferroelectric smectic membranes, *Phys. Rev. E.* **75(3)**, 031706 (2007).

40. P. V. Dolganov, H. T. Nguyen, G. Joly, V. K. Dolganov, and P. Cluzeau, Shape of nematic droplets in smectic membranes, *EPL.* **78**, 66001 (2007).

41. C. Völtz and R. Stannarius, Buckling instability of droplet chains in freely suspended smectic films, *Phys. Rev. E.* **72**, 011705 (2005).

42. R. Stannarius and C. Völtz, Spontaneous buckling of compressible droplet chains in free standing smectic-c films, *Phys. Rev. E.* **72**, 032701 (2005).

43. C. Leier and G. Pelzl, Phasenumwandlungen von kristallin-flüssigen modifikationen durch photochemische isomerisierung, *J. Prakt. Chem.* **321**, 197 (1979).

44. P. Cluzeau, V. Bonnand, G. Joly, V. Dolganov, and H. T. Nguyen, Self-organization of n(*) inclusions in smc(*) free-standing films, *Eur. Phys. J. E.* **10**, 231–240 (2003).

45. P. V. Dolganov, H. T. Nguyen, G. Joly, V. K. Dolganov, and P. Cluzeau, Ferroelectricity-induced effects in interaction and self-organization of inclusions in smectic membranes, *Europhys. Lett.* **76(2)**, 250–256 (2006).

46. K. Harth, B. Schulz, C. Bahr, and R. Stannarius, Atomic force microscopy of menisci of free-standing smectic films., *Soft Matter.* **7**, 7103 (2011).

47. C. Völtz and R. Stannarius, Self-organization of isotropic droplets in smectic-c free-standing films, *Phys. Rev. E.* **70**, 061702 (2004).

48. D. R. Link, N. Chattham, J. E. Maclennan, and N. A. Clark, Effect of high spontaneous polarization on defect structures and orientational dynamics of tilted chiral smectic freely suspended films, *Phys. Rev. E.* **71**, 021704 (2005).

49. C. Bohley and R. Stannarius, Energetics of 2d colloids in free standing smectic-c film, *Eur. Phys. J. E.* **20**, 299–308 (2006).

50. D. Pettey, T. C. Lubensky, and D. R. Link, Topological inclusions in 2d smectic c films, *Liq. Cryst.* **25**, 579–587 (1998).

51. P. Poulin, H. Stark, T. C. Lubensky, and D. A. Weitz, Novel colloidal interactions in anisotropic fluids, *Science.* **275**, 1770–1773 (1997).

52. C. Bohley and R. Stannarius, Colloidal inclusions in smectic films with spontaneous bend, *Eur. Phys. J. E.* **23**, 25–30 (2007).

53. J. Fukuda, Configuration of a chiral smectic-c film with a circular inclusion,

Eur. Phys. J. E. **24**, 91–98 (2007).

54. P. V. Dolganov and P. Cluzeau, Influence of chirality on director configuration and droplet interaction in ferroelectric free-standing films, *Phys. Rev. E.* **78**, 021701 (2008).

55. P. V. Dolganov, V. K. Dolganov, and P. Cluzeau, Behavior of inclusions with different value and orientation of topological dipoles in ferroelectric smectic films, *JETP.* **109**, 169–175 (2009).

56. P. V. Dolganov, E. I. Kats, and P. Cluzeau, Stepwise transition of a topological defect from the smectic film to the boundary of a dipolar inclusion, *Phys. Rev. E.* **81**, 031709 (2010).

57. N. M. Silvestre, P. Patricio, M. M. Telo da Gama, A. Pattanaporkratana, C. S. Park, J. E. Maclennan, and N. A. Clark, Modeling dipolar and quadrupolar defect structures generated by chiral islands in freely suspended liquid crystal films, *Phys. Rev. E.* **80**, 041708 (2009).

58. K. Harth, A. Eremin, and R. Stannarius, Vortex flow in free-standing smectic c films driven by elastic distortions., *Soft Matter.* **7**, 2858 (2011).

59. J. C. Loudet, P. Dolganov, P. Patrício, H. Saadaoui, and P. Cluzeau, Undulation instabilities in the meniscus of smectic membranes, *Phys. Rev. Lett.* **106**, 117802 (2011).

60. K. Harth and R. Stannarius, Deep holes in free-standing smectic c films, *Ferroelectrics.* **468**, 92 (2014).

61. R. B. Meyer and P. S. Pershan, Surface polarity induced domains in liquid crystals, *Solid State Comm.* **13**, 989–992 (1973).

62. J. E. Maclennan, Spontaneous director rotation in freely suspended ferro-electric liquid-crystal films, *Europhys. Lett.* **13**, 435 (1990).

63. I. W. Stewart, *The Static and Dynamic Continuum Theory of Liquid Crystals: A Mathematical Introduction.* CRC Press Inc, Boca Raton, FL (2004). ISBN ISBN-13: 978-0748408962.

64. D. Svensek and S. Zumer, Hydrodynamics of pair-annihilating disclinations in smc films, *Phys. Rev. Lett.* **90**), 155501 (2003).

65. C. W. Oseen, Über die Stokes'sche Formel, und über eine verwandte Aufgabe in der Hydrodynamik, *Ark. Math. Astronom. Fys.* **6**, 29 (1910).

66. P. G. Saffman and M. Delbrück, Brownian motion in biological membranes, *Proc. Nat. Acad. Sci.* **72**, 3111 (1975).

67. P. G. Saffman, Brownian motion in thin sheets of viscous fluid, *J. Fluid Mech.* **73**, 593–602 (1976).

68. B. D. Hughes, B. A. Pailthorpe, and L. R. White, The translational and rotational drag on a cylinder moving in a membrane, *J. Fluid Mech.* **110**, 349 (1981).

69. D. Y. Chan, J. D. Henry, and L. R. White, The interaction of colloidal particles collected at fluid interfaces, *J. Coll. Interf. Sci.* **79**, 410 (1981).

70. K. D. Danov, B. Pouligny, and P. A. Kralchevsky, Capillary forces between colloidal particles confined in a liquid film: The finite-meniscus problem, *Langmuir.* **17**, 6599 (2001).

71. J. Sur and H. K. Pak, Capillary force on colloidal particles in a freely suspended liquid thin film, *Phys. Rev. Lett.* **86**, 4326 (2002).

72. D. G. A. L. Aarts, H. N. W. Lekkerkerker, G. H. W. Guo H, and D. Bonn, Hydrodynamics of droplet coalescence, *Phys. Rev. Lett.* **95**, 164503 (2005).

73. J. D. Paulsen, J. C. Burton, S. R. Nagel, S. Appathurai, M. T. Harris, and O. A. Basaran, The inexorable resistance of inertia determines the initial regime of drop coalescence, *PNAS.* **109**, 6857 (2012).

74. Z. H. Nguyen, A. M. Goldfain, C. S. Park, J. E. Maclennan, M. A. Glaser, K. Harth, R. Stannarius, and N. A. Clark. Coalescence dynamics of fluid drops in two dimensions studied using islands on freely-suspended smectic films. unpublished (2016).

75. R. W. Hopper, Coalescence of two equal cylinders: Exact results for creeping viscous plane flow driven by capillarity, *J. Am. Ceram. Soc.* **67**, C–262 (1984).

76. R. W. Hopper, Plane stokes flow driven by capillarity on a free surface, *J. Fluid Mech.* **213**, 359 (1990).

77. R. W. Hopper, Coalescence of two viscous cylinders by capillarity: Part i, theory, *J. Am. Ceram. Soc.* **76**, 2947 (1993).

78. F. Schneider, Measurement of the viscosity coefficient η_3 in free-standing smectic films, *Phys. Rev. E.* **74**, 021709 (2006).

79. D. Davidov, C. R. Safinya, M. Kaplan, S. S. Dana, R. Schaetzing, R. J. Birgeneau, and J. D. Litster, High-resolution x-ray and light-scattering study of critical behavior associated with the nematic–smectic-a transition in 4-cyano-4'-octylbiphenyl, *Phys. Rev. B.* **19**, 1657 (1979).

80. V. Aksenov, J. Bläsing, R. Stannarius, M. Rössle, and R. Zentel, Strain-induced compression of smectic layers in free-standing liquid crystalline elastomer films, *Liquid Crystals.* **32**, 805 (2005).

81. D. Pociecha, E. Gorecka, N. Vaupotic, M. Cepic, and J. Mieczkowski, Spontaneous breaking of minimal surface condition: Labyrinths in free standing smectic films, *Phys. Rev. Lett.* **95**, 207801 (2005).

82. A. Eremin, U. Kornek, R. Stannarius, W. Weissflog, H. Nádasi, F. Araoka, and H. Takezoe, Labyrinthine instability in freely suspended films of a polarization-modulated smectic phase, *Phys. Rev. E.* **88**, 062512 (2013).

Chapter 12

Liquid crystal-enabled electrophoresis and electro-osmosis

Oleg D. Lavrentovich

Liquid Crystal Institute and Chemical Physics Interdisciplinary Program,
Kent State University, Kent, OH 44242
olavrent@kent.edu

This work presents a comparative review of electrokinetic effects in isotropic and anisotropic (liquid crystalline) electrolytes. A special emphasis is placed on nonlinear electrokinetics with flow velocities growing as the square of the applied electric field. This phenomenon allows one to drive steady motion of particles and fluids with an alternating-current electric field. In isotropic electrolytes, spatial separation of charges that leads to nonlinear electrokinetics is achieved through the properties of the solid component (typically a metal). If the electrolyte is a liquid crystal (LC), its anisotropic properties enable separation of charges in the presence of orientational distortions and under the action of an electric field. LC anisotropy leads to electrically-driven motion of colloidal particles (liquid crystal-enabled electrophoresis, LCEP) and of the LC itself (liquid crystal-enabled electro-osmosis, LCEO). The induced charge is proportional to the applied field, director gradients, anisotropy of conductivity, and anisotropy of permittivity. The electric field acts on the space separated charges to drive the electro-osmotic flows. If the director deformations lack mirror symmetry, the LC enables electrophoresis of free particles and electro-osmotic pumping. The advantage of LC-enabled electrokinetics (LCEK) is that its mechanism lifts many restrictions imposed on the properties of the solid counterpart. For example, LCEP can transport particles even if these particles are deprived of any surface charges; the particles can even be a fluid immiscible with a LC or a gas bubble. In a similar fashion, LCEO can drive flows even if there are no floating electrodes. Ionic currents in LCs which have been traditionally considered an undesirable feature in displays offer a broad platform for versatile applications in electrokinetics of particles and fluids, micropumping and mixing, and lab-on-a-chip analysis.

415

"By 2100, like the gods of mythology, we will be able to manipulate objects with the power of our minds"
Michio Kaku[1]

Contents

1. Introduction

If we would one day be able to manipulate objects with the power of our minds, then the skill would be based on our knowledge of how matter is put into motion by electromagnetic fields. The underlying mechanisms form the subject of electrokinetics.[2–4] If the driving force represents a uniform electric field, one classifies two closely related sub-areas: electro-osmosis, which refers to the dynamics of fluids in contact with solids, and electrophoresis, which refers to the dynamics of dispersed particles in a fluid. Both areas are very active in terms of fundamental science and in practical developments of microfluidics,[5,6] optofluidics,[7] small-scale molecular synthesis,[8] sensing,[9] sorting,[10] and biomedical devices.[11,12] Research and applications focus mainly on isotropic electrolytes such as water[2–4,13–19] or polymer solutions.[20] The goal of this review is to present the exploration of electrokinetics in *anisotropic* electrolytes, namely, in liquid crystals (LCs).

Since the communities exploring liquid crystals and electrokinetics are seldom overlapping, a significant part of the review is dedicated to electrokinetics in isotropic fluids. Linear electrokinetics is a classical example (Section 2), followed by nonlinear effects, such as dielectrophoresis, alternating-current (AC) electrokinetics and induced-charge electrokinetics (ICEK) (Section 3). In all of these effects, the mechanisms driving the motion are crucially dependent on the properties of the solid surfaces or solid particles. If the solid-fluid interface develops electric double layers in the absence of any electric field, spatial separation of opposite charges in the double layer leads to electro-osmotic flows and electrophoretic mobility in the presence of an electric field. This is the case in linear electrophoresis, considered in Section 2. In nonlinear effects, the double layers at the solid-electrolyte interface are induced by the field. The latter is possible when the solid part satisfies certain conditions, for example, it is a metal or an ionic exchanger. The resulting flows grow as the square of the field, as discussed in Section 3.

When the isotropic electrolyte is replaced with a LC electrolyte, a new mechanism of space charge generation appears that is rooted in the anisotropic properties of the LC rather than in the properties of the solid part. These anisotropies are discussed in Section 4. Sections 5 and 6 demonstrate how anisotropic conductivity and dielectric permittivity, combined with the spatially varying orientation of molecules in space, allow the ionic charges of opposite signs to separate in space once the electric field is applied. The field acts on these charges and causes electrokinetic flows that lead either to LC-enabled electrophoresis (LCEP)[21,22] (in the context of freely suspended particles, Section 5) or to LC-enabled electro-osmosis (LCEO)[23] (in the context of fixed boundary conditions, Section 6). Since LC-enabled electrokinetics (LCEK) has a much lesser dependence on the properties of the particles, it has a potentially wider range of applications. For example, LCEK allows one to transport fluid droplets,[24,25] spherically symmetric metallic particles, and particles with zero surface charge.[21,22]

2. Linear electrokinetics in isotropic electrolytes

The mechanism by which an electric field causes electrokinetics in electrolytes depends primarily on how the electric charges are separated in space. In linear electrokinetics, the charges are separated through surface chemistry, and they form an electric double layer.[2–4] The discovery of electro-osmotic flows is attributed to Reuss who in 1809 observed that water could percolate through a porous piece of clay and that small clay particles could move in water when acted upon by an electric field.[26] The clay particles, as many other materials such as glass, polymers, or minerals, become charged when placed in water through dissociation of the surface groups. For example, glass in water (at pH>3) becomes negatively charged by releasing protons and forming SiO^- surface groups. The charges immobilized at the surface attract a cloud of free ions of the opposite polarity. The balance of electrostatic attraction and thermal (Brownian) fluctuations establishes the so-called electric double layer of thickness:

$$\lambda_D = \frac{1}{e}\sqrt{\frac{\epsilon\epsilon_0 k_B T}{\sum_i c_i z_i^2}} \tag{1}$$

(the Debye screening length, see Chap. 3), typically on the order of 0.3-10 nm for aqueous electrolytes.[2-4,26] Here e is the electron charge, ϵ is the dielectric constant of water, $\epsilon_0 = 8.854 \text{ pN/V}^2 = 8.854 \cdot 10^{-12} \frac{C^2}{J \cdot m}$ is the electric constant, c_i and z_i are the concentration and valency of ionic species i in the solution, respectively.

Although an electrolyte in contact with a solid surface or particle remains an electrically neutral system, spatial separation of opposite charges in double layers is sufficient to cause electrokinetics. Consider a charged solid surface screened by counter-ions, Fig. 1. An applied electric field induces a torque on the electric double layer, accelerating counter-ions in the fluid relative to the charges on the substrate until the motion is stabilized by the opposing viscous torque.[27] Figure 1a illustrates the resulting electro-osmotic flow of the electrolyte with respect to the solid substrate. The produced electro-osmotic slip velocity is determined by the Helmholtz-Smoluchowski formula

$$\mathbf{u}_{EO} = -\frac{\epsilon\epsilon_0\zeta}{\eta}\mathbf{E}, \tag{2}$$

where ζ is the so-called zeta potential (electric potential at the slip surface near the solid surface), and η is the electrolyte's viscosity. The slip velocity $\mathbf{u}_{EO}$ is generated in the immediate vicinity of the surface, at a distance about λ_D from it. Note that the slip velocity does not depend on any geometrical length such as the width of a capillary. This is why the electro-osmotic flows have a certain advantage over the pressure-induced

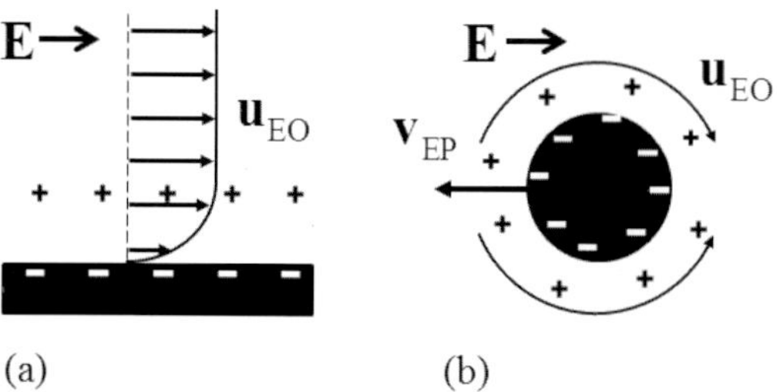

Fig. 1.   (a) Electro-osmosis at a charged surface in electrolyte; (b) linear electrophoresis of a charged sphere.

flows whose velocities $u \propto r^2$ reduce dramatically as the radius r of the channel becomes smaller.[28]

If the solid is a free colloidal sphere, Fig. 1b, then the electro-osmotic slip leads to a swimming motion, called electrophoresis, with the particle's velocity given by the Helmholtz-Smoluchowski equation:[29,30]

$$\mathbf{v}_{EP} = \frac{\epsilon\epsilon_0\zeta}{\eta}\mathbf{E},\tag{3}$$

which is valid when the particle's radius a is much larger than λ_D. It is assumed that the zeta potential is not altered by the applied electric field. Such an approximation is valid when the applied field is much smaller than ζ/λ_D, which is about 10^7 V/m for the typical $\zeta = 100$ mV and $\lambda_D = 10$ nm.[26] The electrophoretic velocity, Eq. (3), does not depend on the size and shape of the particle.[29] Because of this, the well-known separation of DNA molecules by electrophoresis is performed in gels rather than in water solutions, in order to impart different trapping forces on different molecules.

The Helmholtz-Smoluchowski equation (3) has been derived under the assumption of a no-slip condition at the solid surface. At hydrophobic surfaces of materials such as polydimethylsiloxane and poly (methyl methacrylate) used in microfluidic devices, this condition is violated. The liquid actually slips at these surfaces, with the velocity usually described as being proportional to the shear rate at the surface, $u_s = b(\partial u/\partial z)_{z=0}$, where the coefficient b is called the slip length, see, for example, Ref. [31]. Non-zero slip enhances the electro-osmotic flows, multiplying the velocity in Eq. (3) by a factor of $1 + b/\lambda_D$.[31]

It is instructive to rewrite Eq. (3) in terms of the particle fixed charge, $Q = 4\pi\epsilon\epsilon_0\zeta a^2/\lambda_D$ (the replacement is valid for zeta potentials smaller than the so-called thermal potential $V_{\text{th}} = k_B T/e$, equal to 25 mV at room temperature):

$$\mathbf{v}_{EP} = \frac{Q\lambda_D}{4\pi a^2\eta}\mathbf{E}.\tag{4}$$

The last expression shows that for a fixed surface charge, the velocity is reduced in stronger electrolytes, as the Debye length becomes smaller. Furthermore, Eq. (4) can be compared to the velocity of a particle that also carries a charge Q but is placed in a low-conductive (dielectric) medium, so that there is no screening cloud of ions. In the latter case, the electric field imposes a direct Coulomb force on the particle's charge, $\mathbf{F} = Q\mathbf{E}$. If the particle is a sphere, the balance of the Coulomb force and the viscous drag force given by Stokes' formula, $\mathbf{F}_{\text{visc}} = 6\pi a\eta\mathbf{v}$, leads to the velocity estimate (neglecting gravity)

$$\mathbf{v}_{\text{Millikan}} = \frac{Q}{6\pi a\eta}\mathbf{E}, \tag{5}$$

which is larger than the electrophoretic velocity by a factor $\propto a/\lambda_D$. The famous realization of the effect described by Eq. (5) is Millikan's experiment in which the electron charge $e = Q/n$, n=1,2,3,...150, was determined from the velocity of charged oil droplets dispersed in air between two electrodes.[32]

3. Nonlinear electrokinetics in isotropic electrolytes

In classic linear electrokinetics, the field acts on electric charges within the equilibrium electric double layers that exist regardless of field presence. The corresponding relationship between the velocities and the applied electric field is linear, which implies that flows are possible only when driven by a DC electric field. An AC driving would produce no net displacement. It is thus hard to produce steady flows. Furthermore, since the flow velocity is proportional to the electric field everywhere in the bulk of the electrolyte, the electro-osmotic flows are irrotational, $\nabla \times \mathbf{u} = 0$, which makes it difficult to produce vortices for mixing.[27] Among other problems encountered in linear electrokinetics, one often cites poor control of surface charges, relatively low velocities, and undesirable electrochemical reactions at the surfaces.[13,31] These deficiencies explain a growing interest to nonlinear phenomena, especially those in which the electrokinetic flows are proportional to E^2, thus allowing an AC driving. In this section, we consider nonlinear effects in isotropic fluids that can be broadly classified as (1) dielectrophoresis, (2) AC electrokinetics, and (3) induced-charge electrokinetics (ICEK).

3.1. *Dielectrophoresis*

Dielectrophoresis is the motion of a polarizable particle in a non-uniform electric field,[33] Fig. 2. The electric field induces a dipole moment $\mathbf{p}_{\text{DEP}} = \alpha V E$ on the particle, which depends on the particle's polarizability α (relative to the medium) and the volume V. Although the absolute values of the two induced charges are the same, they find themselves in a slightly different electric field. The electrostatic force is larger on the charge that is closer to the maximum of the non-uniform field. As a result, the particle is pulled towards the region with the maximum field by the force

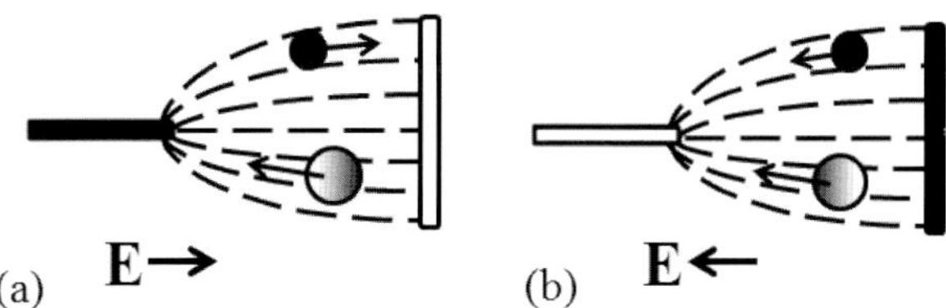

Fig. 2. Dielectrophoresis of a polarizable sphere (red/blue shading) in a non-uniform electric field; reversal of the field direction from (a) to (b) does not change the direction of motion, which is towards the maximum of the field, provided the particle is more polarizable as compared to the medium. Particle with a permanent negative charge (blue, top part) is always moving towards the positive electrode and thus shows no net propulsion when driven by an AC electric field.

$\mathbf{F}_{\mathrm{DEP}} = \frac{1}{2}\alpha V \nabla E^2$.[33] Balance of this force with the viscous drag produces a velocity that for a sphere scales as

$$\mathbf{v}_{\mathrm{DEP}} \propto \frac{\alpha a^2}{\eta} \nabla E^2. \tag{6}$$

If the particle is rod-like, it will also align itself with the long axis parallel to the local field. The dielectrophoretic forces are sufficiently strong to be used for manipulation of relatively small particles. For example, Au nanorods of length 50-70 nm and diameter 10 nm dispersed in toluene and subject to a modest field $E = 10^6$ V/m that changes over the scale of (10-100) μm experience a dielectrophoretic force on the order of (10-100) pN, which is substantially higher (by 2-3 orders of magnitude) than the random forces of Brownian nature.[34] Dielectrophoresis can be used to create locally ordered clouds of metal nanorods with nematic type of order and field-induced birefringence on the order of (-0.1),[34] Fig. 3. Orientationally ordered clouds of metal nanorods with spatially varying refractive indices demonstrate an imperfect "optical cloak" effect, reducing visibility of objects placed inside the cloud,[34,35] Fig. 3.

Studies of dielectrophoresis in LCs have been briefly reviewed in Ref. [36]; an important feature of the LC is that the non-uniform electric field can arise without a special geometry of electrodes (needed in the case of isotropic fluids). Because of LC anisotropy, the dielectrophoretic effect can occur when the LC is located between two flat plates but shows director distortions.[37]

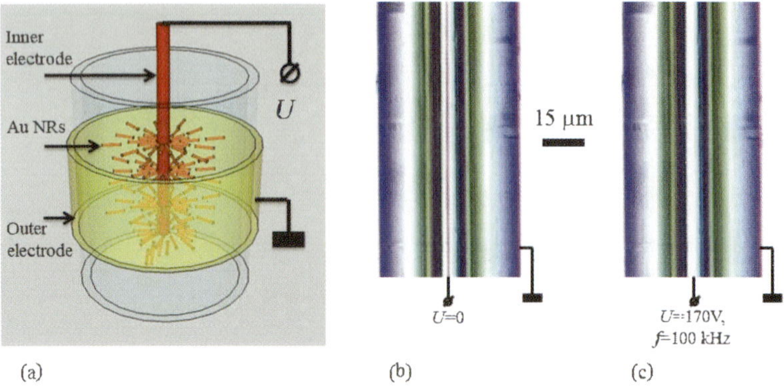

Fig. 3. (a) Dielectrophoresis of gold nanorods in a circular glass cylinder; the electric field is created by a central wire electrode and an outer electrode; the cloud of nanorods is denser near the axis; (b) optical microscopy view of the capillary; no field; (c) applied electric field condenses the nanorods near the axis and reduces the visibility of the central wire. Modified from Ref. [34].

3.2. *AC electrokinetics*

AC electrokinetics (ACEK) and ICEK are two closely related phenomena, both employing polarizable (conductive) surfaces.[31] An electric field acting on such a polarizable surface induces a polarization charge. The charge can be induced on the energized electrodes themselves, in which case one calls the effect AC electrokinetics.[38] Alternatively, the charge can be induced on the 'floating' polarizable particles located in an 'externally' applied electric field; in this case, it is called ICEK. In both effects, the electrokinetic velocities grow as E^2: one power of E induces the charge, while the second power of E drives these charges to trigger hydrodynamic flows or to transport particles. For reviews, see Refs. [14, 27, 31].

AC electro-osmotic flow was observed experimentally by Ramos *et al.*[38] in a simple geometry of two coplanar electrodes in contact with an electrolyte. The mechanism can be presented qualitatively as shown in Fig. 4, following Bazant.[27] At the instant the electrodes are energized, the electric field lines are strictly perpendicular to their surface, Fig. 4a, as the electrodes are equipotential surfaces; there are no electro-osmotic flows, Fig. 4b. The electrolyte solution conducts along the field lines and brings ions to the surface of electrodes, thus inducing double layers, starting with the regions close to the gap, where the field is strongest, Fig. 4c. The remaining un-screened electric field yields a tangential component $\mathbf{E}_t$, Fig. 4c,

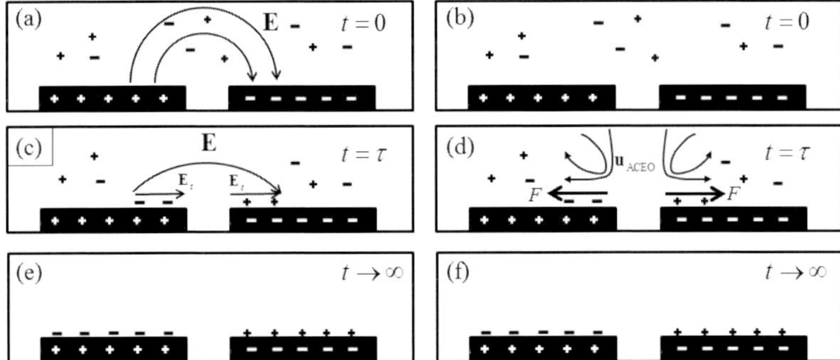

Fig. 4. Mechanism of AC electro-osmosis: (a, b) Initial moment of field application, field lines are perpendicular to the electrodes; no electro-osmotic flows; (c, d) electric field moves the ions to the electrodes, creates electric double layers; tangential component of the field acts on the induced charge to produce flows; (e, f) if the field of the same polarity is applied for a long time, the electrodes are completely screened, and there are no electro-osmotic flows. The left column shows the electric charges and fields; the right column shows the electric charges, Coulomb forces and electro-osmotic flows.

that drives the electro-osmotic slip motion $\mathbf{u}_{ACEO}$, by imposing a Coulomb force $\mathbf{F} = Q\mathbf{E}_t$, where Q is the charge in the double layer, Fig. 4d. Here the subscript stands for AC electro-osmosis (ACEO). If the field is applied for a long time, the electrodes are completely screened, Fig. 4e, and the electro-osmotic flow stops, Fig. 4f. If the system is driven by an AC field of a frequency that is too high, the electrodes have no time to charge, and ACEO does not arise. If the frequency is too low, the potential across the gap is zero, and thus there is no tangential component to drive the flow. As a result, there is an optimum frequency of the AC field that yields maximum velocity $\mathbf{u}_{ACEO}$.[2,39] The velocity does not depend on the polarity of the electric field, as the sign of the induced charge in the double layer is always opposite to that of the charge on the electrode.[40] The scaling of time-averaged ACEO flow is[27,39]

$$\langle \mathbf{u}_{ACEO} \rangle \propto \frac{(\omega/\omega_c)^2}{[1 + (\omega/\omega_c)^2]^2} \frac{\epsilon\epsilon_0 V^2}{\eta L}, \tag{7}$$

where V is the applied voltage amplitude, L is the center-to-center distance between the electrodes, and $\omega_c \approx \frac{\sigma\lambda_D}{\epsilon\epsilon_0 L}$ is the critical frequency inversely proportional to the time needed to charge the double layers.

In the original setting with a pair of symmetric electrodes, ACEO creates two vortices of flow with mirror symmetry with respect to the center plane in Fig. 4. There is no pumping action. Ajdari[41] made an important prediction that a broken symmetry, Fig. 5, would lead to unidirectional pumping. Namely, if a fluid is placed in a locally asymmetric set of electrodes, and driven by an AC electric field of a zero mean time-average value, $V = V_0 \sin(\omega t)$ that causes local ACEO flows, it will experience a global pumping force.[41] The prediction has been confirmed experimentally.[42,43]

Fig. 5.   Asymmetric electrodes create asymmetric ACEO flows (solid arrows) that produce net pumping of the fluid from left to right (dashed arrow).

3.3. *Induced-charge electrokinetics*

In the previously considered example of ACEO, spatial separation of charges occurred at the polarizable surfaces of the electrodes. In contrast to the case of linear electrokinetics, the electric double layers were formed by the applied field. Similar effects of field-induced separation of charges can occur in other settings. In 1987, Dukhin *et al.* discovered that conductive particles of ion-exchangers moved in the electric field much faster than expected from the classic electrophoretic models.[15,44] Their velocities were proportional to the square of the field; larger particles moved faster than smaller ones. Dukhin *et al.*[15,44] explained the effect as the electric field-induced formation of the electric double layer near the particles, with an effective zeta potential $\zeta = 2aE$ proportional to the field and the size of particle. As a result, the slip velocity should grow as:[15,44]

$$v_{\mathrm{EO2}} = \frac{2\epsilon\epsilon_0 a}{\eta} E^2;\tag{8}$$

here the subscript 'EO2' reflects the term 'electro-osmosis of the second kind' coined in Refs. [15, 44].

Charge separation and nonlinear electrokinetics can be caused by the electric field not only around an ionic exchanger[44–47] but also around polarizable objects such as metal spheres.[48–50] Bazant and Squires generalized a broad range of effects in which the field-induced flows occur because of field-induced charge separation, and they called this class of effects ICEK.[14,19]

To understand qualitatively the mechanism of ICEK, consider a metallic disc in an externally applied electric field, following Bazant and Squires,[14,19] Fig. 6. Initially, the electric field is perpendicular to the surface of the metallic sphere and causes the electric carriers within the metal to shift towards the surface, Fig. 6a. The field also drives the ions (of opposite polarity to the carriers inside the metal) present in aqueous electrolyte towards the surface, thus inducing a double layer, Fig. 6a. The double layer expels the field lines, creating a tangential component of the field, Fig. 6b. This component of the field drives the induced charges, thus producing an ICEO flow, Fig. 6c. Around a circular disk, the flow is quadrupolar with four vortices, being of a 'puller' type, Fig. 6c, pulling the fluid towards the poles of the disk and ejecting it into the directions perpendicular to $\mathbf{E}$.[14,18] The field-induced zeta potential is on the order of $\zeta \approx Ea$, and the ICEO

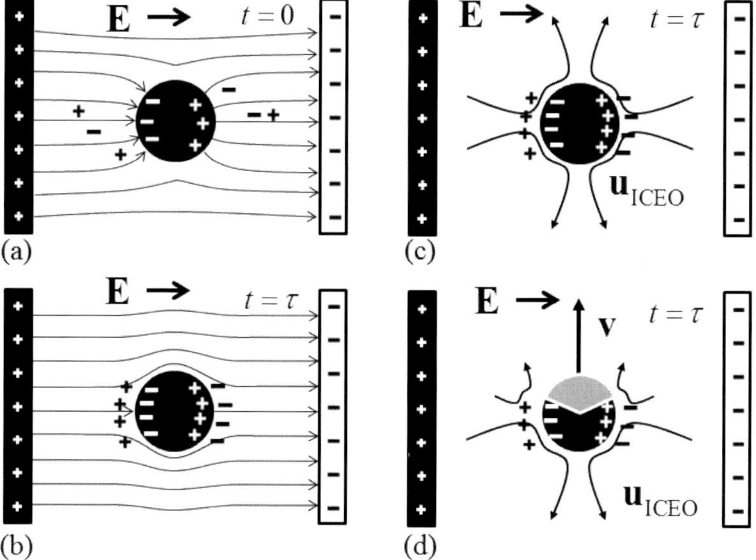

Fig. 6. Mechanism of ICEO around a metal disk: (a) initial moment of field application, field lines are perpendicular to the disk; no electro-osmotic flows; (b) the induced double layers expel the field lines; (c) the tangential component of the electric field drives quadrupolar ICEO flows around the disk; (d) if symmetry is broken, the ICEO flow results in pumping of the fluid around the disk, or electrophoresis with a velocity $\mathbf{v}$ if the polarizable disk is free.

velocities grow with the square of the field:[14,18]

$$u_{\mathrm{ICEO}} = \frac{9\epsilon\epsilon_0 a}{64\eta} E^2. \tag{9}$$

ICEO is thus dramatically different from the linear electro-osmosis in which the zeta potential, determined by the fixed surface charges, does not depend on E, so that $|u_{\mathrm{EO}}| \propto E$, compare Eq. (2) to Eq. (9). The quadratic dependence $u_{\mathrm{ICEO}} \propto E^2$ in Eq. (9) allows one to drive steady flows with a uniform AC field, a clear advantage over DC driving of the standard linear electro-osmosis, which explains the growing interest for ICEO.

Nonlinear electro-osmosis around conductive bodies in a uniform field has been documented experimentally for mercury drops,[51] solid metal spheres,[52,53] metallized 'volcano' posts,[54] and metallic cylinders, either isolated[55,56] or in touching groups.[57] In all these cases, the flows are quadrupolar and produce no net pumping of the fluid. Bazant and Squires made an important prediction that ICEO combined with broken symmetry of particles can result in an AC-driven pumping and electrophoresis of free particles.[13,19] For example, if the disk depicted in Fig. 6d contains a dielectric segment, then the ICEO flows near the less polarizable part will be weaker, which would break the quadrupolar symmetry and result in pumping of the fluid around the disk, towards the bottom of Fig. 6d, provided the disk is immobilized. If the disk is free to move, the broken symmetry would produce its electrophoretic motion upwards, as shown by the vertical arrow in Fig. 6d. This induced-charge electrophoresis (ICEP) was experimentally discovered for dielectric-metal Janus particles by Velev's group.[17] One can also observe spinning of Janus doublets caused by ICEO.[58]

Current understanding of ICEO and the role of symmetry breaking is far from complete, however. Even for the simple case of a homogeneous metallic sphere, it is unclear why the experimental velocities[17,55] are 10–100 times smaller than in Eq. (9), especially when voltages applied across the particle exceed the thermal voltage. Among the potential reasons are surface roughness[59] and nonuniformity of the field-induced potential ζ, changes in viscosity and permittivity of the electrolyte,[60] and surface conductivity effects. Recent numerical simulations[61] suggest that one of the reasons might be the a chaotic flows that develop at high electric fields because of the concentration polarization effect.[62,63] Besides the somewhat reduced velocities, the simulations[61] revealed other features not anticipated by the standard theory, such as asymmetry of inward and outward velocities.

Quantitative experiment analysis of ICEO flow patterns for conductive spheres and metal-dielectric Janus spheres in an aqueous electrolyte has been performed very recently.[53,64] In the experiments by Peng *et al.*,[53] conductive spheres were obtained by depositing a 200 nm Au layer onto dry soda lime spheres of diameter 200 μm. Janus spheres were created by covering only half of the glass spheres with Au. The spheres were placed in ultrapure water-filled (conductivity 10^{-5} S/m) chambers of depth 50, 60, 170, and 500 μm, confined between two glass plates. The experimental ICEO flows and velocity maps, Figs. 7a, b, were recorded by observing the motion of small fluorescent particles with a microscope focused onto the equatorial plane of the spheres immobilized at the bottom plate of the chambers. The applied electric field of frequency 1 kHz varied from 0 to 40 mV/μm. Although the experimental flow pattern of quadrupolar symmetry with four large persistent vortices is similar to the prediction of the standard ICEO theory, there are important qualitative and quantitative differences.

The standard ICEO theory predicts that the radial component of velocity depends on the polar angle θ measured with respect to the field $\mathbf{E} = (E, 0, 0) : u_r \propto 1 + 3\cos 2\theta$ when the conductive particle is a sphere

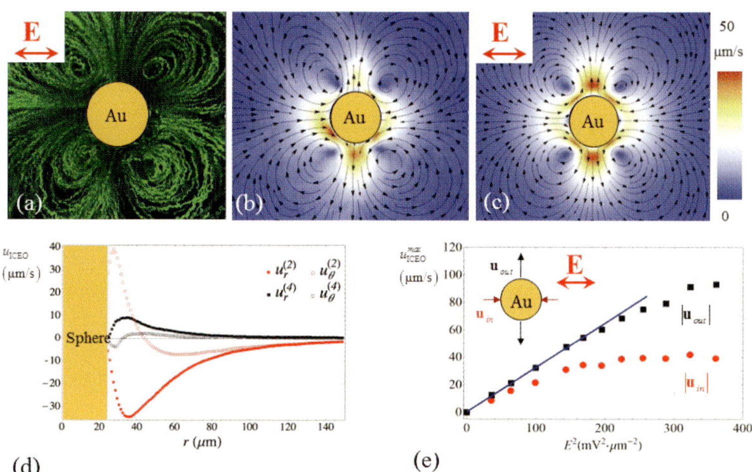

Fig. 7. ICEO flows around a gold sphere of diameter 50 μm in a flat electrolytic chamber of height 60 μm, under the AC electric field $E = 10$ mV/μm, 1 kHz: (a) trajectories of fluorescent markers; (b) ICEO velocity map; (c) numerically reconstructed velocity map with Fourier harmonics $n = 2$ and $n = 4$, Eq. (10); (d) radial dependence of the Fourier coefficients; (e) maximum inwards and outwards velocities as the functions of E^2. Modified from Ref. [53].

in three-dimensional (3D) space, and $u_r \propto \cos 2\theta$ when it is a disk in 2D.[18] The absolute value of the inward $u_{r,in} = u_r(\theta = 0, \pi)$ velocity is expected to be either larger than the outward velocity $u_{r,out} = u_r(\theta = \pm\pi/2)$, or equal to it, namely, $R_{io}^u = |u_{r,in}|/|u_{r,out}| = 2$ for the sphere and $R_{io}^u = 1$ for the disk. For spheres in confined cells of thickness h not much larger than the diameter $2a$ of the sphere, the theoretically expected R_{io}^u should be between 1 and 2. The experimental R_{io}^u determined recently[53] turns out to be *smaller* than 1. For example, when $h = 2a = 50$ μm, i.e., the sphere touches the top and bottom plates of the microfluidic chamber, the experimental value is $R_{io}^u = 0.5$ at the distance 10 μm from the sphere. Increasing the depth of the chamber makes R_{io}^u a bit larger, but still smaller than 1, as demonstrated in Figs. 7d and 7e for the sphere located in a chamber of depth 60 μm; in this case, R_{io}^u varies between 0.6 at the applied field $E = 10$ mV/μm to 0.4 at $E = 19$ mV/μm.

The inward/outward asymmetry is readily seen in the Fourier analysis of the experimental patterns, Figs. 7b, c. The radial $u_r(r, \theta)$ and azimuthal $u_\theta(r, \theta)$ velocity components can be represented in polar coordinates (r, θ) as

$$u_r(r, \theta) = \sum_{n=1}^{\infty} u_r^{(n)}(r) \cos n\theta, \quad u_\theta(r, \theta) = \sum_{n=1}^{\infty} u_\theta^{(n)}(r) \sin n\theta, \qquad (10)$$

where r is the distance from the sphere's center. The experimental velocities for spheres only slightly smaller than the thickness of the cell ($2a = 50$ μm, $h = 60$ μm) are well captured by Eqs. (10) with two even harmonics $n = 2, 4 : u_r(r, \theta) = u_r^{(2)}(r) \cos 2\theta + u_r^{(4)}(r) \cos 4\theta$ and $u_\theta(r, \theta) = u_\theta^{(2)}(r) \sin 2\theta + u_\theta^{(4)}(r) \sin 4\theta$, Figs. 7c, d. Other harmonics are negligibly small. At large distances $r \gg a$, the four Fourier coefficients decay as $u_{r,\theta}^{(n)}(r) \propto r^{-3}$ and obey the condition of incompressibility $\nabla \cdot u|_{r \gg a} = 0$, i.e., $u_r^{(2)} = u_\theta^{(2)}$ and $u_r^{(4)} = 2u_\theta^{(4)}$.

The experimentally determined coefficients $u_r^{(2)}$ and $u_r^{(4)}$ in Eq. (10) are of opposite signs, Fig. 7d, which makes the ratio $R_{io}^u = |u_{r,in}|/|u_{r,out}| = |u_r^{(2)} + u_r^{(4)}|/|-u_r^{(2)} + u_r^{(4)}|$ *smaller* than 1, about 0.58 at $r = 35$ μm and ≈ 0.67 at $r = 43$ μm. The higher the field, the stronger the asymmetry $|u_{r,in}| < |u_{r,out}|$ of the inward and outward velocities. Numerical simulations by Davidson *et al.*[61] show a similar asymmetry $|u_{r,in}| < |u_{r,out}|$ of the inward and outward velocities; it has been suggested[61] that the observed asymmetry might be caused by concentration polarization and development of chaotic flows at high fields. Note, however, that independent numerical simulations of ICEO at high fields do not show chaotic motion.[65]

The concentration polarization effect is associated with the finite conductivity of ions within the electric double layers (either permanent[66] or induced by the field[67]) that becomes relevant at high electric fields. Figure 8a illustrates the situation for the field-induced electric double layers around a metallic sphere. Polarization of the metal sphere leads to the formation of the electric double layers, as explained above. The field component tangential to the surface of the sphere drives the counter-ions in the outer part of the electric double layers from the poles (where the polar angle θ defined in Fig. 8a adopts the values 0 and π) towards the equator of the sphere. The concentration of anions at $\theta = 0$ and cations at $\theta = \pi$ along the diffuse layer is decreased as compared to their concentration near $\theta = \pm\pi/2$. This deficit of charges can be replenished through the normal flux of the ionic species from the neutral bulk towards the outer part of the electric double layer. For the direction of the field shown in Fig. 8a, anions are supplied from the right hand side and cations from the left hand side. At the same time, coions in these regions move away from the sphere

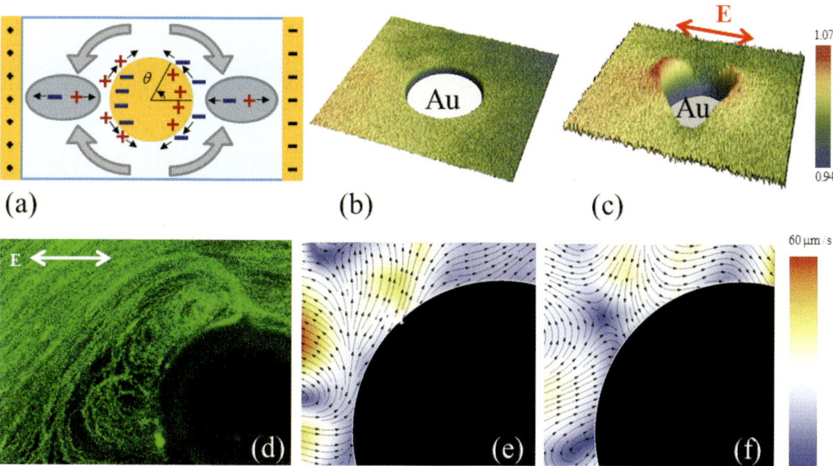

Fig. 8. (a) Scheme of concentration polarization around a metallic sphere acted upon by an AC electric field; the elliptical zones show the regions with depleted concentration of electrolyte; the large block arrows show the direction of chemiosmotic flow; spatial maps of fluorescence intensity caused by dye Rhodamine 6G involved in ICEO around a gold sphere in water, in absence of the electric field (b) and in presence of the AC field, $E = 15$ mV/μm, 1 kHz (c); (d) irregular flows around gold sphere at high AC field, $E = 40$ mV/μm, 8 kHz, visualized by fluorescent polystyrene spherical tracers; (e) and (f) snapshots of flow velocities measured within 40 ms intervals, for the same high AC field. Modified from Ref. [53].

along the directions collinear with the external electric field. The net result
is a decrease in the concentration of salt on the right and left poles of the
sphere, as compared to the concentration in the equatorial regions. The
concentration gradient, extended over the length scale on the order of the
particle size, much larger than the thickness of the electric double layer,
represents the 'concentration polarization'.[66] The concentration gradient
should lead to an 'chemiosmotic' flow of the electrolyte. The effect has
been described by Khair and Squires for linear electrokinetics, in which
the chemiosmotic flow is in the direction from one pole of the sphere to
another, being opposite to the electro-osmotic flow.[68] In Figs. 7 and 8, the
chemiosmotic flow is expected from the equator towards each pole of the
sphere, i.e., against the ICEO flow, thus slowing it down. In the numerical
simulations,[61] formation of concentration gradients was linked to the decreased inward velocities and, at higher fields, with appearance of chaotic
flows that suppressed the ICEO flows. Experimentally, the concentration
gradients can be detected by adding fluorescent ionic dyes as the fluorescence intensity is related to the local tracer concentration.[69] Leinweber *et
al.*[69] observed a local increase of dye concentration around metallic posts
acted upon by an DC electric field; the enrichment was observed along the
direction parallel to the applied field. Similar experiments with an ionic
dye Rhodamine 6G added to the aqueous electrolyte surrounding a gold
sphere and acted upon by an AC field show that the concentration of ions,
while spatially uniform without a field, Fig. 8b, is re-distributed when the
field is present, increasing by about 7% near the sphere poles, at $\theta = 0, \pi$
and decreasing by a similar amount at $\theta = \pm \pi/2$, Fig. 8c,[53] apparently because of the chemiosmotic effect. At high voltages, the experiments[53] also
demonstrate a development of irregular flows and appearance of vortices
near the surface of the sphere, Figs. 8d, e, f. These can be associated with
the hydrodynamic instability of the extended space charge regions formed
as a result of concentration polarization, as suggested in Ref. [61].

The effect of broken symmetry on the ICEO flows is illustrated by a
Janus particle that represents a glass sphere, half of which is coated with
a thin layer of gold, Fig. 9. It is convenient to characterize the structure
by a dipole $\mathbf{P}$ directed from the glass part towards the metallic part. If
the sphere were free, it would realign in the electric field to yield $\mathbf{P} \perp \mathbf{E}$
since this orientation corresponds to the maximum polarizability of the
metallic part.[70] By gluing the Janus sphere to the bottom of the electrolytic
chamber, one can map the ICEO flows around it. The Janus sphere breaks
left-right symmetry of the ICEO flows, creating a pair of strong vortices

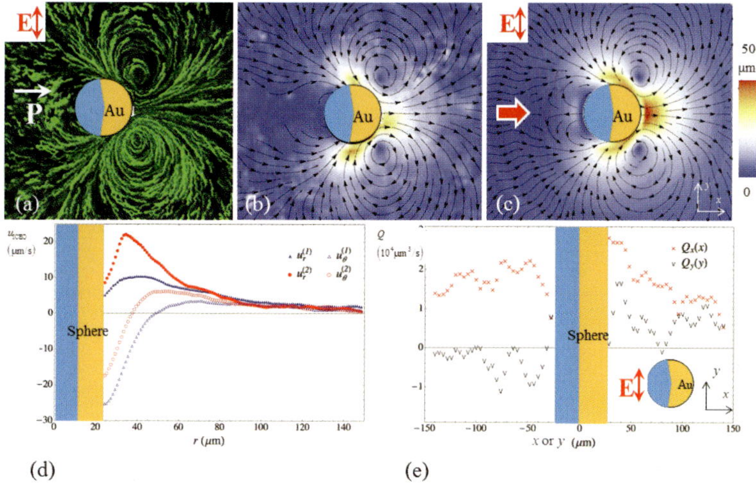

Fig. 9.   Experimental analysis of ICEO flows around a glass-gold Janus sphere of diameter 50 μm in a flat electrolytic chamber of height 60 μm, under the AC electric field, 1 kHz: (a) trajectories of fluorescent markers; (b) ICEO velocity map; (c) numerically reconstructed velocity map with Fourier harmonics $n = 1$ and $n = 2$, Eq. (10); (d) radial dependence of the Fourier coefficients; (e) volumetric flows along the x- and y-axes; note pumping along the x-axis. Horizontal arrow in (c) shows direction of pumping. Modified from Ref. [53].

near the Au hemisphere, Figs. 9a, b, c. Figure 9a shows the trajectories of fluorescent tracers as seen under an optical microscope focused at the midplane of the cell. The velocities near the Au part are much higher than near the SiO_2 part because of the higher polarizability of Au. Only two harmonics, $n = 1, 2$, are needed to reproduce the experimental data, as seen by comparing Fig. 9b to Fig. 9c.

Presence of the $n = 1$ harmonic, Fig. 9c, implies the pumping of water around an immobilized Janus particle. The efficiency of pumping is illustrated by the volumetric flow $Q_x(x)$ passing through the vertical cross-sections of the chamber, presented in Fig. 9e as a function of the horizontal x-distance of these cross-sections from the sphere. The system pumps a fluid volume equal to the volume of the metallic particle, every 3 seconds or so, along a direction orthogonal to **E**, Fig. 9c. The volumetric flow $Q_y(y)$ parallel to the field is an antisymmetric function of the y coordinate; there is no net pumping along this direction. The asymmetry of ICEO flows around the metal-dielectric Janus particles in Fig. 9 supports the ICEK mechanism of electrophoresis of the free Janus particles observed by Velev *et al.*[17]

With the typical $\epsilon = 80, \eta = 1$ mPa·s, $E = 10$ mV/μm, and $a = 25$ μm, Eq. (9) predicts $u_0 \approx 250$ μm/s, while the experimental $|u_{\mathrm{ICEK}}^{\max}| = |u_{out}| \approx 50$ μm/s is much lower, by a factor $\Lambda = u_0/|u_{\mathrm{ICEK}}^{\max}| \approx 5$. The disparity is not well understood; most likely, it is caused by multiple factors. One is concentration polarization,[61] supported by the experiments reported in Ref. [53] in two aspects. First, at moderate voltages, $Ea = 10V_{th}$, the inward velocities are smaller than the outward velocities, Fig. 7e. Second, one observes a field-induced redistribution of ions, Fig. 8. Among other contributing factors are surface contamination[71] and roughness,[59] interactions with walls,[17] confinement-enhanced viscous friction[72] and the assumption of small voltages $V \leq V_{th}$ of the standard theory.

As seen in Figs. 7 and 9, the ICEO flows of isotropic electrolytes around immobilized conductive spheres are controlled by broken symmetries of surface properties. Homogeneous spheres produce quadrupolar flows with a subtle effect of the inward velocities being smaller than the outward velocities. Metal-dielectric Janus spheres produce dipolar flows and pumping effects, with contributions $\sim \cos\theta, \sim \sin\theta$ to the radial and azimuthal components of ICEO velocities, respectively. ICEO-mediated pumping around immobilized particles and nonlinear electrophoresis of free Janus spheres[17] are both rooted in broken symmetry of the particle (such as non-spherical shape or metal-dielectric duality of the surface properties).[13,19]

Strong dependency of ICEO flows on the symmetry of the solid subsystem can be used in practical applications such as non-mechanical pumping of fluids[18,19] and particles[17,18,73–75] and in microfluidic chaotic stirrers.[76] Fluid mixing is a challenging problem at the micron scales, as the typical Reynolds numbers in microfluidics are very low and the flows are of a laminar type. One of the approaches to an effective mixing is to use an ICEO chamber with two different sets of electrodes that would produce two different fluid fields around a metal obstacle in the chamber. By switching between the two configurations back and forth, one can achieve chaotic advection in the chamber and thus facilitate stirring.[76]

To summarize this section, we stress again that in an isotropic electrolyte, the mechanisms of electrokinetics are rooted primarily in the properties of the solid component that produces either equilibrium double layers or facilitates induction of these layers in the applied electric field. The role of the electrolyte is to supply the counter-ions to complete the double layers build-up. When the isotropic electrolyte is replaced with a LC electrolyte, the situation changes rather dramatically, as it is now the anisotropic properties of the fluid that allow the electric charges to be spatially separated;

the nature of the solid part is of lesser importance. Next we consider the electrolytic properties of LCs (Sec. 4), then the effect of particle propulsion in LCEP (Sec. 5), and the LCEO effect, which yields a transparent illustration of the mechanisms involved (Sec. 6).

4. Liquid crystals as anisotropic electrolytes

LCs always contain some amount of ionic impurities.[77,78] They appear as residuals in chemical synthesis, through adsorption from adjacent media (such as alignment layers), and through the injection of charges from electrodes in contact with the LC. Electric conductivity of a typical LC with no added salts varies in a very broad range, $10^{-12} - 10^{-7}$ $\Omega^{-1}\mathrm{m}^{-1}$.[77,78] The lowest conductivity can be achieved by very careful purification; reported ultralow levels are on the order of 10^{-15} $\Omega^{-1}\mathrm{m}^{-1}$.[79] LCs with strong polar groups, such as cyanobiphenyls, typically attract more ions, while lower concentrations can be achieved with fluorinated LCs, which explains their widespread use in active matrix displays.

The LC electrolyte can develop equilibrium double layers near solid surfaces. The Debye screening length λ_D of these double layers is about 0.1-1 μm,[80–82] i.e. larger than the corresponding value in water. Thus in LCs, one should observe linear electrophoresis similar to the case of isotropic electrolytes. However, the studies are limited to very few publications.[83–90]

Rill *et al.*[88] reported on electrophoresis in lyotropic polymer LCs used to separate DNA molecules. The medium was an uncharged triblock copolymer forming micelles arranged into a cubic LC phase. The arrangement of micelles created narrow voids for the DNA to travel. The medium apparently did not change the prime mechanism of electrophoresis, but the presence of well-defined voids guaranteed excellent separation efficiency. Electrophoresis of nanoparticles was observed in lamellar lyotropic LCs by Mizuno *et al.*[84,85] Liao *et al.*[91] demonstrated electrorotation of micron-size particles in LCs, similar to Quincke rotation known for isotropic fluids.[92] Rotation can result in translation, as observed for isotropic, nematic and smectic A phases.[91,93] Dierking *et al.*[86] reported that microspheres dispersed in a nematic move perpendicularly to the applied electric field and suggested that the particle velocity is related to the charges absorbed on the surface of particles. Tatarkova *et al.* used charged microspheres and reported a linear electrophoretic effect.[94] Ryzhkova, Podgornov, and Haase discovered a regime in which the velocity-field relationship had a cubic correction to the linear dependence.[83] A strong effort was undertaken in industry to explore LCs in electrophoretic displays, as reviewed by Klein.[95]

Electric conductivity in a LC depends on the direction of current with respect to the director. As a rule, conductivity along the director is higher than in a perpendicular direction, $\sigma_{||} > \sigma_{\perp}$. Anisotropy of conductivity in LCs is well documented; $\sigma_{||}/\sigma_{\perp}$ typically varies between 1 and 1.8.[78] Anisotropic conductivity explains the so-called Carr-Helfrich effect, i.e., occurrence of an anomalous orientation and a sequence of electrohydro-dynamic convective instabilities observed in a uniformly aligned LC with negative dielectric anisotropy $\Delta\epsilon = \epsilon_{||} - \epsilon_{\perp} < 0$ acted upon by a 'vertical' electric field $\mathbf{E}$ that is perpendicular to the planar director $\hat{\mathbf{n}} = (1,0,0)$.[96–98] At high frequencies of the field, the LC preserves its orientation, $\hat{\mathbf{n}} \perp \mathbf{E}$, as dictated by the negative sign of $\Delta\epsilon$. At low frequencies, anisotropy of conductivity coupled with small fluctuative deviations of the director from the initial orientation, leads to spatial charge separation along the horizontal extension of the cell. Space charge modifies the local electric field, by adding a horizontal component. This component tends to enhance the original fluctuative misalignment of the director (anomalous orientation). Furthermore, the spatial charge experiences the bulk Coulomb force that at sufficiently high fields can overcome the viscous stresses and cause electrohydrodynamic convection. The latter adopts a variety of forms, depending on the amplitude and frequency of the field, from regular well-ordered rolls to more complex dynamic scattering modes (DMS). Scenarios of DMS evolution are currently a subject of intensive studies as they represent an assessable experimental model of the growth phenomena in non-equilibrium systems, see, e.g. [99]. The important difference between the Carr-Helfrich effect and LC-enabled electrokinetics is that in the first case, the director distortions are generated in a fluctuative manner from a uniform state and then enhanced by the applied field, while in the second case, the director distortions are the feature of the equilibrium state, being introduced either by the dispersed colloidal particles or through other means, such as surface anchoring patterns. As a result, the pattern of space separated charges follows the pattern of the director field in a deterministic manner.

Director orientation and its distortions play a decisive role in LC-enabled electrokinetics,[21–25,100] as will be discussed in detail in the next sections. The important role of the director field in statics and dynamics of colloidal particles in LCs has been already clearly established in earlier studies, see, for example, reviews [36,101–103]. Anisotropy of viscous drag for a particle moving parallel and perpendicular to the director has been demonstrated in Refs. [103–109]. Brownian motion in LCs was found to be both anisotropic[110] and anomalous[111] thanks to the director and its fluctuations. Note here that typical velocities involved in the electrically triggered motion of particles in LCs, according to the experimental works,[21–25,83,86,94,100,112] are less than $v \sim 100$ μm/s; the particles are usually smaller than 100 μm. Therefore, the Reynolds number $Re = \rho v R/\eta$, which indicates the relative importance of inertia and viscous terms in the dynamics, is very small. With fluid density $\rho \sim 10^3$ kg/m^3 and viscosity $\eta \sim 0.1$ kg m^{-1}s^{-1},[96,113] one estimates $Re \sim 10^{-5} - 10^{-4}$; the inertia effects can be neglected. This feature leads to the celebrated Scallop Theorem:[114] for a small object to 'swim' in an isotropic fluid, it should exhibit a 'non-reciprocal' stroke that is different when run forward and backwards.

The hydrodynamics of nematics is complicated by velocity-director coupling. The Ericksen number $Er = \eta v R/K$ measures the relative importance of the viscous and elastic forces. With $K = 10$ pN,[96,113] $\eta = 0.1$ kg m^{-1}s^{-1}, $a = 50$ μm, even a modest velocity $v = 2$ μm/s leads to $Er = 1$. For $Er < 1$, one can neglect the nonlinear effects and consider the Stokes drag on the sphere as a linear function of v. However, for $Er > 1$, the coupling between the director and the velocity field makes the Stokes drag nonlinear, which might influence the dynamics of colloidal particles.[115] In what follows, we neglect this coupling, which is justified for small velocities. We also do not consider flexoelectric and backflow effects; although these are important, they do not change the qualitative picture of the LC as an electrolytic medium in which the space charge is induced simply through director distortions and anisotropy of electric conductivity and dielectric permittivity.

5. Liquid crystal-enabled electrophoresis

Consider a solid dielectric sphere in a uniform nematic with an overall director $\hat{\mathbf{n}}_0$, set, for example, by a surface rubbing along the x-axis, Fig. 10. The sphere imposes local anchoring on the director, aligning it perpendicularly to itself. The local radial director field needs to match the uniform director $\hat{\mathbf{n}}_0 = (1,0,0)$ away from the sphere. The frustration is resolved[116] through the formation of a topological point defect, the so-called hyperbolic hedgehog, Fig. 10a.

The hedgehog-sphere pair can be characterized by a structural dipole $\mathbf{p} = (p, 0, 0)$, Figs. 10a, c, directed from the core of the point defect towards the sphere. The dipole $\mathbf{p}$ is parallel to $\hat{\mathbf{n}}_0 = (1,0,0)$ but can be oriented either towards the positive or negative end of the x-axis; the orientation is determined by random factors such as surface irregularities of the parti-

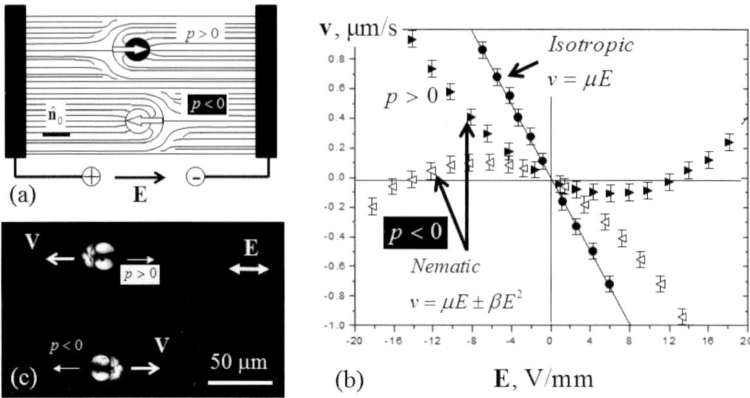

Fig. 10. Liquid crystal-enabled electrophoresis (LCEP): (a) scheme of experiment with a DC field; (b) electrophoretic velocity of glass spheres in isotropic (black circles) and nematic (triangles) phase for two orientations of the structural dipole; (c) AC field-driven electrophoresis with polarity defined by the structural dipoles. Modified from Ref. [21].

cle. Once chosen, the hedgehog's position cannot be changed without very strong perturbations, such as melting of the entire nematic bulk.

If the surface of the sphere carries electric charges, one would expect to observe a linear electrophoretic effect, similar to the case of isotropic electrolytes. Indeed, when the LC is melted into an isotropic fluid, a linear electrophoretic motion of glass and polymer particles with velocity $v = \mu E$ is clearly observed, Fig. 10b; here μ is the mobility. In the nematic phase, the situation changes rather dramatically.[21]

Experiments[21] reveal that the velocity-field dependence is no longer a linear function, but represents a sum of two terms, one linear in the field and one quadratic, Fig. 10b. (In order to mitigate possible director realignment because of dielectric anisotropy $\Delta\epsilon > 0$, the electric field $\mathbf{E} = (E_x, 0, 0)$ is parallel to the overall director $\hat{\mathbf{n}}_0 = (1, 0, 0)$). The sign of the quadratic term depends on the polarity of $\mathbf{p}$ but does not depend on the electric field polarity, Fig. 10b. On the other hand, the sign of the linear term depends on the field polarity but does not depend on $\mathbf{p}$.[21] If an AC driving is used, then the linear term averages to zero, but the quadratic term yields an electrophoretic propulsion with $v \propto E^2$ along the direction opposite to $\mathbf{p}$, with the hedgehog leading the sphere in the case shown in Fig. 10c. The nonlinear term disappears when the LC is melted into an isotropic fluid; the electrophoretic velocity shows only a linear dependence on the applied field. Furthermore, the electrophoretic activity disappears if the particles are placed in shallow cells of thickness comparable to their diameter.[21] In this case, the normally anchored sphere produces more symmetric quadrupolar director distortions (the so-called Saturn ring configurations[117,118]). LC-enabled electrophoresis is thus deeply rooted in the type of director distortions around the sphere.

A separate study of a nematic with $\Delta\epsilon < 0$ revealed how LCEP depends on mutual orientations of $\mathbf{p}$, $\mathbf{E}$, and $\hat{\mathbf{n}}_0$.[22] Let us choose $\hat{\mathbf{n}}_0 = (0,1,0)$, Fig. 11. In a LC with $\Delta\epsilon < 0$, the electric field can be applied along any direction perpendicular to $\hat{\mathbf{n}}_0 = (0,1,0)$ without causing any realignment in the far field and associated backflow.[119,120] There are two differently directed components of electrophoretic mobility in this case,[22] presented in Figs. 11a and b, respectively.

First, if the particle is charged, it moves collinearly with the applied field $\mathbf{E} = (E_x,0,0)$, as in standard electrophoresis, Fig. 11a. The velocity of small particles of diameter $2a = 5$ μm grows linearly with the field. This behavior indicates that the electrophoretic mobility along the field direction is caused by equilibrium electric double layers around the charged particle,

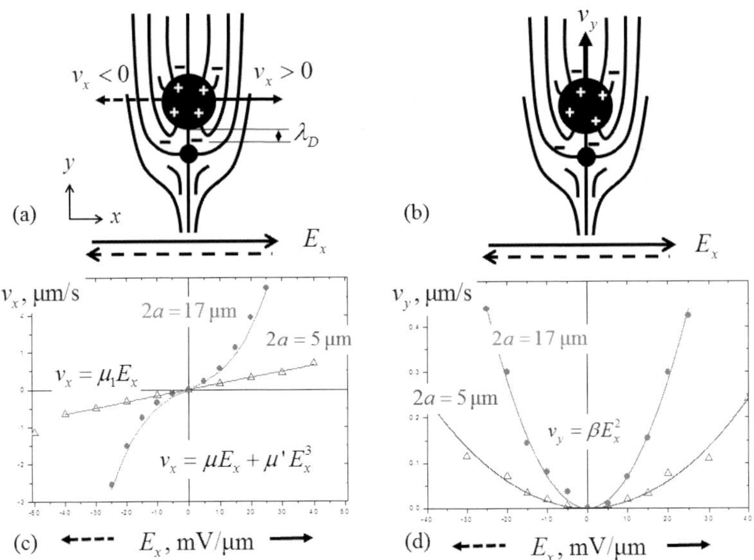

Fig. 11. Electrophoresis of a sphere in a nematic with negative dielectric anisotropy: (a) linear electrophoretic velocity component parallel to the field; (b) quadratic (in field) velocity component perpendicular to the electric field. Modified from Ref. [22].

as described in Sec. 2, Fig. 1b. If the particle is large, $2a = 17$ μm, the field dependence acquires a cubic term, Fig. 11c, $v_x = \mu E_x + \mu' E_x^3$. This velocity component is parallel to the applied electric field, Fig. 11a. The cubic term is observed also in isotropic electrolytes. The phenomenon, called the Stotz-Wien effect[121,122] is explained by the field-induced polarization of the electric double layers.[123] A similar effect is natural for a LC medium, where it can also be enhanced by the dielectric torques $\propto \Delta\epsilon E^2$ realigning the director. The field-induced change $\propto E^2$ of the linear mobility μ is equivalent to the appearance of the cubic coefficient μ'.[22]

The most intriguing feature is that the particle also moves *perpendicularly* to the field, Fig. 11b, with a velocity $v_y = \beta E_x^2$ that obviously does not depend on the field polarity, Fig. 11d. Such a motion is simply impossible in linear electrophoresis.[2–4] If the nematic is melted into the isotropic fluid, the quadratic component disappears; the effect thus cannot be explained by the existence of equilibrium electric double layers around the particle. As discussed in the next section, the phenomenon is caused by the field-induced separation of charges in the LC surrounding the particle.

The fact that the applied electric field causes two different directions of motion, parallel and perpendicular to itself, and that the corresponding velocities show dependencies of the type $v_x \propto E$ and $v_y \propto E^2$, allows one to control electrophoretic trajectories in 3D space by simply applying AC and DC electric fields. An example is presented in Fig. 12.[22] A planar nematic cell is subject to the vertical electric field acting along the axis z perpendicular to the plates of the cell. The nematic is of a negative dielectric anisotropy, $\Delta\epsilon < 0$. The cell contains dispersed glass spheres with normal surface anchoring that create point defect hedgehogs either on the left or the right side of the sphere, see the inset in Fig. 12. A DC field applied across the cell controls the z-component of velocity and the z-coordinate of the levitating sphere through linear electrophoresis. However, if the electric field applied in the same direction is of the AC type, it will drive the spheres along the horizontal direction parallel to the overall director, thanks to LCEP caused by broken left-right symmetry of the sphere with the hedgehog on its side. The in-plane motion can be predesigned by patterned director alignment; as an example, Ref. [21] demonstrates circular electrophoresis of particles in nematic cells with circular surface treatment.

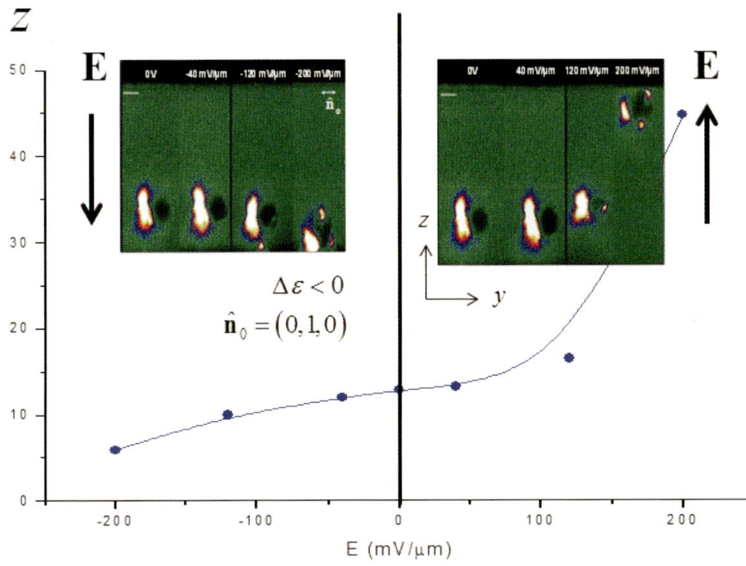

Fig. 12. Electrophoretically controlled levitation of a positively charged borosilicate glass sphere of diameter 9.6 μm in a planar nematic cell with negative dielectric anisotropy; the vertical DC field pushes the sphere either downwards ($E < 0$) or upwards ($E > 0$). The insets show fluorescent confocal polarizing microscopy textures of the samples in the vertical cross-section; the glass sphere is seen as a dark spot; the hedgehog is seen as a bright region. Redrawn from Ref. 22.

6. Liquid crystal-enabled electro-osmosis

Any form of electrokinetics requires separation of electric charges. In classic electrophoresis, the charges are separated by dissociation at the fluid-solid interface or by different affinity of dissolved positive and negative ions to the solid substrates. In ICEK, the charges are separated by the electric field thanks to the special properties of the particle, which can be an ionic exchanger[15,16] or a metal[13,14,17,18] (the latter case includes the AC electrokinetics at metal electrodes[38]). In LCEK, the mechanism of space charge formation is rooted in anisotropy of the medium itself, namely, in anisotropy of electric conductivity and dielectric permittivity, as well as spatially varying molecular orientation director.[23]

The essence can be understood by considering a disk-like particle placed in a 2D LC cell with a uniform director $\hat{\mathbf{n}}_0$. The lateral surface of the particle provides a certain anchoring direction, either normal to itself, Fig. 13a,

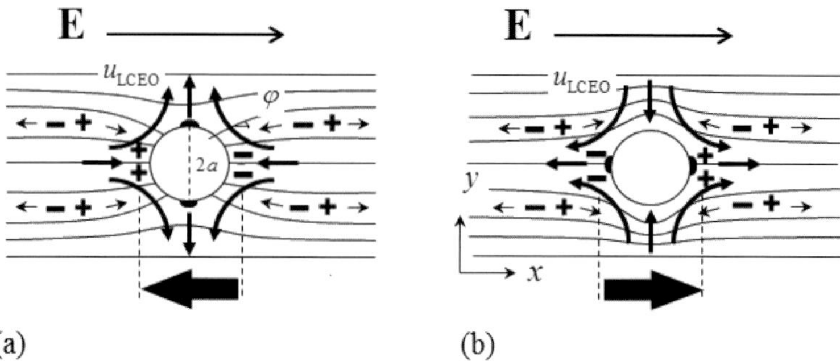

Fig. 13.   Anisotropy of conductivity induces space charge in the electric field, in a LC distorted around: (a) a disk with normal anchoring and quadrupolar director distortions; (b) a disk with tangential anchoring. Space separated charges form electric double layers of large spatial extension (comparable to the diameter of the sphere). The induced dipole moment, shown by block arrows underneath the figures, is either antiparallel to the applied electric field or parallel to it, depending on the director gradients. The dipoles reverse their polarity when the electric field is reversed. Electro-osmotic flows of steady directionality are shown by thick arrows; their direction does not change when the polarity of the applied electric field is reversed.

or tangential, Fig. 13b. To match the near- and far-fields, the director acquires distortions of a quadrupolar type. Suppose that the dielectric anisotropy is zero, $\Delta\epsilon = 0$, so that the electric field does not realign the director; its only action is to drive the ions. If $\Delta\sigma > 0$, the ions prefer to move along the director lines. As a result, positive and negative charges gather in different regions of the space, Fig. 13. For the disk with normal boundary conditions, the director field lines are converging on the left and right sides, Fig. 13a. In this case, for the electric field applied in the direction from left to right, $E_x > 0$, the accumulated charges are positive at the left side of the disk and negative on its right side, Fig. 13a. For the disk with tangential anchoring, the director lines are diverging; the signs of the separated charges in Fig. 13b are opposite to that ones in Fig. 13a. Comparison of Fig. 13a and Fig. 13b illustrates clearly that polarity of space charge is determined by the sign of director gradients. In LCEK, the field-driven charge separation occurs in a deterministic manner, following the pre-existing equilibrium pattern of spatially-varying director, such as the patterns shown in Figs. 13a, b.

Once the charges are separated in space, the electric field drives them by inserting the Coulomb force of density $f \propto \rho(E)E$, which yields an electro-osmotic flow of the nematic, Fig. 13; here $\rho(E) \propto E$ is the charge density that is proportional to the field that induced it. Reversing the field polarity alters the sign of the induced charge $\rho \propto E$ at a given location, but the product $\rho E \propto E^2$ remains polarity-insensitive. For example, if the field direction shown in Fig. 13a is reversed, $E_x < 0$, then the left side of the disk would accumulate negative ions and the right side would accumulate positive ions; the product ρE would remain the same. Therefore the forces and flows are polarity independent, growing as E^2. Of course, polarity reversal of charge clouds takes some time, thus the forces and flows decay as the frequency of the AC field increases.

As follows from discussion above, the induced space charge is sensitive to the sign of director distortions $\partial \varphi / \partial y$, where φ is the angle between the unperturbed $\hat{\mathbf{n}}_0$ and the actual director, Fig. 13a. As a result of opposite charge patterns, the two disks with different surface anchoring produce opposite polarities of flows. The LCEO flow is of a 'puller' type around the normally anchored disk with the converging director, i.e., the inward velocities are collinear with $\mathbf{E}$, Fig. 13a. The tangential disk with the diverging director configuration produces a 'pusher' pattern of flow, as the inward velocities are normal to the field, Fig. 13b.

Experiments[23] with two types of surface anchoring at the surface of dielectric spheres placed in shallow nematic LC cells confirm the prediction of 'puller' and 'pusher' flows: the sphere with a Saturn ring in Fig. 14b is a puller and the sphere with tangential anchoring in Fig. 14d is a pusher. In both cases the flows are of quadrupolar symmetry with four vortices.

The LCEO flow pattern can be analyzed using Eq. (10). Since electric conductivity and viscosity of LC are anisotropic, one would expect some elongation of the four vortices in the direction of the applied field and $\hat{\mathbf{n}}_0 = (1, 0, 0)$. As a result, the Fourier description of Fig. 14b requires three even harmonics ($n = 2, 4, 6$) to produce a close match of the experiment. Far from the sphere, the coefficients $u_{rc}^{(2)}(r) = u_{\theta s}^{(2)}(r), u_{rc}^{(4)}(r) = 2u_{\theta s}^{(4)}(r)$ and $u_{rc}^{(6)}(r) = 3u_{\theta s}^{(6)}(r)$ show dependencies $\propto 1/r^3$ and satisfy the incompressibility condition.

The principle of symmetry connection between the director gradients and the ensuing LCEO patterns can be extended to the dipolar director field formed around a normally anchored sphere in a thick cell that produces a hyperbolic hedgehog in its vicinity,[116] Fig. 15. Since the left-right symmetry is broken, the nematic LC is pumped around the sphere, Figs. 15b, c. The LCEO pattern contains odd harmonics describing this pumping effect. The coefficients of the first harmonic $n = 1$ decay with the distance

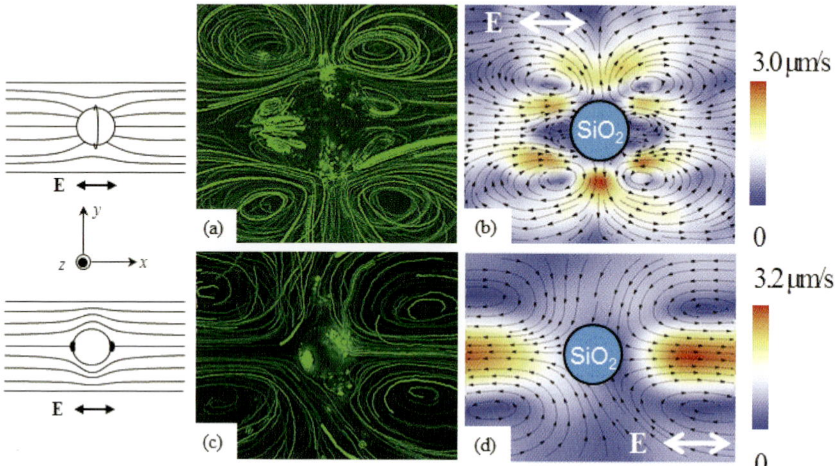

Fig. 14. LCEO streamlines and velocity maps around glass spheres of diameter 50 µm. (a),(b) perpendicular anchoring; (c),(d) tangential anchoring. Velocity patterns are of puller (b) and pusher (d) type. AC field driving of frequency 5 Hz and amplitude 26 mV/µm. Modified from Ref. [23].

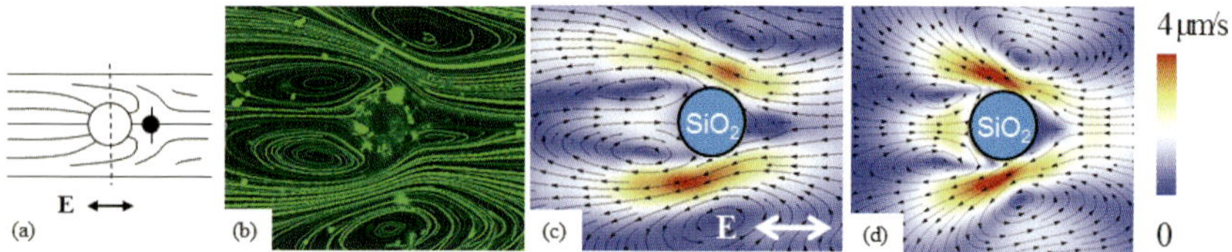

Fig. 15. (a) Director field around a sphere with perpendicular surface anchoring and a hyperbolic hedgehog on the right-hand side; the director lines are converging on the left and diverging on the right-hand side, breaking the mirror symmetry with respect to the vertical axis shown by a dashed line. LCEO streamlines (b) and velocity maps (c,d) around an immobilized glass sphere of diameter 50 µm with perpendicular surface anchoring. Horizontal AC field of frequency 5 Hz and amplitude 26 mV/µm pumps the nematic from right to left. Part (b) shows the experimentally determined velocity map, part (c) shows the velocity field reconstructed with three harmonics of the Fourier analysis. Modified from Ref. [23]

as $u_{rc}^{(1)}(r) = u_{\theta s}^{(1)}(r) \propto 1/r^2$, while the coefficients with $n = 2$ to 6 decay faster, $\propto 1/r^3$, satisfying the incompressibility condition. A similar pumping effect is expected for a Janus sphere, one half of which is tangentially anchored, while the other half is normally anchored.[124] In principle, any type of asymmetric director field would produce LCEO flows and pumping effects.

The pumping effect around an immobilized sphere with normal surface anchoring implies that if the particle is free, it will move with velocity $v \propto E^2$, as observed in Ref. [21], Fig. 10. Both LCEO and LCEP are caused by the same mechanism: spatial separation of charges in a distorted anisotropic LC electrolyte.

How do the LCEO and LCEP velocities depend on the materials properties? To answer this question, let us first estimate the density ρ of charges created as a result of conductivity anisotropy and establish how it depends on the typical scale a of director distortions, E, and $\Delta\sigma$. For simplicity, consider 2D geometry and assume that the dielectric anisotropy is small, $\Delta\epsilon \ll \bar{\epsilon}$, where $\bar{\epsilon} = (\epsilon_{||} + \epsilon_{\perp})/2$, and that the director distortions are weak, $\hat{\mathbf{n}} = (1, \varphi)$, where $\varphi = \varphi(x, y)$ is a small tilt angle between the director and the x-axis, Fig. 13a. The field, applied along the x-axis, drives ionic currents $J_i = \sigma_{ij} E_j$, where $\sigma_{ij} = \sigma_{\perp}\delta_{ij} + \Delta\sigma n_i n_j$ is the conductivity tensor; i and j stand for x and y. For small φ, the current components are $J_x = \sigma_{||} E_x + \Delta\sigma\varphi E_y$ and $J_y = \sigma_{\perp} E_y + \Delta\sigma\varphi E_x$; the field component E_y is induced by separation of charges. Using the charge conservation law $\mathrm{div}\mathbf{J} = 0$ and Poisson's equation $\mathrm{div}\mathbf{D} = \rho$ (where $\mathbf{D}$ is the electric displacement), one obtains the charge density $\rho(x, y)$ caused by anisotropy of the LC and director gradients $|\partial\varphi/\partial y| \sim 1/a$ in the presence of an electric field:[23]

$$\rho(x, y) = \left(-\frac{\Delta\sigma}{\bar{\sigma}} + \frac{\Delta\epsilon}{\bar{\epsilon}}\right)\epsilon_0\bar{\epsilon}E_x\frac{\partial\varphi}{\partial y}; \tag{11}$$

here $\bar{\sigma} = (\sigma_{||} + \sigma_{\perp})/2$ is the average conductivity. The induced charge density is thus proportional to the director gradients, anisotropy of conductivity and permittivity, and the field itself. The amplitude of LCEO velocity around a sphere of radius a then follows from the balance of the driving bulk force $f \propto \rho E$ and viscous resistance $\eta u/a^2$:[23]

$$|u_{\mathrm{LCEO}}| = \frac{\alpha\epsilon_0\bar{\epsilon}a}{\eta}\left|\frac{\Delta\sigma}{\bar{\sigma}} - \frac{\Delta\epsilon}{\bar{\epsilon}}\right|E^2. \tag{12}$$

The numerical coefficient $\alpha \sim 1$ is introduced to account for the replacement of anisotropic LC viscosity with its average value η and for other approximations, such as using $1/a$ as a measure of director gradients.

Experiments show that the amplitude $|u_{\mathrm{LCEO}}^{\max}|$ of LCEO velocities is linearly proportional to a, Fig. 16a, and to E^2, Fig. 16b, as expected from Eq. (12). The theoretical estimate, Eq. (12), with typical $\alpha = 1, \Delta\sigma/\bar{\sigma} =$

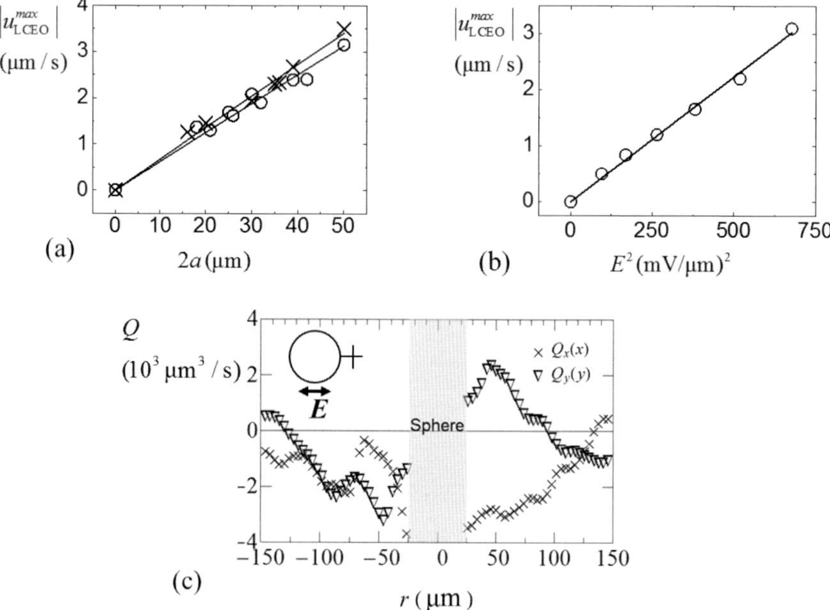

Fig. 16. Quantitative parameters of LCEO around a glass sphere subject to a uniform AC electric field of frequency 5 Hz. (a) Maximum LCEO velocity around tangentially anchored (circles) and perpendicularly anchored (crosses) spheres increases linearly with the diameter $2a$ of the sphere; velocity patterns are of quadrupolar symmetry in both cases; $E = 26$ mV/mm. (b) Maximum LCEO velocity around a tangentially anchored sphere of diameter $2a = 50$ microns grows as E^2. (c) Volume of the LC flow around a sphere with perpendicular anchoring and a dipolar structure (diameter 50 microns), shown in Fig. 15, passing along the x axis parallel to the dipole and along the y axis perpendicular to the dipole. The LC is pumped from right to left. Modified from Ref. [23].

$0.3, \bar{\epsilon} = 6, \Delta\epsilon = 0, \eta = 0.07$ kg m^{-1}s^{-1}, $a = 25$ μm, predicts a characteristic velocity $|u^{\max}_{\text{LCEO}}| = 3.9$ μm/s when the field is $E = 26$ mV/μm, close to the experimental $|u^{\max}_{\text{LCEO}}| \approx 3$ μm/s, Fig. 16b.

LCEO flows shown in Figs. 14–16 are all created with dielectric particles; there are no metal/conductive elements in the LC cell except for the two electrodes to apply the field. Since the charge separation occurs because of the medium, the strongly polarizable parts such as the metal particles in ICEK discussed in Sec. 3 are not needed. This feature has important implications for potential applications. For example, LCEK can be used to transport droplets of other fluids that are not miscible with the LCs.[24,25] In the case of thermotropic LCs, these inclusions might be water and various aqueous solutions. For example, Hernandez-Navarro *et al.*[25] demonstrated controlled transport of water-based 'microreactors' dispersed in a nematic LC, propelled through the mechanism of LCEK.

It is of interest to compare the efficiency of LCEO vs ICEO in an isotropic electrolyte, when the embedded particle is dielectric. A dielectric particle in an isotropic electrolyte can cause ICEO, with the typical velocity $u_{\text{ICEO, diel}} \sim \epsilon\epsilon_0 \lambda_D E^2/\eta$ being a factor of λ_D/a smaller than the velocity around an ideally polarizable metal particle, Eq. (9).[13] For a comparable electric field, the ratio of the LCEO and ICEO velocities is $\frac{|u_{\text{LCEO}}|}{|u_{\text{ICEO, diel}}|} \approx \frac{\epsilon_{\text{LC}}\eta_{\text{water}}a}{\epsilon_{\text{water}}\eta_{\text{LC}}\lambda_D}$, where the subscripts refer to the medium. Despite the fact that $\epsilon_{\text{LC}}/\epsilon_{\text{water}} \sim 0.1$ and $\eta_{\text{water}}/\eta_{\text{LC}} \sim 0.1$, it is the large ratio $a/\lambda_D \sim 10^4$ that makes the LCEO velocities about two orders of magnitude higher as compared to ICEO velocities around dielectric bodies with equilibrium double layers, thanks to the separation of charges over the scales $\sim a$.

7. Conclusion

The overview of electrokinetic phenomena in isotropic and liquid crystalline electrolytes demonstrates that there are many different mechanisms by which the applied electric field can cause motion of a fluid with ionic species past a solid obstacle or propel an inclusion within the electrolyte. In the simplest case of linear electrokinetics, the separation of charges is produced by physical and chemical processes at the interfaces and the formation of electric double layers in the absence of an externally applied electric field. In this case, field-induced flow velocities grow mostly linearly with the applied electric field.

Nonlinear electrokinetics with quadratic field dependencies of the velocities implies that the separation of charges is produced by the electric field itself, so that the ensuing charge density is in the first approximation proportional to the electric field, $\rho \propto E$. Effects such as AC electrokinetics and ICEK are gaining attention because of the possibility to create steady flows at the microscales, an important requirement for microfluidic applications. In isotropic electrolytes, induced-charge electrokinetics is triggered in the presence of strongly polarizable (metal) surfaces or particles. Without these polarizable components, the effects are not very efficient. For example, replacing a metal sphere with a dielectric reduces the ICEO velocities by a factor of λ_D/a.[18] Electrophoretic motion based on ICEK requires some symmetry breaking on the part of the particles. For example, the particle can exhibit asymmetry of polarizability, as in the experiments with metal-dielectric Janus particles performed by Velev.[17]

LCs used as anisotropic electrolytes offer a plethora of new effects. The most important feature is that the field-induced separation of charges in the LC occurs without the need for polarizable surfaces/particles. All that is needed to create a charge density $\rho \propto E$ is a non-uniform director pattern and a reasonable anisotropy of electric conductivity or permittivity. The ensuing electro-osmotic flows of velocities $\propto E^2$ depend on the director gradients, in particular, on their sign and symmetry, Eqs. (11, 12). For example, director distortions with dipolar symmetry produce electro-osmotic pumping. In the case of electrophoresis, dipolar deformations of molecular orientation occur even around an absolutely spherically symmetric particle. The fact that a spherical particle, either solid[21,22] or fluid,[25] shows electrophoretic activity with velocities $\propto E^2$ in the LC, but not in an isotropic electrolyte, underlines the principal difference in the origin of charge separation, which is the medium in LCEK and the particle in ICEK.

LCEP demonstrates other features not met in isotropic-medium electrophoresis. In particular, a spherical particle with a hyperbolic hedgehog moves in a uniform nematic LC cell in the same direction until it reaches the edge of the sample (where it can make a u-turn and move in the opposite direction, if the director field in the edge region is supporting such a realignment). The director lines serve as a guiding rail, and the polarity of motion is determined by the location of the point-defect hedgehog. Once the hedgehog is formed on the left or right hand side of the sphere, that location cannot be switched without a strong perturbation such as complete melting of the LC. This feature allows one to pattern the director field at the surface of the LC cells and to design 3D trajectories.[21,23,24]

In LCEK presented in this review, the charges are separated because of director distortions introduced by colloidal particles with certain surface anchoring. The space charge density is proportional to the electric field and the director gradients, $\rho \propto E(\partial\varphi/\partial y)$, Eq. (11). An attractive feature of the LCEK is that the director distortions $\propto (\partial\varphi/\partial y)$ can be created by many other means, such as patterned surface alignment, as demonstrated recently by Peng *et al.*[125] Control through light irradiation[24] is especially promising, as different patterns of the director field can be written, erased and re-written again, see, for example, Refs. [126, 127].

The LCEK velocities are determined by a number of LC material parameters, the most important of which, according to the proposed model,

Eq. (11), are (i) anisotropy of electric conductivity, $\Delta\sigma = \sigma_{||} - \sigma_\perp$ and (ii) dielectric anisotropy $\Delta\epsilon = \epsilon_{||} - \epsilon_\perp$. An intriguing feature is that the LCEK velocity u is predicted[23] to depend linearly on both $\Delta\sigma$ and $\Delta\epsilon$, Eq. (12). Therefore, varying the absolute value and, what is even more interesting, the signs of $\Delta\sigma$ and $\Delta\epsilon$, one can change the amplitude and direction of the electrically induced flows in LC cells. For example, with the same predesigned pattern shown in Fig. 9a, one can reverse the direction of LCEO flows in Fig. 9d by changing the sign of $\Delta\epsilon$, frequency of the field, composition, or by temperature; $\Delta\epsilon$ can be also adjusted simply by mixing LCs with $\Delta\epsilon > 0$ (such as pentylcyanobiphenyl) and $\Delta\epsilon < 0$ (such as 4'-butyl-4-heptyl-bicyclohexyl-4-carbonotrile), see, for example, Ref. [128].

LCEK should depend on the concentration and type of ions, but so far, there are no studies published to elucidate these dependencies. It would be important to establish how the concentration of ions is distributed in space when the electric field is applied. As discussed in Sec. 3, even in an isotropic electrolyte, this distribution is rather complex and leads to effects such as the difference in 'inflow' and 'outflow' electro-osmotic velocities.[53,61]

What might be the future of LCEK? From the fundamental point of view, after more than a hundred years of applying the linear Helmholtz-Smoluchowski relationship $v \propto E$ to the overwhelming majority of electrokinetic phenomena, it is exciting to see that a simple replacement of an isotropic fluid with a LC leads to a conceptually different quadratic relationship $v \propto E^2$. It is even more exciting that the origin of this nonlinear relationship is in the mechanism of space charge formation rooted in the properties of the electrolyte rather than solid inclusions in it. The field of LCEK appears to be wide and fertile for future developments. Exploration of LCEK might help to better understand the complex world of LC electrohydrodynamics, the relationship between anisotropic surface interactions and bulk elasticity, coupling of the director and flow, and mechanisms of ionic transport in an anisotropic medium, which is a part of a more general area of charge transport in organic matter that embraces photosynthesis and transport within proteins and across biomembranes.[129]

It is probably too early to speculate on concrete devices that might be built on the basis of LCEK. From a general standpoint, advantages of using LC electrolytes instead of their isotropic counterparts appear to be as following. First, the LCEK allows one to use an AC driving which sustains steady flows. Second, the flow patterns can be pre-designed through the control of director patterns. Third, the thermotropic LC medium, being hydrophobic in nature, allows one to transport water droplets with dissolved chemicals. Fourth, the LCEK flows, in particular, the direction of pumping, can be controlled through the temperature/field frequency dependence of material parameters such as conductivity and dielectric permittivity anisotropy. One can envision that these new features might be in demand for the laboratory-on-a-chip devices, where steady flows of different geometries can be used in precise microfluidic applications.

The last few decades have seen an important shift in the LC research paradigm, associated with hybrid systems, such as LC droplets in isotropic environment[130–132] or colloidal inclusions in LCs.[116,133] These studies explored mostly equilibrium states. Current research is increasingly focusing on dynamics of LCs and generally soft systems as evidenced by achievements in the science of artificial and natural (bacteria) micro-swimmers and active nematics.[112,134–139] LCEK is an intrinsic part of this field, although with its own well-defined mechanisms. LCEK has expanded over the last few years from pioneering observations of unusually complex electric-field-induced dynamics of colloids in LCs[85,86,94] to established relationships such as the quadratic dependency of velocity on the electric field[21,22,25] and reversal of flow directions by the sign of director gradients,[23] followed by the demonstration of LCEK controlled by patterned molecular orientation.[125] The LCEK area is very active today thanks to research groups exploring LCEP,[24,25] nonlinear electrophoresis in LCs in general,[89] and motion of colloidal assemblies in the electric field.[100] Very close to this research are studies on electrically induced back-flow effects[37,119,120] and microfluidics based on dielectric reorientation.[102] There is little doubt that the field will bring new exciting developments in the years to come.

Acknowledgments

The research presented in this review would be impossible without the contributions of I. Lazo, C. Peng, O. Pishnyak, S. Shiyanovskii, and J. Xiang, to whom I am very thankful. The work was supported by NSF grants DMR-1507637 and DMS-1434185.

8. List of abbreviations used in the text and in subscripts

2D two-dimensional
3D three-dimensional
AC alternating current
ACEK alternating current electrokinetics
ACEK alternating current electro-osmosis
DC direct current
DEP dielectrophoresis
EO electro-osmosis
EP electrophoresis
EO2 electro-osmosis of the second type
ICEK Induced charge electrokinetics
ICEO Induced charge electro-osmosis
ICEP Induced charge electrophoresis
LCEK Liquid crystal-enabled electrokinetics
LCEO Liquid crystal-enabled electro-osmosis
LCEK Liquid crystal-enabled electrophoresis

References

1. M. Kaku, *Physics of the Future.* Doubleday, New York (2011).
2. H. Morgan and N. Green, *AC Electrokinetics: colloids and nanoparticles.* Research Studies Press, Baldock, UK (2003).
3. A. Ramos, *Electrokinetics and Elecrohydrodynamics in Microsystems.* Springer, Wien (2011).
4. W. Russel, D. Saville, and W. Schowalter, *Colloidal Dispersions.* Cambridge University Press, Cambridge (1989).
5. H. A. Stone, A. D. Stroock, and A. Ajdari, Engineering flows in small devices: microfluidics toward a lab-on-a-chip, *Annu. Rev. Fluid Mech.* **36**, 381–411 (2004).
6. G. M. Whitesides, The origins and the future of microfluidics, *Nature.* **442**, 368–373 (2006).
7. D. Psaltis, S. R. Quake, and C. Yang, Developing optofluidic technology through the fusion of microfluidics and optics, *Nature.* **442**(7101), 381–386 (2006).
8. A. J. Demello, Control and detection of chemical reactions in microfluidic systems, *Nature.* **442**(7101), 394–402 (2006).
9. J. M. Karlinsey, Sample introduction techniques for microchip electrophoresis: A review, *Anal. Chim. Acta.* **725**, 1–13 (2012).
10. P. Sajeesh and A. K. Sen, Particle separation and sorting in microfluidic devices: a review, *Microfluidics and nanofluidics.* **17**(1), 1–52 (2014).

11. H. Craighead, Future lab-on-a-chip technologies for interrogating individual molecules, *Nature.* **442**(7101), 387–393 (2006).

12. J. El-Ali, P. K. Sorger, and K. F. Jensen, Cells on chips, *Nature.* **442**(7101), 403–411 (2006).

13. M. Z. Bazant and T. M. Squires, Induced-charge electrokinetic phenomena: Theory and microfluidic applications, *Phys. Rev. Lett.* **92**(6), 066101 (2004).

14. M. Z. Bazant and T. M. Squires, Induced-charge electrokinetic phenomena, *Curr. Opin. Colloid Interface Sci.* **15**(3), 203–213 (2010).

15. S. Dukhin, N. Mishchuk, A. Tarovskii, and A. Baran, Electrophoresis of the 2nd kind, *Colloid J USSR.* **49**(3), 544–545 (1987).

16. S. Dukhin, N. Mishchuk, and P. Takhistov, Electroosmosis of the second kind and unrestricted current increase in the mixed monolayer of an ion exchanger, *Colloid J USSR.* **51**(3), 540–542 (1989).

17. S. Gangwal, O. J. Cayre, M. Z. Bazant, and O. D. Velev, Induced-charge electrophoresis of metallodielectric particles, *Phys. Rev. Lett.* **100**(5), 058302 (2008).

18. T. M. Squires and M. Z. Bazant, Induced-charge electro-osmosis, *J. Fluid Mech.* **509**, 217–252 (2004).

19. T. M. Squires and M. Z. Bazant, Breaking symmetries in induced-charge electro-osmosis and electrophoresis, *J. Fluid Mech.* **560**, 65–101 (2006).

20. C. Zhao and C. Yang, Electrokinetics of non-newtonian fluids: a review, *Adv. Colloid Interface Sci.* **201**, 94–108 (2013).

21. O. D. Lavrentovich, I. Lazo, and O. P. Pishnyak, Nonlinear electrophoresis of dielectric and metal spheres in a nematic liquid crystal, *Nature.* **467** (7318), 947–950 (2010).

22. I. Lazo and O. D. Lavrentovich, Liquid-crystal-enabled electrophoresis of spheres in a nematic medium with negative dielectric anisotropy, *Philosophical Transactions of the Royal Society a-Mathematical Physical and Engineering Sciences.* **371**(1988), 20120255 (2013).

23. I. Lazo, C. H. Peng, J. Xiang, S. V. Shiyanovskii, and O. D. Lavrentovich, Liquid crystal-enabled electro-osmosis through spatial charge separation in distorted regions as a novel mechanism of electrokinetics, *Nat. Commun.* **5**, 5033 (2014).

24. S. Hernàndez Navarro, P. Tierno, J. A. Farrera, J. Ignés Mullol, and F. Sagués, Reconfigurable swarms of nematic colloids controlled by photoactivated surface patterns, *Angew. Chem.* **126**(40), 10872–10876 (2014).

25. S. Hernàndez-Navarro, P. Tierno, J. Ignés-Mullol, and F. Sagués, AC electrophoresis of microdroplets in anisotropic liquids: transport, assembling and reaction, *Soft Matter.* **9**(33), 7999–8004 (2013).

26. S. Ghosal, Fluid mechanics of electroosmotic flow and its effect on band broadening in capillary electrophoresis, *Electrophoresis.* **25**(2), 214–228 (2004).

27. M. Z. Bazant. Induced-charge electrokinetic phenomena. In ed. A. Ramos, *Electrokinetics and Electrodynamics in Microsystems*, pp. 221–297. Springer, Wien (2011).

28. T. M. Squires, Induced-charge electrokinetics: fundamental challenges and

opportunities, *Lab Chip.* **9**(17), 2477–2483 (2009).

29. J. L. Anderson, Colloid transport by interfacial forces, *Annual review of fluid mechanics.* **21**(1), 61–99 (1989).

30. A. V. Delgado, F. González-Caballero, R. Hunter, L. Koopal, and J. Lyklema, Measurement and interpretation of electrokinetic phenomena, *J. Colloid Interface Sci.* **309**(2), 194–224 (2007).

31. C. Zhao and C. Yang, Advances in electrokinetics and their applications in micro/nano fluidics, *Microfluidics and nanofluidics.* **13**(2), 179–203 (2012).

32. R. A. Millikan, The isolation of an ion, a precision measurement of its charge, and the correction of Stokes's law, *Physical Review (Series I).* **32**(4), 349 (1911).

33. H. Pohl, *Dielectrophoresis.* Cambridge University Press, Cambridge (1978).

34. A. B. Golovin and O. D. Lavrentovich, Electrically reconfigurable optical metamaterial based on colloidal dispersion of metal nanorods in dielectric fluid, *Appl. Phys. Lett.* **95**(25), 254104 (2009).

35. A. B. Golovin, J. Xiang, H. S. Park, L. Tortora, Y. A. Nastishin, S. V. Shiyanovskii, and O. D. Lavrentovich, Electro-optic effects in colloidal dispersion of metal nano-rods in dielectric fluid, *Materials.* **4**(2), 390–416 (2011).

36. O. D. Lavrentovich, Transport of particles in liquid crystals, *Soft Matter.* **10**(9), 1264–1283 (2014).

37. O. P. Pishnyak, S. V. Shiyanovskii, and O. D. Lavrentovich, Inelastic collisions and anisotropic aggregation of particles in a nematic collider driven by backflow, *Phys. Rev. Lett.* **106**(4), 047801 (2011).

38. A. Ramos, H. Morgan, N. G. Green, and A. Castellanos, AC electric-field-induced fluid flow in microelectrodes, *J. Colloid Interface Sci.* **217**(2), 420–422 (1999).

39. A. González, A. Ramos, N. Green, A. Castellanos, and A. Ramos, Fluid flow induced by nonuniform ac electric fields in electrolytes on microelectrodes. II. a linear double-layer analysis, *Phys. Rev. E.* **61**, 4019–4028 (2000).

40. A. Ramos, H. Morgan, N. G. Green, and A. Castellanos, Ac electrokinetics: a review of forces in microelectrode structures, *J Phys D Appl Phys.* **31**, 2338–2353 (1998).

41. Ajdari, Pumping liquids using asymmetric electrode arrays, *Phys Rev E Stat Phys Plasmas Fluids Relat Interdiscip Topics.* **61**(1), R45–8 (2000).

42. A. Brown, C. Smith, and A. Rennie, Pumping of water with ac electric fields applied to asymmetric pairs of microelectrodes, *Phys. Rev. E.* **63**(1 Pt 2), 016305 (2001).

43. A. Ramos, A. González, A. Castellanos, N. Green, and H. Morgan, Pumping of liquids with ac voltages applied to asymmetric pairs of microelectrodes, *Phys. Rev. E.* **67**(5 Pt 2), 056302 (2003).

44. S. Dukhin, N. Mishchuk, A. Tarovskii, and A. Baran, The 2nd-kind electrophoresis, *Dopov Akad Nauk B.* pp. 42–44 (1987).

45. S. Dukhin, E. K. Zholkovsky, and N. A. Mishchuk, A secondary double electric layer and secondary electroosmosis, *Dopov Akad Nauk B.* pp. 45–48 (1986).

46. N. A. Mishchuk, T. Heldal, T. Volden, J. Auerswald, and H. Knapp, Microfluidic pump based on the phenomenon of electroosmosis of the second kind, *Microfluid Nanofluid.* **11**, 675–684 (2011).

47. N. Mishchuk, F. Gonzalez-Gaballero, and P. Takhistov, Electroosmosis of the second kind and current through curved interface, *Colloid Surface A.* **181**, 131–144 (2001).

48. N. Gamayunov and V. Murtsovkin, Motion of disperse particles in a uniform alternating electric-field, *Colloid J USSR.* **49**, 543–544 (1987).

49. V. Murtsovkin and G. Mantrov, Study of the motion of anisometric particles in a uniform variable electric-field, *Colloid J USSR.* **52**, 933–936 (1990).

50. I. L. Simonov and V. N. Shilov, Theory of low-frequency dielectric-dispersion of a suspension of ideally polarizable spherical-particles, *Colloid J USSR.* **39**, 775–780 (1977).

51. V. Murtsovkin and G. Mantrov, Steady flows in the neighborhood of a drop of mercury with the application of a variable external electric-field, *Colloid J USSR.* **53**, 240–244 (1991).

52. N. Gamayunov, G. Mantrov, and V. Murtsovkin, Study of flows induced in the vicinity of conducting particles by an external electric-field, *Colloid J USSR.* **54**, 20–23 (1992).

53. C. H. Peng, I. Lazo, S. V. Shiyanovskii, and O. D. Lavrentovich, Induced-charge electro-osmosis around metal and janus spheres in water: Patterns of flow and breaking symmetries, *Phys. Rev. E.* **90**(5), 051002(R) (2014).

54. C. Harnett, J. Templeton, K. Dunphy-Guzman, Y. Senousy, and M. Kanouff, Model based design of a microfluidic mixer driven by induced charge electroosmosis, *Lab Chip.* **8**(4), 565–572 (2008).

55. C. Canpolat, S. Qian, and A. Beskok, Micro-PIV measurements of induced-charge electro-osmosis around a metal rod, *Microfluid Nanofluid.* **14**, 153–162 (2013).

56. J. Levitan, S. Devasenathipathy, V. Studer, Y. Ben, T. Thorsen, T. Squires, and M. Bazant, Experimental observation of induced-charge electro-osmosis around a metal wire in a microchannel, *Colloid Surface A.* **267**, 122–132 (2005).

57. C. Canpolat, M. Zhang, W. Rosen, S. Qian, and A. Beskok, Induced-charge electroosmosis around touching metal rods, *J Fluid Eng-T Asme.* **135** (2013).

58. A. Boymelgreen, G. Yossifon, S. Park, and T. Miloh, Spinning janus doublets driven in uniform ac electric fields, *Phys. Rev. E.* **89**(1), 011003 (2014).

59. R. Messinger and T. Squires, Suppression of electro-osmotic flow by surface roughness, *Phys. Rev. Lett.* **105**(14), 144503 (2010).

60. M. Bazant, M. Kilic, B. Storey, and A. Ajdari, Towards an understanding of induced-charge electrokinetics at large applied voltages in concentrated solutions, *Adv. Colloid Interface Sci.* **152**(1-2), 48–88 (2009).

61. S. Davidson, M. Andersen, and A. Mani, Chaotic induced-charge electro-osmosis, *Phys. Rev. Lett.* **112**(12), 128302 (2014).

62. S. Dukhin, Electrokinetic phenomena of the 2nd kind and their applications, *Adv. Colloid Interface Sci.* **35**, 173–196 (1991).

63. N. Mishchuk, Concentration polarization of interface and non-linear electrokinetic phenomena, *Adv. Colloid Interface Sci.* **160**(1-2), 16–39 (2010).

64. A. Boymelgreen and G. Yossifon, Observing electrokinetic janus particle-channel wall interaction using microparticle image velocimetry, *Langmuir.* **31**(30), 8243–8250 (2015).

65. H. Sugioka, dc step response of induced-charge electro-osmosis between parallel electrodes at large voltages, *Phys. Rev. E.* **90**(1), 013007 (2014).

66. J. Lyklema, *Fundamentals of Interface and Colloid Science: Solid-Liquid Interfaces (Volume 2).* Academic Press (1995).

67. S. Dukhin, Nonequilibrium electric surface phenomena, *Adv. Colloid Interface Sci.* **44**, 1–134 (1993).

68. A. Khair and T. Squires, The influence of hydrodynamic slip on the electrophoretic mobility of a spherical colloidal particle, *Physics of Fluids.* **21**, 042001 (2009).

69. F. Leinweber, J. Eijkel, J. Bomer, and A. van den Berg, Continuous flow microfluidic demixing of electrolytes by induced charge electrokinetics in structured electrode arrays, *Anal. Chem.* **78**(5), 1425–1434 (2006).

70. S. Gangwal, O. Cayre, and O. Velev, Dielectrophoretic assembly of metallodielectric janus particles in AC electric fields, *Langmuir.* **24**(23), 13312–13320 (2008).

71. A. Pascall and T. Squires, Induced charge electro-osmosis over controllably contaminated electrodes, *Phys. Rev. Lett.* **104**(8), 088301 (2010).

72. J. Happel and H. Brenner, *Low Reynolds number hydrodynamics.* Martinus Nijhoff Publishers, The Hague (1983).

73. H. Zhao and H. Bau, On the effect of induced electro-osmosis on a cylindrical particle next to a surface, *Langmuir.* **23**(7), 4053–4063 (2007).

74. E. Yariv, Induced-charge electrophoresis of nonspherical particles, *Physics of Fluids.* **17**, 051702 (2005).

75. D. Saintillan, E. Darve, and E. Shaqfeh, Hydrodynamic interactions in the induced-charge electrophoresis of colloidal rod dispersions, *J. Fluid Mech.* **563**, 223–259 (2006).

76. H. Zhao and H. Bau, Microfluidic chaotic stirrer utilizing induced-charge electro-osmosis, *Phys. Rev. E.* **75**(6 Pt 2), 066217 (2007).

77. C. Neyts and F. Beunis. Ion transport in liquid crystals. In eds. J. W. Goodby, P. J. Collings, T. Kato, C. Tschierske, H. Gleeson, and P. Raynes, *Handbook of Liquid Crystals, 8 Volume Set,* pp. 357–382. Wiley-VCH (2014).

78. L. Blinov and V. Chigrinov, *Electrooptic Effects in Liquid Crystal materials.* Springer, New York (1994).

79. H. De Vleeschouwer, A. Verschueren, F. Bougrioua, K. Neyts, G. Stojmenovik, S. Vermael, and H. Pauwels, Dispersive ion generation in nematic liquid crystal displays, *Jpn. J. Appl. Phys. 1.* **41**, 1489–1494 (2002).

80. R. Thurston, J. Cheng, R. Meyer, and G. Boyd, Physical-mechanisms of dc switching in a liquid-crystal bistable boundary-layer display, *J. Appl. Phys.* **56**, 263–272 (1984).

81. G. Barbero, A. Neto, J. Le Digabel, and O. Martins, Ionic relaxation in nematic liquid crystal cells, *Liq. Cryst.* **34**, 343–348 (2007).

82. F. Ciuchi, A. Mazzulla, A. Pane, and J. Reyes, AC and DC electro-optical response of planar aligned liquid crystal cells, *Appl. Phys. Lett.* **91**, 232902 (2007).

83. A. V. Ryzhkova, F. V. Podgornov, and W. Haase, Nonlinear electrophoretic motion of dielectric microparticles in nematic liquid crystals, *Appl. Phys. Lett.* **96**(15), 151901 (2010).

84. D. Mizuno, Y. Kimura, and R. Hayakawa, Electrophoretic microrheology of a dilute lamellar phase: Relaxation mechanisms in frequency-dependent mobility of nanometer-sized particles between soft membranes, *Phys. Rev. E.* **70**, 011509 (2004).

85. D. Mizuno, Y. Kimura, and R. Hayakawa, Electrophoretic microrheology in a dilute lamellar phase of a nonionic surfactant, *Phys. Rev. Lett.* **87**, 088104 (2001).

86. I. Dierking, G. Biddulph, and K. Matthews, Electromigration of microspheres in nematic liquid crystals, *Phys. Rev. E.* **73**(1), 011702 (2006).

87. I. Dierking, P. Cass, K. Syres, R. Cresswell, and S. Morton, Electromigration of microspheres in ferroelectric smectic liquid crystals, *Phys. Rev. E.* **76**(2), 021707 (2007).

88. R. Rill, B. Locke, Y. Liu, and D. Van Winkle, Electrophoresis in lyotropic polymer liquid crystals, *Proc. Natl. Acad. Sci. U. S. A.* **95**(4), 1534–1539 (1998).

89. A. Ryzhkova and I. Musevic, Particle size effects on nanocolloidal interactions in nematic liquid crystals, *Phys. Rev. E.* **87**, 032501 (2013).

90. A. V. Ryzhkova, F. V. Podgornov, A. Gaebler, R. Jakoby, and W. Haase, Measurements of the electrokinetic forces on dielectric microparticles in nematic liquid crystals using optical trapping, *Journal of Applied Physics.* **113**(24), 244902 (2013).

91. G. Liao, I. I. Smalyukh, J. R. Kelly, O. D. Lavrentovich, and A. Jakli, Electrorotation of colloidal particles in liquid crystals, *Phys. Rev. E.* **72**(3), 031704 (2005).

92. T. Jones, *Electromechanics of Particles.* Cambridge University Press, Cambridge (1995).

93. A. Jakli, B. Senyuk, G. X. Liao, and O. D. Lavrentovich, Colloidal micromotor in smectic a liquid crystal driven by DC electric field, *Soft Matter.* **4**(12), 2471–2474 (2008).

94. S. A. Tatarkova, D. R. Burnham, A. K. Kirby, G. D. Love, and E. M. Terentjev, Colloidal interactions and transport in nematic liquid crystals, *Phys. Rev. Lett.* **98**(15), 157801 (2007).

95. S. Klein, Electrophoretic LC displays: How far are we?, *Liquid Crystals Reviews.* **1**(1), 52–64 (2013).

96. P. de Gennes and J. Prost, *The Physics of Liquid Crystals.* Clarendon Press, Oxford (1993).

97. E. F. Carr, Influence of electric fields on molecular alignment in liquid crystal p-(anisalamino)-phenyl acetate, *Mol. Cryst. Liq. Cryst.* **7**, 253 (1969).

98. W. Helfrich, Conduction-induced alignment of nematic liquid crystals - basic model and stability considerations, *J. Chem. Phys.* **51**, 4092 (1969).

99. K. Takeuchi, M. Kuroda, H. Chaté, and M. Sano, Experimental realization of directed percolation criticality in turbulent liquid crystals, *Phys. Rev. E.* **80**(5 Pt 1), 051116 (2009).

100. Y. Sasaki, Y. Takikawa, V. Jampani, H. Hoshikawa, T. Seto, C. Bahr, S. Herminghaus, Y. Hidaka, and H. Orihara, Colloidal caterpillars for cargo transportation, *Soft Matter.* **10**(44), 8813–8820 (2014).

101. C. Blanc, D. Coursault, and E. Lacaze, Ordering nano- and microparticles assemblies with liquid crystals, *Liquid Crystals Reviews.* pp. 1–27 (2013).

102. A. Sengupta, S. Herminghaus, and C. Bahr, Liquid crystal microfluidics: surface, elastic and viscous interactions at microscales, *Liquid Crystals Reviews.* **2**, 73–110 (2014).

103. G. Foffano, J. Lintuvuori, A. Tiribocchi, and D. Marenduzzo, The dynamics of colloidal intrusions in liquid crystals: a simulation perspective, *Liquid Crystals Reviews.* **2**, 1–27 (2014).

104. H. Stark, D. Ventzki, and M. Reichert, Recent developments in the field of colloidal dispersions in nematic liquid crystals: the stokes drag, *J. Phys.-Condens. Matter.* **15**(1), S191–S196 (2003).

105. J. Fukuda, H. Stark, M. Yoneya, and H. Yokoyama, Dynamics of a nematic liquid crystal around a spherical particle, *J. Phys.-Condens. Matter.* **16**(19), S1957–S1968 (2004).

106. J. Kotar, M. Vilfan, N. Osterman, D. Babic, M. Copic, and I. Poberaj, Interparticle potential and drag coefficient in nematic colloids, *Phys. Rev. Lett.* **96**(20), 207801 (2006).

107. M. Vilfan, N. Osterman, M. Copic, M. Ravnik, S. Zumer, J. Kotar, D. Babic, and I. Poberaj, Confinement effect on interparticle potential in nematic colloids, *Phys. Rev. Lett.* **101**(23), 237801 (2008).

108. R. W. Ruhwandl and E. M. Terentjev, Friction drag on a particle moving in a nematic liquid crystal, *Phys. Rev. E.* **54**(5), 5204–5210 (1996).

109. I. Lazo and O. Lavrentovich, Liquid crystal-enabled electrophoresis of spheres in a nematic medium with negative dieletric anisotropy, *Phil. Trans. R. Soc. A.* **371**, 20120255 (2013).

110. J. C. Loudet, P. Hanusse, and P. Poulin, Stokes drag on a sphere in a nematic liquid crystal, *Science.* **306**(5701), 1525–1525 (2004).

111. T. Turiv, I. Lazo, A. Brodin, B. Lev, V. Reiffenrath, V. Nazarenko, and O. Lavrentovich, Effect of collective molecular reorientations on brownian motion of colloids in nematic liquid crystal, *Science.* **342**(6164), 1351–1354 (2013).

112. S. Zhou, A. Sokolov, O. D. Lavrentovich, and I. S. Aranson, Living liquid crystals, *Proc. Natl. Acad. Sci. U. S. A.* **111**(4), 1265–1270 (2014).

113. M. Kleman and O. D. Lavrentovich, *Soft Matter Physics: An Introduction.* Springer, New York (2003).

114. E. M. Purcell, Life at low reynolds-number, *American Journal of Physics.* **45**(1), 3–11 (1977).

115. H. Stark and D. Ventzki, Non-linear stokes drag of spherical particles in a nematic solvent, *Europhys. Lett.* **57**(1), 60–66 (2002).

116. P. Poulin, H. Stark, T. C. Lubensky, and D. A. Weitz, Novel colloidal

interactions in anisotropic fluids, *Science.* **275**(5307), 1770–1773 (1997).

117. O. V. Kuksenok, R. W. Ruhwandl, S. V. Shiyanovskii, and E. M. Terentjev, Director structure around a colloid particle suspended in a nematic liquid crystal, *Phys. Rev. E.* **54**(5), 5198–5203 (1996).

118. Y. D. Gu and N. L. Abbott, Observation of saturn-ring defects around solid microspheres in nematic liquid crystals, *Phys. Rev. Lett.* **85**(22), 4719–4722 (2000).

119. O. P. Pishnyak, S. V. Shiyanovskii, and O. D. Lavrentovich, Aggregation of colloidal particles in a non-equilibrium backflow induced by electrically-driven reorientation of the nematic liquid crystal, *Journal of Molecular Liquids.* **164**(1-2), 132–142 (2011).

120. O. P. Pishnyak, S. Tang, J. R. Kelly, S. V. Shiyanovskii, and O. D. Lavrentovich, Levitation, lift, and bidirectional motion of colloidal particles in an electrically driven nematic liquid crystal, *Phys. Rev. Lett.* **99**(12), 127802 (2007).

121. A. Dukhin and S. Dukhin, Aperiodic capillary electrophoresis method using an alternating current electric field for separation of macromolecules, *Electrophoresis.* **26**(11), 2149–2153 (2005).

122. S. Stotz, Field dependence of the electrophoretic mobility of particles suspended in low-conductivity liquids, *J. Colloid Interface Sci.* **65**, 118–130 (1978).

123. T. Simonova and S. Dukhin, Nonlinear polarization of diffusion part of thin double-layer of a spherical-particle, *Colloid J USSR.* **38**, 65–70 (1976).

124. M. Conradi, M. Ravnik, M. Bele, M. Zorko, S. Zumer, and I. Musevic, Janus nematic colloids, *Soft Matter.* **5**(20), 3905–3912 (2009).

125. C. H. Peng, Y. Guo, C. Conclin, J. Viñals, S. V. Shiyanovskii, Q.-H. Wei, and O. D. Lavrentovich, Liquid crystals with patterned molecular orientation as an electrolytic active medium, *Phys. Rev. E.* **92**, 052502 (2015).

126. M. Han, S. Morino, and K. Ichimura, Factors affecting in-plane and out-of-plane photoorientation of azobenzene side chains attached to liquid crystalline polymers induced by irradiation with linearly polarized light, *Macromolecules.* **33**, 6360–6371 (2000).

127. S. V. Shiyanovskii, A. Glushchenko, Y. Reznikov, O. D. Lavrentovich, and J. L. West, Tensor and complex anchoring in liquid crystals, *Phys. Rev. E.* **62**(2), R1477–R1480 (2000).

128. M. Gu, Y. Yin, S. V. Shiyanovskii, and O. D. Lavrentovich, Effects of dielectric relaxation on the director dynamics of uniaxial nematic liquid crystals, *Phys. Rev. E.* **76**(6), 061702 (2007).

129. G. Whitesides and D. Lipomi, Soft nanotechnology: "structure" vs. "function", *Faraday Discuss.* **143**, 373–384 (2009).

130. J. Doane, N. Vaz, B. Wu, and S. Zumer, Field controlled light-scattering from nematic microdroplets, *Appl. Phys. Lett.* **48**, 269–271 (1986).

131. O. D. Lavrentovich, Topological defects in dispersed liquid crystals, or words and worlds around liquid crystal drops, *Liq. Cryst.* **24**(1), 117–125 (1998).

132. G. E. Volovik and O. D. Lavrentovich, The topological dynamics of defects - boojums in nematic drops, *Zhurnal Eksperimentalnoi I Teoreticheskoi*

Fiziki. **85**(6), 1997–2010 (1983).

133. H. Stark, Physics of colloidal dispersions in nematic liquid crystals, *Physics Reports-Review Section of Physics Letters.* **351**(6), 387–474 (2001).

134. S. Ramaswamy, The mechanics and statistics of active matter, *Annual Review of Condensed Matter Physics.* **1**, 323–345 (2010).

135. T. Sanchez, T. N. Chen, Daniel, J. DeCamp, Stephen, M. Heymann, and Z. Dogic, Spontaneous motion in hierarchically assembled active matter, *Nature.* **491**(7424), 431 (2012).

136. M. C. Marchetti, J. F. Joanny, S. Ramaswamy, T. B. Liverpool, J. Prost, M. Rao, and R. A. Simha, Hydrodynamics of soft active matter, *Rev. Mod. Phys.* **85**(3), 1143 (2013).

137. F. Keber, E. Loiseau, T. Sanchez, S. DeCamp, L. Giomi, M. J. Bowick, M. C. Marchetti, Z. Dogic, and A. R. Bausch, Topology and dynamics of active nematic vesicles, *Science.* **345**, 1135–1139 (2014).

138. I. S. Aranson, Active colloids, *Phys-Usp+.* **56**, 79–92 (2013).

139. O. D. Lavrentovich, Active colloids in liquid crystals, *Curr. Opin. Colloid Interface Sci.* **21**, 97–109 (2016).

Subject index